e Text

s and Problems
es and Problems, Teacher's Annotated Edition
ing Performance Objectives)
HYSICS
HYSICS, Teacher's Annotated Edition
ciples and Problems, Evaluation Program (Spirit Duplicating Masters)
YSICS CHART

Lynn Berberich
Karen Ragni
Larry P. Koons
Dick Smith

r Photo

This colorful hot air balloon is drifting slowly and quietly over the rolling countryside below. y through knowledge and understanding of certain basic laws of physics is the flight of this lloon accomplished.

Physics is the study of the interrelationships of matter and energy. From everyday experience you are already familiar with some of the basic laws of physics. You find applications of these laws in many of the devices which you use every day. Examples of these devices are telephones, cars, electric lights, TV sets, and electronic calculators.

Through a study of physics you will gain greater knowledge and awareness of the world around you. When called upon to do so, you will be able to make intelligent decisions regarding issues such as energy and environment which are so vital both to us and to future generations.

Photo by James M. Jackson

Chapter Opening Photo Descriptions and Credits

1 **Sunset** William Maddox
2 **Antarctic Studies** Ian Whillans, Institute of Polar Studies, Ohio State University
3 **Moving Automobile** U.S. Energy Research and Development Administration
4 **Weather Mapping** NOAA
5 **Sailboat** Rich Brommer
6 **Hang Glider** James M. Jackson
7 **Bowling Ball Hitting Pins** American Bowling Congress
8 **Fountain** Meston
9 **Parachutist** William Maddox
10 **Mountain Climber** SPORTS ILLUSTRATED Photo by Mark Kauffman © Time, Inc.
11 **Water-Powered Flour Mill** Photo by Robert Neulieb, Courtesy of Clifton Mills®, Inc., Clifton, Ohio
12 **Mountain Scene** Orville Andrews
13 **Threading Steel** Kennametal Corporation
14 **Splashing Milk Drop** Courtesy of Harold E. Edgerton, Massachusetts Institute of Technology

15 **Parade Balloon** Bruce Coleman, Inc.
16 **Waves** Rich Brommer
17 **Light Through Trees** William Maddox
18 **Lake St. Marie, Glacier National Park** Meston
19 **Cat Peering Through a Glass of Water** Nina Leen for Time-Life Books © Time, Inc.
20 **Night Lights** W. Keith Turpie
21 **Diver With Lamp** Joe Jacques
22 **Lightning** Westinghouse Electric Corporation
23 **Overhead Electric Wires** USDA Photo
24 **Line Amplifier-Signal Splitter for TV** W. Keith Turpie
25 **Electromagnet** Navarre Macomb
26 **Train Model** W. Keith Turpie
27 **Radio Telescope Antenna** British Information Services
28 **Satellite With Solar Panels** NASA
29 **Field-Ion Emission Pattern** Courtesy of Dr. Edwin Müller, Pennsylvania State University
30 **Nuclear Power Plant** Connecticut Yankee Atomic Power Plant

ISBN 0-675-07485-1

Published by
Charles E. Merrill Publishing Co.
A Bell & Howell Company

Columbus, Ohio 43216

PHYSICS
Principles and Problems

JAMES T. MURPHY
Chairman, Science Department
Reading Memorial High School
Reading, Massachusetts

Consultant
ROBERT C. SMOOT
Chairman, Science Department
McDonogh School
McDonogh, Maryland

Charles E. Merrill Publishing Co.
A Bell & Howell Company
Columbus, Ohio

Preface

PHYSICS: Principles and Problems provides a clear and straight-forward presentation of the basic concepts of physics. The central theme, the interrelationship between matter and energy, is applicable to all sciences. The essential concepts of physics are developed in an orderly manner so as to present a unified, logical sequence. Excessive detail has been omitted where it would obscure or confuse the main idea. Memorization has been minimized.

The most up-to-date notation has been used throughout **PHYSICS: Principles and Problems.** Only SI units and those units currently accepted for use with the SI system are presented. In keeping with this policy of using SI notation, spaces are used instead of commas in indicating place value in numerals throughout the book.

Mechanics, needed to interpret most phenomena, is the first concept presented. Then, each form of energy — heat, light, electric, nuclear — and the basic structure of matter are intertwined. As these interrelationships are developed, the conservation laws are demonstrated and emphasized.

Before students can solve specific problems, they must understand certain principles. Therefore, **PHYSICS: Principles and Problems** presents each principle clearly before introducing related problems. The authors have written this text to bridge the gap between the understanding of a general statement, theory, or law and the application of principles to the solution of problems. Reasoning based on experience and experiment leads students to an awareness of these principles and how they interrelate with physical phenomena. Photographs and artwork, many of them in full color, are used extensively throughout the text to illustrate physics principles and their applications to situations encountered both in research and in everyday living.

Often, it is necessary to apply more than one principle in solving a problem. **PHYSICS: Principles and Problems** helps students understand the application of several principles and thus to arrive at a solution. When students understand both the problem and the principles to be applied, they can solve any of the problems presented. More complex problems are developed as combinations of fundamental concepts. Each problem emphasizes the thinking involved in setting up a logical solution.

Because mathematics is the language of science, a basic background in this subject is necessary to understand physics. To make the text self-sustaining, a brief review of algebra and trigonometry is provided in Chapter 1. Thus, use of outside resources has been eliminated.

Each chapter is introduced with a photograph and a thought-provoking paragraph which relate the theme of the chapter to the world of the student. Through this introduction, students become aware of the relevance of the concepts to be explored within the chapter.

A **Goal** statement appears in the margin at the beginning of each chapter. This statement gives an overall purpose for the study of the chapter.

Margin notes are carefully positioned throughout the text to highlight important terms and ideas and to further assist students in organizing study and review. New terms are printed in boldface type, spelled phonetically, and defined within the text when introduced.

Examples with step-by-step solutions are provided throughout the chapter to guide students in mastery of problem-solving. These sample problems are immediately reinforced with review problems which enable students to check independently their understanding of the material just studied.

An extensive **Summary,** which provides a chapter overview, appears at the end of each chapter. Comprehensive **Questions** and **Problems** sections are also included at the end of each chapter to provide further opportunity for students to check their knowledge and understanding of concepts. A **Projects** section and a **Readings** section provide students with opportunities to expand their knowledge through a variety of individualized activities and reading experiences.

Appendices as well as **Answers to Odd-Numbered Problems** and the **Index** appear at the end of the text. Information in the Appendices includes trigonometric tables, tables of the elements and physical constants, and important equations. A new feature of this text is an Appendix devoted to the subject of careers. This section includes descriptions of a variety of physics-related careers and the general education requirements of each.

Physics and its practical applications are basic and vital to all students whatever their educational goals. Conscious of both the science-oriented student and the nonscience-oriented student, the authors of **PHYSICS: Principles and Problems** have designed this text to appeal to students with a wide range of interests. Within this wide range, the text can be used successfully for both classroom and individual study.

The text also reflects the consensus of recent recommendations made by committees studying the physics curriculum and by teachers using this material in a variety of teaching situations. Following these guidelines, the authors have designed a physics program which is both manageable and realistic in terms of its expectations of students.

The authors wish to express their sincere thanks to the many physics students, teachers, and science educators who have made suggestions for changes based on their use of the first edition of **PHYSICS: Principles and Problems.**

Contents

1 Fundamental Mathematics   2

1:1 Solving Equations Algebraically, p. 3; **1:2** Scientific Notation, p. 4; **1:3** Addition and Subtraction in Scientific Notation, p. 6; **1:4** Multiplication and Division in Scientific Notation, p. 7; **1:5** Trigonometry of Right Triangles, p. 8; **1:6** The Law of Cosines, p. 9; **1:7** The Law of Sines, p. 10; **1:8** Units and Equations, p. 11

2 Measurement   14

2:1 Measurement and the Scientific Method, p. 15; **2:2** Fundamental and Derived Units, p. 16; **2:3** The Metric System, p. 16; **2:4** Prefixes Used With Metric Units, p. 18; **2:5** Errors in Measurement, p. 20; **2:6** Accuracy and Precision, p. 21; **2:7** Significant Digits, p. 22; **2.8** Operations With Significant Digits, p. 23; **2:9** Graphs, p. 24; **2:10** Linear and Direct Variation, p. 25; **2:11** Inverse Variation, p. 26

3 Motion In A Straight Line   30

3:1 Motion, p. 31; **3:2** Average and Instantaneous Speed, p. 32; **3:3** Uniform Acceleration, p. 34; **3:4** Final Velocity After Uniform Acceleration, p. 36; **3:5** Distance Traveled During Uniform Acceleration, p. 37; **3:6** Uniform Acceleration—Starting and Stopping, p. 38; **3:7** Acceleration Due to Gravity, p. 41

4 Graphical Analysis Of Motion   46

4:1 Distance-Time Graph for Constant Speed, p. 47; **4:2** Slope of a Distance-Time Graph, p. 48; **4:3** Distance-Time Graph for a Complete Trip, p. 49; **4:4** Speed-Time Graph for Constant Speed, p. 50; **4:5** Speed-Time Graph for Uniform Acceleration, p. 51; **4:6** Distance-Time Graph for Uniform Acceleration, p. 52; **4:7** Acceleration-Time Graph for Uniform Acceleration, p. 53

5 Vectors   58

5:1 Vector Quantities, p. 59; **5:2** Vector Addition—Graphical Method, p. 60; **5:3** Distance and Displacement, p. 62; **5:4** Speed and Velocity, p. 62; **5:5** The Independence of Vector Quantities, p. 63; **5:6** Vector Addition of Forces, p. 63; **5:7** Vector Addition—Mathematical Methods, p. 66; **5:8** Addition of Several Vectors, p. 68; **5:9** Equilibrium, p. 69; **5:10** The Equilibrant, p. 70; **5:11** Perpendicular Components of Vectors, p. 71; **5:12** Non-Perpendicular Components of Vectors, p. 74

6 Dynamics   78

6:1 Forces, p. 79; **6:2** Newton's First Law, p. 80; **6:3** Newton's Second Law, p. 82; **6:4** Units of Force, p. 83; **6:5** Weight and Mass, p. 84; **6:6** Net Forces and Acceleration, p. 86; **6:7** Two Ways to Measure Mass, p. 88

7 Momentum And Its Conservation   92

7:1 Momentum, p. 93; **7:2** Newton's Third Law of Motion, p. 96; **7:3** Law of Conservation of Momentum, p. 97; **7:4** Internal Forces—External Forces, p. 100; **7:5** Conservation of Momentum in General, p. 103

8 Motion In Two Dimensions   108

8:1 Projectile Motion, p. 109; **8:2** Projectiles Fired at an Angle, p. 113; **8:3** Uniform Circular Motion, p. 114; **8:4** Placing a Satellite in Orbit, p. 119; **8:5** Simple Harmonic Motion, p. 121

9 Universal Gravitation   126

9:1 Kepler's Laws of Planetary Motion, p. 127; **9:2** Universal Gravitation, p. 128; **9:3** Newton's Test of the Inverse Square Law, p. 132; **9:4** The Cavendish Experiment, p. 133; **9:5** The Law of Universal Gravitation and Weight, p. 134; **9:6** Gravitational Fields, p. 135

10 Work And Power   138

10:1 Work, p. 139; **10:2** Work and the Direction of Force, p. 141; **10:3** Power, p. 143

11 Energy And Its Conservation — 146

11:1 Energy—The Capacity to Do Work, p. 147; **11:2** Potential Energy, p. 148; **11:3** Base Levels, p. 150; **11:4** Energy Units—Work Units, p. 150; **11:5** Kinetic Energy, p. 152; **11:6** Conservation of Energy, p. 153; **11:7** Conservation of Matter and Energy, p. 156; **11:8** Elastic Collisions, p. 157

12 Measurement Of Heat — 164

12:1 What is Heat? p. 165; **12:2** Temperature and Heat, p. 166; **12:3** Thermometry, p. 168; **12:4** The Celsius Temperature Scale, p. 169; **12:5** The Kelvin Temperature Scale, p. 169; **12:6** The First Law of Thermodynamics, p. 170; **12:7** The Second Law of Thermodynamics, p. 171; **12:8** Heat Units, p. 171; **12:9** Specific Heat, p. 172; **12:10** Conservation in Heat Transfer, p. 174; **12:11** Latent Heat and Change of State, p. 176

13 Heat As Energy — 182

13:1 The Mechanical Equivalent of Heat, p. 183; **13:2** The Joule as a Universal Unit of Energy, p. 189

14 Kinetic Theory — 192

14:1 Assumptions of the Kinetic Theory, p. 193; **14:2** Thermal Expansion of Matter, p. 194; **14:3** Surface Tension, p. 198; **14:4** Vaporization, p. 200; **14:5** The Solid State, p. 202; **14:6** Plasma, p. 203; **14:7** Electric Resistance and Superconductivity, p. 205; **14:8** Studying the Unobservable, p. 207

15 The Gas Laws — 210

15:1 Standard Pressure, p. 211; **15:2** Boyle's Law, p. 212; **15:3** Charles' Law, p. 215; **15:4** The General Gas Law, p. 217

16 Waves And Energy Transfer — 220

16:1 All Waves Follow the Same Rules, p. 221; **16:2** Mechanical and Electromagnetic Waves, p. 222; **16:3** Transverse and Longitudinal Waves, p. 222; **16:4** Pulses and Waves, p. 223; **16:5** Wave Characteristics, p. 224; **16:6** Sound Waves, p. 225; **16:7** Energy and the Amplitude of a Wave, p. 226; **16:8** Wave Speed in a Medium, p. 227; **16:9** Behavior of Waves at Boundaries, p. 228; **16:10** The Transmitted Wave, p. 231; **16:11** Interference, p. 231; **16:12** Nodes, p. 232; **16:13** Ripple Tanks, p. 233; **16:14** The Law of Reflection, p. 234; **16:15** Refraction of Waves, p. 235; **16:16** Diffraction of Waves, p. 236; **16:17** The Doppler Effect, p. 237

17 The Nature Of Light — 242

17:1 Light—An Electromagnetic Wave, p. 243; **17:2** Transmission and Absorption of Light, p. 244; **17:3** The Speed of Light, p. 245; **17:4** Light Travels in a Straight Line, p. 247; **17:5** Illumination by a Point Source, p. 248; **17:6** Color and Light, p. 251; **17:7** Light—Waves or Particles? p. 252; **17:8** Interference in Thin Films, p. 254; **17:9** Polarization of Light, p. 255; **17:10** The Dual Nature of Light, p. 256

18 Reflection And Refraction — 260

18:1 The Law of Reflection, p. 261; **18:2** Diffuse and Regular Reflection, p. 261; **18:3** Refraction of Light, p. 262; **18:4** Snell's Law, p. 264; **18:5** Index of Refraction and the Speed of Light, p. 266; **18:6** Total Internal Reflection, p. 267; **18:7** Effects of Refraction, p. 269; **18:8** Dispersion of Light, p. 270

19 Mirrors And Lenses — 274

19:1 Plane Mirrors, p. 275; **19:2** Converging Mirrors, p. 277; **19:3** Spherical Aberration, p. 278; **19:4** Real and Virtual Images, p. 279; **19:5** Images Formed by Converging Mirrors, p. 279; **19:6** Virtual Images in a Converging Mirror, p. 281; **19:7** Diverging Mirrors, p. 282; **19:8** Lenses, p. 285; **19:9** Converging Lenses, p. 286; **19:10** Virtual Images Produced by a Converging Lens, p. 288; **19:11** Diverging Lenses, p. 289; **19:12** Derivation of the Lens Equation, p. 290; **19:13** Chromatic Aberration, p. 290; **19:14** Optical Devices, p. 290

20 Diffraction Of Light — 294

20:1 Diffraction and Interference, p. 295; **20:2** Measuring the Wavelength of a Light Wave, p. 297; **20:3** Single-Slit Diffraction, p. 300; **20:4** Resolving Power of Lenses, p. 302

21 The Origin Of Light — 306

21:1 Charged Particles Generate Light, p. 307; **21:2** The Excitation of Atoms, p. 308; **21:3** Means by Which Atoms Are Excited, p. 309; **21:4** Fluorescence and Phosphorescence, p. 309; **21:5** Allowed Transitions, p. 310; **21:6** Emission Spectra, p. 312; **21:7** Absorption Spectra, p. 313; **21:8** Fraunhofer Lines, p. 314; **21:9** Lasers and Masers, p. 314

22 Static Electricity 320

22:1 Micro-structure of Matter, p. 321; **22:2** Charging Bodies Electrically, p. 322; **22:3** Electrostatic Demonstrations, p. 323; **22:4** Charged Bodies Attract Neutral Bodies, p. 324; **22:5** Grounding, p. 325; **22:6** Conductors and Insulators, p. 326; **22:7** Concentration of Charge, p. 327; **22:8** Electric Potential Energy, p. 327; **22:9** Electric Circuits, p. 328; **22:10** The Coulomb, p. 329; **22:11** Coulomb's Law, p. 330; **22:12** Electric Fields, p. 332; **22:13** Electric Field Intensity, p. 334; **22:14** The Electric Field Between Two Parallel Plates, p. 334

23 Electric Currents 338

23:1 Difference in Potential, p. 339; **23:2** Work and Energy, p. 341; **23:3** The General Plan of an Electric Circuit, p. 342; **23:4** The Ampere and Electric Power, p. 344; **23:5** Ohm's Law, p. 345; **23:6** Diagramming Electric Circuits, p. 346; **23:7** Controlling Current in a Circuit, p. 347; **23:8** Heating Effect of Electric Currents, p. 348; **23:9** Transmission of Current Over Long Distances, p. 350; **23:10** The Electronvolt, p. 351

24 Series And Parallel Circuits 354

24:1 Series Circuits, p. 355; **24:2** Voltage Drops in a Series Circuit, p. 357; **24:3** Parallel Circuits, p. 359; **24:4** Characteristics of Parallel Circuits, p. 361; **24:5** Series-Parallel Circuits, p. 364; **24:6** Ammeters and Voltmeters, p. 367

25 The Magnetic Field 372

25:1 General Properties of Magnets, p. 373; **25:2** Magnetic Fields Around Permanent Magnets, p. 374; **25:3** Magnetic Fields Between Like and Unlike Poles, p. 375; **25:4** Electromagnetism, p. 375; **25:5** Magnetic Fields Around a Current-Bearing Wire, p. 376; **25:6** Magnetic Field Around a Coil, p. 377; **25:7** Theory of Magnetism, p. 378; **25:8** Interaction of Magnetic Fields, p. 379; **25:9** The Direction of the Force, p. 381; **25:10** Measuring the Force on the Wire, p. 382; **25:11** The Force on a Single Charged Particle, p. 383; **25:12** Electric Motors, p. 385; **25:13** Electric Meters, p. 386

26 Electromagnetic Induction 390

26:1 Faraday's Discovery, p. 391; **26:2** Direction of a Current in a Wire, p. 392; **26:3** Induced EMF, p. 393; **26:4** The Electric Generator, p. 394; **26:5** Alternating Current Generator, p. 396; **26:6** Generators and Motors, p. 398; **26:7** Lenz's Law, p. 399; **26:8** Self-Induction, p. 400; **26:9** Transformers, p. 400

27 Electromagnetic Field Applications 406

27:1 Generation of Electromagnetic Waves, p. 407; **27:2** The Discovery of X Rays, p. 408; **27:3** Transmission of Electromagnetic Waves, p. 411; **27:4** Millikan's Oil-Drop Experiment, p. 415; **27:5** Determining the Mass of an Electron, p. 417; **27:6** The Mass Spectrograph, p. 421

28 The Quantum Theory 426

28:1 The Photoelectric Effect, p. 427; **28:2** The Quantum Theory of Light, p. 431; **28:3** The Compton Effect, p. 432; **28:4** The Heisenberg Uncertainty Principle, p. 433; **28:5** Matter Waves, p. 434

29 The Atom 438

29:1 Radioactivity, p. 439; **29:2** Discovery of the Nucleus, p. 440; **29:3** The Neutron, p. 442; **29:4** Planetary Model of the Atom, p. 442; **29:5** Isotopes, p. 443; **29:6** The Bohr Model of the Atom, p. 444; **29:7** Bohr's Equations, p. 446; **29:8** Success of Bohr's Model of the Atom, p. 449; **29:9** Present Model of the Atom, p. 450

30 The Nucleus 454

30:1 Atomic Number and Mass Number, p. 455; **30:2** Radioactive Transmutation, p. 456; **30:3** Nuclear Equations, p. 457; **30:4** Nuclear Bombardment, p. 458; **30:5** The Cyclotron, p. 459; **30:6** Linear Accelerators, p. 460; **30:7** Particle Detectors, p. 461; **30:8** Artificial Transmutation, p. 463; **30:9** Artificial Radioactivity, p. 464; **30:10** Half-Life, p. 465; **30:11** Binding Force Within the Nucleus, p. 466; **30:12** Calculating Binding Energy, p. 467; **30:13** Nuclear Particles, p. 468; **30:14** Nuclear Fission, p. 470; **30:15** The Nuclear Reactor, p. 471; **30:16** Breeder Reactors, p. 474; **30:17** Nuclear Fusion, p. 474; **30:18** Controlled Fusion, p. 475

Appendix A   Trigonometric Functions   482
Appendix B   International Atomic Masses   483
Appendix C   Physical Constants and Conversion Factors   484
Appendix D   Useful Equations   485
Appendix E   Physics-Related Careers   486
Answers to Odd-Numbered Problems   489
Index   497

Through the ages, people have watched the sun rise and set regularly. They have observed many other phenomena take place over and over. By analyzing these observations, people have attempted to gain a better understanding of the world around them. As a result, in recent years scientists have concluded that certain laws are basic to all sciences. Mathematics is a very useful tool which scientists use to test these laws. In what ways do you find mathematics useful?

FUNDAMENTAL MATHEMATICS

During the past several centuries, scientists have explored almost every aspect of our world. One of the most exciting discoveries is that all of science is tied together by a few simple and fundamental relationships. The relationships that describe the movement of the earth around the sun also describe how electrons move through a TV set. Even the flow of blood through your veins can be described by these same relationships. Scientists have also found that sunlight, radio waves, sound waves, and the ripples in a puddle of water act very much alike and show the same relationships. In short, there are laws that are basic to all the sciences. The science that examines these fundamental laws is called physics.

Through your study of physics you will learn about the fundamental laws that tie science together. You may plan to major in science or in a nonscience field of study. In either case, an understanding of physics concepts is important. Almost every vocation is now affected by recent scientific findings. Also, many of the decisions that we, as citizens, will have to make call for an understanding of science.

GOAL: You will review the basic mathematics operations needed to solve quickly and successfully problems associated with this physics course.

Physics is the science that examines the relationships of matter and energy.

1:1 Solving Equations Algebraically

Suppose that you need to solve an equation for an unknown. For example, you may need to find the value of a in the equation

$$F = ma$$

To do this, the equation must be solved for a. We can do this by remembering that whenever any operation is performed on one side of an equation, the same operation must also be done on the

Practice this meth
equations un'
them on si

3

other side of the equation. In the present example, we first divide both sides of the equation by m. This gives us the equation

$$\frac{F}{m} = a$$

The unknown is usually placed on the left side of an equation. Thus, this should be rewritten

$$a = \frac{F}{m}$$

If an equation contains several factors, the same process is followed until the unknown is isolated.

Example: Solving Equations

Solve the following equation for x: $\qquad\qquad \dfrac{ay}{x} = \dfrac{cb}{s}$

Solution:

   (Multiply both sides by x) $\qquad\qquad\qquad ay = \dfrac{cbx}{s}$

   (Multiply both sides by s) $\qquad\qquad\qquad ays = cbx$

   (Divide both sides by cb) $\qquad\qquad\qquad \dfrac{ays}{cb} = x$

   (Rewrite with x on the left side) $\qquad\qquad x = \dfrac{ays}{cb}$

PROBLEMS

1. You know that $2 = \dfrac{8}{4}$. Use the method described above to solve this equation for (a) 8, and (b) 4.

2. Solve the following equations for v:

   (a) $s = vt$, (b) $t = \dfrac{s}{v}$, (c) $a = \dfrac{v^2}{2s}$ and, (d) $\dfrac{v}{a} = \dfrac{b}{c}$

3. Solve the equation $s = \dfrac{at^2}{2}$ for (a) t^2, (b) a, and (c) 2.

4. Solve each of these equations for E: (a) $f = \dfrac{E}{s}$,

   (b) $m = \dfrac{2E}{v^2}$, and (c) $m = \dfrac{E}{c^2}$.

5. Solve the equation $P = hD$ for (a) h, and (b) D.

6. Solve the equation $v^2 = 2as$ for (a) s, (b) a, and (c) v.

1:2 Scientific Notation

Scientists often work with very large and very small numbers. For example, the mass of the earth is about 6 000 000 000 000 000 000 000 000 kg and the mass of an electron is 0.000 000 000 000 000 000 000 000 000 000 911 kg. In this form, numbers take up much

FIGURE 1-1. The Androm-
eda Galaxy (a) is thought
to have a diameter of
about 200 000 light years,
or 1.9×10^{18} kilometers.
The human hair (b) pass-
ing through the eye of
this needle has a diameter
of about 0.1 mm, or 1.0×10^{-4} m.

space and are difficult to use in calculations. To work with such
numbers more easily, you can write them in a shortened form by
expressing decimal places as powers of ten. This method of expressing numerals is called **scientific notation.**

To write numbers in good scientific notation, move the decimal
point until only one digit appears to the left of the decimal point.
Count the number of places you moved the decimal point and use
that number as the exponent of the power of ten. Thus, the mass
of the earth can also be expressed as 6×10^{24} kg. Note that the
exponent is positive when the decimal point is moved to the left.

Place one digit to the left of the
decimal point in scientific notation.

$$1\ 000\ 000 = 1 \times 10^6$$
$$96\ 000 = 9.6 \times 10^4$$
$$365 = 3.65 \times 10^2$$

A positive exponent shows the
number of places the decimal
point has been moved to the
left.

To write the mass of the electron in scientific notation the decimal point is moved 31 places to the right. Thus, the mass of the
electron can also be written as 9.11×10^{-31} kg. Note that the exponent is negative when the decimal point is moved to the right.

$$0.000\ 63 = 6.3 \times 10^{-4}$$
$$0.007 = 7 \times 10^{-3}$$
$$0.000\ 000\ 95 = 9.5 \times 10^{-7}$$

A negative exponent shows the
number of places the decimal
point has been moved to the
right.

PROBLEMS

Express the following numbers in scientific notation.

7. (a) 5800   (b) 450 000   (c) 60 000   (d) 86 000 000 000
8. (a) 0.000 58   (b) 0.000 000 45   (c) 0.0036   (d) 0.004
9. (a) 300 000 000   (b) 186 000   (c) 93 000 000
10. (a) 0.0073   (b) 0.000 87   (c) 0.0032
11. (a) 5 000 000 000 000 000 000 000 000
    (b) 0.000 000 000 000 000 000 166

1:3   Addition and Subtraction In Scientific Notation

Suppose you need to add or subtract numbers expressed in scientific notation. If they have the same exponent they are added and subtracted by simply adding or subtracting the coefficients and keeping the same power of ten.

Examples: Adding and Subtracting With Like Exponents

$$\text{(a)} \quad 4 \times 10^8 \; + 3 \times 10^8 \; = 7 \times 10^8$$
$$\text{(b)} \quad 4 \times 10^{-8} + 3 \times 10^{-8} = 7 \times 10^{-8}$$
$$\text{(c)} \quad 8 \times 10^6 \; - 4 \times 10^6 \; = 4 \times 10^6$$
$$\text{(d)} \quad 8 \times 10^{-6} - 4 \times 10^{-6} = 4 \times 10^{-6}$$

If the powers of ten are not the same, they must be made the same before the numbers are added or subtracted. This is done by moving the decimal points until the exponents are the same.

Examples: Adding and Subtracting With Unlike Exponents

$$\text{(a)} \quad 4.0 \times 10^6 \; + 3 \times 10^5 \; = 4.0 \times 10^6 \; + 0.3 \times 10^6 \; = 4.3 \times 10^6$$
$$\text{(b)} \quad 4.0 \times 10^6 \; - 3 \times 10^5 \; = 4.0 \times 10^6 \; - 0.3 \times 10^6 \; = 3.7 \times 10^6$$
$$\text{(c)} \quad 4.0 \times 10^{-6} - 3 \times 10^{-7} = 4.0 \times 10^{-6} - 0.3 \times 10^{-6} = 3.7 \times 10^{-6}$$

FIGURE 1-2. Examples of calculators in use today are (a) the abacus which has been used in a variety of forms since the Middle Ages, and (b) this modern electronic calculator.

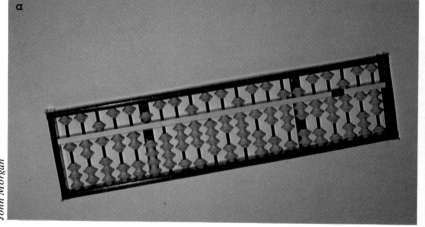

John Morgan

William Maddox

PROBLEMS

Find the value of each of the following equations. (Express your answers in scientific notation.)

12. (a) $5 \times 10^7 + 3 \times 10^7$ (c) $4.2 \times 10^4 + 3.6 \times 10^4$
     (b) $6 \times 10^8 + 2 \times 10^8$ (d) $1.8 \times 10^9 + 2.5 \times 10^9$

13. (a) $5 \times 10^{-7} + 3 \times 10^{-7}$ (c) $1.66 \times 10^{-19} + 2.30 \times 10^{-19}$
     (b) $4 \times 10^{-3} + 3 \times 10^{-3}$ (d) $7.2 \times 10^{-12} + 2.6 \times 10^{-12}$

14. (a) $6 \times 10^8 - 4 \times 10^8$ (c) $5.8 \times 10^9 - 2.8 \times 10^9$
      (b) $3.8 \times 10^{12} - 1.9 \times 10^{12}$

15. (a) $6 \times 10^{-8} - 4 \times 10^{-8}$ (c) $5.8 \times 10^{-9} - 2.8 \times 10^{-9}$
      (b) $3.8 \times 10^{-12} - 1.9 \times 10^{-12}$

16. (a) $6.0 \times 10^8 + 4 \times 10^7$ (c) $4 \times 10^4 + 3.0 \times 10^5$
      (b) $7.0 \times 10^4 + 2 \times 10^3$

17. (a) $5.0 \times 10^{-7} + 4 \times 10^{-8}$ (c) $3.0 \times 10^{-14} + 2 \times 10^{-15}$
      (b) $6.0 \times 10^{-3} + 2 \times 10^{-4}$

18. (a) $5.0 \times 10^{-7} - 4 \times 10^{-8}$ (c) $3.0 \times 10^{-14} - 2 \times 10^{-15}$
      (b) $6.0 \times 10^{-3} - 2 \times 10^{-4}$

1:4   Multiplication and Division in Scientific Notation

Numbers expressed in scientific notation can be multiplied even when the exponents are not the same. First, multiply the numbers preceding the powers of ten. Then, add the exponents of ten to obtain the correct power of ten for the product.

Examples: Multiplication Using Scientific Notation

    (a) $(3 \times 10^6)\ (2 \times 10^3) \ = 6 \times 10^9$

    (b) $(2 \times 10^{-5})\ (4 \times 10^9) \ = 8 \times 10^4$

    (c) $(4 \times 10^3)\ (5 \times 10^{11}) \ = 20 \times 10^{14} = 2 \times 10^{15}$

When multiplying in scientific notation, the exponents of 10 are added.

Numbers expressed in scientific notation can also be divided even when the exponents are not the same. First, divide the numbers preceding the powers of ten. Then, subtract the exponent in the denominator from the exponent in the numerator. The result is the power of ten for the answer.

Examples: Division Using Scientific Notation

    (a) $\dfrac{8 \times 10^6}{2 \times 10^3} = 4 \times 10^{6-3} = 4 \times 10^3$

    (b) $\dfrac{8 \times 10^6}{2 \times 10^{-2}} = 4 \times 10^{6-(-2)} = 4 \times 10^8$

When dividing in scientific notation, the exponents of 10 are subtracted.

PROBLEMS

Find the value of each of the following:

19. (a) $(2 \times 10^4)\ (4 \times 10^8)$
      (b) $(3 \times 10^4)\ (2 \times 10^6)$
      (c) $(6 \times 10^{-4})\ (5 \times 10^{-8})$
      (d) $(2.5 \times 10^{-7})\ (2.5 \times 10^{16})$

20. (a) $\dfrac{6 \times 10^8}{2 \times 10^4}$ (b) $\dfrac{6 \times 10^8}{2 \times 10^{-4}}$ (c) $\dfrac{6 \times 10^{-8}}{2 \times 10^4}$ (d) $\dfrac{6 \times 10^{-8}}{2 \times 10^{-4}}$

21. (a) $\dfrac{(3 \times 10^4)\,(4 \times 10^4)}{6 \times 10^4}$ (c) $\dfrac{(2.5 \times 10^6)\,(6 \times 10^4)}{5 \times 10^2}$

     (b) $\dfrac{(3 \times 10^4)\,(4 \times 10^4)}{6 \times 10^{-4}}$ (d) $\dfrac{(6 \times 10^{12})\,(6 \times 10^{-6})}{1.2 \times 10^6}$

1:5   Trigonometry of Right Triangles

Trigonometry is the study of the properties of triangles.

Trigonometry (trig uh NAHM uh tree) deals with the relations between angles and sides of triangles. Look at the right triangle in Figure 1-3. A right triangle is one which contains a 90° angle. In Figure 1-3, the angles are labeled A, B, and C. The side opposite angle A is labeled a. The side opposite angle B is labeled b. The side opposite angle C is labeled c.

FIGURE 1-3

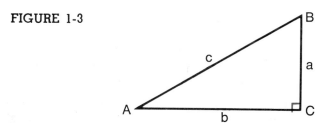

Sine, cosine, and tangent are 3 common functions of angles.

Three common functions of an angle are called the sine (sin), cosine (cos), and tangent (tan). For angle A, these functions are expressed as

$$\text{sine } A = \frac{\text{opposite side}}{\text{hypotenuse}} \quad \text{or} \quad \sin A = \frac{a}{c}$$

$$\text{cosine } A = \frac{\text{adjacent side}}{\text{hypotenuse}} \quad \text{or} \quad \cos A = \frac{b}{c}$$

$$\text{tangent } A = \frac{\text{opposite side}}{\text{adjacent side}} \quad \text{or} \quad \tan A = \frac{a}{b}$$

Example:

Angle A in Figure 1-3 is 30°. The hypotenuse is 8 cm. What is the length of side a and of side b? (The sine and cosine of 30° are found in Table A-1 of Appendix A.)

Solution:

(a) $\sin A = \dfrac{a}{c}$ (b) $\cos A = \dfrac{b}{c}$

     $a = c \sin A$ $b = c \cos A$

       $= 8 \text{ cm} \times 0.50$ $= 8 \text{ cm} \times 0.866$

       $= 4 \text{ cm}$ $= 7 \text{ cm}$

PROBLEMS

22. Use Table A-1 of Appendix A, to find the size of the angles associated with each trigonometric function below. The Greek letter theta, θ, is used to designate the unknown angle.

(a) $\sin \theta = 0.500$ (e) $\tan \theta = 1.00$

(b) $\sin \theta = 0.985$ (f) $\tan \theta = 0.364$

(c) $\cos \theta = 0.707$ (g) $\tan \theta = 2.050$

(d) $\sin \theta = 0.707$ (h) $\cos \theta = 0.866$

23. One angle of a right triangle is 20°. The length of the hypotenuse is 6 cm. (a) Construct the triangle graphically and measure the lengths of the other two sides. (b) Use trigonometry to calculate the lengths of these two sides.

24. One acute angle of a right triangle is 40°. The length of the hypotenuse is 12 cm. (a) Construct the triangle and measure the lengths of the other two sides. (b) Use trigonometry to calculate the lengths of these two sides.

25. One angle of a right triangle is 60°. The length of the hypotenuse is 15 cm. Calculate the lengths of the other two sides.

26. One acute angle of a right triangle is 35°. The length of the side opposite the angle is 14 cm. Use the tangent of 35° to calculate the length of the side adjacent to the angle.

27. One acute angle of a right triangle is 37°. The length of the side opposite the angle is 12 cm. (a) Calculate the length of the side adjacent to the angle. (b) Calculate the length of the hypotenuse.

1:6 The Law of Cosines

To use the trigonometry of the right triangle, two of the sides of a triangle must be perpendicular. That is, you must have a right triangle. But sometimes you will need to work with a triangle that is not a right triangle. The **law of cosines** applies to *all*

The law of cosines applies to all triangles.

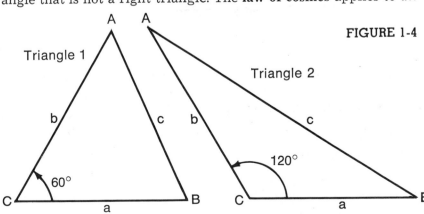

FIGURE 1-4

FIGURE 1-5. Survey teams make use of trigonometric functions in their measurements.

triangles. Consider the two triangles shown in Figure 1-4. They are not right triangles. When angle C is known, the lengths of the sides obey the following relationship.

$$c^2 = a^2 + b^2 - 2ab \cos C$$

When the angle C is larger than 90°, its cosine is negative and is numerically equal to the cosine of its supplement. In triangle 2, Figure 1-4, angle C is 120°. Therefore, its cosine is the negative of the cosine of (180° − 120°) or 60°. The cosine of 60° is 0.500. Thus, the cosine of 120° is −0.500.

PROBLEMS

28. In triangle 1 of Figure 1-4, let the length of side a be 7 cm, the length of side b be 8 cm, and the angle C be 60°. (a) Construct this triangle graphically and measure side c. Record the value. (b) Use the law of cosines to calculate the length of side c. Compare the measured and calculated values.

29. In triangle 2 of Figure 1-4, let the length of side a be 8 cm, the length of side b be 10 cm, and angle C be 120°. (a) Construct this triangle graphically and measure the length of side c. (b) Use the law of cosines to calculate the length of side c. Compare this solution with your graphical solution.

1:7 The Law of Sines

The law of sines applies to all triangles.

Just as the law of cosines applies to all triangles, the **law of sines** applies to all triangles. The relationship is

$$\frac{a}{\sin A} = \frac{b}{\sin B} = \frac{c}{\sin C}$$

PROBLEMS

30. In triangle 1 of Figure 1-4, the length of side a is 7 cm, and the length of side b is 8 cm. If angle A is 53°, calculate the value of angle B.

31. In triangle 2 of Figure 1-4, the length of side b is 10 cm, and the length of side a is 8 cm. Angle A is 26°. Calculate the value of angle B. (For the sine of 120°, use the sine of its supplement, 60°.)

32. The three included angles of a triangle are angle $A = 55°$, angle $B = 55°$, and angle $C = 70°$. If the length of side c is 20 cm, what are the lengths of sides a and b?

1:8　Units and Equations

In mathematics you learned not to mix units if you wanted meaningful answers to problems. To find the area of a rectangle, you cannot multiply the length by the width if the two sides are measured in different units. You have to change one of the units to agree with the remaining unit in order to obtain a reasonable answer. How can you multiply 12 meters by 60 centimeters? You must first change the units so they are all the same. Thus, our example might be written 12 meters times 0.60 meters. This gives a meaningful answer of 7.2 square meters. Similar quantities must be expressed in the same units in calculations.

Units must be uniform when solving a problem.

Quantities such as length, speed, and area are called *dimensional quantities*. A measured dimensional quantity has a numerical value that depends upon the system of units used. For example, a given area can be stated as either 1 square meter or 10 000 square centimeters. When making a measurement, the most convenient unit is used.

Examples of dimensional quantities are length, speed, and area.

When writing an equation in physics, you must state the units as well as the numerical values. This helps you to keep consistent units in the equation. This also tells you if the equation is dimensionally correct.

All equations in physics must agree dimensionally.

Example: Dimensionally Correct Equation

$$\text{mass} = \text{density} \times \text{volume}$$

$$\text{kg} = \frac{\text{kg}}{\text{m}^3} \times \text{m}^3$$

$$\text{kg} = \text{kg}$$

Units divide out as factors to give the correct label in the solution.

Note that the units on the right side of the equation divide out. This shows that the dimensions on both sides of the equation are the same. The equations are dimensionally correct.

Example: Dimensionally Incorrect Equation

$$\text{velocity} = \text{distance} \times \text{time}$$

$$\frac{m}{sec} = m \times sec$$

$$\frac{m}{sec} \neq \text{m-sec}$$

Notice that the units on the right sides do not agree with those on the left sides. By inspecting the dimensions you should be immediately aware that the equations are not correct.

PROBLEM

33. Substitute suitable units into the following equations and state which are dimensionally correct.
   (a) area $=$ length $\times$ width $\times$ height
   (b) time $= \dfrac{\text{distance}}{\text{velocity}}$
   (c) distance $=$ velocity $\times$ time squared

SUMMARY

Physics is the study of the basic scientific laws that can be applied to all the sciences. A knowledge of physics is important to all individuals in gaining an understanding of the world around them. It also makes us, as citizens, better able to make decisions about science-related questions.

The physicist often works with numbers. Some of these numbers are very large and others are very small. Expressed in scientific notation, these numbers can easily be read and handled in calculations.

Trigonometry is useful in calculations involving triangles. There are simple relationships between the sides and angles of right triangles. The law of cosines can be used for calculations on other types of triangles.

Units should always be included in physics problems. These units can then be checked for dimensional accuracy. This will tell you if you have used correct equations and units.

QUESTIONS

1. Define physics.
2. Write a paragraph explaining how equations may be solved for an unknown quickly and efficiently.
3. How may an equation be checked to tell whether or not it is written correctly?

PROBLEMS

1. Solve each of these equations for x.

   (a) $W = fx$ (b) $g = \dfrac{f}{x}$ (c) $m = \dfrac{x}{y}$ (d) $s = \dfrac{ax^2}{2}$

2. Express these numbers in scientific notation.
   (a) 650 000   (c) 226
   (b) 5 000 000   (d) 4500

3. Write these numbers in scientific notation.
   (a) 0.025   (c) 0.0006
   (b) 0.000 25   (d) 0.000 000 000 000 19

4. Find the value of:
   (a) $6 \times 10^8 + 3 \times 10^8$
   (b) $2.2 \times 10^4 + 3.6 \times 10^4$
   (c) $5.0 \times 10^8 + 6.0 \times 10^7$
   (d) $9.8 \times 10^5 + 2.0 \times 10^4$

5. Subtract:
   (a) $8.4 \times 10^{-8} - 3.2 \times 10^{-8}$
   (b) $5.4 \times 10^7 - 3.4 \times 10^7$
   (c) $6.0 \times 10^{-8} - 6.0 \times 10^{-9}$
   (d) $2.2 \times 10^{12} - 8.0 \times 10^{11}$

6. Multiply:
   (a) $(3 \times 10^4)(2 \times 10^4)$
   (b) $(4 \times 10^6)(6 \times 10^4)$
   (c) $(2.2 \times 10^{12})(3.6 \times 10^{20})$
   (d) $(9.5 \times 10^{14})(6.0 \times 10^8)$

7. Divide:
   (a) $(6 \times 10^{14}) \div (3 \times 10^7)$
   (b) $(9.9 \times 10^{12}) \div (4.5 \times 10^{-6})$
   (c) $(2.6 \times 10^{-8}) \div (4.0 \times 10^{-4})$
   (d) $(5.8 \times 10^3) \div (6.0 \times 10^{-2})$

8. Consult Table A-1 of Appendix A to find the number of degrees associated with these trigonometric functions.
   (a) $\sin \theta = 0.0848$
   (b) $\sin \theta = 0.5150$
   (c) $\sin \theta = 0.3090$
   (d) $\cos \theta = 0.9816$
   (e) $\cos \theta = 0.7771$
   (f) $\cos \theta = 0.2588$
   (g) $\tan \theta = 0.3640$
   (h) $\tan \theta = 1.000$
   (i) $\tan \theta = 3.0777$

9. One acute angle of a right triangle is 26°. The hypotenuse is 10 cm. Calculate the lengths of the other two sides.

10. One angle of a right triangle is 50°. The length of the side opposite the 50° angle is 8.5 cm. Calculate the length of the adjacent side and the hypotenuse.

11. The three included angles of a triangle are, angle $A = 39°$, angle $B = 31°$ and angle $C = 110°$. If the length of side c is 14.7 cm, what is the length of side a and of side b?

12. Substitute any suitable and consistent units into each of the following equations and then state which are correct and which are incorrect.
   (a) $\text{velocity} = \dfrac{\text{distance}}{\text{time}}$
   (b) $\text{area} = \dfrac{\text{height}}{\text{volume}}$
   (c) $\text{pressure} = \dfrac{\text{area}}{\text{force}}$
   (d) $\text{time} = \sqrt{\dfrac{\text{length}}{\text{length/sec}^2}}$

PROJECTS

1. List as many formulas as you can think of from your mathematics courses that deal with volume and area. Can you show, by substituting units for the symbols, that they are dimensionally correct?

2. The development of light-emitting-diodes (LED) and integrated circuits (IC) have made modern calculators portable, inexpensive, and available everywhere. Not all calculators are the same. Some have more desirable features than others. Try using several different calculators where they are offered for sale. Also, look at calculator advertisements in catalogs and newspapers. In view of your present and future needs, make a list of the important features that you would look for in a calculator.

READINGS

De Long, Howard, "Unsolved Problems in Arithmetic." *Scientific American,* March, 1971.

Gardner, Martin, *Mathematical Carnival.* Westminster, Maryland, Alfred A. Knopf, Inc., 1975.

Toth, Imre, "Non-Euclidean Geometry Before Euclid." *Scientific American,* November, 1969.

Measuring devices are constantly being improved, and standard units of measurement are becoming accepted internationally. As a result, we are able to learn more about our world and to share this knowledge with others. This scientist is making measurements during a study of glaciers. In what ways do you depend on measurements in your daily life?

MEASUREMENT

Our knowledge of science has grown rapidly during the last 300 years. This growth is due to the wide use of a special method of studying the world around us. This method involves experimentation. In order to do meaningful experiments, early scientists had to develop measuring devices and standards for measurement. This finally led to the development of the metric system of measurement. The metric system is now used by scientists all over the world. As improved measuring devices and standards are developed, we will be able to find out much more about our world.

GOAL: You will gain knowledge and understanding of the metric system, the basic process of measurement, significant digits, and the graphing of data.

2:1 Measurement and the Scientific Method

Physics received great impetus during the sixteenth and seventeenth centuries. At that time, scientists began to realize that all physical events follow understandable laws. One of the first scientists to understand this was Galileo Galilei (1564-1642). While still at the university, he challenged so-called knowledge that was based on little, if any, observation or experimentation. He questioned the belief that the earth is the center of the universe. He doubted Aristotle's views on physics, especially the idea that objects of large mass fall faster than objects of small mass.

Galileo was dismissed from the university before he could complete his studies. But this did not cause him to change his ideas. He knew that he could answer his critics only by showing them proof that could not be denied. To do this, he developed a systematic method of observation and analysis. He carefully measured the way in which small spheres roll down smooth ramps and kept a record of his observations. Analysis of this data showed that all objects fall at the same speed regardless of their masses. Galileo also studied motion. He found that all motion follows a simple set of laws. We now call this set of laws the science of **kinematics** (kin uh MAT iks). He observed the heavens with a telescope. He confirmed the theory of Copernicus that the earth travels around the sun while spinning on its axis. This discovery did not agree

Kinematics is the study of motion.

15

The Bettmann Archive, Inc.

FIGURE 2-1. The scientific method of studying natural events was developed by Galileo. He kept detailed records of his observations.

with the religious belief of that day. As a result, Galileo was brought before the Inquisition. He was kept a prisoner in his home for the rest of his life.

The method developed by Galileo to study natural events is known today as the **scientific method.** It is based on systematic experimentation through careful measurement and analysis. From the analyses, conclusions are drawn. These conclusions are then tested to find out if they are valid. Since Galileo's time, scientists all over the world have used this method to gain a better understanding of the universe.

Scientific method requires careful measurement and analysis.

2:2 Fundamental and Derived Units

In mechanics, three fundamental units are used to measure the quantities mass, length, and time.

Derived units are combinations of fundamental units.

In mechanics, three **fundamental units** are used to measure quantities. These are the units for the quantities mass, length, and time. Units for all other quantities are expressed in terms of these three basic units and thus are called **derived units**. For example, area is found by multiplying length by width. Volume can be found by multiplying length by width by height. Density can be expressed as mass divided by volume.

2:3 The Metric System

The metric system is a decimal system of measurement.

The three basic units in the MKS system are the meter, the kilogram, and the second.

In 1790, French scientists created the metric system of measurement. The metric system is easy to use because units of different sizes are related by powers of 10. One form of the metric system of measurement uses the meter, the kilogram, and the second as its fundamental units. This system is known as the *MKS system.* The MKS system will be used throughout this text.

FIGURE 2-2. Metric units for length (a), mass (b), and volume (c) are widely used today.

The standard unit of length in the MKS system is the meter (m). At first, it was defined as one ten-millionth (10^{-7}) of the distance from the north pole to the equator as measured along a line passing through Paris. This length was marked off on a platinum-iridium bar by making two scratches on the bar. The distance between these two scratches when the bar is at 0° Celsius is the standard meter. It is necessary to state the temperature because metals expand and contract with changes in temperature.

The meter is not exactly one ten-millionth of the distance from the north pole to the equator. The first measurement of this distance was slightly in error. In 1960, the meter was redefined as

The meter (m) is the standard unit of length.

FIGURE 2-3. The United States Bureau of Standards maintains prototype metric length, mass, and volume standards.

Heinz Zinram, Time-Life Books, © Time Inc.

FIGURE 2-4. Timing devices have been used for centuries. Examples are (a) this 10th century sundial with a peg which can be repositioned for different months of the years and (b) the modern cesium clock.

The kilogram (kg) is the standard unit of mass.

The second (sec) is the standard unit of time.

The SI system is a revision of the MKS system of units. It is used internationally.

1 650 763.73 times the wavelength of orange light emitted by a krypton-86 atom.

The mass of an object is the quantity of matter it contains. The standard unit of mass is the kilogram (kg). This is the mass of a platinum-iridium cylinder kept near Paris. One thousandth of this mass is called a gram (g).

In all systems of measurement, the standard unit of time is the second (sec). At first, the second was defined as 1/86 400 of the mean solar day. A mean solar day is the average length of the day over a period of one year. In 1967, the second was redefined in terms of one type of radiation emitted by a cesium-133 atom.

Today, the exchange of scientific knowledge is worldwide. This has led to a need for a system of measurement which is accepted throughout the world. Thus, in 1960, the General Conference of Weights and Measures adopted a revised form of the MKS system for international use. This system of units is called the **International System of Units.** The units are called SI units.

2:4   Prefixes Used With Metric Units

The advantage of the metric system over the English system is that it is a decimal system. Each fraction or multiple of a metric unit is a power of ten. Thus, a tenth of a meter is a decimeter, a hundredth of a meter is a centimeter, and a thousandth of a meter is a millimeter. You can see each of these divisions on a meter stick. It is common practice to express a length as 53 centimeters, not as 5 decimeters and 3 centimeters. This is like saying 53 cents rather than 5 dimes and 3 cents.

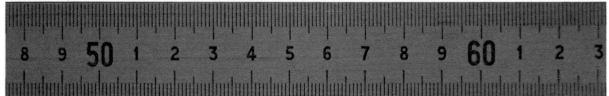

FIGURE 2-5. Fifty-three centimeters can also be expressed as 530 millimeters.

Table 2-1

PREFIXES USED WITH METRIC UNITS

Prefix	Symbol	Meaning	Example
		Fractions	
deci	d	1/10 or 10^{-1}	decimeter (dm)
centi	c	1/100 or 10^{-2}	centimeter (cm)
milli	m	1/1 000 or 10^{-3}	milligram (mg)
micro	μ	1/1 000 000 or 10^{-6}	microgram (μg)
nano	n	1/1 000 000 000 or 10^{-9}	nanometer (nm)
		Multiples	
deka	da	10 or 10^{1}	dekagram (dag)
hecto	h	100 or 10^{2}	hectogram (hg)
kilo	k	1 000 or 10^{3}	kilometer (km)
mega	M	1 000 000 or 10^{6}	megameter (Mm)
giga	G	1 000 000 000 or 10^{9}	gigameter (Gm)

Units in the metric system are related by powers of 10.

FIGURE 2-6. Scientists make observations and measurements in studies conducted (a) in the laboratory, as well as (b) in the field.

2:5   Errors in Measurement

Data (singular, datum) are recorded observations.

Scientists are constantly measuring quantities and comparing the data they obtain. If relationships are found, they must be confirmed through experimentation. Only then do these findings become accepted scientific theories. Our knowledge of the universe and our ability to cope with our surroundings increase through these theories.

All measurements are in error to some degree.

When measuring, recall that every measurement is subject to error. The length of a ruler can change with changes in temperature. An electric measuring device is affected by any magnetic fields near it. In one way or another, all instruments are subject to external influence. Errors in measurement are to be expected.

In addition to error due to external causes, accuracy of measurement depends on the person taking the reading. In a car, the passenger's reading of the gas gauge and the driver's reading of the same gauge can be quite different. From the passenger's seat, the gauge may read empty. From the driver's seat, the gauge may read one-quarter full. The driver's reading is the more correct one.

Parallax is the apparent shift in position of an object as it is viewed from different angles.

Measuring devices must be read by looking at them straight on. If they are not read straight on, an error due to **parallax** (PAR uh laks) is possible. Parallax is the apparent shift in the position of an object when it is viewed from different angles. An object does not move when it is viewed from various angles. It is the reference points behind the object that differ. Thus, the object looks as if it has moved. When sitting next to the driver, you line up the gauge needle on the empty mark. But if you move to the driver's seat, you will line up the needle on the one-quarter-full mark.

FIGURE 2-7. A parallax example. (a) A gasoline gauge as seen from the passenger's seat; (b) the same gauge as seen from the driver's seat. Note the apparent difference in readings.

John Morgan   *John Morgan*

Edwin L. Shay

FIGURE 2-8. The accuracy of this spring scale calibrated in newtons is being checked with a standard weight of 9.8 newtons.

2:6 Accuracy and Precision

Accuracy is the extent to which a measured value agrees with the accepted value for a quantity. For example, the accepted value of π to six digits is 3.141 59. Suppose you determine the value of π to six digits as 3.141 76. Only the first four digits of your value agree with the accepted value. Thus, your value is accurate to only four places.

Precision is the degree of exactness with which a quantity is measured. Precision need not be an indication of accuracy. Your value for π is just as precise as the accepted value because both values contain six digits.

The precision of a measuring device is limited by the finest division on its scale. The finest division on a meter stick is a millimeter. Thus, a measurement of any smaller length with a meter stick can be only an estimate. There is a limit to the precision of even the best instruments.

The accuracy of a measuring device depends upon how well the value obtained by using the instrument agrees with the accepted value. Thus, when a measurement is to be made, the measuring device should first be checked for accuracy. This can be done by using the instrument to measure quantities whose values are known. The measured values are then compared with the known values.

Errors in measurement affect the accuracy of a measurement. But the precision is not affected since values are still stated in terms of the smallest division on the instrument.

Accuracy is the degree of agreement between a measured value and the true value.

Precision is the degree of the instrument's exactness.

FIGURE 2-9. A micrometer caliper can be used to obtain very precise and accurate measurements.

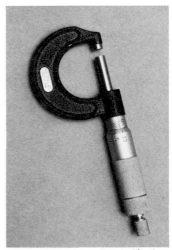

Bruce Charlton

2:7 Significant Digits

Because the precision of all measuring devices is limited, the number of digits that can be assumed for any measurement is also limited. When making a measurement, read the instrument to its finest division and then estimate to within a part of that finest division. The figures that you write down for the measurements are called **significant digits.**

Suppose you want to measure the length of a strip of metal with a meter stick. The metal strip in Figure 2-10 is somewhat longer than 5.6 cm. Looking closely at the scale, you can see that the end of the metal strip is four-tenths of the way between 5.6 cm and 5.7 cm. Therefore, the length of the strip is 5.64 cm. The last digit is an estimate. Either 5.6 cm or 5.7 cm would be more in error than 5.64 cm. The readings of 5.6 cm and 5.7 cm are at least 0.03 cm and probably 0.04 cm in error. It is not likely that a reading of 5.64 cm is more than 0.01 cm in error.

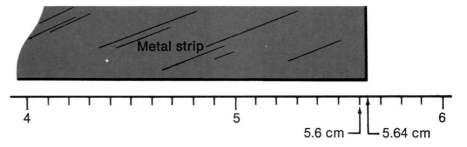

Suppose that the end of the metal strip is right on the 5.6-cm mark. In that case, you can write the measurement as 5.60 cm. The zero indicates that the strip is not 0.01 cm more or less than 5.6 cm. Therefore, the zero is a significant digit for it has meaning. It is the uncertain digit because you are still guessing. The last digit written down for any measurement is the uncertain digit. *All nonzero digits in a measurement are significant.*

Zeroes are often a problem. The zero mentioned in 5.60 cm is significant. However, a zero that only serves to locate the decimal point is not significant. Thus, the value of 0.0026 kg contains two significant digits. The measurement of 0.002060 kg contains four significant digits, the final zero indicating a probable value.

There is no way to tell how many of the zeroes in the number 186 000 are significant. The 6 may have been the estimated digit and the three zeroes may be needed only to place the decimal point. Or, all three zeroes may be significant. To avoid this problem, such measurements are written in **scientific notation.** In the number that appears before the power of ten, all the digits are significant. Thus, 1.860×10^5 has four significant digits.

PROBLEMS

1. State the number of significant digits in each measurement:
   - (a) 2804 m
   - (b) 2.84 m
   - (c) 0.0029 m
   - (d) 0.003 068 m
   - (e) 4.6×10^5 m
   - (f) 4.06×10^5 m
2. State the number of significant digits in each measurement:
   - (a) 75 m
   - (b) 75.00 cm
   - (c) 0.007 060 kg
   - (d) 1.87×10^6 m
   - (e) 1.008×10^8 m
   - (f) 1.20×10^{-4} m

2:8   Operations with Significant Digits

The results of any mathematical operation with measured quantities cannot be more accurate than the least accurate of the quantities involved. Assume that you must add the lengths 6.48 m and 18.2 m. The length 18.2 m is accurate only to a tenth of a meter. Therefore, the sum of the two lengths can be accurate only to a tenth of a meter. To add the two lengths, round off 6.48 m to 6.5 m. Then add 6.5 m to 18.2 m. This gives the sum 24.7 m. Subtraction is handled in the same way. To add or subtract measured quantities, first round off all values to correspond in accuracy to the least accurate value involved.

Example: Significant Digits—Addition

Add: 24.686 m + 2.34 m + 3.2 m

Solution: 24.7 m
           2.3 m
           3.2 m
          ———
        30.2 m

Before adding or subtracting, round off each value to agree in accuracy with the least accurate value.

To multiply or divide two measured quantities, perform the operation before rounding. Then, keep in the product or quotient only as many significant digits as are in the factor with the lesser number of significant digits.

Example: Significant Digits—Multiplication

Multiply: 3.22 cm $\times$ 2.1 cm

Solution: 3. 2 ② cm
             2.① cm
         ——————
          ③②②
      6 4④
      ——————
      6.⑦⑥② cm²

After multiplying or dividing, round off each value to agree in accuracy with the least accurate value.

Note that each digit circled in the example is either a doubtful digit or was obtained by using a doubtful digit. A doubtful digit becomes more doubtful when it is multiplied. Since the 7 in the product is doubtful, the 6 and 2 which represent even finer divisions are certainly not significant. The answer is best stated as 6.8 cm².

PROBLEMS

3. Add: 6.201 cm + 7.4 cm + 0.68 cm + 12.0 cm

4. Add: 28.662 m + 32.34 m + 17.5 m

5. Add: 26.38 kg + 14.531 kg + 30.8 kg

6. The sides of a rectangular plot of land are measured. Their lengths are found to be 132.68 m, 48.3 m, 132.736 m, and 48.37 m. What is the perimeter of the plot of land as can best be determined with these measurements?

7. Subtract: 10.8 g − 8.264 g

8. Subtract: 44.12 ml − 26.82 ml

9. A tank has a mass of 3.64 kg when empty and a mass of 51.8 kg when filled to a certain level with water. What is the mass of the water in the tank?

10. Multiply:
   (a) 1.31 cm × 2.3 cm
   (b) 6.87 cm × 2.2 cm
   (c) 3.2145 km × 4.23 km

11. Divide:
   (a) 20.2 cm ÷ 7.41 cm
   (b) 3.1416 cm ÷ 12.4 cm
   (c) 64.39 m ÷ 13.6 m

12. Measurements of a rectangular floor show the length is 15.72 m and the width is 4.40 m. Calculate the area of the floor to the best possible value using these measurements.

2:9   Graphs

Quantitative experiments are done to learn what relationships exist between measured quantities. During the experiment, one quantity called the *independent variable* is carefully varied. The value of another quantity called the *dependent variable* is measured for each variation of the independent variable. Both values are recorded in a table. The independent variable is placed in the first column and the dependent variable is placed in the second column. A graph can then be plotted from the table. *The values of the independent variable are plotted horizontally (x axis). The values of the dependent variable are plotted vertically (y axis).* The curve that best fits the plotted points is then drawn. Often, the shape of this curve clearly shows the mathematical relation-

The independent variable is plotted horizontally. The dependent variable is plotted vertically.

ship that exists between the dependent and independent variables. A *straight line* passing through the origin shows that the dependent variable y varies directly with the independent variable x. A *hyperbola* shows that the dependent variable varies inversely with the independent variable. A *parabola* shows that the dependent variable varies with the square of the independent variable.

2:10   Linear and Direct Variation

The most general form for a linear equation is

$$y = kx + b$$

where k and b are constants. The graph of a linear equation is a straight line. For example, the graph of the equation $y = 3x + 2$ is shown in Figure 2-11. The values used to plot this table are given in Table 2-2.

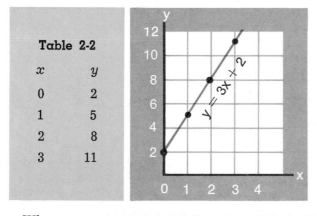

Table 2-2

x	y
0	2
1	5
2	8
3	11

FIGURE 2-11.

When one quantity varies directly with another, it increases or decreases in proportion to an increase or a decrease in the other quantity. The general equation for direct variation is

$$y = kx$$

where k is a constant. The graph of direct variation is always a straight line passing through the origin.

A good example of direct variation is provided by a law discovered by Sir Robert Hooke (1635-1703). Hooke's law states that the stretching of a spring varies directly with the force acting on the spring. Thus, if a force of 1 newton (N) causes a spring to stretch 1.5 cm, a force of 2 N will cause it to stretch 3.0 cm, and a force of 3 N will cause it to stretch 4.5 cm.

In a test of this law, the force acting on a spring was varied and the resulting changes in length were measured. The data is shown in Table 2-3.

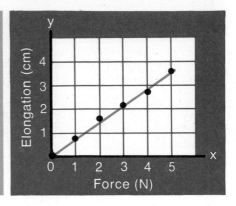

Table 2-3

Force (N)	Elongation (cm)
0	0.0
1	0.7
2	1.5
3	2.1
4	2.7
5	3.5

FIGURE 2-12

By plotting the independent variable (force) on the x axis, and the dependent variable (change in length) on the y axis, we obtain the straight-line graph shown in Figure 2-12. This line passes through the origin. The change in length varies directly with the applied force.

2:11 Inverse Variation

Inverse variation:
   as x increases, y decreases
or as x decreases, y increases

When one quantity varies inversely with another, the second quantity will either decrease as the first increases or increase as the first decreases. The general equation for inverse variation is

$$y = \frac{k}{x}$$

where k is a constant.

The behavior of a gas under varying pressures shows inverse variation. When the pressure acting on a gas is doubled, the volume of the gas is reduced to one-half its initial volume. Conversely, when the pressure on the gas is reduced to one-half the original pressure, the volume of the gas is doubled. Further reductions in pressure cause corresponding increases in volume. Table 2-4 lists data collected during an experiment with a gas. The corresponding graph is a hyperbola.

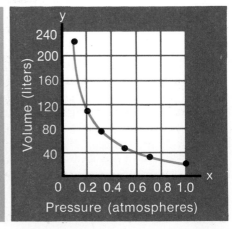

Table 2-4

Pressure (atmospheres)	Volume (liters)
0.1	225
0.2	110
0.3	74.9
0.5	44.6
0.7	32.0
1.0	22.4

FIGURE 2-13

26

Scientific studies show that physical events follow a few fundamental laws. These studies involve the use of the scientific method. This method makes use of experimentation. Measurement is basic to experimentation.

The three basic units of measurement in mechanics are those of length, mass, and time. Other units are combinations of these units and are called derived units. Physicists all over the world use the metric system for the measurements. In this system, the basic units of length, mass, and time are the meter (m), the kilogram (kg), and the second (sec). Metric units are easy to use because larger and smaller units are based on powers of ten.

Accuracy is the extent to which a measured value agrees with the accepted value for a quantity. Precision is the degree of certainty with which a quantity is measured. In making a reading, the number of meaningful digits is limited by the size of the divisions on the scale of the measuring device. The last digit in a reading is an estimate. In a reading, all certain figures and one estimated figure are called significant digits.

Graphs can be plotted to show relationships between independent and dependent variables. The independent variable is plotted on the x axis. The dependent variable is plotted on the y axis. Two typical graphs often result. A straight line graph shows that the quantities are directly proportional to one another. A hyperbola indicates that one quantity varies inversely wih the other.

1. Distinguish between a fundamental unit and a derived unit.
2. What are the fundamental units in the MKS system of measurement?
3. Express speed in terms of fundamental units.
4. What is the importance of the International System of Units?
5. Give the proper name for each multiple of the meter listed:
   (a) 1/100 m   (b) 1/1000 m   (c) 1000 m
6. (a) What is mass? (b) What is the standard unit of mass in the MKS system?
7. (a) Which digit of a measured quantity is the doubtful digit? (b) Is this digit significant?
8. (a) Why is it difficult to tell how many significant digits are in a measured value such as 76 000? (b) How can the number of significant digits in such a number be made clear?
9. During a laboratory experiment, as one quantity is varied the change in the value of a second quantity is measured. What are each of these quantities called?
10. When plotting a graph, (a) what quantity is plotted vertically? (b) what quantity is plotted horizontally?
11. Aristotle wrote (without performing any experiments) that the rate at which an object falls varies inversely with the density of the medium in which it is falling. What would this mean in terms of an object falling through a vacuum? Can you guess why Aristotle wrote that there can be no such thing as a vacuum?

1. State the number of significant digits in each of these measurements:
   (a) 248 m   (b) 64.01 m   (c) 0.000 03 m   (d) 80.001 m
2. State the number of significant digits in the following measurements:
   (a) 2.40×10^6 kg   (b) 6×10^8 kg   (c) 4.07×10^{16} m
3. Add: 16.2 m + 5.008 m + 13.48 m
4. Add: 5.006 m + 12.0077 m + 8.0084 m

5. Subtract: 78.05 cm² − 32.046 cm²

6. Subtract: 15.07 kg − 12.0 kg

7. Multiply:
  (a) 1.42 cm × 1.2 cm   (c) 74.0 cm × 2.54 cm
  (b) 6.8 m × 3.145 m   (d) 8.002 cm² × 1.50 cm

8. Multiply:
  (a) 4.3 cm × 8.26 cm   (c) 0.000 50 m/sec × 0.0030 sec
  (b) $(2.0 \times 10^8$ m$)$ $(1.6 \times 10^7$ m$)$

9. The length of a room is 16.40 m, its width is 4.5 m, and its height is 3.26 m. What volume of air does the room contain?

10. Gold has a density of 19.3 g/cm³. A cube of gold measures 4.23 cm on each edge. (a) What is the volume of the cube? (b) What is its mass?

11. One cubic centimeter of silver has a mass of 10.5 g. (a) What is the mass of 65 cm³ of silver? (b) When placed on a beam balance, a chunk of silver is shown to have a mass of only 616 g. What part of it is hollow?

12. During a laboratory experiment, a student measured the mass of 10 cm³ of water. The student then measured the mass of 20 cm³ of water. In this way, the data in Table 2-5 were collected.

Table 2-5

Volume (cm³)	Mass (g)
10	10.0
20	20.1
30	29.8
40	40.2
50	50.3

(a) Plot the values given in the table and draw the curve that best fits all points. (b) What is the resulting curve called? (c) According to the graph, what is the relationship between the volume of the water and the mass of the water?

13. During a science demonstration, an instructor placed a 1-kg mass on a horizontal table that was nearly frictionless. The instructor then applied various horizontal forces to the mass and measured the rate at which the mass gained speed (was accelerated) for each force applied to it. The results of the experiment are shown in Table 2-6.

Table 2-6

Force (N)	Acceleration (m/sec²)
5.0	4.9
10.0	9.8
15.0	15.2
20.0	20.1
25.0	25.0
30.0	29.9

(a) Plot the values given in the table and draw the curve that best fits all points. (b) According to the graph, what is the relationship between the force applied to a mass and the rate at which it gains speed?

14. The instructor who performed the experiment in Problem 13 then changed the procedure. The mass was varied while the force was kept constant. The rate at which each mass gained speed was then recorded. The results are shown in Table 2-7.

Table 2-7

Mass (kg)	Acceleration (m/sec²)
1.0	12.0
2.0	5.9
3.0	4.1
4.0	3.0
5.0	2.5
6.0	2.0

(a) Plot the values given in Table 2-7 and draw the curve that best fits all points. (b) What is the resulting curve called? (c) According to the graph, what is the relationship between mass and the acceleration produced by a constant force?

PROJECTS

1. Tony's Pizza Shop ordered new 22.86-cm diameter pizza pans. By mistake, 25.40-cm pans were delivered. Tony says that the difference is too small to worry about. As Tony's accountant, what would you say?

2. Debate the following statement: The United States should adopt the metric system of measurement for all commercial transactions.

3. Make a table in which you list the surface areas and volumes of cubes having sides which measure 1 m, 2 m, 3 m, 4 m, 5 m, and 6 m respectively. Add a third column in which you list the ratio of the surface area to volume for each cube. (For example, the first ratio is six to one.)

Now suppose that you are a member of a committee in charge of designing a new high school building for a town which has cold winters Part of the committee is in favor of a one-floor building consisting of many wings. A second group wants a cube-shaped building of several stories. You know that heating is a major cost in the operation of a school and that heat loss takes place through the walls of buildings. How would you cast your vote on the matter?

READINGS

Ambler, Ernest, "Measurement Standards, Physical Constants, and Science Teaching." *The Science Teacher,* November, 1971.

Astin, Allen V., "Standards of Measurement." *Scientific American,* June, 1968.

Dirac, P. A. M., "The Evolution of the Physicist's Picture of Nature." *Scientific American,* May, 1963.

Gardner, Martin, "Can Time Go Backward?" *Scientific American,* January, 1967.

Haber-Schaim, Uri, et al; *PSSC Physics,* 4th ed. Boston, D.C. Heath and Co., 1976.

Page, C. H., and Vigoureux, P., eds., *The International System of Units (SI).* National Bureau of Standards (U.S.), Special Publication 330, July, 1974.

Ritchie-Calder, Lord, "Conversion to the Metric System." *Scientific American,* July, 1970.

Motion describes the movement of an object. An object can have a variety of motions. For example, a car can be moving steadily. It can also be speeding up or slowing down. It can even be standing still. During a trip, a car will probably undergo all of these motions. All of these motions can be described in terms of four quantities. These quantities are speed, acceleration, time, and distance. This car is being driven along a straight stretch of highway. For what reasons might the driver want to know the values of speed, acceleration, time, and distance during an extended trip?

MOTION IN A STRAIGHT LINE

Everything in the universe is in a state of motion. The earth itself is filled with moving things. The earth also spins on its axis. The earth and the other planets of our solar system orbit the sun. Our solar system moves through space as part of the Milky Way Galaxy. Stars and galaxies move away from one another. It might seem impossible to find a simple way to describe and understand the motions of all these objects. But this is just what physicists have done! A few simple equations apply to all motions. They are basic to everything the physicist studies. The amazing thing about physics is that the laws of nature tend to be simple, not complex. An understanding of physics begins with an understanding of motion.

GOAL: You will gain knowledge and understanding of the fundamentals of motion.

3:1 Motion

A body can have only two types of motion. There is no third type of motion. A body can be moving either with a **constant velocity** or with a changing velocity. A change in velocity is called **acceleration** (ak sel uh RAY shuhn). In this chapter, you will study these two types of motion. By applying this knowledge you can understand all motion.

This chapter deals only with motion in a straight line. Motion along a curved path is discussed in Chapter 8. Motion in a curved path is simply straight line motion in two or more directions. For example, follow the path of a baseball as it leaves the player's bat. The ball follows a curved path. This motion can be easily understood. As the ball moves forward in a straight line, it also rises and falls in a straight line. All curved motion can be viewed in this way. An understanding of straight line motion will enable you to understand motion along curved paths.

An object can move either with constant velocity or with acceleration.

Acceleration is the rate of change of velocity.

Curved motion is simply straight line motion in more than one direction.

31

Library of Congress

FIGURE 3-1. One of the first series of high-speed photographs was taken in 1878. The vertical lines are 68 cm apart. The time between exposures is 1/25 sec. What is the average speed of the horse in m/sec?

Instantaneous speed is the speed at a given instant.

Average speed is figured over a time period.

The horizontal bar in $\bar{v}$ means "average."

3:2 Average and Instantaneous Speed

In this chapter the terms speed and velocity are used interchangeably. A detailed discussion of these quantities appears in Chapter 5.

The *instantaneous speed* of a moving body is the actual speed at which it is moving at any given instant. For a car, this is the reading of the speedometer at a given moment. Often a body in motion does not move at a constant speed. During even a short trip, a car speeds up (accelerates) and slows down (decelerates). Thus, the total distance traveled by a body during a period of time is often the result of an average speed. The *average speed* of a body during a time period can be calculated with the equation

$$\bar{v} = \frac{s}{t}$$

Here, $\bar{v}$ is the average speed, s is the distance traveled, and t is the time spent traveling. If the speed is truly constant, the small bar over the v is dropped. Thus, v shows uniform speed.

FIGURE 3-2. This modern high-speed official finish-line photo shows the winning runner of the mile race clocked at 3.54.54 and the second runner clocked at 3.54.75. Officials using hand-operated stop watches had clocked both runners with an identical time of 3.54.6.

Bulova Watch Company

Example: Average Speed

A car travels a distance of 450 km during a 10-hr period. What is its average speed?

Solution:

$$\overline{v} = \frac{s}{t}$$
$$= \frac{450 \text{ km}}{10 \text{ hr}}$$
$$= 45 \text{ km/hr}$$

During some calculations, you may need to change kilometers per hour to meters per second. Recall that a given quantity divided by its equivalent is equal to one. Recall also that the value of any quantity when multiplied by one does not change. We have seen that 1 km = 1000 m, and 1 hr = 3600 sec. It follows that 1000 m ÷ 1 km = 1, and 1 hr ÷ 3600 sec = 1. To change 45 km/hr to m/sec, first multiply by a distance factor whose value is one. Then multiply by a time factor whose value is one.

$$45 \frac{\text{km}}{\text{hr}} \times \frac{1000 \text{ m}}{1 \text{ km}} \times \frac{1 \text{ hr}}{3600 \text{ sec}} = 12.5 \frac{\text{m}}{\text{sec}}$$

This method of converting one unit to an equivalent unit is called the *factor-label method of unit conversion*. Note that unit labels are also treated as factors and can be divided out. If the final units do not make sense, check your factors. You will find that a factor has either been inverted or stated incorrectly.

In the factor-label method, units are divided out as factors.

PROBLEMS

1. A motorist travels a distance of 406 km during a 7-hr period. What was the average speed in (a) km/hr and (b) m/sec?

2. During a canoe race, a camper paddles a distance of 406 m in 70 sec. What is the average speed in (a) m/sec and (b) km/hr?

3. A rocket launched into outer space travels a distance of 240 000 km during the first 6 hr after the launching. What is the average speed of the rocket in (a) km/hr and (b) m/sec?

4. An electron traverses a vacuum tube with a length of 2 m in 2×10^{-3} sec. What is the average speed of the electron during this time in (a) m/sec and (b) cm/sec?

5. Light from the sun requires 8.3 min to reach the earth. The speed of light is 3.0×10^8 m/sec. In kilometers, how far is the earth from the sun?

6. A bullet leaves the muzzle of a rifle and 5 sec later becomes embedded in the trunk of a tree 3000 m away. What is the average speed of the bullet in (a) m/sec and (b) km/hr?

3:3 Uniform Acceleration

Acceleration is the change in velocity per unit time.

Acceleration is the rate at which velocity (or speed) is changing with time. If the speed of a body is increasing, the acceleration is positive. If the speed is decreasing, the acceleration is negative.

The way in which acceleration is expressed may seem confusing at first. Do not confuse acceleration with velocity. They are not the same. Acceleration is the rate of change in speed (or velocity.) It is correctly expressed as meters per second per second. This is the number of meters per second added to or taken away from a body's speed during each second of the acceleration period. Similarly, acceleration might be expressed as kilometers per hour per second. These expressions are usually written as m/sec² and km/hr-sec respectively.

The MKS unit for acceleration is m/sec².

You should think through acceleration equations. Acceleration is the rate of change of speed. Therefore, to find acceleration you divide the change in speed of a body by the time needed to make the change.

$$a = \frac{\Delta v}{t}$$

The symbol Δ denotes "change in."

Here, a represents the acceleration, Δv (read "delta vee") is the change in speed, and t is the time required to make the speed change. In the strictest sense, the change in speed of a body, and therefore its acceleration, occur in spurts. That is, the acceleration is not always constant. In this chapter, we will think of all accelerations as uniform. Here, a will denote constant acceleration.

The change in speed of a body is the difference between its final speed (v_f) and its original speed (v_o). Thus, Δv is simply $v_f - v_o$. By substitution,

$$a = \frac{v_f - v_o}{t}$$

FIGURE 3-3. A multiple exposure photograph of an object moving along a track. Notice that as the object moves to the right the distance traveled between exposures becomes less. Is the object speeding up or slowing down?

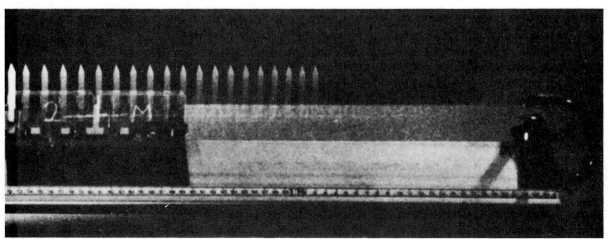

The Ealing Corporation

FIGURE 3-4. From speed and time data, the acceleration of this car can easily be determined.

Example: Positive Acceleration

During an 11-sec period, the speed of a race car is increased uniformly from 44 m/sec to 88 m/sec. What is the acceleration?

Solution:

$$a = \frac{v_f - v_o}{t} = \frac{88 \text{ m/sec} - 44 \text{ m/sec}}{11 \text{ sec}}$$
$$= \frac{44 \text{ m/sec}}{11 \text{ sec}}$$
$$= 4 \text{ m/sec}^2$$

Consider what happens when the racing car slows down uniformly from 88 m/sec to 44 m/sec during the 11 seconds. The same equation can be used again. Subtracting the original speed from the final speed gives a negative value for Δv. This means that the acceleration is negative.

Negative acceleration is deceleration.

Example: Negative Acceleration

During an 11-sec period, the speed of a racing car is decreased uniformly from 88 m/sec to 44 m/sec. What is the acceleration?

Solution:

$$a = \frac{v_f - v_o}{t} = \frac{44 \text{ m/sec} - 88 \text{ m/sec}}{11 \text{ sec}}$$
$$= \frac{-44 \text{ m/sec}}{11 \text{ sec}}$$
$$= -4 \text{ m/sec}^2$$

PROBLEMS

7. What is the acceleration of a racing car if its speed is increased uniformly from 44 m/sec to 66 m/sec over an 11-sec period?

8. What is the acceleration of a racing car if its speed is decreased uniformly from 66 m/sec to 44 m/sec over an 11-sec period?

9. A train moving at a speed of 15 m/sec is accelerated uniformly to 45 m/sec over a 12-sec period. What is its acceleration?

10. A plane starting from rest ($v_o = 0$) is accelerated uniformly to its takeoff speed of 72 m/sec during a 5-sec period. What is the plane's acceleration?

11. A bullet leaves the muzzle of a rifle in a direction straight up with a speed of 700 m/sec. Ten seconds later its speed straight up is only 602 m/sec. At what rate does the earth's gravitational field decelerate the bullet?

12. An arrow is shot straight up with an initial speed of 98 m/sec. Nine seconds later its speed straight up is only 9.8 m/sec. At what rate is the arrow decelerated by the pull of the earth's gravitational field?

13. In a vacuum tube, an electron is accelerated uniformly from rest to a speed of 2.6×10^5 m/sec during a time period of 6.5×10^{-2} sec. Calculate the acceleration of the electron.

3:4 Final Velocity After Uniform Acceleration

In some cases where the uniform acceleration is known, it may be desirable to calculate the final speed of a body at the end of an acceleration period. The equation for acceleration is

$$a = \frac{v_f - v_o}{t}$$

Solving for v_f,
$$v_f - v_o = at$$
$$v_f = v_o + at$$

Example: Final Velocity After Uniform Acceleration

A ball rolling down an incline undergoes a uniform acceleration of 4 m/sec² for 5 sec. If the ball has an initial speed of 2 m/sec when it starts down the incline, what is its final speed?

Solution:

$$v_f = v_o + at$$
$$= 2\,\text{m/sec} + (4\,\text{m/sec}^2 \times 5\,\text{sec})$$
$$= 22\,\text{m/sec}$$

PROBLEMS

14. A car is uniformly accelerated at the rate of 2 m/sec² for 12 seconds. If the original speed of the car is 36 m/sec, what is its final speed?

15. An airplane flying at 90 m/sec is accelerated uniformly at the rate of 0.5 m/sec² for 10 seconds. What is its final speed?

16. A race car traveling at 45 m/sec is slowed uniformly at the rate of −1.5 m/sec² for 10 seconds. What is its final speed in (a) m/sec and (b) km/hr?

17. A spacecraft traveling at 1200 m/sec is uniformly accelerated at the rate of 150 m/sec² by burning its second-stage rocket. If the rocket burns for 18 seconds, what is the final speed of the craft?

3:5   Distance Traveled During Uniform Acceleration

The distance traveled by a body during any given time period can be calculated from the average speed of the body during that time period. Solving the average speed equation for s, we obtain

$$s = \bar{v}t$$

If a body is being uniformly accelerated, its average speed is easy to find.

Consider a car that is accelerated uniformly from 40 m/sec to 60 m/sec during a 10-sec period. The car passes smoothly through the whole set of speeds between 40 m/sec and 60 m/sec. Half of these speeds are less than 50 m/sec. Half are more than 50 m/sec. The average speed is the middle speed, 50 m/sec. The average speed of a uniformly accelerating body is always the middle speed.

Distance is the product of average speed and time.

The average speed of a body which is accelerating uniformly is its middle speed.

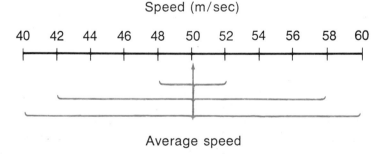

Speed (m/sec)

Average speed

The middle speed of the car can be found by adding the final speed and the initial speed and dividing the sum by two. This can be written

$$\bar{v} = \frac{v_o + v_f}{2}$$

FIGURE 3-5. The average speed of a uniformly accelerated body is the middle speed.

Thus, the average speed of the car in our example is

$$\bar{v} = \frac{40 \text{ m/sec} + 60 \text{ m/sec}}{2} = 50 \text{ m/sec}$$

To find the distance traveled by the body during the acceleration period, substitute the expression for average velocity into the equation $s = \bar{v}t$. This expression becomes

$$s = \left(\frac{v_o + v_f}{2}\right)t$$

Example: Distance Traveled During Uniform Acceleration

What distance is traveled by a train as it is accelerated uniformly from 22 m/sec to 44 m/sec in a 20-sec period?

Solution:

$$s = \left(\frac{v_o + v_f}{2}\right)t$$

$$= \frac{22 \text{ m/sec} + 44 \text{ m/sec}}{2} \times 20 \text{ sec}$$

$$= 660 \text{ m}$$

PROBLEMS

18. A car traveling at 44 m/sec is uniformly decelerated to a speed of 22 m/sec over an 11-sec period. What distance does it travel during this time?

19. A racing car starts from rest ($v_o = 0$) and is accelerated uniformly to 40 m/sec in 8 sec. What distance does the car travel?

20. A plane flying at the speed of 150 m/sec is accelerated uniformly at a rate of 5 m/sec². (a) What is the plane's speed at the end of 10 sec? (b) What distance has it traveled?

21. A rocket traveling at 88 m/sec is accelerated uniformly to 132 m/sec over a 15-sec period. What distance in meters does the rocket travel during this time?

22. An engineer is to design a runway to accommodate airplanes that must gain a ground speed of 60 m/sec before they can take off. If these planes are capable of being accelerated uniformly at the rate of 1.5 m/sec², (a) how long will it take them to achieve take-off speed? (b) What must be the minimum length of the runway?

3:6   Uniform Acceleration—Starting and Stopping

Consider the special case of a body that is accelerated from rest. In this case, $v_o = 0$ and the general equation $v_f = v_o + at$ becomes

$$v_f = at$$

The general equation for the distance traveled by a body with uniform acceleration is

$$s = \left(\frac{v_o + v_f}{2} \right) t$$

But for a body starting from rest, $v_o = 0$ and $v_f = at$. So we can rewrite the above to read

$$s = \left(\frac{at}{2} \right) t$$

This can also be written

$$s = \tfrac{1}{2} at^2$$

Thus, for a body starting from rest, the distance the body travels in any given time can be calculated if its acceleration is known. The same distance will be traveled whether a body starts from rest and is accelerated to 40 m/sec in 10 sec or starts at 40 m/sec and is decelerated to 0 m/sec in 10 sec. The equation can be used for both cases, starting from rest and going to rest.

> The equation, $s = \tfrac{1}{2}at^2$ is used for an object starting from rest or going to rest.

Example: Distance When Acceleration and Time Are Known

A car starting from rest is accelerated at a constant rate of 6.2 m/sec². What distance does the car travel during the first 7 sec of acceleration?

Solution:

$$s = \tfrac{1}{2} at^2$$
$$= \frac{(6.2 \text{ m/sec}^2)(7 \text{ sec})^2}{2}$$
$$= 152 \text{ m}$$

PROBLEMS

23. An airplane starts from rest and undergoes a uniform acceleration of 3 m/sec² for 30 sec before leaving the ground. What distance does it travel during the 30 sec?

24. A jet plane lands on a runway traveling at 88 m/sec and is decelerated uniformly to rest in 11 sec. Calculate (a) its deceleration in m/sec², and (b) the distance it travels.

25. The Tokyo express is accelerated from rest at a constant rate of 1 m/sec² for 1 min. How far does it travel during this time?

26. Starting from rest, a racing car travels a distance of 200 m in the first 5 sec of uniform acceleration. At what rate is it being accelerated?

27. In an emergency, a driver brings a car to a full stop in 5 sec. The car is traveling at a rate of 38 m/sec when braking begins. (a) At what rate is the car decelerated? (b) How far does it travel before stopping?

28. A stone is dropped from an airplane at a height of 490 m. It requires 10 sec to reach the ground. At what rate does gravity accelerate the stone?

The general equations for final velocity (v_f) and total distance (s) can be combined to form an equation for finding the final velocity of a body that starts from rest. Recall that

$$v_f = v_o + at \quad \text{and} \quad s = \frac{v_f + v_o}{2} t$$

When v_o is zero, the equations for v_f and s may be written

$$v_f = at \quad \text{and} \quad s = \frac{v_f}{2} t$$

Solving for t: $\qquad t = \frac{v_f}{a} \quad \text{and} \quad t = \frac{2s}{v_f}$

Therefore $\qquad\qquad \frac{v_f}{a} = \frac{2s}{v_f}$

and, $\qquad\qquad\qquad v_f^2 = 2as$

$$\text{or}$$

$$v_f = \sqrt{2as}$$

For an object coming to rest ($v_f = 0$), the initial velocity can be given in terms of the distance traveled and the deceleration

$$v_o^2 = 2as$$

Example: Acceleration When Distance and Initial Velocity Are Known

An airplane flying at 63 m/sec lands on a runway and travels 1000 m before stopping. At what rate is the plane decelerated? (Note: Let a represent deceleration.)

Solution:

$$\text{Since } v_o^2 = 2as$$

$$a = \frac{v_o^2}{2s}$$

$$= \frac{(63 \text{ m/sec})^2}{2 \times 1000 \text{ m}}$$

$$= 2.0 \text{ m/sec}^2$$

PROBLEMS

29. A plane is accelerated from rest at the constant rate of 3.0 m/sec^2 over a distance of 500 m. What is its speed after traveling this distance?

30. Decelerating a plane at the uniform rate of 8 m/sec^2, a pilot stops the plane in 484 m. How fast was the plane going before braking began?

31. A box falls off the tailgate of a truck and slides along the street for a distance of 62.5 m. Friction decelerates the box at 5.0 m/sec². At what speed was the truck moving when the box fell?

32. A light plane flying at 40 m/sec touches down on a runway and travels 100 m before stopping. At what rate is the plane decelerated?

33. Suppose you are driving along a highway at 45 m/sec and the best deceleration your brakes can produce is 4.5 m/sec². What minimum distance will you travel during an emergency stop?

3:7 Acceleration Due to Gravity

All freely falling bodies that are close to the surface of the earth gain speed toward the earth at the same rate (neglecting any frictional effects of air). Hence, it is worthwhile for you to memorize the value of gravitational acceleration. In the MKS system, acceleration due to gravity is 9.8 m/sec². All equations discussed in this chapter apply to gravitational acceleration. It is usual to replace the a used in acceleration equations with g when working with the acceleration of gravity. Hence

$$v_f = v_o + gt \text{ and } v_f^2 = 2gs$$

The rate of acceleration is common to all free-falling bodies.

The acceleration of a free-falling body due to gravity in MKS units is 9.8 m/sec².

Example: Acceleration Due to Gravity

(a) What is the speed (in m/sec) of a brick that drops from a high scaffold after 4 sec of free fall? (b) How far does the brick fall during the first 4 sec? (Being dropped, the brick starts from rest.)

Solution:

(a) $v_f = v_o + gt$
$= 0 \text{ m/sec} + (9.8 \text{ m/sec}^2 \times 4 \text{ sec})$
$= 39 \text{ m/sec}$

(b) $s = \dfrac{gt^2}{2}$
$= \dfrac{9.8 \text{ m/sec}^2 \ (4 \text{ sec})^2}{2}$
$= 78 \text{ m}$

The acceleration of gravity is always 9.8 m/sec² towards the earth. It does not depend on the direction an object is moving— up or down. An object shot straight up is decelerated at the rate of 9.8 m/sec² until it comes to rest. It then is accelerated down at the same rate of 9.8 m/sec². Suppose an arrow leaves an

Acceleration due to gravity is always directed toward the center of the earth.

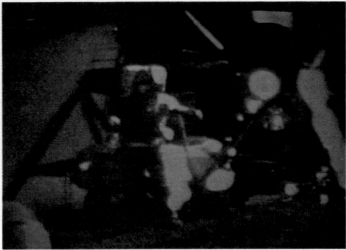

FIGURE 3-6. While on the moon, one of these astronauts dropped a hammer and a feather from the same height at the same time. Both objects hit the ground at the same time. Thus, it was shown that the two objects of unequal mass are accelerated equally by the moon's gravity.

archer's bow with a speed of 49 m/sec straight up. Each second, gravity removes 9.8 m/sec from its speed. After 5 seconds, the arrow will have a speed of 0 m/sec. For an instant it is at rest. Then the arrow is accelerated downward, the same as any falling body starting from rest. It will fall for just 5 sec before reaching the point from which it left the bow. At that point it has a speed of 49 m/sec (5 sec × 9.8 m/sec²). The arrow spends 10 sec in the air. It rises to the same height during the 5 sec of rise that an object falls from rest in 5 sec. To find out how high a body will rise when shot straight up, first find the time it takes gravity to bring the body to rest. Then calculate the distance the body, starting from rest, will fall during this same time.

Example: Deceleration Due to Gravity

A mortar shell is shot straight up with an initial speed of 98 m/sec. (a) How long does the shell remain in the air? (b) How high does the shell rise?

Solution:

(a) Calculate the time it takes an object, starting from rest, to reach a speed of 98 m/sec when it falls freely. Since $v_f = gt$, it follows that

$$t = \frac{v_f}{g}$$
$$= \frac{98 \text{ m/sec}}{9.8 \text{ m/sec}^2}$$
$$= 10 \text{ sec}$$

Gravity takes 10 sec to bring the shell to a halt and another 10 sec to bring it back to the earth. The time spent in the air by the shell is 20 sec.

(b) Since the shell rises for 10 sec, the height it reaches equals the distance an object, starting from rest, falls in in 10 sec. Hence,

$$s = \frac{gt^2}{2}$$
$$= \frac{9.8 \text{ m/sec}^2 (10 \text{ sec})^2}{2}$$
$$= 4.9 \text{ m} \times 100$$
$$= 490 \text{ m}$$

PROBLEMS

34. A stone is dropped straight down from a high cliff. What is its speed (m/sec) after 5 sec of free-fall?

35. Suppose that a stone is thrown straight downward from a high cliff. If its speed at the time it is released is 20 m/sec, what is its speed after 4 sec of free-fall?

36. A stone falls from rest for 4 sec. How far does it fall?

37. A stone is dropped from a high tower and 3 sec later hits the ground. How high is the tower in meters?

38. While flying a plane parallel to the ground, a pilot releases a fuel tank in order to reduce the plane's mass. What is the tank's vertical velocity after falling (a) 10 m, and (b) 1000 m?

39. A stone is thrown straight down from a cliff with an initial speed of 8 m/sec. (a) What is the stone's velocity after 3 sec? (b) How far does the stone travel during the 3 sec?

40. What is the final speed of an object that starts from rest and falls freely for a distance of 64 m?

41. A mortar shell is accidentally shot straight up with an initial speed of 147 m/sec. (a) How long does it take the acceleration of gravity to reduce its vertical speed to zero? (b) How high does the shell rise?

SUMMARY

All motion can be described by a few universal equations. These equations deal with either constant velocity or changing velocity (acceleration). There is no other type of motion. Motion in a curved path is simply a body undergoing straight line motion in at least two directions at the same time.

Instantaneous speed is the actual speed of a body at any given instant. Average speed is the effective speed over a period of time. The distance traveled over a time period is found by multiplying the average speed by the time.

Acceleration is the rate at which velocity changes with time. When a body is speeding up, its acceleration is positive. When it is slowing down, its acceleration is negative. Negative acceleration is also called deceleration. If the acceleration is always the same, it is called uniform acceleration.

The average speed of a body undergoing uniform acceleration is always its middle speed. The middle speed is found by adding the initial and final speeds and dividing by two.

In the MKS system of measurement the acceleration of gravity is 9.8 m/sec². The acceleration of gravity is treated in the same way as any other acceleration.

QUESTIONS

1. What do you think is the most important aspect of the few simple equations presented in this chapter?
2. How does an understanding of straight line motion make it possible to understand curved motion?
3. Write the equations for (a) acceleration (b) the final velocity of a uniformly accelerating body, and (c) the distance traveled by a moving body during an acceleration period. You should be able to reason these out.
4. Four cars are started from rest. Car A is accelerated at 6 m/sec². Car B is accelerated at 5.4 m/sec². Car C is accelerated at 8.0 m/sec², and car D speeds up at 12 m/sec². In the first column of a table, show the speed of each car at the end of 2 sec. In the second column, show the distance each car travels during the same two seconds. What conclusion do you reach about the speed attained and the distance traveled by a body starting from rest at the end of the first two seconds of acceleration?
5. A body shot straight up rises for 7 sec before gravity brings it to a halt. A second body falling from rest takes 7 sec to reach the ground. What do the two bodies have in common?

PROBLEMS

1. The speed of a car is increased at a constant rate. If the speed is increased by 42 m/sec over a 7 sec period, what is the acceleration?
2. Find the uniform acceleration of a body that will cause its speed to change uniformly from 32 m/sec to 96 m/sec in an 8-sec period.
3. An electron, initially at rest, leaves a cathode and is uniformly accelerated in a straight line toward an anode. It reaches the anode in 0.01 sec traveling with a speed of 2000 m/sec. What was its acceleration?
4. A car traveling at a speed of 20 m/sec is accelerated uniformly at the rate of 1.6 m/sec² for 6.8 sec. What is its final speed?
5. Determine the final speed of a proton that has an initial speed of 264 m/sec and then is decelerated uniformly in an electric field at the rate of 16 m/sec² for 15 sec.
6. A supersonic jet flying at 200 m/sec is accelerated uniformly at the rate of 23.1 m/sec² for 20 sec. (a) What is its final speed? (b) The speed of sound is 331 m/sec in air. How many times the speed of sound is the plane's final speed?
7. Determine the distance traveled during constant acceleration by a plane that is accelerated from 66 m/sec to 88 m/sec in 12 sec.
8. How far does a plane fly while being decelerated uniformly from 140 m/sec to 70 m/sec in 15 sec?
9. Starting from rest, a rocket is accelerated at the uniform rate of 18 m/sec² for 5 sec. What distance does it travel during this time?
10. A plane flying at 110 m/sec touches down and travels 302 m before coming to rest. At what rate was the plane decelerated?
11. If a bullet leaves the muzzle of a rifle with a speed of 600 m/sec, and the barrel of the rifle is 0.9 m long, at what rate is the bullet accelerated while in the barrel?

12. A car comes to rest after uniform deceleration at the rate of 9 m/sec² for 8 sec. What distance does it travel during this time?

13. A plane travels a distance of 500 m while being accelerated uniformly from rest at the rate of 5 m/sec². What final speed does it attain?

14. A stone falls freely from rest for 8 sec. (a) Calculate its final speed. (b) What distance does the stone fall during this time?

15. A pack of instruments is dropped from a weather balloon and hits the ground with a speed of 73.5 m/sec (a) How high is the balloon when the instruments are released? (b) How long do the instruments fall?

16. During a baseball game a batter hits a long fly ball. If the ball remains in the air for 6 sec, how high does it rise?

17. A student drops a rock from a bridge 120 m high. With what speed does the stone strike the water below?

18. Just as a traffic light turns green, a waiting car starts off with a constant acceleration of 6 m/sec². At the instant the car begins to accelerate, a truck with a constant velocity of 21 m/sec passes in the next lane. (a) How far will the car travel before it overtakes the truck? (b) How fast will the car be traveling when it overtakes the truck?

PROJECTS

1. Ask other students to help you in an activity to test reflexes. Find out if they can catch a dollar bill which is held half-way between their open fingers when it is dropped. They will not be able to snap their fingers together in time because reaction time for people is at least 0.15 seconds and it takes the bill only 0.13 seconds to fall through their hand.

2. Now that you know about acceleration, test your reaction time. Ask a friend to hold a ruler just even with the top of your open fingers. Then have your friend drop the ruler. Taking the number of centimeters that the ruler falls before you can catch it, calculate your reaction time. An average of several trials will give more accurate results.

3. Take a weight and a piece of paper and drop them from the same height. Which reaches the floor first? Now crumple up the paper and try again.

4. Calculate the average velocity of a faucet drip.
   (a) Adjust a faucet so that it drips.
   (b) Measure the distance from the tip of a hanging drop to the bottom of the sink. Use a deep sink, if possible. With a stopwatch, measure the time it takes for a drop to fall.
   (c) Calculate the final velocity of a drop.
   (d) Using your measurements from part (b) and the equation $s = gt^2/2$, calculate a value for g. How does this experimental value compare with the accepted value?

READINGS

Bixby, William, *The Universe of Galileo and Newton* (Horizon Caravel Books). New York, Harper and Row Pubs., Inc., 1964.

Daich, C. B., *Learn Science Through Ball Games*. New York, Sterling Publishing Co., 1972.

Fermi, Laura, and Bernadini, Gilberto, *Galileo and the Scientific Revolution*. New York, Basic Books, Inc., 1961.

Haber-Schaim, Uri, et al, *PSSC Physics*, 4th ed. Boston, D. C. Heath and Co., 1976, Chapter 9.

March, Robert H., *Physics for Poets*. New York, McGraw-Hill Book Co., 1970, Chapter 2.

Graphs are often used to analyze relationships between quantities. For example, by graphing data related to a developing storm, a scientist can learn about the path and speed of the storm and thus can predict which areas will be affected by the storm and when. In what situations have you used graphs to analyze data?

GRAPHICAL ANALYSIS OF MOTION

Graphs are very useful to scientists. They can be used to show relationships between quantities. They can also be used to find out how quantities are related. Many graphs have special shapes. In your work with graphs, keep in mind what each **axis** stands for. Then, you will often be able to see at a glance how the graphed quantities are related.

GOAL: You will gain knowledge and understanding of the uses of graphs and will learn to recognize the type of relationship between variables from the shape of their graph.

4:1 Distance-Time Graph for Constant Speed

A body moving at a constant speed travels the same distance during each second of motion. Therefore, the total distance traveled varies directly with the elapsed time. A graph of distance as a function of time is a straight line passing through the origin.

When speed is constant, distance varies directly with time.

Consider a plane flying at a constant speed of 60 m/sec. Table 4-1 lists the time of travel and the total distance (s) traveled during a 5-sec interval. Figure 4-1 is a plot of this data. The curve is a straight line passing through the origin.

Table 4-1	
Time (seconds)	Distance (meters)
0	0
1	60
2	120
3	180
4	240
5	300

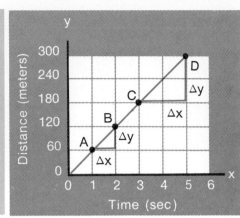

FIGURE 4-1. A distance-time graph for a body traveling at constant speed.

4:2 Slope of a Distance-Time Graph

The steepness of a graph is called the **slope** of the graph. Slope is the vertical change or rise (Δy) divided by the corresponding horizontal change or run (Δx) between any two points on the graph. For example, between points A and B in Figure 4-1, the rise is 120 m − 60 m, or 60 m. The run is 2 sec − 1 sec, or 1 sec. Using these two points to determine the slope,

$$\text{slope} = \frac{\text{rise}}{\text{run}} = \frac{\Delta y}{\Delta x} = \frac{\Delta s}{\Delta t} = \frac{60 \text{ m}}{1 \text{ sec}} = 60 \text{ m/sec}$$

Between points C and D,

$$\text{slope} = \frac{\text{rise}}{\text{run}} = \frac{\Delta s}{\Delta t} = \frac{300 \text{ m} - 180 \text{ m}}{5 \text{ sec} - 3 \text{ sec}} = \frac{120 \text{ m}}{2 \text{ sec}} = 60 \text{ m/sec}$$

Thus, the slope of a distance-time graph gives the speed of the object. When the curve is a straight line, the slope is the same all along its length. Therefore, a straight line graph tells you that the speed of the object is constant.

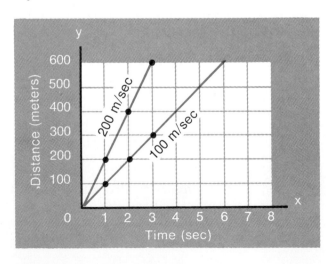

FIGURE 4-2. The steeper the slope of a distance-time graph, the higher the speed.

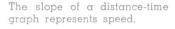

Figure 4-2 shows the distance-time graph for two planes. One is traveling at 100 m/sec while the other is traveling at 200 m/sec. The slope of the line representing the faster plane is steeper than the slope of the line representing the slower plane. A steeper slope indicates that a body is traveling a greater distance per unit time. For any distance-time graph, the steepest slope corresponds to the fastest speed.

A steep slope for a distance-time graph indicates a high speed.

4:3 Distance-Time Graph for a Complete Trip

The distance-time graph in Figure 4-3 represents a short car trip. During the first 10 sec, a car travels a distance of 200 m from its point of origin. Thus, the speed of the car for the entire 10-sec period is

$$\text{slope} = \frac{\Delta s}{\Delta t} = \frac{200 \text{ m}}{10 \text{ sec}} = 20 \text{ m/sec}$$

Between points B and C, the car is at rest. Its distance from its point of origin does not change. Since $\Delta s = 0$, the slope $\Delta s/\Delta t$ must also be zero. Thus, the speed of the car between the tenth and twentieth second of the trip is zero.

When the slope of a distance-time graph is zero, the object is at rest.

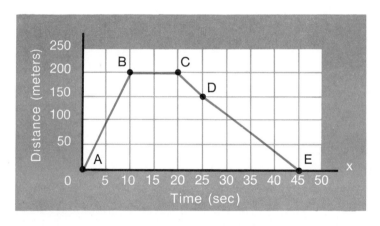

FIGURE 4-3. A distance-time graph for a body traveling at changing speed.

Between points C and D, the distance of the car from the point of origin decreases. Thus, Δs is negative. Therefore, the slope ($\Delta s/\Delta t$) is also negative. This means that the car is traveling in a direction opposite to its original direction. Between points C and D,

$$\text{slope} = \frac{\Delta s}{\Delta t} = \frac{-50 \text{ m}}{5 \text{ sec}} = -10 \text{ m/sec}$$

A negative slope for a distance-time graph shows that an object is moving in a direction opposite to its original direction.

At point D, the speed of the car decreases and the slope of the line is less steep thereafter. Between points D and E,

$$\text{slope} = \frac{\Delta s}{\Delta t} = \frac{-150 \text{ m}}{20 \text{ sec}} \qquad -7.5 \text{ m/sec}$$

Note that at point E the car is back at its origin.

Suppose the line of the graph went below the x axis. This would indicate that the car had passed its point of origin and was moving in a direction opposite to that of its motion during the first 10 sec of the trip.

4:4   Speed-Time Graph for Constant Speed

Consider a plane flying at a constant speed of 60 m/sec. Figure 4-4 plots its speed against the time of travel. Since the speed is constant, every point on the line has the same vertical position. Therefore, the line through these points is parallel to the x axis.

The speed-time graph for constant speed is a line parallel to the x axis.

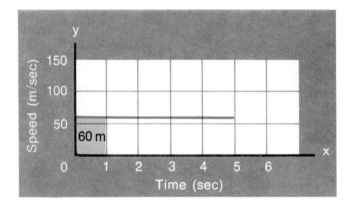

FIGURE 4-4. The speed-time graph for a body moving with constant speed.

A speed-time graph is useful because the area between the curve and the x axis represents the distance (s) traveled by the body. For example, notice the shaded area under the line in Figure 4-4. The vertical side of this area is the speed, $v = 60$ m/sec. The horizontal side is the time, $t = 1$ sec. The area of this box is vt, or 60 m. This is the distance the plane travels in 1 sec.

At the end of 3 sec, the area under the line would be $vt = 60$ m/sec $\times$ 3 sec $= 180$ m. The area under the curve of a speed-time graph represents distance.

The area under a speed-time graph represents distance.

PROBLEMS

1. A plane flies in a straight line with a constant speed of 50 m/sec. (a) Construct a table showing the total distance the plane travels at the end of each second for a 20-sec period. (b) Use the data from the table to plot a distance-time graph. (c) Show that the slope of the line gives the speed of the plane. Use at least two different sets of points along the graph. (d) Plot a speed-time graph of the plane's motion for the first 12 sec of the 20-sec interval. (e) Find the distance the plane travels between the eighth and eleventh second.

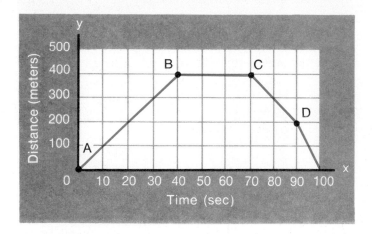

FIGURE 4-5. Use this graph for Problems 2, 3, 4, and 5.

2. Use the distance-time graph in Figure 4-5 to find (a) how far the body travels between $t = 0$ sec and $t = 40$ sec, (b) how far it travels between $t = 40$ sec and $t = 70$ sec, and (c) how far it travels between $t = 90$ sec and $t = 100$ sec.

3. Use Figure 4-5 to find (a) the speed of the body during the first 40 sec, (b) the speed of the body between $t = 40$ sec and $t = 70$ sec, (c) the speed of the body between $t = 70$ sec and $t = 90$ sec, and (d) the speed of the body between $t = 90$ sec and $t = 100$ sec.

4. If the slope of the line between points A and B in Figure 4-5 is positive, what must be true of the slope of the line between points C and D?

5. Use the distance-time graph of Figure 4-5 to construct a table showing the speed of the plane for each 10-sec interval over the entire 100 sec.

6. As a solution to Problem 5, plot a speed-time graph using the table you constructed.

7. A car moves along a straight road at a constant speed of 40 m/sec. (a) Plot its distance-time graph for a 10-sec interval. (b) Find the slope of the graph at two different places along the line. (c) Plot a speed-time graph for the car. What does the area under the line of the graph represent? (d) Calculate the area under the line of the graph between the fifth and sixth sec. What does this area represent?

4:5   Speed-Time Graph for Uniform Acceleration

Consider a jet plane that starts from rest on a runway. It is accelerated uniformly at the rate of 20 m/sec^2. Table 4-2 shows the speeds of the plane over a 5-sec period. Figure 4-6 is a plot of these speeds against time. This speed-time graph for uniformly

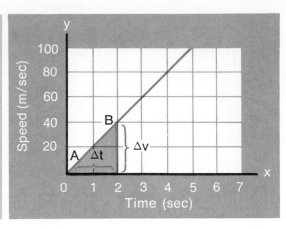

Table 4–2	
Time (sec)	Speed (m/sec)
0	0
1	20
2	40
3	60
4	80
5	100

FIGURE 4-6. A speed-time graph for uniformly accelerated motion.

The speed-time graph of constant acceleration is a straight line which passes through the origin.

The slope of a speed-time graph represents acceleration.

accelerated motion is a straight line passing through the origin. This means that during uniform acceleration the speed varies directly with time.

For uniform acceleration, the slope of a speed-time graph is constant along its entire length. Note that the slope gives the acceleration of the object. Between points A and B,

$$\text{slope} = \frac{\text{rise}}{\text{run}} = \frac{\Delta v}{\Delta t} = \frac{40 \text{ m/sec}}{2 \text{ sec}} = 20 \text{ m/sec}^2$$

You can find the acceleration of any object by taking the slope of its speed-time graph.

In Section 4:4 you found that, for a body moving with constant speed, the area under the speed-time curve gives the distance the body travels. This is also true of a body undergoing uniform acceleration. The area under the speed-time curve still gives the distance the body travels. In fact, the area under any speed-time curve gives distance regardless of the type of motion.

Look at the shaded area under the line between points A and B. Consider the entire rectangle of which the shaded area is half. The vertical limit of the rectangle is the speed of 40 m/sec. This limit is the speed attained by the jet plane when it is accelerated at the rate of 20 m/sec² for 2 sec. So v can be expressed in terms of acceleration and time, or $v = at$. Thus, the vertical side of the rectangle equals at. The horizontal limit of the rectangle is the time, 2 sec. The area of the rectangle is its vertical side multiplied by its horizontal side, or $at \times t = at^2$. But the area under the line is half this, or $at^2/2$. This is the distance an accelerating body covers when starting from rest (Section 3:5).

4:6 Distance-Time Graph for Uniform Acceleration

Now let us plot a distance-time graph for the jet plane discussed in Section 4:5. The total distance the plane has traveled at the end of each section can be found in two ways. It can be

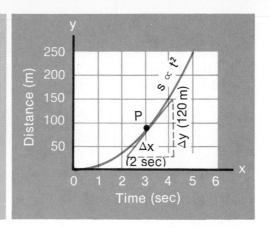

Table 4–3

Time (seconds)	Distance (meters)
0	0
1	10
2	40
3	90
4	160
5	250

FIGURE 4-7. A distance-time graph for uniformly accelerated motion.

calculated with the equation $s = at^2/2$. It can also be found by determining the area under the speed-time curve of Figure 4-6. The results are given in Table 4-3. The data from Table 4-3 is used to plot a distance-time graph (Figure 4-7).

The curve in the distance-time graph is half a parabola. A parabola always shows that one quantity varies directly with the square of the other. In this case, the distance traveled by the accelerating body varies directly with the square of time.

The slope of any distance-time graph yields the speed. When the speed is constant, the distance-time graph is a straight line. Figure 4-1 shows how to find the slope of the line. However, when a body is accelerating, it travels a greater distance each second than it did the second before. The steepness of the curve changes constantly. The resulting smooth curve is a parabola. The slope of this curve is more difficult to find than the slope of a straight line. Often it is found by drawing a tangent to the curve at the point where the slope is wanted. The slope of the tangent gives the instantaneous speed at the point on the curve that the tangent touches. In Figure 4-7 a tangent is drawn at point P. The slope of the tangent at this point is

The distance-time graph for uniform acceleration is a half-parabola (s varies directly with t^2).

The slope of a parabola can be found by drawing a tangent to the curve at the point where the speed is desired.

$$\frac{\Delta s}{\Delta t} = \frac{150 \text{ m} - 30 \text{ m}}{4 \text{ sec} - 2 \text{ sec}} = \frac{120 \text{ m}}{2 \text{ sec}} = 60 \text{ m/sec}$$

Point P coincides with the end of 3 sec of travel. The speed to expect at the end of 3 sec for a body which accelerates at the rate of 20 m/sec^2 from rest is 60 m/sec. Note also that it is the speed shown on the speed-time graph for the same body after 3 sec.

4:7 Acceleration-Time Graph for Uniform Acceleration

Acceleration that does not change with time is called uniform acceleration. Because the acceleration is constant, an acceleration-time graph is a line parallel to the x axis.

The acceleration-time graph for uniform acceleration is a line parallel to the x axis.

In Figure 4-8, the acceleration of the jet plane of Section 4:5 is plotted against time. As expected, the acceleration-time line is a straight line parallel to the x axis.

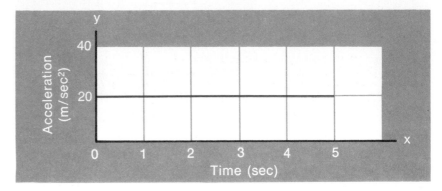

FIGURE 4-8. An acceleration-time graph for uniformly accelerated motion.

The area under an acceleration-time graph represents velocity.

Notice that the area under the line of the acceleration-time graph represents the speed of the plane. At any point along the x axis, the area under the line is a rectangle with sides a and t. Therefore, the area of the rectangle is at. Since $v = at$, the area gives the speed. For example, at the end of 3 sec the speed of the car is 3 sec $\times$ 20 m/sec^2, or 60 m/sec.

The situation shown in Figure 4-8 is a very simple one. When acceleration is not uniform, such graphs become even more useful.

SUMMARY

Many graphs have characteristic shapes. From these special shapes, certain relationships can easily be seen. The distance-time graph for a body moving at constant speed is a straight line passing through the origin. The slope of a distance-time graph gives the speed of the body. If the distance-time graph is parallel to the x axis, the slope is zero. Therefore, this type of graph indicates that the speed of the body is zero.

For a body moving at a constant speed, the speed-time graph is a line parallel to the x axis. The area under the line represents the distance traveled.

The speed-time graph for uniformly accelerated motion is a straight line passing through the origin. This indicates that speed varies directly with time. Since the slope is $\Delta v/\Delta t$, the slope of the line gives the acceleration. The area under the line represents the distance traveled and corresponds to $at^2/2$.

In a distance-time graph for uniformly accelerated motion, the curve is half of a parabola. This curve indicates that distance varies with the square of the time.

When uniform acceleration is plotted against time, the acceleration-time line is a straight line parallel to the x axis. The area under the line represents the speed of the accelerating body.

QUESTIONS

1. Define the slope of a graph.

2. What does the slope of a distance-time graph indicate?

3. What quantity is represented by the area under a speed-time graph?

4. What does the slope of a speed-time graph indicate?
5. If a speed-time curve is a straight line parallel to the x axis, what can be said about the acceleration?
6. What quantity can be found by determining the area under an acceleration-time curve?

PROBLEMS

1. The speed of an automobile changes over an 8-sec time period as shown in Table 4-4 below. (a) Plot the speed-time graph of the motion. (b) Determine the distance the car travels during the first 2 sec. (c) What distance does the car travel during the first 4 sec? (d) What distance does the car travel during the entire 8 sec? (e) Find the slope of the line between $t = 0$ sec and $t = 4$ sec. What does this slope represent? (f) Find the slope of the line between $t = 5$ sec and $t = 7$ sec. What does this slope represent?

Table 4–4		Table 4–5	
Time (sec)	Speed (m/sec)	Time (sec)	Distance (m)
0	0	0	0
1	4	1	2
2	8	2	8
3	12	3	18
4	16	4	32
5	20	5	50
6	20		
7	20		
8	20		

2. The total distance a steel ball rolls down an incline at the end of each second of travel is given in Table 4-5 above. (a) Make a distance-time graph of the motion of the ball. Use five divisions for each 10 m of travel on the y axis. Use five divisions for each second of time on the x axis. (b) What type of curve is the line of the graph? (c) What distance has the ball rolled at the end of 2.2 sec? (d) Find the slope of the line at $t = 3$ sec. What does this slope show?

3. Use Figure 4-9 to find the acceleration of the moving body during (a) the first 5 sec of travel, (b) during the second 5 sec of travel, (c) between the tenth and the fifteenth sec of travel, and (d) between the twentieth and twenty-fifth sec of travel.

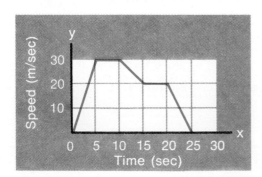

FIGURE 4-9. Use this graph with Problems 3 and 4.

4. Refer to Figure 4-9 to find the distance the moving body travels (a) between $t = 0$ and $t = 5$ sec, (b) between $t = 5$ sec and $t = 10$ sec, (c) between $t = 10$ sec and $t = 15$ sec, and (d) between $t = 0$ and $t = 25$ sec.

5. Use the intervals marked on the graph in Figure 4-10 to describe the entire trip of the moving body.

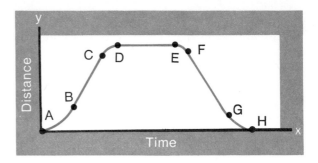

FIGURE 4-10. Use this graph with Problem 5.

6. Make a table of the speeds of a body (m/sec) at the end of each second for the first 5 sec of free-fall from rest. (a) Use the data in your table to plot a speed-time graph. (b) What does the total area under the graph represent?

7. (a) Compute the total distance the body in Problem 6 travels at the end of each second for the first 5 sec of the free-fall. (b) Use the distances calculated in Part (a) to plot a distance-time graph. (c) Find the slope of the curve at the end of 2 and 4 sec. What are the approximate slopes? Do these values agree with the table of speeds in Problem 6?

8. Use the data prepared in Problem 7 to plot the distance versus time squared. (a) What kind of curve is obtained? (b) Does this agree with the equation $s = at^2/2$? (c) Find the slope of the curve at any point. Explain the significance of the value you obtain.

9. Look at Figure 4-11 below. (a) What kind of motion does this graph represent? (b) What does the slope of the graph represent?

10. Look at Figure 4-12 below. (a) What kind of motion does this graph represent? (b) What does the area under the line of the graph represent?

11. Look at Figure 4-13 below. (a) What kind of motion does this graph represent? (b) What does the slope of the line represent? (c) What does the area under the line represent?

12. Look at Figure 4-14 below. What does the area under the line of this graph represent?

13. Look at Figure 4-15. (a) What type of curve does this graph represent? (b) What does the slope of the line taken at any point represent? (c) How would slopes taken at higher points on the line differ from those taken at lower points?

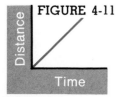

FIGURE 4-11

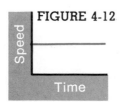

FIGURE 4-12

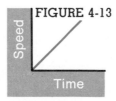

FIGURE 4-13

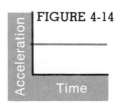

FIGURE 4-14

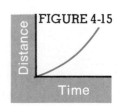

FIGURE 4-15

1. Match each of the following situations to one of the curves below.
   (a) A student buys a bank and saves $1.00 per day.
   (b) A student adds nothing per day to a bank containing $5.00.
   (c) A car speeds up uniformly from rest.
   (d) A moving car comes to a smooth stop.
   (e) Gravitational field intensity varies inversely with the square of the distance from the center of the earth.
   (f) The distance a dropped stone falls from rest is directly proportional to the square of the time it falls.

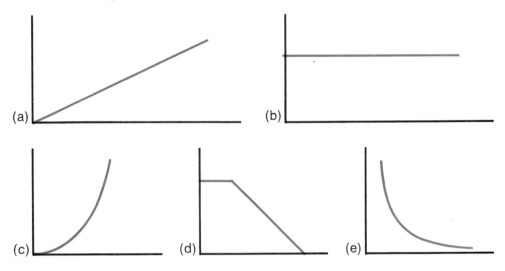

FIGURE 4-16.
For Project 1.

2. To accompany each of the graphs shown below draw (a) a speed-time graph and (b) an acceleration-time graph.

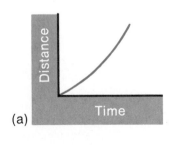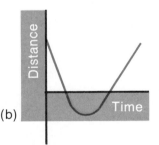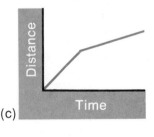

FIGURE 4-17.
For Project 2.

READINGS

Chester, Michael, *Relativity, an Introduction for Young Readers.* New York, W. W. Norton and Co., Inc., 1967.

Drake, Stillman, "Galileo's Discovery of the Law of Free Fall." *Scientific American,* May, 1973.

Haber-Schaim, Uri, et al, *PSSC Physics,* 4th ed. Boston, D.C. Heath and Co., 1976, Chapter 9.

Ickx, Jacques, "The Great Automobile Race of 1895." *Scientific American,* May, 1972.

Wilson, Curtis, "How Did Kepler Discover His First Two Laws?" *Scientific American,* March, 1972.

This sailboat moves from one place to another. When this happens, the displacement, or change in position of the boat, is given by an expression which contains three parts — a number, a unit, and a direction. This kind of quantity is called a vector quantity. Some other examples of vector quantities are velocity, acceleration, and force. What are some other examples of vector quantities?

VECTORS

You are already used to working with scalars. For example, twelve dollars plus twelve dollars is twenty-four dollars. A dollar is a scalar quantity. It is not affected by anything other than its magnitude or size. You may wonder how a twelve-newton force plus a twelve-newton force can equal a twelve-newton force. Vectors are controlled by their directions as well as by their magnitudes. Thus, when vectors are added, twelve plus twelve can equal any value between zero and twenty-four. Scientists are constantly dealing with vector quantities. An understanding of vectors is fundamental to an understanding of many of the basic physics principles.

GOAL: You will gain knowledge and understanding of the meaning and use of vector algebra needed to solve quickly and successfully physics problems requiring the use of vectors.

5:1 Vector Quantities

Scientists deal with both scalar and vector quantities. A **scalar quantity** is completely described by its magnitude. The magnitude is made up of a number and an appropriate unit. Mass, volume, and distance are scalar quantities. Examples of these scalar quantities are 10 grams, 12 liters, and 15 kilometers. Each is made up of a number and a unit. A **vector quantity** is characterized by both magnitude and direction. Force is a vector quantity because a force must always act in some direction. A force is described completely only when both its magnitude and direction are stated. Other vector quantities are velocity and momentum.

Scalar quantities have magnitude only.

Vector quantities have both magnitude and direction.

Scalar quantities are added according to the rules of ordinary arithmetic. Thus, 2 liters plus 2 liters is 4 liters. But the sum of two vector quantities depends on their directions as well as their

Scalars are added algebraically.

59

magnitudes. Consider a plane that is flying due east at 90 km/hr. At the same time this plane is being blown south by the wind at 50 km/hr. The plane has two velocities but they cannot be added algebraically. The plane is not flying with a velocity of 140 km/hr. Nor is its direction east or south. The magnitudes and directions of the two velocities produce a vector sum that must be determined by a process called vector addition.

5:2   Vector Addition—Graphical Method

A vector quantity can be represented by an arrow-tipped line segment. The length of the arrow represents the magnitude of the quantity. The direction of the arrow represents the direction of the quantity. This arrow-tipped line segment is called a vector. Figure 5–1 shows some typical vectors.

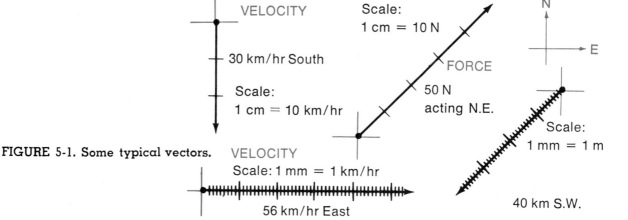

FIGURE 5-1. Some typical vectors.

The vector sum of any two vectors can be found graphically. In Figure 5–2, vectors **a** and **b** represent the two velocities of the plane flying east at 90 km/hr and being blown south at 50 km/hr. The vectors are added by placing the tail of one vector at the head of the other vector. Neither the direction nor the length of either vector is changed. A third vector is drawn connecting the tail of the first vector to the head of the second vector. This vector represents the sum of the two vectors. This third vector is called the **resultant** of $\vec{a}$ and $\vec{b}$. The resultant is always drawn from the tail of the first vector to the head of the second vector. To find the magnitude of the resultant, measure its length and evaluate it according to the same scale used to draw vectors $\vec{a}$ and $\vec{b}$. Its direction is found by using a protractor. In Figure 5–2, the resultant velocity is 103 km/hr in the direction 29° south of east.

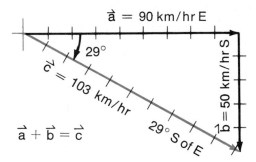

Scale: 1 division = 10 km/hr

FIGURE 5-2. Vector addition.

In algebraic addition, the order of addition is of no consequence. This is also true of vector addition. The tail of vector $\vec{a}$ could have been placed at the head of vector $\vec{b}$. Figure 5–3 illustrates that the same sum would result.

Regardless of the order in which vectors are added, the sum will be the same.

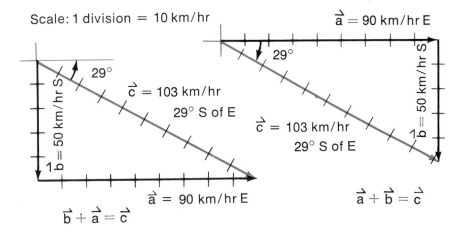

FIGURE 5-3. The vector sum of $\vec{b}$ + $\vec{a}$ is the same as the vector sum of $\vec{a}$ + $\vec{b}$.

When two vector quantities act in the same or in opposite directions, their numerical sum is the same as their algebraic sum. That is, if a plane flies at 90 km/hr due east and the wind blows it along at 50 km/hr due east, its velocity is 140 km/hr due east. If the wind is blowing due west and the plane must fly directly into it, the plane's velocity is 90 km/hr + (− 50 km/hr) = 40 km/hr east. A minus sign is placed in front of 50 km/hr to show that this velocity is opposite in direction to the 90 km/hr velocity.

FIGURE 5-4. When two vectors act in the same or opposite directions, their resultant is numerically just the algebraic sum of the two.

Scale: 1 division = 10 km/hr

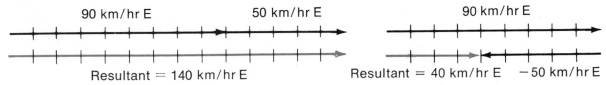

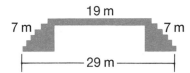

FIGURE 5-5. The total distance a person walks in crossing this freeway by way of the foot bridge is 33 meters. The displacement of the person from stairway to stairway is 29 meters directly across the freeway.

Distance is a scalar quantity; displacement is a vector quantity.

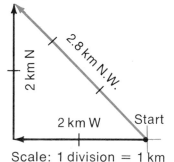

Scale: 1 division = 1 km

FIGURE 5-6. A hiker walks a distance of 4 kilometers. The displacement of the hiker is 2.8 kilometers north of west.

Speed is a scalar quantity; velocity is a vector quantity.

5:3 Distance and Displacement

Distance and displacement are not the same. Distance is a scalar quantity. Displacement is a vector quantity. Let us look at the difference between the two quantities. Suppose you leave your home one morning to take a walk. If you walk 2 km due west and then turn and walk 2 km due north, you will have walked a total distance of 4 km. But you will not be 4 km from your home. Instead, you will be a little over 2.8 km northwest of your home. The **distance** is the length of the actual path traveled. In this case, the distance is 4 km. Displacement is quite different from distance. A straight line from the starting position to the final position is called the **displacement**. In order to describe the displacement, both the length of this line and its direction must be given. In this case, the displacement is 2.8 km northwest.

5:4 Speed and Velocity

The **speed** of a moving body is the distance it travels per unit time. Speed is stated in kilometers per hour or meters per second. The direction is not stated. Speed is a scalar quantity.

The **velocity** of a moving body is the distance it travels per unit time in a given direction. Note that in stating the velocity, both magnitude and direction are given. Velocity is a vector quantity. Speed is the magnitude of velocity.

5:5   The Independence of Vector Quantities

Vectors, when added, produce a resultant effect, but never change each other's values. Consider a motorboat that heads due east at 8 m/sec across a river flowing due south at 5 m/sec. The boat will travel 8 meters due east in one second. It will also travel 5 meters due south in the same second. The southerly velocity cannot change the easterly velocity. Neither can the easterly velocity change the southerly velocity. Each velocity is independent of the other and acts as if it were the only velocity. This is known as the independence of velocities. All vector quantities behave in the same way.

Vectors act independently.

In Figure 5–7, the two velocities of the boat are represented by vectors. When these vectors are added, the resultant velocity is 9.4 m/sec in the direction 32° south of east. In one second, this resultant velocity will carry the motorboat 8 meters due east and 5 meters due south. You can think of the boat as traveling east at 8 m/sec and south at 5 m/sec at the same time. You can also think of it as traveling 9.4 m/sec in the direction 32° south of east. Both statements mean exactly the same thing.

Suppose that the river being crossed by the boat is 80 meters wide. Since the boat's velocity is 8 m/sec at all times, it will take the boat 10 seconds to cross the river. The boat will also be carried 50 meters downstream during this 10 seconds. However, in no way does this change its velocity across the river.

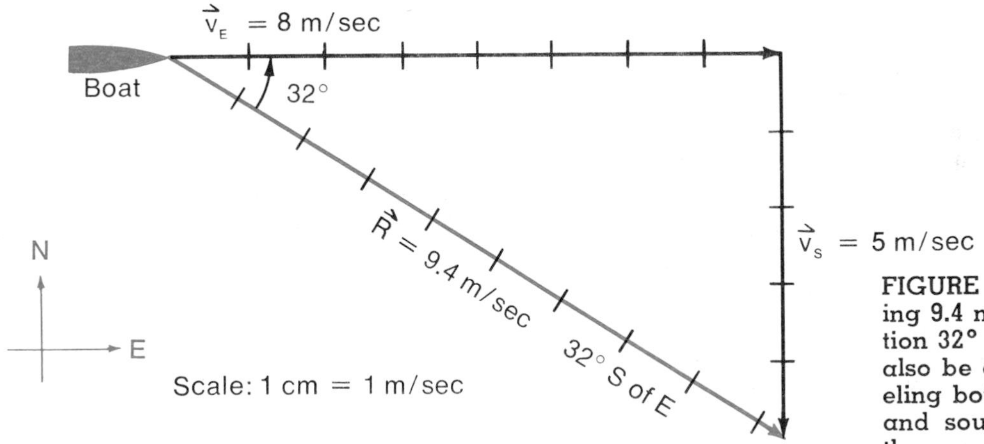

FIGURE 5-7. A boat traveling 9.4 m/sec in the direction 32° south of east can also be described as traveling both east at 8 m/sec and south at 5 m/sec at the same time.

5:6   Vector Addition of Forces

Force vectors, and other kinds of vectors, are added in the same ways as velocity vectors. Forces which act on the same point at the same time are called **concurrent** (kahn KUHR uhnt) **forces**. In the MKS system of measurement, the unit of force is the newton (N).

Concurrent forces act on the same point at the same time.

The newton is the MKS unit of force.

Example: Vector Addition of Forces

A force of 40 N and a force of 60 N act concurrently on a point P. The 60-N force acts in the direction due east. The 40-N force acts in the direction 60° north of east. What is the magnitude and direction of their resultant?

Solution:

The sum of the two forces is found by moving vector $\vec{b}$ parallel to itself until the tail of $\vec{b}$ is located at the head of vector $\vec{a}$. The resultant is then drawn and interpreted in terms of the scale used.

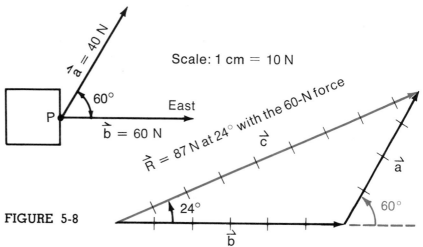

FIGURE 5-8

PROBLEMS

Draw vector diagrams to solve each problem. Use a protractor, a sharp pencil, and a metric ruler.

1. A plane flying due north at 100 m/sec is blown due west at 50 m/sec by a strong wind. Find the plane's resultant velocity (speed and direction).

2. A hiker leaves camp and walks 10 km due north. The displacement at this point is 10 km north. The hiker then walks 10 km due east. This adds a second displacement of 10 km east to the first displacement. (a) What is the total distance walked by the hiker? (b) Determine the total displacement from the starting point.

3. A motorboat heads due east at 16 m/sec across a river that flows due south at 9 m/sec. (a) What is the resultant velocity (speed and direction) of the boat? (b) If the river is 136 m wide, how long does it take the motorboat to reach the other side? (c) How far downstream is the boat when it reaches the other side of the river?

4. An airplane flies due west at 120 km/hr. At the same time, the wind blows it due north at 40 km/hr. What is the plane's resultant velocity?

5. A salesperson leaves the office and drives 26 km due north along a straight highway. A turn is made onto a highway that leads in a direction 30° north of east. The driver continues on the highway for a distance of 62 km and then stops. What is the total displacement of this person from the office?

6. Two soccer players kick the ball at exactly the same time. One player's foot exerts a force of 60 N north. The other's foot exerts a force of 80 N east. What is the magnitude and direction of the resultant force on the ball?

7. Two forces of 60 N each act concurrently on a point P. Determine the magnitude of the resultant force acting on point P when the angle between the forces is as follows:
   (a) 0°   (d) 90°
   (b) 30°   (e) 180°
   (c) 60°

8. In Problem 7, what happens to the resultant of two forces as the angle between them increases?

9. A weather team releases a weather balloon. The balloon's buoyancy accelerates it straight up at 15 m/sec². A wind accelerates it horizontally at 6.5 m/sec². What is the magnitude and direction (with reference to the horizontal) of the resultant acceleration?

10. A meteoroid passes between the moon and the earth. A gravitational force of 600 N pulls the meteoroid toward the moon. At the same time, a gravitational force of 480 N pulls it toward the earth. The angle between the two forces is 130°. The moon's force acts perpendicularly to the meteoroid's original path. What is the resultant magnitude and direction of the force acting on the meteoroid? State the direction in reference to the meteoroid's original path. (The diagram below is *not* a vector diagram. It is intended to show direction only.)

FIGURE 5-9. For Problem 10.

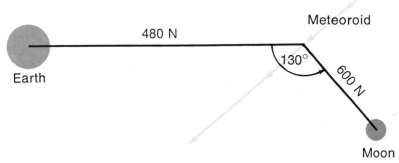

5:7 Vector Addition—Mathematical Methods

The vector sum of any two vectors can be determined mathematically as well as graphically. If two vectors act perpendicularly, a right triangle is formed when the tail of one vector is placed at the head of the second vector. Then the magnitude of their resultant is found by using the **Pythagorean** (puh thag uh REE uhn) **theorem.**

The Pythagorean theorem can be used to find the length of the third side of a right triangle.

$$c^2 = a^2 + b^2$$

The direction of their resultant is found by using the definition of tangent.

$$\tan \theta = \frac{\text{opposite side}}{\text{adjacent side}}$$

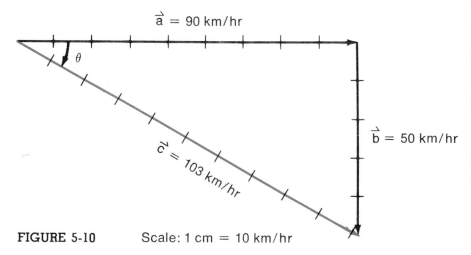

$\vec{a} = 90$ km/hr

θ

$\vec{c} = 103$ km/hr

$\vec{b} = 50$ km/hr

FIGURE 5-10   Scale: 1 cm = 10 km/hr

Again, consider the airplane that is flying due east at 90 km/hr and is being blown due south at 50 km/hr. In what direction and at what speed is the airplane actually flying?

$$c^2 = a^2 + b^2$$
$$c = \sqrt{(90 \text{ km/hr})^2 + (50 \text{ km/hr})^2}$$
$$= \sqrt{10\ 600} \text{ km/hr}$$
$$= 103 \text{ km/hr}$$

To find the direction of the resultant, find the tangent of the angle θ.

$$\tan \theta = \frac{\text{opposite side}}{\text{adjacent side}}$$
$$= \frac{50 \text{ km/hr}}{90 \text{ km/hr}}$$
$$= 0.566$$
$$\text{thus,} \quad \theta = 29°$$

In this case, tan $\theta = 0.566$. Table A-1 in Appendix A shows that 0.556 is the tangent of 29°. Therefore, the angle θ is 29°. The resultant is described as 103 km/hr at 29° south of east.

When two vectors do not act at a right angle, the magnitude and direction of the resultant is determined by use of the law of cosines or the law of sines (Sections 1:6 and 1:7).

The law of cosines and the law of sines can be used to find the third side of any triangle.

Example: Vector Addition of Non-Perpendicular Forces

A force of 40 N and a force of 60 N act concurrently on a point P. The 60-N force acts in the direction due east. The 40-N force acts in the direction 60° north of east. What is the magnitude and direction of their resultant?

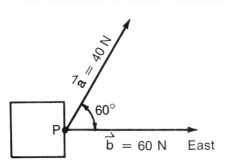

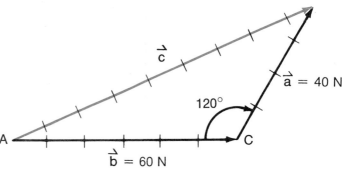

Scale: 1 cm = 10 N   **FIGURE 5-11**

Solution:

To determine the magnitude of $\vec{c}$, use the law of cosines.

$$c^2 = a^2 + b^2 - 2ab \cos C$$
$$= (40\text{ N})^2 + (60\text{ N})^2 - 2(40\text{ N})(60\text{ N})(-0.50)$$
$$c = \sqrt{1600 + 3600 + 2400}\ \text{N}$$
$$= \sqrt{7600}\ \text{N}$$
$$= 87\text{ N}$$

To determine the direction of $\vec{c}$, use the law of sines to find angle A.

$$\frac{a}{\sin A} = \frac{c}{\sin C}$$
$$\sin A = \frac{a \sin C}{c}$$
$$= \frac{40\text{ N} \times \sin 120°}{87\text{ N}}$$
$$= \frac{40\text{ N} \times 0.866}{87\text{ N}}$$
$$= 0.398$$

Angle $A = 23°$

Thus, the direction of $\vec{c}$ is 23° north of east.

PROBLEMS

Solve graphically or mathematically depending upon your instructor's directions.

11. A 100-N force and a 50-N force act on point *P*. The 100-N force acts due north. The 50-N force acts due east. What is the magnitude and direction of the resultant force?

12. A motorboat travels at 40 m/sec. It heads straight across a river 320 m wide. (a) If the water flows at the rate of 8 m/sec, what is the boat's velocity with respect to the shore? (b) How long does it take the boat to reach the opposite shore?

13. A boat heads directly across a river 40 m wide at 8 m/sec. The current is flowing at 3.8 m/sec. (a) What is the resultant velocity of the boat? (b) How long does it take the boat to cross the river? (c) How far downstream is the boat when it reaches the other side?

14. An airplane flies at 150 km/hr and heads 30° south of east. A 50 km/hr wind blows in the direction 25° west of south. What is the resultant velocity of the plane with respect to the earth?

15. Two 10-N forces act concurrently on point *P*. Find the magnitude of their resultant when the angle between them is
    (a) 0°   (b) 30°   (c) 90°   (d) 120°   (e) 180°

5:8   Addition of Several Vectors

The same procedure is always used regardless of the number of vectors to be added.

The order of vector addition is unimportant.

FIGURE 5-12. Determining the resultant of three concurrent forces.

Often three or more forces act concurrently on the same point. To determine the resultant of three or more vectors, follow the same procedure you use to add two vectors. Place the vectors head-to-tail. The order of addition is **not** important. In Figure 5–12a, the three forces $\vec{a}$, $\vec{b}$, and $\vec{c}$, act concurrently on point P. In Figure 5–12b and c, the vectors are added graphically. Note that the resultant is the same in both parts although two different orders of addition are used. In placing the vectors head-to-tail, their directions must be maintained.

(a)

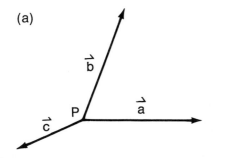

(b)

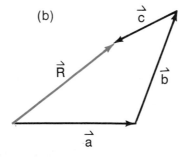

(c)

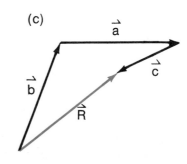

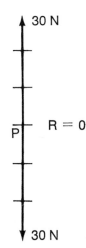

FIGURE 5-13. In this tug of war, the dog pulls with a force of 30 N. A 30-N force is exerted by a student in the opposite direction. The resultant force is zero.

5:9 Equilibrium

When two or more forces act concurrently on a body and their vector sum is zero, the body is in **equilibrium** (ee kwuh LIB ree uhm). An example of equilibrium is the case in which two equal forces act in opposite directions on point P (Figure 5–13).

For a second example, consider three forces acting on point P (Figure 5–14a). The 3-N force and the 4-N force are at right angles to each other. Their resultant is a 5-N force to the right. Vector $\vec{c}$ is a 5-N force to the left. The resultant of these two 5-N forces

Equilibrium is a zero resultant of forces.

(a)

(b)

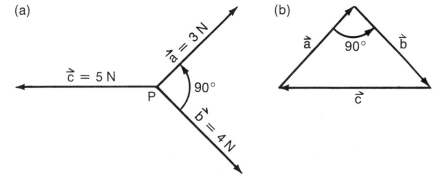

FIGURE 5-14. Vectors in equilibrium give a resultant of zero.

is zero. Therefore, the three forces produce no net force on point P. Thus, point P is in equilibrium. When the three vectors are added head-to-tail, they form a closed triangle (Figure 5–14b). A resultant cannot be drawn because the vector sum is zero.

FIGURE 5-15. Because all of the forces acting concurrently on this bridge are in equilibrium, this bridge remains motionless.

An equilibrant force offsets forces acting on a given point to produce equilibrium.

The equilibrant is numerically equal to the resultant, but opposite in direction.

5:10 The Equilibrant

When two or more forces act on a point and their vector sum is not zero, an **equilibrant** (ee KWIL uh bruhnt) **force** can be found. The equilibrant force is the single additional force which, when applied at the same point as the other forces, will produce equilibrium. In Figure 5–16, the equilibrant is a 5-N force whose direction is opposite to the direction of the resultant.

To find the equilibrant of two or more concurrent forces, first find the resultant of the forces. The equilibrant is a force equal in magnitude to the resultant, but opposite in direction.

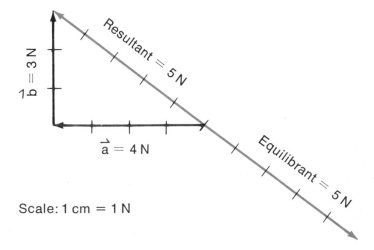

FIGURE 5-16. Determining the equilibrant of two forces acting at an angle of 90° with each other.

Scale: 1 cm = 1 N

PROBLEMS

16. A force of 50-N acts due west. What single force places this force in equilibrium?

17. Two forces act concurrently on a point P. One force is 60 N due east. The second force is 80 N due north. (a) Find the magnitude and direction of their resultant. (b) What is the magnitude and direction of their equilibrant?

18. A 60-N force acting at 30° east of north and a second 60-N force acting in the direction 60° east of north are concurrent forces. (a) Determine the resultant force. (b) What is the magnitude and direction of their equilibrant?

19. A 60-N force acts 45° west of south. An 80-N force acts 45° north of west. The two forces act on the same point. What is the magnitude and direction of their equilibrant?

20. A 30-N force acting due north and a 40-N force acting 30° east of north act concurrently on point P. What is the magnitude and direction of a third force that places these two forces in equilibrium?

5:11 Perpendicular Components of Vectors

In order to move an object in a given direction, it may be necessary to apply a force in quite a different direction. This applied force can be thought of as the sum of two or more forces. The forces which together give a resulting force are called **component** (kuhm POH nuhnt) **forces**.

Component forces, when added, give the resultant force.

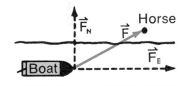

William Maddox

FIGURE 5-17. A boat is pulled through a canal by a horse walking along the bank ahead of the boat. The tension in the rope between the boat and the horse can be thought of as the sum of two component forces. One of these forces operates in the direction of the canal and the other operates in the direction of the bank.

FIGURE 5-18. Resolving a force into its vertical and horizontal components.

(a)

(b)

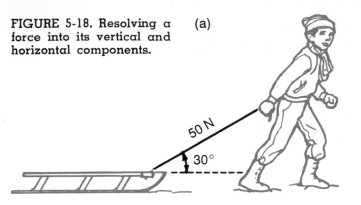

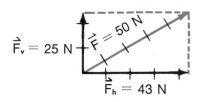

Scale: 1 division = 10 N

$\vec{F}_v = 25$ N $\vec{F} = 50$ N

$F_h = 43$ N

Consider the sled being pulled in Figure 5–18a. A 50-N force is being exerted on a rope held at an angle of 30° with the horizontal. The purpose of the 50-N force is to pull the sled forward. However, not all of the 50-N force does this. Part of the force acts in an upward direction. The only force that pulls the sled forward is the horizontal component ($\vec{F}_h$) of the 50-N force.

A single force may be resolved into perpendicular components.

The values of the horizontal and vertical components of $\vec{F}$ can be found by first drawing a set of perpendicular axes (Figure 5–18b). One axis represents the horizontal direction. The other axis represents the vertical direction. The vector to represent the force ($\vec{F}$) in the rope is then drawn at the proper angle with the horizontal axis. To resolve that force into the components $\vec{F}_v$ and $\vec{F}_h$, draw lines perpendicularly from each axis to the tip of the force vector. The magnitudes of the two components are then found in terms of the scale used for $\vec{F}$. (Note that the resultant of $\vec{F}_v$ and $\vec{F}_h$ is the original force vector $\vec{F}$.)

As the direction of a force changes, the magnitude of each of the component forces changes.

The size of the horizontal component is increased when the person pulling the sled lowers the rope. But if the angle between the rope and the horizontal is increased to 60°, the horizontal component is decreased to 25 N. Thus, the magnitudes of the components change as the direction of the force changes.

Scale: 1 cm = 10 N

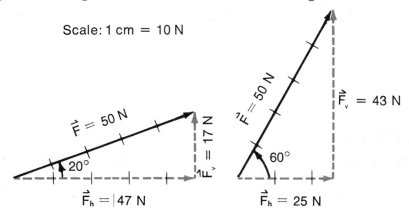

FIGURE 5-19. The horizontal and vertical components of a force depend upon its direction.

$\vec{F} = 50$ N 20° $\vec{F}_h = 47$ N $F_v = 17$ N

$\vec{F} = 50$ N 60° $\vec{F}_v = 43$ N $\vec{F}_h = 25$ N

In resolving velocity and displacement vectors, let one axis represent a north-south direction. Let the second axis represent an east-west direction.

Example: Resolving a Velocity Vector Into Its Components

A wind with a velocity of 40 km/hr blows 30° north of east. What is the north component of the wind's velocity? What is the east component of the wind's velocity?

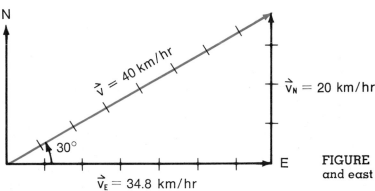

FIGURE 5-20. Resolving $\vec{v}$ into north and east components.

Scale: 1 cm = 5 km/hr

Solution:
   To find the north component (v_N), use the relation

$$\sin 30° = \frac{v_N}{v}$$

Then, $v_N = v \sin 30°$
               $= 40 \text{ km/hr} \times 0.50$
               $= 20 \text{ km/hr}$

To find the east component (v_E), use the relation

$$\cos 30° = \frac{v_E}{v}$$

Then, $v_E = v \cos 30°$
               $= 40 \text{ km/hr} \times 0.87$
               $= 34.8 \text{ km/hr}$

PROBLEMS

21. A heavy box is pulled across a wooden floor with a rope. The rope forms an angle of 60° with the floor. A tension of 80 N is maintained on the rope. What force actually is pulling the box across the floor?

22. The rope in Problem 21 is lowered until it forms an angle of 30° with the floor. A force of 80 N is maintained on the rope. What force pulls the box across the floor?

23. An airplane flies 30° north of west at 500 km/hr. At what rate is the plane moving (a) north, (b) west?

24. A ship sails from Norfolk harbor. It maintains a direction of 45° north of east for a distance of 100 km. How many kilometers has the ship progressed from Norfolk (a) north, (b) east?

25. A lawnmower is pushed with a force of 70 N applied to the handle. Find the horizontal component of this force when the handle is held at an angle with the lawn of (a) 60°, (b) 40°, (c) 30°.

26. A guy wire helps to hold a television tower in place. The wire forms an angle of 40° with the tower. It is under a tension of 4000 N. (a) What force tends to support the tower? (b) What force tends to pull the tower over?

27. A water skier is towed by a speedboat. The skier moves to one side of the boat in such a way that the towrope forms an angle of 55° with the wake of the boat. The tension on the rope is 350 N. What would be the tension on the rope if the skier were directly behind the boat?

5:12 Non-Perpendicular Components of Vectors

In Section 5:11, a single vector was resolved into two components at right angles to each other. However, a vector can be resolved into components that lie in any directions as long as their vector sum is equal to the original vector. In some cases, it may be necessary for you to resolve a vector into components that are not at right angles to each other.

A sign that weighs 40 N is supported by ropes A and B (Figure 5-21a). Three forces act on the sign. These are the force in rope A,

FIGURE 5-21. Resolving the force $\vec{R}$ into the non-perpendicular components $\vec{a}$ and $\vec{b}$.

Scale: 1 division = 10 N

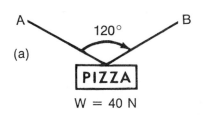

(a)

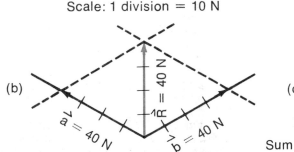

(b)

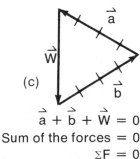

(c)

$$\vec{a} + \vec{b} + \vec{W} = 0$$
Sum of the forces = 0
$$\Sigma F = 0$$

the force in rope B, and the force due to gravity (the weight of the sign). The weight of the sign (40 N) acts in the direction straight down. Because the sign is in equilibrium, the forces in the two ropes must produce a resultant (R) of 40 N in the direction straight up to balance the weight of the sign. Thus, the magnitude and direction of the resultant of the forces in the two ropes is known, although the actual force in each rope is not known.

Figure 5–21b shows how the vector $\vec{R}$ can be resolved into two components to find the force in each rope. Three lines are drawn. These are the known vector $\vec{R}$ and two lines which represent the directions of ropes A and B.

The vector $\vec{R}$ is then resolved into two components—one in the direction of rope A and one in the direction of rope B. This is done by constructing a parallelogram. The broken lines in this diagram represent the parallel sides that must be drawn to complete the parallelogram. These broken lines intersect the lines in the direction of ropes A and B. In so doing, they define the components of $\vec{R}$. The two components $\vec{a}$ and $\vec{b}$ are then interpreted in terms of the scale of the diagram to find the force in each rope.

In this case, the force turns out to be 40 N in each rope. The fact that the force in each rope is equal to the weight is due to the choice of angles. At other angles, the forces in the ropes will vary. Note that when the vectors $\vec{a}$, $\vec{b}$, and $\vec{W}$ are added as in Figure 5–21c, they form a closed triangle. This indicates a vector sum of zero. Thus, the sign is in equilibrium. No net force implies no acceleration.

SUMMARY

Quantities may be either scalar quantities or vector quantities. Scalar quantities have magnitude only. Vector quantities have both magnitude and direction. Scalar quantities are added algebraically. Vector quantities are added by a special method called vector addition.

A vector quantity can be represented by an arrow-tipped line segment called a vector. In vector addition, vectors are added head-to-tail. The vector sum, or resultant, is drawn from the tail of the first vector to the head of the last vector. Vectors can be added in any order. The order in which they are added does not affect the sum of the vectors.

Vectors, when added, produce a resultant. However, each vector remains completely independent of the others. The resultant merely indicates the combined effect of the vectors.

When two or more forces act concurrently on a body and their vector sum is zero, the body is in equilibrium. If their vector sum is not zero, the body is not in equilibrium. In this case, there exists a single, additional force that can be applied to the body to produce equilibrium. This additional force is called the equilibrant.

A vector can be resolved into component vectors, or components. These components, when added, give a resultant which is the original vector. Components can be selected in any direction, as long as their vector sum is equal to the original vector.

QUESTIONS
1. Distinguish between vector quantities and scalar quantities.
2. How are vectors always added?
3. When two vectors are added, what is the rule for drawing the resultant vector?
4. A boat travels at 10 m/sec. It heads straight across a river which flows at 3 m/sec. What is the resultant velocity of the boat across the river?
5. What is meant by the term concurrent forces?
6. How does the resultant of two vectors change as the angle between the two vectors increases?
7. A lawnmower is pushed across a lawn. Can the horizontal component of the force be increased without changing the total force applied to the handle of the mower? How?
8. What is the sum of three vectors that form a closed triangle? Assume that the vectors are force vectors. What does this imply about the object upon which the forces act?
9. How can the equilibrant of two or more concurrent forces be found?
10. A gardener may find that it is easier to pull a lawnroller across the lawn than it is to push the same roller across the lawn. Explain.

PROBLEMS
1. What is the vector sum of a 65-N force acting due east and a 30-N force acting due west?
2. A plane flies due north at 200 km/hr. A wind blows it due east at 50 km/hr. What is the magnitude and direction of the plane's resultant velocity?
3. A boat travels at 8 m/sec and heads straight across a river 240 m wide. The river flows at 4 m/sec. (a) What is the boat's resultant speed with respect to the riverbank? (b) How long does it take the boat to cross the river? (c) How far downstream is the boat when it reaches the other side?
4. Determine the magnitude of the resultant of a 40-N force and a 70-N force acting concurrently when the angle between them is
   (a) 0°   (d) 90°
   (b) 30°   (e) 180°
   (c) 60°
5. Three people attempt to haul a heavy sign to the roof of a building by means of three ropes attached to the sign. Person A stands directly above the sign and pulls straight up on a rope. Person B and person C stand on either side of Person A. Their ropes form 30° angles with person A's rope. A force of 100 N is applied on each rope. What is the net upward force acting on the sign?
6. An electron in the picture tube of a television set is subjected to a magnetic force of 2.6×10^{-24} N acting horizontally and an electric force of 3.0×10^{-24} N acting vertically. What is the magnitude of the resultant force acting on the electron?
7. A plane travels 40° north of east for a distance of 300 km. How far north and how far east does the plane travel?
8. A descent vehicle landing on the moon has a vertical velocity toward the surface of the moon of 30 m/sec. At the same time it has a horizontal velocity of 55 m/sec. (a) At what speed does the vehicle move along its descent path? (b) At what angle with the vertical is this path?

9. A lawnmower is pushed across a lawn by applying a force of 90 N to the handle of the mower. The handle makes an angle of 60° with the horizontal. (a) What are the horizontal and vertical components of the force? (b) The handle is lowered so that it makes an angle of 30° with the horizontal. What are the horiontal and vertical components of the force?

10. A force of 90 N is exerted on a heavy box by means of a rope. The rope is held at an angle of 45° with the horizontal. What are the vertical and horizontal components of the 90-N force?

11. A river flows due south. A riverboat pilot heads the boat 27° north of west and is able to go straight across the river at 6 m/sec. (a) What is the speed of the current? (b) What is the speed of the boat?

12. A street lamp weighs 150 N. It is supported by two wires which form an angle of 120° with each other. What is the tension of each of these wires?

13. If the angle between the wires in Problem 12 is changed to 60°, what is the tension of each of the wires?

14. Three forces act concurrently on point P. Force $\vec{a}$ has a magnitude of 80 N and is directed 30° east of north. Force $\vec{b}$ has a magnitude of 70 N and is directed due east. Force $\vec{c}$ has a magnitude of 40 N and is directed 45° south of east. (a) Graphically add these three forces in the order $\vec{a} + \vec{b} + \vec{c}$. (b) Graphically add these three forces in the order $\vec{c} + \vec{b} + \vec{a}$. (c) What is noted about the solutions in each case?

PROJECTS

1. At county fairs, the "strong man" often performs a feat of strength in which he places four or five people at each end of a long rope. Holding the middle of the rope in his teeth, he defies the people to pull him forward. He is very careful not to let the angle between the two lengths of rope to each side of him drop below 140°. Draw a vector that represents this stunt. Use it to explain why the strong man cannot be moved.

2. Your neighbor is clearing stones from a sandy lot before landscaping the lot. You notice that your neighbor is having a difficult time pushing a stone-filled wheelbarrow across the lot. Now that you are a vector expert, what advice can you give your neighbor that will make the work much easier?

READINGS

Bonner, et al, *Principles of Physical Science* (Physics and Physical Science Series). Reading, Mass., Addison-Wesley Publishing Co., Inc., 1971, Chapter 3.

Daich, C. B., *Learn Science Through Ball Games*. New York, Sterling Publishing Co., 1972.

Gans, Carl, "How Snakes Move." *Scientific American,* June, 1970.

Haber-Schaim, Uri, et al, *PSSC Physics,* 4th ed., Boston, D.C. Heath and Co., 1976, Chapter 10.

March, Robert H., *Physics for Poets*. New York, McGraw-Hill Book Co., 1970, Chapter 3.

Rutherford, F. J., et al, *The Project Physics Course,* text ed. New York, Holt, Rinehart and Winston, Inc., 1970, Chapter 3.

Through the centuries, humans have dreamed of soaring into space like a bird. One ancient legend tells of a person who built wings of wax, flew too close to the sun, and fell into the sea when the wax wings melted. Modern attempts at flight have been much more successful. Through observation and experimentation, we have learned much about the relationships between forces and the motions of bodies. What forces contribute to the successful flight of this hang glider?

DYNAMICS

This chapter introduces the most basic of all scientific concepts, the interaction between forces and matter. If the magnitude and direction of a force are known, the effect on a given mass can be determined. This is done by using two laws first stated by Sir Isaac Newton.

Newton's laws of motion are basic to the study of **dynamics** (dy NAM iks). Dynamics deals with the causes of motion (forces) rather than motion itself. In this chapter we will study Newton's first two laws of motion. In Chapter 7 we will study his third law of motion.

Sir Isaac Newton (1642–1727) was born in the same year that Galileo died. By the age of eighteen, he had discovered the binomial theorem. He then went on to develop the law of universal gravitation and to explain the motions of the planets, comets, and the moon. Newton also explained the nature of light and invented a system of calculus. Few scientists have contributed as much to science as has Sir Isaac Newton.

GOAL: You will gain knowledge and understanding of Newton's first two laws of motion and of the distinction between mass and weight.

Dynamics is the study of forces which cause motion.

6:1 Forces

Forces are needed to produce all the motions that we see every day. Most people observe thousands of forces every day of their lives. But, there are not a large number of different forces. In fact, there are only five forces known to science. Three of these —*gravitational, electric,* and *magnetic*—cause most observable interactions. The other two forces are the *nuclear* and *weak interaction* forces. They are rarely observed because they exist only inside the nucleus.

The five forces known to scientists are the gravitational, electric, magnetic, nuclear, and weak interaction forces.

An electric force results from the electron repulsion of two objects.

The force that appears when you push on something with your hand is an electric force. This electric force of repulsion develops as the electrons of the hand are brought close to the electrons of an object. In the same way, the force between an automobile's tires and the road is an electric force.

Gravitational force is the weakest of the five forces.

Gravitational force is an extremely weak force in comparison to the other forces. If two tennis balls are held one meter apart, the gravitational force between them is only 0.000 000 000 01 newton. Electric forces, on the other hand, can be very large. If one extra electron could be added to each of the atoms in the two tennis balls, the resulting electric force between them would be 500 000 000 000 000 000 000 newtons. We could never put such a charge on the tennis balls. They would be forced apart long before the charging was completed.

Magnetic and electric forces are closely related.

Magnetic forces, like electric forces, are very large in comparison to gravitational forces. In fact, magnetic forces are produced by moving electric charges. Electric and magnetic forces are very closely related. At the present time, this relationship is not completely understood.

A nuclear force is the strongest of the five forces. It holds the nucleus of an atom together.

Nuclear forces are much stronger than any of the other forces. The nuclear force holds the nucleus of an atom together in spite of the strong electric force of repulsion between its protons. Sometimes nuclei of atoms change by gaining or losing particles. When this happens, a huge amount of nuclear energy is released. Today, nuclear power plants use this energy to provide electricity for some cities.

Scientists believe that a second force exists inside the nucleus. This is called the weak interaction force. It is believed to be the force that causes some atoms to break apart. We know little about the process involved. It is hard to find out what happens inside the extremely small nucleus of an atom.

Forces act through a distance.

One unusual thing about forces is their ability to act through distances. The gravitational force between the earth and the moon keeps the moon in its orbital path over a distance of roughly 400 000 kilometers. Likewise, one magnet can affect a second magnet through a distance. This ability of forces to act through empty space is one of nature's most puzzling phenomena.

6:2 Newton's First Law

Galileo was the first to introduce the idea of acceleration. Galileo guessed that the speed of falling bodies increases uniformly with time. But, at that time, precise clocks had not yet been invented. Thus, Galileo had no way to measure the speeds of falling bodies. He got around this difficulty by rolling metal balls down smooth ramps. When the ramps formed small angles with the

Dick Smith

FIGURE 6-1. Galileo studied acceleration due to gravity by rolling metal balls down smooth ramps and timing them with a water clock.

Kinematics is the study of motion.

horizontal, the speeds of the rolling balls were slow enough to measure by using a water clock. For different time intervals, he measured both the speeds of the balls and the distances traveled. In this way Galileo was able to prove that the balls gained speed uniformly with time. Gradually he worked out the equations of motion we studied in Chapter 3. These relationships are basic to **kinematics** (kin uh MAT iks), the study of motion.

Galileo noticed that when a ball left one of the ramps it rolled for a long distance. The ball lost very little speed as it rolled across the stone floor. Galileo reasoned that if the floor were frictionless and endless, the ball would never stop moving. This observation required a remarkable amount of insight because nothing on the earth behaves in this way. Friction is an ever-present force. Friction always causes a moving body to come to rest unless a propelling force is constantly applied to the body. Friction thus creates the false idea that it is a "natural tendency" for a body in motion to come to rest. Galileo introduced the idea of **inertia** (in UHR shuh). Inertia is the tendency of a body to resist a change in its motion.

Inertia is a body's resistance to change in motion.

Newton's **first law of motion** states: *A body continues in its state of rest, or of uniform motion in a straight line, unless it is acted upon by a net external force.* This laws says that it is the natural tendency of a body to retain the motion it has. A body will resist any change in its state of motion. The first law also makes the function of forces very clear. A force is capable of changing the state of motion of a body.

Newton's first law of motion is also known as the law of inertia.

6:3 Newton's Second Law

Newton's first law of motion implies that there is no fundamental difference between a body at rest and one that is moving with uniform velocity. Consider the two cars in Figure 6-2. One car is at rest while the other one moves in a straight line at a constant 60 km/hr. The car at rest is acted upon by two forces. The force of gravity pulls it downward. The force of the road pushes it upward. The two forces are equal and opposite. Therefore, their vector sum is zero and the car is in equilibrium.

An object at rest is in equilibrium.

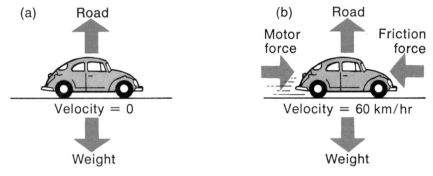

(a) Road — Velocity = 0 — Weight

(b) Road — Motor force — Friction force — Velocity = 60 km/hr — Weight

FIGURE 6-2. When forces are in equilibrium, there is no acceleration.

An object moving at a constant velocity is in equilibrium.

Four forces act on the car that moves in a straight line at a constant 60 km/hr. In the vertical direction, the same two forces are present that act on the car at rest. They are equal and opposite. In the horizontal direction, the force of the motor drives the car forward while the force of friction opposes the forward motion. These two forces must be equal and opposite because the velocity of the car is constant. By Newton's laws, a net force would accelerate the car. Thus, the motor force and the friction force are equal and opposite. The vector sum of all of the forces is zero. The moving car and the car at rest are both in equilibrium. If the driver changes the motor force, the car will accelerate or decelerate. Just as Newton's first law of motion states, any unbalanced force causes acceleration.

Newton's second law of motion tells us that an unbalanced force causes acceleration.

Newton was the first to recognize that a net force always causes acceleration and not just motion. Newton then formulated his **second law of motion:** *When an unbalanced force acts on a body, the body will be accelerated.* The acceleration will vary directly with the applied force and will be in the same direction as the applied force. It will vary inversely with the mass of the body. The mathematical expression of Newton's second law is

$$a = \frac{F}{m}$$

More often, Newton's second law of motion is written:

$$F = ma$$

6:4   Units of Force

A force accelerates a mass. A force is measured in terms of the acceleration it gives to a standard mass. Suppose a 1-kg mass is located on a frictionless, horizontal surface. The force that will cause this 1-kg mass to accelerate at the rate of 1 m/sec² is called one newton.

$$F = ma$$
$$= 1 \, \text{kg} \times 1 \, \text{m/sec}^2$$
$$= 1 \, \text{newton}$$

The **newton** (N) is the MKS unit of force.

A force of one newton will accelerate a 1-kg mass at the rate of 1 m/sec².

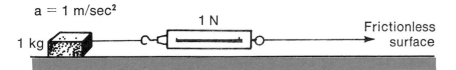

$a = 1 \, \text{m/sec}^2$

1 N

1 kg

Frictionless surface

FIGURE 6-3. Units of force are defined in terms of the acceleration they give to standard masses.

Example: Using Newton's Second Law to Find Force

A force gives a 2-kg mass an acceleration of 5 m/sec². What is the magnitude of the force?

Solution:

$$F = ma$$
$$= 2 \, \text{kg} \times 5 \, \text{m/sec}^2$$
$$= 10 \, \text{kg-m/sec}^2$$
$$= 10 \, \text{N}$$

Example: Using Newton's Second Law to Find Mass

A force of 20 N gives a stone an acceleration of 4 m/sec². What is the mass of the stone?

Solution:

$$F = ma$$
$$m = \frac{F}{a}$$
$$= \frac{20 \, \text{N}}{4 \, \text{m/sec}^2}$$
$$= \frac{20 \, \text{kg-m/sec}^2}{4 \, \text{m/sec}^2}$$
$$= 5 \, \text{kg}$$

PROBLEMS

1. A net force of 25 N is applied to a 10-kg mass. What is the acceleration given to the mass?

2. A 16-N net force is applied to a 2-kg mass. What is the acceleration of the mass?

3. An athlete exerts a force of 150 N on a shot-put giving it an acceleration of 20 m/sec². What is the mass of the shot-put?

4. A 1.5-kg mass accelerates across a smooth table at 15 m/sec². What is the net force applied to it?

5. What acceleration does a net force of 20 N impart to a mass of
   (a) 5 kg   (d) 40 kg
   (b) 10 kg   (e) 100 kg
   (c) 20 kg

6. What force gives a 1-kg mass an acceleration of 9.8 m/sec²?

7. An artillery shell has a mass of 8 kg. The shell is fired from the muzzle of a gun with a speed of 700 m/sec. The gun barrel is 3.5 m long. What is the average force on the shell while it is in the gun barrel? (Hint: use $v^2 = 2as$)

8. A racing car has a mass of 700 kg. It starts from rest and travels 120 m in 2 sec. The car undergoes uniform acceleration during the entire 2 sec. What force is applied to it? (Ignore friction; use $s = at^2/2$.)

Mass is the quantity of matter in a body.

Weight is the earth's gravitational force on a body.

The unit for mass is the kilogram.

FIGURE 6-4. The international standard of mass is a platinum-iridium cylinder which is defined as having a mass of exactly one kilogram.

National Bureau of Standards

A 1-kg mass has a weight of 9.8 N on the earth's surface.

6:5   Weight and Mass

It is important to clearly understand the distinction between weight and mass. **Mass** depends upon the amount of matter in a body. It is related to the actual number of protons, neutrons, and electrons that makes up the body. **Weight** refers to the gravitational force exerted on the body by the earth. Weight is a special name for gravitational force. It is measured in newtons as are other forces. Mass, however, is measured in kilograms.

Consider the force that must act on a 1-kg mass allowed to fall freely from some point near the earth's surface. The mass accelerates at the rate of 9.8 m/sec². By Newton's second law of motion, the force needed to accelerate a 1-kg mass at the rate of 9.8 m/sec² is

$$F = ma$$
$$= 1 \text{ kg} \times 9.8 \text{ m/sec}^2$$
$$= 9.8 \text{ kg-m/sec}^2$$
$$= 9.8 \text{ N}$$

Thus, the earth must exert a force of 9.8 N on the 1-kg mass. The mass weighs 9.8 N. If you hang a 1-kg mass on a spring scale, you will find that it does indeed weigh 9.8 N. If you hang a 2-kg mass on the spring scale, you will find that it weighs 19.6 N. A force of 19.6 N is the force needed to give a 2-kg mass an acceleration of 9.8 m/sec². In the same way, a 3-kg mass weighs 29.4 N. Thus, mass and weight are proportional.

The acceleration of gravity is 9.8 m/sec².

Note that all masses accelerate at the same rate, even though the earth pulls with a greater force on large masses. This happens because a greater force is needed to accelerate a large mass than a small mass.

To determine the weight of a mass, write Newton's second law in the form $W = mg$. Here, W represents the weight, m represents the mass, and g represents the acceleration of gravity. The weight of a 5-kg mass is

$$W = mg$$
$$= 5 \text{ kg} \times 9.8 \text{ m/sec}^2$$
$$= 49 \text{ kg-m/sec}^2$$
$$= 49 \text{ N}$$

When dealing with gravity, F=ma can be written W=mg.

The weight of a body varies with the location of the body. An object weighs slightly less in an airplane in flight than it would at sea level. An object on the moon weighs only one-sixth as much as it does on the earth. But, the mass of an object is always the same. Moving an object from one place to another never changes the mass of the object.

Weight varies with location. Mass does not.

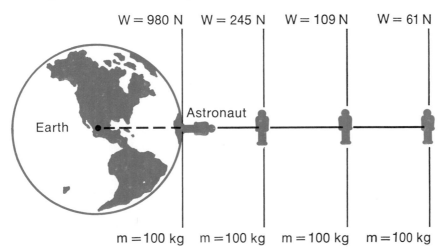

W = 980 N   W = 245 N   W = 109 N   W = 61 N

Earth   Astronaut

m = 100 kg   m = 100 kg   m = 100 kg   m = 100 kg

FIGURE 6-5. The weight of this astronaut varies with the location of the astronaut. The mass of this astronaut does not change with location.

PROBLEMS

Use Newton's second law, expressed as W = mg, to solve these problems.

9. Determine the weight of a 4.8-kg mass.

10. A stone weighs 98 N. What is its mass?

11. What is the weight of a 20-kg mass?

12. An economy car has a mass of 800 kg. What is the weight of the car?

13. A car has a mass of 1000 kg. What is its weight in newtons?

14. A small yacht weighs 4900 N. What is its mass in kilograms?

15. An 8-kg mass weighs 78.4 N. At what rate does the weight of the mass accelerate the mass?

16. (a) A car has a mass of 1200 kg. What is the weight of the car? (b) Disregarding friction, what force must the car motor apply to accelerate the car along a level highway at the rate of 4 m/sec²?

6:6 Net Forces and Acceleration

A net force acting on a mass causes the acceleration of the mass.

In Newton's second law of motion, $F = ma$, the force F which causes the mass to accelerate is the net force acting on the mass. Consider a 10-kg mass, resting on a smooth, horizontal surface. If a 100-N force is applied to the mass, then the acceleration is

$$a = \frac{F}{m} = \frac{100 \text{ N}}{10 \text{ kg}}$$
$$= \frac{100 \text{ kg-m/sec}^2}{10 \text{ kg}}$$
$$= 10 \text{ m/sec}^2$$

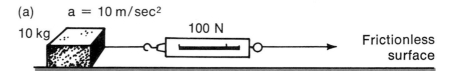

(a) $a = 10 \text{ m/sec}^2$

10 kg   100 N   Frictionless surface

(b) $a = 8 \text{ m/sec}^2$

10 kg   100 N   Rough surface

FIGURE 6-6. When acted upon by a 100-N force, the acceleration of a 10-kg mass resting on a frictionless surface (a) is greater than the acceleration of a 10-kg mass resting on a rough surface (b).

Suppose the 10-kg mass rests on a rough surface. Then when the 100-N force is applied, a friction force will also be present. The resulting acceleration will be caused by the net force, which is the difference between the applied force and the friction force. If the friction force is 20 N, then

$$F_{net} = 100 \text{ N} - 20 \text{ N} = 80 \text{ N}$$

and

$$a = \frac{F}{m} = \frac{80 \text{ N}}{10 \text{ kg}}$$
$$= \frac{80 \text{ kg-m/sec}^2}{10 \text{ kg}}$$
$$= 8 \text{ m/sec}^2$$

Friction is not the only agent that prevents the total force applied to a body from being the net force acting on it. The stone in Figure 6-7 weighs 98 N. This means that the earth pulls down on the stone with a force of 98 N. If someone lifts up on the stone with a force of 148 N, the net force acting on it is 50 N upward. The acceleration given to the 10-kg mass by the net force of 50 N will be in accord with the second law of motion, $F = ma$,

$$a = \frac{F}{m} = \frac{50 \text{ N}}{10 \text{ kg}}$$

$$= \frac{50 \text{ kg-m/sec}^2}{10 \text{ kg}}$$

$$= 5 \text{ m/sec}^2$$

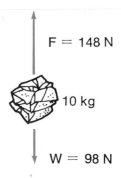

$F = 148$ N

10 kg

$W = 98$ N

FIGURE 6-7. A mass is accelerated upward if the total force exerted upward is greater than the weight.

PROBLEMS

17. A stone weighs 4.9 N. (a) What is its mass? (b) At what rate is the stone accelerated straight up if a 69-N force is applied to it in that direction?

18. A car located on a level highway has a mass of 400 kg. The friction force opposing the motion of the car is 750 N. What acceleration will a force of 2250 N produce on the car?

19. A small rocket weighs 14.7 N. (a) What is its mass? (b) The rocket is fired from a high platform but its engine fails to burn properly. The rocket gains a total upward force of only 10.2 N. At what rate and in what direction is the rocket accelerated?

20. A force of 90 N is exerted straight up on a stone that weighs 7.35 N. Calculate (a) the mass of the stone, (b) the net force acting on the stone, and (c) the acceleration of the stone.

21. The instruments attached to a weather balloon have a mass of 5 kg. (a) What do the instruments weigh? (b) The balloon is released on a calm day and exerts an upward force of 98 N on the instruments. At what rate does the balloon with instruments accelerate straight up? (c) After 10 seconds of acceleration, the weather instruments are released automatically. What is the magnitude and direction of their velocity at that instant? (d) What net force acts on the instruments after their release? (e) What time elapses before the instruments begin to fall straight down?

22. A rocket which weighs 7840 N on the earth is fired. The force of propulsion is 10 440 N. Determine (a) the mass of the rocket, (b) the upward acceleration of the rocket, and (c) the velocity of the rocket at the end of 10 sec.

FIGURE 6-8. A beam balance compares masses. The unknown mass is placed on the left and compared with known masses placed on the right. The masses are equal when the weights are equal and the beam is balanced.

Ohaus Scale Corp.

6:7 Two Ways to Measure Mass

There are two fundamentally different ways to measure the mass of a body. One method is to use a beam balance. An unknown mass is placed on a pan at the end of a beam. Known masses are placed on the pan at the other end of the beam. When the pans balance, the force of gravity is the same on each pan. Then the masses on either side of the balance must also be the same. The beam-balance method is a method of comparison. The variations of gravitational force from place to place do not affect measurements made in this way. The same result for a measurement by the beam-balance method is obtained anywhere. The mass found by the beam-balance method is called the **gravitational mass** of the body.

Gravitational mass is determined by comparing the unknown mass with a known mass.

The second method to determine the mass of a body is quite different. It uses the property of inertia. An unknown is placed on a frictionless, horizontal surface. Then a known force is applied to it and the acceleration of the mass is measured. The mass of the body can then be calculated using the equation $m = F/a$. When mass is measured in this way it is said to be the **inertial mass** of the body. This second method is seldom used because it involves both a frictionless surface and a difficult measurement of acceleration. The gravitational method of measuring mass is easier and more widely used.

Inertial mass is calculated with the equation $F=ma$. In this case, F is known and a is measured.

Gravitational mass

1.5 kg

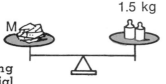

Inertial mass

$F = 3$ N $a = 2$ m/sec²

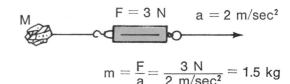

$$m = \frac{F}{a} = \frac{3\ N}{2\ m/sec^2} = 1.5\ kg$$

FIGURE 6-9. Measuring gravitational and inertial mass.

Gravitational mass and inertial mass are two essentially different concepts. But for a given mass, they are always numerically equal. This implies that an important relationship exists between gravitational mass and inertial mass. For a long time, this equivalence was thought to be one of nature's most remarkable coincidences. But Albert Einstein (1879–1955) realized that this was more than a coincidence. Einstein used this phenomenon as the foundation for his general theory of relativity.

Gravitational mass and inertial mass represent two different concepts. Numerically, however, they are equal.

SUMMARY

A force is needed to cause any motion. There are only five forces in nature. These are the gravitational, electric, magnetic, nuclear, and weak interaction forces. Of these, gravitational forces are the weakest and nuclear forces are the strongest.

Newton stated certain laws of motion. These laws apply to all interactions of force with matter. Newton's first law of motion states that a body will keep its state of motion unless acted upon by a net external force. This tendency of a body to resist a change in its motion is called the inertia of the body. Newton's second law of motion states that when a net external force acts on a body, the body will be accelerated according to the equation $F = ma$. A newton (N) is that force which will accelerate a 1-kg mass at the rate of 1 m/sec^2.

Mass is the amount of matter a body contains. Weight is the gravitational force acting on the body. Mass is measured in kilograms. Weight is measured in newtons. A 1-kg mass weighs 9.8 N.

Gravitational mass and inertial mass are two essentially different concepts. However, for a given mass, they are always numerically equal. Einstein used this phenomenon as the foundation for his general theory of relativity.

QUESTIONS

1. A ball is rolled across the top of a table and slowly comes to a stop. Considering Newton's first law of motion, explain why the ball stops. How could the ball have remained in motion?
2. Generally speaking, how do gravitational forces compare with electric and magnetic forces?
3. If gravitational forces are so weak, why don't we fall off the earth?
4. What does a net force greater than zero always produce? Why can't you pull a battleship through the desert if this is so?
5. The speedometer of your car indicates a constant 50 km/hr. Why can you say that you are not accelerating?
6. An object on Earth has a mass of 3 kg. What would be the mass of the object if it were taken to Jupiter where the pull of gravity is 10 times that of Earth?
7. What is the difference between uniform velocity and uniform acceleration?
8. Why do you fall backward on a bus when it accelerates from rest? Why do you fall forward when the driver decelerates to rest?
9. Why does a car burn more gasoline traveling in a city than it does traveling on an interstate highway?
10. What is the difference between mass and weight?

11. A person weighing 490 N stands on a scale in an elevator.
    (a) What does the scale read when the elevator is at rest?
    (b) The elevator starts to ascend and accelerates the person upward at 2 m/sec². What does the scale read now?
    (c) When the elevator reaches a desirable speed it no longer accelerates. What is the reading on the scale as the elevator rises uniformly?
    (d) The elevator begins to slow down as it reaches the proper floor. Do the scale readings increase or decrease?
    (e) The elevator starts to descend. Does the scale reading increase or decrease?
    (f) What does the scale read if the elevator descends at a constant speed?
    (g) If the cable snaps and the elevator falls freely, what would the scale read?

PROBLEMS

1. Determine the acceleration that a force of 25 N gives to a 4-kg mass. The friction force to be overcome is 5 N.
2. What net force gives an acceleration of 8 m/sec² to a 750 kg racing car?
3. Determine the weights of these masses:
   (a) 14 kg
   (b) 0.43 kg
   (c) 0.7 kg
4. Determine the mass of these weights:
   (a) 98 N
   (b) 80 N
   (c) 0.98 N
5. How much force is needed to keep a 20-N stone from falling?
6. What applied force accelerates a 20-kg stone straight up at 10 m/sec²?
7. A rocket weighs 9800 N. (a) What is its mass? (b) What force gives it a vertical acceleration of 4 m/sec²?
8. A car weighing 9800 N travels at 30 m/sec. (a) What braking force brings it to rest in 100 m? (b) in 10 m?
9. A 20-kg sled is pulled along level ground. The sled's rope makes an angle of 60° with the snow-covered ground and pulls on the sled with a force of 180 N. Find the acceleration of the sled if the friction force to be overcome is 15 N.
10. The mass of an elevator plus occupants is 750 kg. The tension in the cable is 8950 N. At what rate does the elevator accelerate upward?
11. Determine the acceleration of the system in Figure 6–10.

FIGURE 6-10

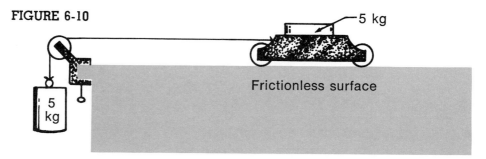

5 kg

Frictionless surface

5 kg

12. A 75-kg person is lowered down the side of a cliff with a rope. The rope being used can support a maximum of 595 N. (a) In order to prevent the rope from breaking, at what minimum rate must the climber be accelerated downward? (b) If the climber is lowered at this rate, to a ledge 20 m below, at what speed will the person strike the ledge?

13. An astronaut 100 m from the spaceship observes a 200-kg meteoroid that drifts toward the ship at 10 m/sec. If the astronaut can gain a hold on the meteroid and the astronaut's rocket gun is capable of delivering a force of 100 N, can the meteoroid be stopped before it hits the spaceship? (Neglect the mass of the astronaut.)

PROJECTS

1. Using a scale, notice and record the changes in your weight readings as you go up and down in an elevator. Discuss your findings in class.

2. Most car ads now include mileage ratings, one for highway driving and one for city driving. Why is the city-driving rating always less than the highway-driving rating?

3. Bend over and grasp your left ankle with your left hand and your right ankle with your right hand. Either lift yourself off the floor or write a paragraph explaining why Newton's first law of motion contains the word "external."

4. Aristotle said that heavy objects are pulled by the earth with greater force than light objects and therefore fall faster (he meant they have a greater acceleration). Write Aristotle a letter and explain to him that he has made a very basic error.

READINGS

Anrade, E. N., *Sir Isaac Newton*. New York, Doubleday and Co., Inc., 1958.

Bixby, William, *The Universe of Galileo and Newton* (Horizon Caravel Books). New York, Harper and Row Publishers, Inc., 1964.

Bonner, et al, *Principles of Physical Science* (Physics and Physical Science Series). Reading, Mass., Addison-Wesley Publishing Co., Inc., 1971, Chapter 2.

Haber-Schaim, Uri, et al, *PSSC Physics*, 4th ed. Boston, D.C. Heath and Co., 1976, Chapter 11.

Manuel, Frank E., *A Portrait of Isaac Newton*. Cambridge, Mass., Harvard University Press, 1968.

March, Robert H., *Physics for Poets*. New York, McGraw-Hill Book Co., 1970, Chapter 6.

Sciama, Dennis, "Inertia." *Scientific American*, February, 1957.

All objects in motion have momentum. Momentum is actually a calculated quantity. It is the product of the mass and the velocity of an object. When objects collide, the sum of the momenta of the objects after collision is equal to the sum of the momenta of the objects before collision. This relationship is known as the law of conservation of momentum. Why does the bowling average of a player tend to increase when the bowler uses a ball with larger mass?

MOMENTUM AND ITS CONSERVATION

The quantity known as momentum is one of the cornerstones of physics. It is a concept that explains much of the behavior of matter. The idea of momentum was first introduced by Newton in his studies of motion. Further studies of motion led to the law of conservation of momentum. The law of conservation of momentum is equal in importance to the law of conservation of energy, which you will study in a later chapter.

GOAL: You will gain knowledge and understanding of momentum, Newton's third law of motion, and the law of conservation of momentum.

7:1 Momentum

It is harder to stop a heavy truck than it is to stop a car moving at the same speed. A high-speed bullet needs a much stronger interaction with a tree to bring it to a halt than does a small stone thrown at a tree. This aspect of moving bodies is what we mean when we speak of **momentum** (moh MENT uhm). In physics, momentum has a very precise definition. Momentum is the product of the mass of a body and its velocity.

Momentum is the product of a body's mass and its velocity.

$$\text{Momentum} = \text{Mass} \times \text{Velocity}$$
$$= mv$$

A moving object has a large momentum if its mass is large, its velocity is large, or both its mass and velocity are large. If a heavy truck and a car are both moving at the same speed, the truck has more momentum than the car because of its larger mass. On the other hand, if the car moves very fast and the truck moves very slowly, they could both have the same momentum. A high-speed bullet and a slow-moving train can both have large momenta.

SPORTS ILLUSTRATED, Photo by J. G. Zimmerman © Time Inc.

USDA Photo

a

b

FIGURE 7-1. A skier on a steep slope (a) has more momentum than a skier on a low beginner's slope (b).

Momentum changes whenever velocity changes. If the velocity of a body is changing, this means that the body is being accelerated. Since acceleration is caused by a net force, a momentum change must be caused by a net force. Substituting the expression $a = \Delta v/t$ into Newton's second law of motion,

$$F = ma = \frac{m\Delta v}{t}$$

Thus, $$Ft = m\Delta v$$

An unbalanced force causes a change in momentum.

This equation is the momentum form of Newton's second law of motion. It says that an unbalanced force acting on a body causes a change in the momentum of the body. The direction of the momentum change will be the same as the direction of the applied force. The magnitude of the momentum change will be proportional to the force and the length of time that the force acts.

FIGURE 7-2. A great change in the momentum of a baseball occurs when the baseball bat exerts a force on the baseball over a period of time. For this reason, a batter follows through on his swing in attempting to hit a home run.

SPORTS ILLUSTRATED, Photo by Heinz Kluetmeier © Time Inc.

The quantity Ft is called **impulse**. An impulse produces a change in momentum $(m\Delta v)$. The statement above is read:

Impulse is the product of force and time.

$$\text{Impulse} = \text{Change in Momentum}$$

This relationship is very useful. If we know what change in velocity must be given to a mass, we can calculate the impulse needed. Or, if we measure a change in momentum, we can calculate the force that was involved.

An impulse produces a change in momentum.

Example: Impulse and Change in Momentum

A force of 20 N acts on a 2-kg mass for 10 sec. Compute (a) the impulse and (b) the change in speed of the mass.

Solution:

(a) $Ft = 20\,\text{N} \times 10\,\text{sec} = 200\,\text{N-sec}$

(b) $Ft = m\Delta v$

$$\Delta v = \frac{Ft}{m}$$
$$= \frac{200\,\text{N-sec}}{2\,\text{kg}}$$
$$= \frac{200\,\text{kg-m/sec}^2\,(\text{sec})}{2\,\text{kg}}$$
$$= 100\,\text{m/sec}$$

PROBLEMS

1. A car weighs 7840 N. (a) What is its mass? (b) The car's velocity is 25 m/sec eastward. What is its momentum? (c) The car was accelerated from rest to 25 m/sec by a force of 1000 N. How long did the force act to give it this velocity?

2. A force of 6 N acts on a body for 10 sec. (a) What is the body's change in momentum? (b) The mass of the body is 3 kg. What is its change in speed?

3. A car of mass 1100 kg moves at 22 m/sec. What braking force is needed to bring the car to a halt in 20 sec? (Neglect friction.)

4. A net force of 2000 N acts on a rocket of mass 1000 kg. How long does it take this force to increase the rocket's speed from 0 m/sec to 200 m/sec?

5. A snow-scooter has a mass of 250 kg. A constant force acts upon it for 60 sec. The scooter's initial speed is 6 m/sec and its final speed is 28 m/sec. (a) What change in momentum does it undergo? (b) What is the magnitude of the force which acts upon it?

6. A car weighing 15 680 N and moving at 20 m/sec is acted upon by a 640-N force until it is brought to a halt. (a) What is the

car's mass? (b) What is its initial momentum? (c) What change in the car's momentum does the force bring about? (d) How long does the braking force act on the car to bring it to a halt?

7. A constant force acts on a 600-kg mass for 68 sec. The speed of the mass is 10 m/sec before the force is applied. Its final speed is 44 m/sec. (a) What change in momentum does the force produce? (b) What is the magnitude of the force?

7:2 Newton's Third Law of Motion

Newton's third law of motion is also known as the law of action and reaction.

A single force can never exist. Every force is accompanied by an equal and opposite force.

Newton's first two laws of motion were introduced in Chapter 6. Newton's **third law of motion** is called the law of action and reaction. It states that *every force is accompanied by an equal and opposite force.* According to this law, there is no such thing as a single force. A body can produce a force only if there is some other body to exert its force upon. Your hand pushes a ball. A magnet repels a second magnet. A charged body repels another charged body. Every interaction involves at least two bodies.

Newton's second law of motion states that when one body exerts a force on another, the second body accelerates. But, a fact often overlooked is that the body exerting the force also accelerates. For example, a golf ball is hit with a golf club. The ball is

FIGURE 7-3. At the same time the golf club exerts a force on the golf ball, the golf ball exerts a force on the golf club.

Courtesy of Harold E. Edgerton, Massachusetts Institute of Technology

accelerated. But so is the club. The club is accelerated, but in a direction opposite to the ball. While striking the ball, the club slows down. The force exerted on the club by the ball gives the club a negative acceleration. If *A* produces a force on *B*, then *B* exerts an equal and opposite force on *A*. Walking is a good example of Newton's third law of motion. As you walk, you attempt to push the earth away from you. The reaction force of the earth on your feet propels you forward.

7:3   Law of Conservation of Momentum

Consider the two freight cars of equal mass shown in Figure 7-4. At first, one car moves at 20 km/hr while the other car is at rest on the track. Then, the two cars collide and are coupled together. How does the velocity of the coupled cars (v') compare with the velocity of the single freight car (v) before the collision? This question can be answered by using the law of conservation of momentum.

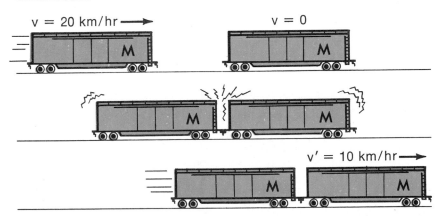

FIGURE 7-4. The total momentum of the freight car system after collision is the same as the total momentum of the system before collision.

The **law of conservation of momentum** states that *the total momentum of an isolated system cannot change.* The freight cars, if they are considered together, form an isolated system. The total momentum of the freight car system cannot be any greater or any less after the cars collide than it was before they collided.

According to the law of conservation of momentum, the total momentum of an isolated system always remains the same.

Total momentum$_{\text{before collision}}$ = Total momentum$_{\text{after collision}}$

Let *M* represent the mass of each freight car and let v' represent the velocity of the coupled cars. Substituting the known quantities into the equation, we obtain

$$M \times 20 \text{ km/hr} = 2M \times v'$$

Solving for v', we find that the coupled freight cars have a velocity of 10 km/hr after collision.

The law of conservation of momentum always holds. Nothing else can happen. For this reason, scientists consider this law to be of great importance. It lets them understand what happens during all collisions. Since all interactions are collisions in one form or another, the law of conservation of momentum is a powerful tool.

Newton's third law of motion is a way of stating the law of conservation of momentum. According to the third law, exactly equal and opposite forces appear whenever two bodies interact. The equal and opposite forces act for the same time. One never exists without the other. Thus the impulse (Ft) given to one body must be exactly the same as the impulse given to the second body, but in the opposite direction.

For Body A		For Body B
Ft	$=$	$-Ft$

and therefore: $m\Delta v$ $=$ $-m\Delta v$

It follows from this that a gain in momentum by one body occurs only through the loss of the same amount of momentum by a second body.

To better understand the law of conservation of momentum, consider a system consisting of many bodies, such as the molecules in a small container of gas. The gas particles are constantly colliding and changing one another's momentum. But each particle can gain only the momentum lost by another particle during a collision. Therefore, the total momentum of the system does not change. The total momentum of an isolated system is constant. An isolated system is a system upon which no outside force is acting.

When two particles collide, one particle can gain only the momentum lost by the other. Therefore, the momentum of the first particle plus the momentum of the second particle must be the same after the collision as it was before the collision. This can be expressed as

$$m_1v_1 + m_2v_2 = m_1v_1' + m_2v_2'$$

Where m_1 and m_2 are the masses of the two particles, v_1 and v_2 are their initial velocities, and v_1' and v_2' are their velocities after collision.

Example: Conservation of Momentum in a Collision

A glass ball of mass 5 g moves with a speed of 20 cm/sec. This ball collides with a second glass ball of mass 10 g which is moving along the same line with a speed of 10 cm/sec. After the collision, the 5 g mass still is moving along the same line, but with a speed of 8 cm/sec. What is the velocity (speed and direction) of the 10 g mass?

John Morgan

FIGURE 7-5. A wrecking ball transfers momentum to the wall of this building during the wrecking process. However, the total momentum of the wrecking ball-wall system after collision is the same as the total momentum of the system just before collision.

Solution:

$$m_1v_1 + m_2v_2 = m_1v_1' + m_2v_2'$$

$$(5 \text{ g}) (20 \text{ cm/sec}) + (10 \text{ g}) (10 \text{ cm/sec}) = (5 \text{ g}) (8 \text{ cm/sec}) + (10 \text{ g}) v_2'$$

$$200 \frac{\text{g-cm}}{\text{sec}} = 40 \frac{\text{g-cm}}{\text{sec}} + (10 \text{ g}) v_2'$$

$$160 \frac{\text{g-cm}}{\text{sec}} = (10 \text{ g}) v_2'$$

$$v_2' = 16 \text{ cm/sec in its original direction}$$

PROBLEMS

8. A plastic ball of mass 200 g moves with a speed of 30 cm/sec. This plastic ball collides with a second plastic ball of mass 100 g which is moving along the same line with a speed of 10 cm/sec. After the collision, the velocity of the 100-g mass is 26 cm/sec along the same line. What is the velocity (speed and direction) of the 200-g mass?

9. An ivory ball of mass 10 g moving with a speed of 20 cm/sec collides with a second ivory ball of mass 20 g moving along the same line in the same direction with a speed of 10 cm/sec. After the collision, the first ball is still moving in its original direction, but it has a speed of only 8 cm/sec. Determine the velocity (speed and direction) of the second ball after the collision.

10. A steel glider of mass 5 kg moves along an air-track with a speed of 15 m/sec. It overtakes and collides with a second steel glider of mass 10 kg moving in the same direction along the track with a speed of 7.5 m/sec. After the collision the first glider continues along the same line at 7 m/sec. (a) With what velocity (speed and direction) did the second steel glider leave the collision? (b) What is the change in momentum of the first glider? (c) What is the change in momentum of the second glider?

11. A car of mass 700 kg travels at 20 m/sec. The car collides with a stationary truck of mass 1400 kg. The two vehicles interlock as a result of the collision. What is the velocity speed and direction) of the car-truck system?

12. A bullet of mass 50 g strikes a wooden block of mass 5 kg. The bullet becomes embedded in the block. The block with the bullet in it then flies off at 10 m/sec. What was the original velocity of the bullet?

13. A billiard ball of mass 200 g travels at 40 cm/sec. This ball overtakes a second billiard ball of mass 150 g which is traveling along the same line at 15 cm/sec. After the collision, the 200 g ball moves along the same line at 20 cm/sec. What is the velocity of the second ball?

7:4   Internal Forces—External Forces

An internal force cannot change the total momentum of a system.

The law of conservation of momentum tells us that an outside force is needed to change the total momentum of a system. An internal force can never change the momentum of a system. Consider the two skaters of Figure 7–6a. One skater has a mass of 30 kg and the second has a mass of 60 kg. They are standing still on

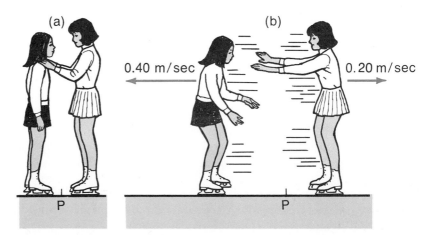

FIGURE 7-6. The internal forces exerted by these skaters cannot change the total momentum of the system.

(a)

(b)

0.40 m/sec

0.20 m/sec

P

P

smooth ice. The 60-kg skater pushes the 30-kg skater and moves backward as the 30-kg skater moves forward. The larger skater applied an internal force to the system. The total momentum of the system was zero before the internal force was applied. Thus, it must be zero after the internal force is applied. The forward momentum of the smaller skater is 30 kg × 0.40 m/sec and must equal the backward momentum of the larger skater which is 60 kg × 0.20 m/sec. If forward is a positive direction, then backward is a negative direction. Thus, the sum of the momenta of the two skaters is zero in Figure 7–6b.

Note that the momentum of each skater is changed. But, the total momentum of the system does not change. The force between the two skaters was an internal force in the two-skater system. If we consider the system to be only one of the skaters, the force would be an external force. Whether a force is internal or external depends upon whether we define the system to be just one of the bodies which are interacting or all of the interacting bodies. If a snowball hit you on the back, you would consider the force to be external to you. But if a friend considers you and the snowball together as a system, the force is internal. In this system, you gain momentum and the snowball loses momentum. The total momentum does not change.

A force can be internal or external depending on the definition of the system.

FIGURE 7-7. The external force exerted on the boat sails increases the momentum of these sailboats.

The momentum of the universe remains unchanged. This is the meaning of the law of conservation of momentum in its broadest sense.

Suppose we consider all the particles in the universe as one large system. Then all forces would be internal forces and there could never be a change in the total momentum of the universe. This is the meaning of the law of conservation of momentum in its broadest sense—the total momentum of the universe is constant.

Example: Conservation of Momentum—Bodies Initially at Rest

A 20-kg projectile leaves a 1200-kg launcher with a velocity of 600 m/sec forward. What is the recoil velocity of the launcher?

Solution:

$$\text{Momentum}_{\text{before firing}} = \text{Momentum}_{\text{after firing}}$$
$$m_1v_1 + m_2v_2 = m_1v_1' + m_2v_2'$$
$$(1200\text{ kg} \times 0) + (20\text{ kg} \times 0) = (1200\text{ kg} \times v_1') +$$
$$(20\text{ kg} \times 600\text{ m/sec})$$
$$0 = 1200\text{ kg} \times v_1' + 12\,000\text{ kg-m/sec}$$
$$\text{Then, } v_1' = -10\text{ m/sec}$$

The negative sign means that the direction of the launcher is in a direction opposite to that of the projectile.

PROBLEMS

14. A 40-kg projectile leaves a 2000-kg launcher with a velocity of 800 m/sec forward. What is the recoil velocity (speed and direction) of the launcher?

15. Upon launching, a model rocket expels 50 g of oxidized fuel from its exhaust at an average speed of 600 m/sec. If the mass of the rocket is 4 kg, what is its vertical speed after the launch? (Disregard gravitational effects.)

16. A neutron of mass 1.67×10^{-27} kg is ejected from a boron nucleus of mass 17.0×10^{-27} kg. If the neutron leaves the nucleus with a velocity of 2.0×10^4 m/sec, what is the recoil velocity of the nucleus?

17. Two campers dock a canoe. One camper steps onto the dock. This camper has a mass of 80 kg and moves forward at 4 m/sec. With what velocity will the canoe and the other camper with a combined mass of 110 kg move away from the dock?

18. A locomotive with a rocket engine is being tested on a smooth, horizontal track. The mass of the locomotive is 12 000 kg. Starting from rest, the engines are fired for 20 sec. During this time they expel 500 kg of oxidized kerosene. The kerosene particles are expelled at an average speed of 1200 m/sec. Find the speed of the locomotive at the end of the 20-sec period.

19. A thread holds two carts together on a frictionless surface as in Figure 7–8. A compressed spring acts upon the carts. The thread is burned. The 1.5-kg cart moves with a velocity of 27 cm/sec to the left. What is the velocity of the 4.5-kg cart?

1.5 kg   4.5 kg

FIGURE 7-8

7:5   Conservation of Momentum in General

Thus far, our treatment of the law of conservation of momentum has covered only interactions that take place along the same line. But the law of conservation of momentum holds for all interactions. Momentum is conserved regardless of the directions of the particles before and after they collide.

Figure 7–9a shows a spray can exploding after being thrown from a spacecraft into the near-vacuum conditions of space. We will assume that the can breaks into only two pieces. Before the explosion, the momentum of the can is represented by the vector $m\vec{v}$. After the explosion, the momenta of the two pieces are represented by the vectors $\vec{a}$ and $\vec{b}$. Notice that the y components of $\vec{a}$ and $\vec{b}$ are equal and opposite and have a vector sum of zero. The vector sum of the x components of $\vec{a}$ and $\vec{b}$ is equal to the original momentum of the can.

Momentum is conserved in all interactions, regardless of the directions of the bodies involved.

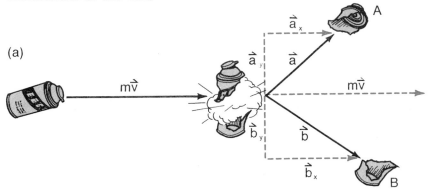

(a)

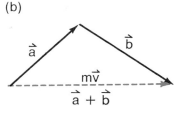

(b)

FIGURE 7-9. The momentum of the can before it explodes is the same as the sum of the momenta of the pieces of the can after it explodes.

As shown in Figure 7–9b, the vectors representing the momenta of the two pieces can be added. The resultant is the original momentum of the can. Even if the can breaks into many pieces, the vector sum of the momenta of all the pieces will still be equal to the initial momentum of the can.

Figure 7–10 shows how the vector sum of the momenta of a system remains constant when collisions are at an angle rather than head-on. A 2-kg steel ball moves at 5 m/sec across a smooth surface toward a second stationary steel ball of mass 2 kg. The bodies collide and move off in the directions shown. Since the mass of each ball is 2 kg and the velocity of each can be measured, it is possible to calculate the momentum of each after the collision takes place. The vectors $\vec{a}$ and $\vec{b}$ of the diagram represent the momenta after the collision. In part (b) these vectors are added. Their vector sum is equal to the momentum of the original ball. Thus, the momentum of the system is the same after the collision as it was before the collision. If the collision had taken place between more than two steel balls at the same time, the result

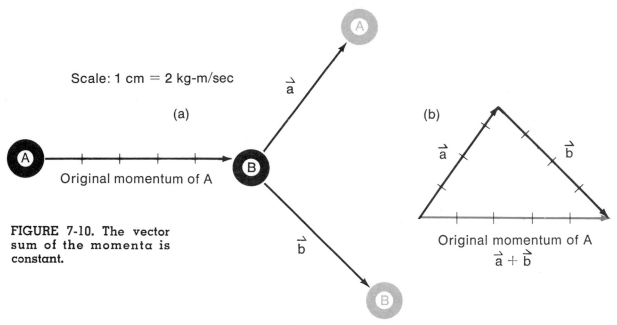

Scale: 1 cm = 2 kg-m/sec

(a)

Original momentum of A

$\vec{a}$

$\vec{b}$

(b)

$\vec{a}$ $\vec{b}$

Original momentum of A

$\vec{a} + \vec{b}$

FIGURE 7-10. The vector sum of the momenta is constant.

would be the same. The vector sum of the momenta before the collision would be the same as the vector sum of the momenta after the collision.

Example: Conservation of Momentum—Collisions at an Angle

Ball A of mass 2 kg moves at a speed of 5 m/sec. Ball A collides with stationary ball B, also of mass 2 kg (Figure 7–11). After the collision, ball A moves off in a direction 30° to the left of its original direction. Ball B moves off in a direction 60° to the right of ball A's original direction. (a) Draw a vector diagram to find the momentum of ball A and of ball B after the collision. (b) What is the speed of each ball after collision?

Solution:

(a) The vector sum of ball A's momentum and ball B's momentum after the collision must equal the vector sum of the momenta of the balls before the collision. Ball B was at rest prior to the collision. Thus, the total momentum before the collision must be equal to the momentum of ball A prior to the collision. Vectors $\vec{a}$ and $\vec{b}$ represent the momenta of balls A and B after the collision. The vector sum of $\vec{a}$ and $\vec{b}$ is equal to the momentum of ball A before the collision. Direct measurement to scale yields the magnitudes of the momenta:

$$a = 8.5 \text{ kg-m/sec}$$
$$b = 5.0 \text{ kg-m/sec}$$

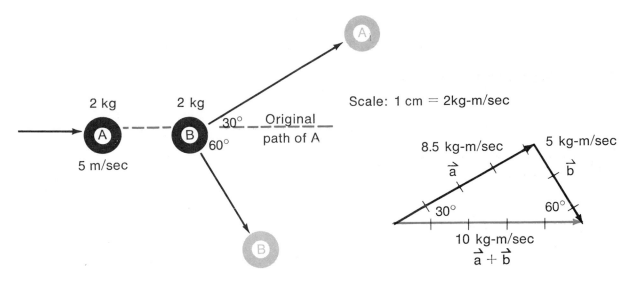

FIGURE 7-11

(b) The masses of balls A and B are 2 kg each. Thus, we can calculate the velocity of each.

$$\text{Momentum of } A = 2 \text{ kg} \times v = 8.5 \text{ kg-m/sec}$$
$$\text{thus, } v = 4.25 \text{ m/sec}$$
$$\text{Momentum of } B = 2 \text{ kg} \times v = 5.0 \text{ kg-m/sec}$$
$$\text{thus, } v = 2.5 \text{ m/sec}$$

PROBLEMS

20. Ball A of mass 5 kg moves at a speed of 4 m/sec. It collides with a second stationary ball B, also of mass 5 kg. After the collision, ball A moves off in the direction 45° to the left of its original direction. Ball B moves off in the direction 45° to the right of ball A's original direction (a) Draw a vector diagram to determine the momentum of ball A and of ball B after the collision. (b) What is the speed of each ball after the collision?

21. Body A of mass 6 kg moves at a speed of 3 m/sec. It collides with a second body B, also of mass 6 kg. After the collision, body A moves off in the direction 50° to the left of its original direction. Body B moves off in the direction 40° to the right of body A's original direction. (a) Draw a vector diagram to determine the momentum of body A and of body B. (b) What is the speed of each body after the collision?

22. A billiard ball of mass 0.5 kg moves at a speed of 10 m/sec.. It collides with a second stationary billiard ball, also of mass 0.5 kg. After the collision, the first ball moves off in a direction 60° to the left of its original direction. The second ball

From PSSC PHYSICS, D. C.
Heath & Company, Lexington, 1965

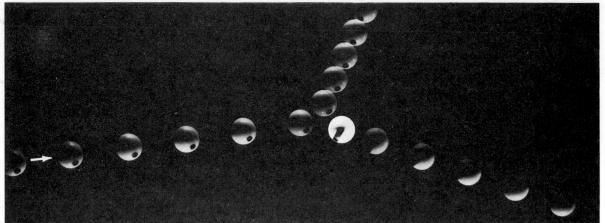

FIGURE 7-12. This photograph accompanies Problem 22.

moves off in a direction 30° to the right of the first ball's original direction. (a) Draw a vector diagram to determine the momentum of each billiard ball. (b) What is the speed of each ball after the collision?

SUMMARY

Momentum is the product of the mass of an object and its velocity. When a body is in a collision, its change in momentum ($m\Delta v$) is equal to the impulse (Ft) that acts on the body.

Newton's third law of motion states that every force is accompanied by an equal and opposite force. Forces always occur in pairs. Paired forces are equal in magnitude but opposite in direction. Opposing forces exist for equal periods of time. It follows from this that when two bodies interact they receive equal and opposite impulses. Therefore, an increase in the momentum of one body can only occur if the momentum of the second body decreases. The total momentum of the two bodies is the same after the collision as it was before the collision. This is the law of conservation of momentum.

An internal force can never change the total momentum of an isolated system. Only an outside force can change the total momentum of a system. If the universe is considered to be a closed system, then according to the law of conservation of momentum, all the particles in the universe can only exchange momentum. Thus, the total momentum of the universe remains constant.

Momentum is a vector quantity. According to the law of conservation of momentum, the vector sum of the momenta of any closed system cannot change.

QUESTIONS

1. If only an external force can change the momentum of a body, how can the internal force of a car's brakes bring the car to a stop?

2. A student stands on a turntable and holds a mass in each hand. The masses are held to the side at arm's length and at shoulder height. Another student slowly turns the turntable. As the student draws the masses in to each side, the table begins to rotate much faster. Explain the increase in speed of rotation.

3. An astronaut on a "space walk" finds that the rope connecting him to the space capsule has broken. Using a pistol, the astronaut manages to get back to the capsule. Explain.

FIGURE 7-13

4. Explain why the cannoneers in Figure 7–13 have found that their giant cannon is useless.
5. Billiard ball *A* travels across a pool table and collides with a stationary billiard ball *B*. The mass of ball *B* is equal to the mass of ball *A*. After the collision, ball *A* is at rest. What must be true of ball *B*?
6. Is it possible for a bullet to have the same momentum as a truck? Explain.

PROBLEMS

1. A force of 50 N is applied to a hockey puck for 2 sec. Calculate the magnitude of the impulse.
2. Assume the puck in Problem 1 has a mass of 0.5 kg and is at rest before the impulse acts upon it. With what speed does it move across the ice after the 2-sec period?
3. A 1500-kg car leaves a parking lot. Thirty seconds later it is moving along a highway at 72 km/hr. (a) What is the car's change in momentum? (b) What average force does the motor produce to bring about this change in momentum?
4. A force of 8.0 N acts on a 2.0-kg mass for 5 sec. (a) What is the change in momentum of the mass? (b) What is the change in the speed of the mass?
5. The mass of a car is 1600 kg. The car's velocity is 20 m/sec. (a) What is its momentum? (b) How long must a force of 800 N act on the car to give it this momentum? (Assume the direction of the force and the direction of the motion are the same.)
6. A plastic ball of mass 100 g moves with a speed of 20 cm/sec. A second plastic ball of mass 40 g is moving along the same path at 10 cm/sec. The two balls collide. After the collision, the 100-g mass has a velocity of 15 cm/sec in its original direction. What is the velocity (speed and direction) of the 40-g ball after the collision?
7. A cesium nucleus emits a beta particle of mass 9.1×10^{-31} kg with a velocity of 1.5×10^7 m/sec. The resulting barium nucleus has a mass of 2.2×10^{-25} kg. What is the recoil velocity of the barium nucleus?

PROJECTS

1. Using an air-hockey game or a pool table, observe momentum conservation when a collision takes place. Notice that the total momentum in the original direction is constant. The components of momenta perpendicular to the original direction always cancel to zero.
2. For this activity you will need a golf-ball, a golf club, and a large field. Drive the ball several times using "follow through." Note the average distance the ball travels. Then drive the ball without using "follow through." Compare the average distances the ball travels. If you have no golf clubs, a baseball and bat can be used.

READINGS

Bonner, et al, *Principles of Physical Science* (Physics and Physical Science Series). Reading, Mass., Addison-Wesley Publishing Co., Inc., 1971, Chapter 10.

Haber-Schaim, Uri, et al, *PSSC Physics,* 4th ed. Boston, D.C. Heath and Co., 1976, Chapter 14.

Lerner and Gosselin, "Giordano Bruno." *Scientific American,* April, 1973.

March, Robert H., *Physics for Poets.* New York, McGraw-Hill Book Co., 1970, Chapter 3.

Streams of water form graceful arches as they rise and fall into a pond at the base of this fountain. Note the variety of shapes of these streams. Some of them rise steeply and fall sharply back to the pond. Other streams arch gently, do not rise as high as others, but fall farther away from their sources. You can easily understand these motions if you think of all curved motion as being simply straight line motion in two directions at the same time. Using this reasoning, how can you explain the shapes of the different paths traced by these streams of water?

motion in two dimensions

All curved motion is the result of a force that causes an object to deviate from its straight-line motion. This principle is in accord with Newton's laws of motion. The first law says that an object in motion will travel in a straight line unless acted upon by an unbalanced force. From this we can conclude that an object moving in a curved path must be acted upon by a net force. Thus, the curved path followed by an object depends only upon the direction and size of the unbalanced force that causes the object to change directions.

GOAL: You will gain knowledge and understanding of motion in two dimensions and will apply this knowledge to the study of projectile motion, uniform circular motion, and simple harmonic motion.

8:1 Projectile Motion

Projectile (proh JEK tyl) **motion** includes all cases of bodies thrown or otherwise projected into the air. Examples of projectiles are baseballs and artificial satellites. To begin the study of projectile motion, consider an object thrown in a horizontal direction. The object will not remain at the same height from which it was thrown. Instead it will at once begin to fall toward the earth. The path followed by such an object is called its trajectory. The vertical and horizontal motions are **independent** of one another. To understand this concept, consider the two golf

Projectile motion is the curved motion of a body that is projected into the air.

A trajectory is the path of a projectile.

Vertical motion and horizontal motion are independent.

109

FIGURE 8-1. This sky diver has both a horizontal velocity and a vertical velocity. These velocities are independent of one another.

balls shown in Figure 8-2. The two balls are released at the same time. One ball is projected horizontally. The other ball is dropped. Strobe photography shows the path followed by each ball. Even though the projected ball moves to the right, its vertical position is, at all times, the same as the vertical position of the dropped ball. Vertically, the projected ball acts as if it has no horizontal velocity and is simply falling. Note also that the projected ball moves the same distance to the right during each time interval. The falling motion does not change the rate at which the ball moves to the right. Both the horizontal and vertical velocities of the ball act as if the other velocity did not exist.

Vertical velocity is constantly changing because of gravity.

Horizontal velocity remains constant.

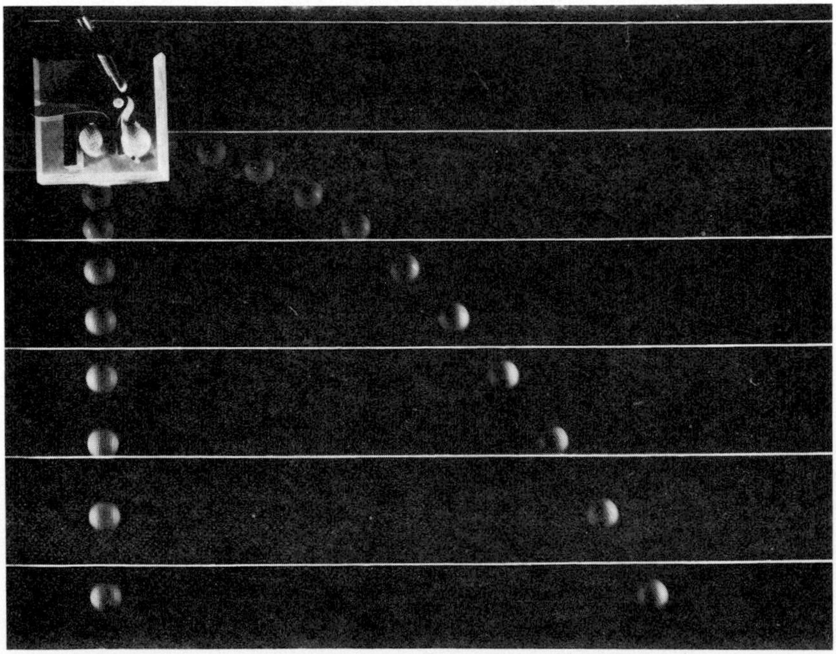

FIGURE 8-2. A flash photograph of two golf balls released simultaneously. Both balls were allowed to fall freely, but one was projected horizontally with an initial velocity of 2.00 m/sec. The light flashes were 1/30 sec apart.

From PSSC PHYSICS, D.C. Heath & Company, Lexington, 1965.

To find the horizontal distance (s_h) a projectile moves while it is falling, you must know both the horizontal velocity (v_h) and the time the body is in the air. Then the horizontal distance is the horizontal velocity times the time of fall.

Example: Projectile Thrown Horizontally

A stone is thrown horizontally at 15 m/sec. It is thrown from the top of a cliff 44 m high. (a) How long does it take the stone to reach the bottom of the cliff? (b) How far from the base of the cliff does the stone strike the ground?

When solving problems, the component velocities are treated separately.

Solution:
  (a) Find the time it takes for an object starting from rest to fall 44 m.

$$s_v = \frac{gt^2}{2}$$

$$t = \sqrt{\frac{2s_v}{g}}$$

$$= \sqrt{\frac{2 \times 44\,\text{m}}{9.8\,\text{m/sec}^2}}$$

$$= \sqrt{9\,\text{sec}^2}$$

$$= 3\,\text{sec}$$

  (b) The stone moves horizontally at 15 m/sec all the time that it is falling.

$$s_h = v_h t$$

$$= 15\,\text{m/sec} \times 3\,\text{sec}$$

$$= 45\,\text{m}$$

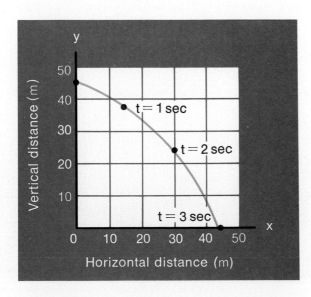

FIGURE 8-3. The path of the projectile for the above example.

PROBLEMS

1. A steel projectile is shot horizontally at 20 m/sec from the top of a 49-m high tower. How far from the base of the tower does it hit the ground?

2. A stone is thrown horizontally at a speed of 10 m/sec from the top of a cliff 78.4 m high. (a) How long does it take the stone to reach the bottom of the cliff? (b) How far from the base of the cliff does the stone strike the ground?

3. At a height of 784 m, sky divers fall from an airplane flying horizontally at 30 m/sec. What horizontal distance do the divers travel before striking the ground? (Neglect air resistance.)

4. A car traveling at 20 m/sec rolls off the edge of a cliff. The cliff is 44.1 m above the ocean. How far from the base of the cliff does the car strike the water?

5. A person standing on a cliff that is 49 m high throws a stone with a horizontal speed of 15 m/sec. How far from the base of the cliff does the stone hit the ground?

6. A plane drops a rubber raft to the survivors of a shipwreck. The plane is flying at a height of 1960 m and at a speed of 90 m/sec. The raft lands next to the survivors. How far away from the shipwreck was the plane when the raft was dropped?

7. An arrow is fired directly at the bull's-eye of a target 60 m away. The arrow has a speed of 89 m/sec. When it is fired, the arrow is 1 m above the ground. How far short of the target does it strike the ground?

FIGURE 8-4. The velocity of this ski jumper can be resolved into horizontal and vertical components.

SPORTS ILLUSTRATED Photo by Jerry Cooke © Time, Inc.

8:2   Projectiles Fired at an Angle

When a projectile is fired at an angle with the horizontal, the principle of independence of velocities still holds. The initial velocity of the projectile can be resolved into two components. One component is directed vertically. The second is directed horizontally. These component velocities are treated separately when solving problems.

Example: Projectile Fired at an Angle

A famous motorcyclist plans to jump across a canyon, 3.5 km wide. To do this, the cyclist plans to leave a 30° ramp on one side of the canyon at a speed of 196 m/sec. If the motorcycle can attain this speed, will it reach the other side of the canyon on the jump?

Solution:

First, find the horizontal and vertical components of the velocity.

$$v_v = v \sin 30°$$
$$= (196 \text{ m/sec}) (0.5)$$
$$= 98 \text{ m/sec}$$

Scale: 1 cm = 30 m/sec

$$v_h = v \cos 30°$$
$$= (196 \text{ m/sec}) (0.866)$$
$$= 170 \text{ m/sec}$$

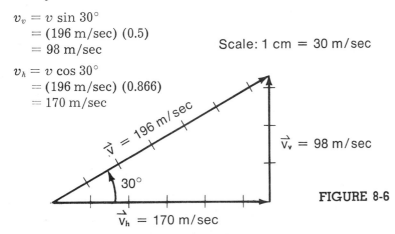

$\vec{v} = 196$ m/sec

$\vec{v_v} = 98$ m/sec

30°

$\vec{v_h} = 170$ m/sec

FIGURE 8-6

Courtesy of Harold E. Edgerton, Massachusetts Institute of Technology

FIGURE 8-5. The path of this diver can be analyzed by treating the diver as a projectile fired at an angle with the horizontal.

The velocity of a projectile can be resolved into horizontal and vertical components.

Secondly, find the total time the bike is in the air. Since, $a = \Delta v/t$, the time needed for the bike to reach its greatest height is

$$t_{up} = \frac{\Delta v_v}{a}$$
$$= \frac{\Delta v_v}{g}$$
$$= \frac{98 \text{ m/sec}}{9.8 \text{ m/sec}^2}$$
$$= 10 \text{ sec}$$

It will take another 10 sec for the bike to return to the earth. Thus, the total time in the air is 20 sec.

Third, find the horizontal distance the bike travels. The horizontal velocity of 170 m/sec is constant. Since the bike spends 20 seconds in the air, the horizontal distance it travels is

$$s_h = v_h t$$
$$= (170 \text{ m/sec}) (20 \text{ sec})$$
$$= 3400 \text{ m}$$
$$= 3.4 \text{ km}$$

Since the distance across the canyon is 3.5 km, the bike will miss the rim of the canyon by 0.1 km.

PROBLEMS

Assume no frictional effects.

8. A projectile is fired at such an angle that the vertical component of its velocity is 49 m/sec. The horizontal component of its velocity is 60 m/sec. (a) How long does the projectile remain in the air? (b) What horizontal distance does it travel?

9. A projectile is fired with a speed of 196 m/sec at an angle of 60° with the horizontal. Calculate (a) the vertical velocity and the horizontal velocity of the projectile, (b) the time the projectile is in the air, and (c) the horizontal distance the projectile travels.

10. A projectile is fired at an angle of 53° with the horizontal. The speed of the projectile is 200 m/sec. Calculate (a) the time the shell remains in the air, and (b) the horizontal distance it travels.

11. While standing on an open bed of a truck moving at 35 m/sec, an archer sees a duck flying directly overhead. The archer shoots an arrow at the duck and misses. The arrow leaves the bow with a vertical velocity of 98 m/sec. (a) How long does it remain in the air? (b) The truck maintains a constant speed of 35 m/sec and does not change its direction. Where does the arrow finally land? (c) What horizontal distance does the arrow travel while it is in the air?

FIGURE 8-7. Each point along the rotating wheel of the gyroscope is accelerated toward the center of rotation. The centripetal acceleration is associated with the centripetal force acting toward the center.

The Brush Beryllium Company

8:3   Uniform Circular Motion

When studying motion of any sort, you must keep in mind that motion is *always* governed by Newton's laws of motion. If a body is accelerating it is always because a net force is acting on the body ($F = ma$). In this section we will derive and use the equations that deal with the conditions for circular motion. A force is needed to make an object move in a circular path. This force turns out to be $F = mv^2/r$, where m is the mass of the object, v

is the speed with which the object goes around the circle, and r is the radius of the circle. Although this equation looks different from $F = ma$, it is not. The acceleration of an object that is moving in a circle is found to be v^2/r. Therefore, $F = ma$ becomes $F = mv^2/r$. This equation is a more usable form of $F = ma$. Here, the acceleration is expressed in terms of the quantities that must be measured to calculate its value.

Uniform circular motion results when a net force, acting on a mass moving with a constant speed, changes direction in such a way that it is always acting at a right angle to the direction in which the mass is moving.

Circular motion, like all motion, is governed by Newton's laws of motion.

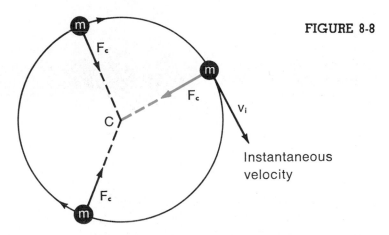

FIGURE 8-8

Instantaneous velocity

Consider Figure 8-8. A stone is tied to the end of a string. Then the stone is swung in a horizontal circle. The force which keeps the stone in its circular path is called **centripetal** (sen TRIP uht uhl) **force** (F_c). Centripetal means center-seeking. This force is exerted on the stone through the string. If this force is removed, the stone travels off in a straight line at its point of release. This is in accord with the first law of motion. The straight line path is tangent to the circle at the point of release.

Centripetal force is a force directed toward the center.

Note that the centripetal force always acts at right angles to the instantaneous velocity of the stone. Therefore, the centripetal force cannot change the magnitude of the velocity. But the force does change the direction of the velocity. Since velocity is a vector quantity, a change in direction is a change in velocity ($\Delta \vec{v}$). A change in the velocity of the stone means that the stone is being accelerated. According to the second law of motion, acceleration is always in the same direction as the applied force. The force (F_c) acting on the stone is always directed toward the center of the circle. Thus, the acceleration is always directed toward the center of the circle. This acceleration is called **centripetal acceleration**.

In circular motion, the centripetal force must be perpendicular to the object's instantaneous velocity.

Centripetal acceleration, like centripetal force, is always directed toward the center of the circle.

SPORTS ILLUSTRATED Photo by Jerry Cooke © Time, Inc.

FIGURE 8-9. This discus thrower swings the discus in a circular path before releasing it. At what point along the circular path does the athlete release the discus?

By drawing a vector diagram, we can analyze uniform circular motion. That is, we can derive equations for the magnitude of both the centripetal acceleration and the centripetal force.

The equations for centripetal acceleration and centripetal force can be derived by drawing a vector diagram.

In Figure 8-10a, A and B are two successive positions of a mass that is moving with uniform circular motion. The radius of the circle is r. The vector $\vec{v}_1$ represents the instantaneous velocity of the mass at A. The vector $\vec{v}_2$ represents the velocity of the mass at B. Note that $\vec{v}_1$ and $\vec{v}_2$ are identical in magnitude, but their directions are different. The magnitude will be denoted by the symbol v.

In Figure 8-10b, the vectors $\vec{v}_1$ and $\vec{v}_2$ have been placed tail to tail. We learned in Chapter 5 that by placing vectors head to tail, we could find their vector sum. By placing two vectors tail to tail, we can find their vector difference. This is one method of

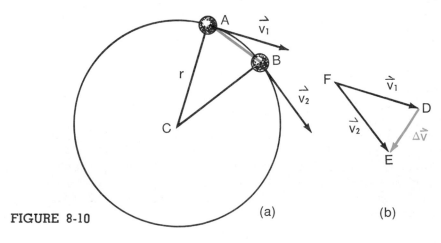

FIGURE 8-10

(a)

(b)

subtracting vectors. Here, the change in velocity ($\Delta\vec{v}$) is found. By drawing the vector $\Delta\vec{v}$, you can see that the vector $\vec{v}_2$ is the resultant of $\vec{v}_1$ and $\Delta\vec{v}$. Because $\vec{v}_1 + \Delta\vec{v} = \vec{v}_2$, it is apparent that $\Delta\vec{v} = \vec{v}_2 - \vec{v}_1$. Therefore, $\Delta\vec{v}$ is the vector difference between $\vec{v}_1$ and $\vec{v}_2$.

The triangles ABC and DEF are similar triangles because the corresponding sides of angles C and F are perpendicular. Thus,

$$\frac{\Delta v}{v} = \frac{\text{chord AB}}{r}$$

The arc AB is the distance s the mass moves during the time interval Δt. The distance s may be expressed as $v\Delta t$. If we choose A and B such that they are very close together, the chord AB and the arc AB become the same length within a small margin of error. Thus, we may express the chord AB as $v\Delta t$. Then

$$\frac{\Delta v}{v} = \frac{v\Delta t}{r}$$

So,

$$\frac{\Delta v}{\Delta t} = \frac{v^2}{r}$$

Since $\dfrac{\Delta v}{\Delta t} = a$. Then,

$$a = \frac{v^2}{r}$$

This equation allows us to find the magnitude of the centripetal acceleration of any body moving in a circle if the radius of the circle and the speed of the body are known.

Vectors are subtracted by placing them tail to tail.

Great Adventure Amusement Park

FIGURE 8-11. Centripetal force holds these people in position on this rapidly rotating wheel.

The period, T, is the time it takes a body to travel once around a circular path.

The velocity of a moving body is distance divided by time ($v = s/t$). The time it takes for a body to traverse the circumference of its circular path once is called its period (T). The distance the body travels in a single revolution is the circumference of the circle, $2\pi r$. Thus, its speed is $2\pi r/T$. This expression for v can be substituted into the equation for centripetal acceleration to yield a form that is often useful.

$$
\begin{aligned}
a &= \frac{v^2}{r} \\
&= \frac{(2\pi r/T)^2}{r} \\
&= \frac{4\pi^2 r}{T^2}
\end{aligned}
$$

The magnitude of any force is equal to ma. Thus, the centripetal force must be

$$
\begin{aligned}
F_c &= ma \\
&= \frac{mv^2}{r} \\
&= \frac{m4\pi^2 r}{T^2}
\end{aligned}
$$

Example: Centripetal Force

In a laboratory, wires are tested for tensile strength. Tensile strength is a measure of the force needed to break a wire. In doing this, a 1.5-kg mass is attached to the end of each wire. Then the mass is swung in a horizontal circle. If the wires tested are 2 m long, what force is each wire subjected to when the mass is swung at a rate of 2 rev/sec?

Solution:

First, find the period (T), the time needed for the mass to complete one revolution. Since the mass completes 2 rev/sec, its period is 0.5 sec. Then calculate the value of F_c.

$$
\begin{aligned}
F_c &= \frac{m4\pi^2 r}{T^2} \\
&= \frac{1.5 \text{ kg} \times 4 \times 9.9 \times 2 \text{ m}}{(0.5 \text{ sec})^2} \\
&= \frac{119 \text{ kg-m}}{0.25 \text{ sec}^2} \\
&= 476 \text{ N}
\end{aligned}
$$

PROBLEMS

12. A 1-kg mass is attached to a string 1 m long and swings in a horizontal circle at a rate of 4 rev/sec. (a) Find the centripetal acceleration of the mass. (b) Calculate the centripetal force (the tension in the string).

13. What is the centripetal acceleration of an object moving in a circular path of 20 m radius with a speed of 20 m/sec?

14. A 2-kg mass is attached to a string 1 m long and swings in a circle parallel to the horizontal. If the mass goes around its path once each 0.8 sec, (a) what is its centripetal acceleration, and (b) what tension is in the string?

15. It takes a 600-kg racing car 10 sec to travel at a uniform speed around a circular racetrack of 50 m radius. (a) What average force must the car's tires exert against the track to maintain its circular motion? (b) What is the acceleration of the car?

16. A child twirls a yo-yo about his head. The yo-yo has a mass of 0.2 kg and is attached to a string 0.8 m long. (a) If the yo-yo makes one complete revolution each second, what tension must exist in the string? (b) If the child increases the speed of the yo-yo to two revolutions per second, what tension must be in the string? (c) What is the ratio of the solution of (b) to (a)? Why?

17. The radius of the moon's path about the earth is about 3.6×10^8 m. The moon's period is 2.3×10^6 seconds (27.3 days). Find the centripetal acceleration of the moon.

8:4   Placing a Satellite in Orbit

To place an artificial satellite in orbit about the earth, certain conditions must be met. The conditions are the same as those for any circular motion. Since a satellite is to circle the earth, it must be acted upon by a centripetal force (F_c) that is always directed

A satellite's weight provides the centripetal force to maintain its circular motion.

FIGURE 8-12. An orbiting satellite is acted upon by a centripetal force directed toward the center of the earth.

NASA

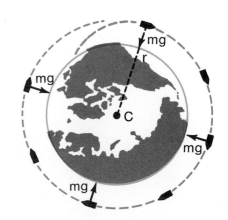

toward the center of the earth. The gravitational force (or weight) that acts on the satellite provides just such a force. Thus, the weight of a space capsule is what keeps it in its orbital path.

The equation for circular motion is $F_c = mv^2/r$. Because it is the weight (mg) of a satellite that must provide the necessary centripetal force to keep it in its orbital path, we may write

$$mg = \frac{mv^2}{r}$$

This equation reduces to

$$g = \frac{v^2}{r}$$

Thus, the velocity a satellite must have to orbit the earth is

$$v = \sqrt{gr}$$

where g is the acceleration of gravity and r is roughly the radius of the earth. It will be left to the student to verify that his "orbital velocity" is about 2.9×10^4 km per hour. This will be done in Problem 18.

A satellite's mass does not affect its orbital velocity.

Note that the mass of the satellite does not affect its orbital velocity. A more massive satellite weighs more. The centripetal force increases in exact accord with the increased mass. As shown above, the mass of the satellite drops out of the equation.

Satellites must be accelerated to orbital velocity by large rockets such as the Saturn V. The acceleration of any mass follows Newton's second law ($F = ma$). Thus, a massive satellite requires a large force to accelerate it to orbital velocity. The mass of the satellites that can be launched is limited by the capabilities of the rockets that are developed. Large space platforms could be placed in orbit by using several rockets. Each would carry parts of the platform to be assembled in orbit.

Most satellites are placed in orbit at a height of more than 320 km above the earth's surface. At such heights there is very little atmosphere to cause friction and reduce the speed of the satellite. Thus, once launched, a satellite will orbit the earth for long periods of time with no need for further power input.

PROBLEMS

18. Calculate the velocity at which a satellite must be launched in order to achieve an orbit about the earth. Use 9.8 m/sec² as the acceleration of gravity and 6500 km as the earth's radius.

19. During the lunar landings, the command module orbited the moon while waiting for the lunar module to return from the moon's surface. If the diameter of the moon is 3570 km and the acceleration of gravity on the moon is 1.6 m/sec², at what velocity did the command module orbit the moon?

8:5   Simple Harmonic Motion

The swinging of a pendulum and the vibrating of a guitar string are both examples of vibrational motion. In this type of motion, the bodies swing back and forth over the same path. This type of motion is related to circular motion.

The **frequency** of a vibrating body is the number of vibrations per unit of time. The standard unit for frequency is the hertz. A **hertz** (Hz) is equal to one cycle per second. For a pendulum, a single vibration begins at the highest point of swing on one side. It continues to the highest point of swing on the other side and then returns to its first position. If a pendulum completes five such cycles in one second, its frequency is 5 cycles/sec or 5 Hz.

The **period** of a vibrating body is the time required for one vibration. The period is the reciprocal of the frequency. Thus, for the pendulum just described, the period would be 1/5 sec or 0.2 sec.

The **amplitude** of vibration is the distance from the vibrating body's rest position to its point of greatest displacement.

Vibrational motion is the to and fro movement of a body over the same path.

Frequency is vibrations per unit time. The unit for frequency is the hertz.

Period is the time needed for one vibration. The period is the reciprocal of the frequency.

Amplitude is the greatest displacement from the rest position.

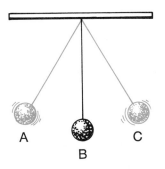
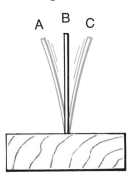
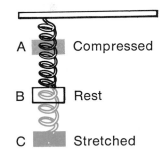

A   B   C

A   Compressed

B   Rest

C   Stretched

FIGURE 8-13. Vibrating bodies undergo simple harmonic motion.

SHM is one type of vibrational motion.

Simple harmonic motion (SHM) is a special kind of vibrational motion. In SHM the acceleration of the body is directly proportional to its displacement (x) from its rest position. In this way, SHM differs from other vibrational motions. When the mass hanging from the spring in Figure 8-13 is pulled down, the force tries to restore the mass to its rest position. This force increases in direct proportion to the distance the mass is pulled from its rest position. Since the force increases directly, the acceleration of the mass must do likewise because $F = ma$. Thus, the acceleration varies directly with the displacement and this is an **example** of SHM. The acceleration of the mass is greatest at C, zero at B, and in full magnitude again at A. Note that, at all times, the acceleration is directed toward the rest position. This is another characteristic of SHM.

The relationship between SHM and circular motion is diagrammed in Figure 8-14a. A body is shown going around a circle

In SHM, the acceleration varies directly with the displacement.

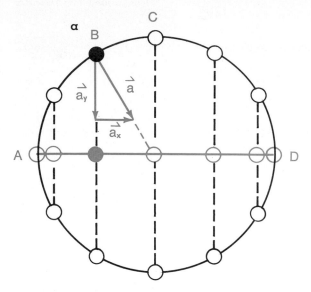

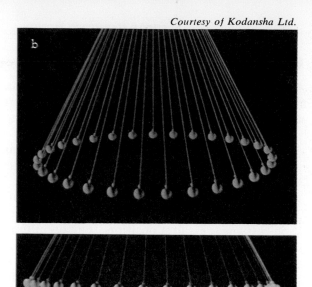

Courtesy of Kodansha Ltd.

FIGURE 8-14. (a) A diagram of uniform circular motion. (b) The uniform circular motion of a mass as viewed from above and from the side.

SHM can be explained as the projection of circular motion.

FIGURE 8-15

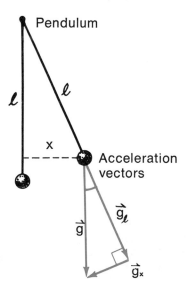

with uniform speed. The acceleration of the body is directed toward the center of the circle at all times. However, at B, we can consider the acceleration to consist of the x and y components shown. The x component, a_x, is always directed parallel to the diameter AD. Notice that a_x is zero at C and greatest at its maximum displacement from C. In between, a_x fluctuates smoothly between zero and maximum.

Consider a body moving back and forth along the axis AD in such a way as to always be perpendicularly beneath the mass going around the circle. At any position, its acceleration would be the same as a_x, and it would be undergoing SHM. Simple harmonic motion can be described as the projection of circular motion on one axis.

The period of the body undergoing uniform circular motion and the body undergoing SHM would be the same. That is, it would take one body as long to go back and forth along its axis as it would take the other body to go around the circle. We have found that, for uniform circular motion, $a = 4\pi^2 r/T^2$. Thus, the period of both circular motion and SHM must be given as

$$T^2 = \frac{4\pi^2 r}{a}$$

To show the usefulness of the relationship between circular motion and SHM, we will use the pendulum of Figure 8-15. In this figure, the gravitational acceleration $\vec{g}$ is resolved into two components. The component $\vec{g}_x$ is at a right angle to the direction of the string. Since the motion of the pendulum is always at a right angle to the direction of the string, $\vec{g}_x$ represents the acceleration of the pendulum.

National Bureau of Standards

Since the two triangles of Figure 8-15 are similar triangles,

$$\frac{g_x}{x} = \frac{g}{l}$$

or, $g_x = \frac{gx}{l}$

The equation for the period of a pendulum can be derived.

$$T^2 = \frac{4\pi^2 r}{a}$$

$$= \frac{4\pi^2 x}{(g/l)x}$$

$$= \frac{4\pi^2 l}{g}$$

thus, $T = 2\pi \sqrt{\dfrac{l}{g}}$

Notice that the period of a pendulum does not depend on the mass of the body nor on the amplitude of the swing. In any one location, the period depends only on the length of the pendulum (g being constant for a given location). Note also that a simple pendulum can be used to measure the acceleration of gravity.

Example: The Period of a Pendulum

Determine the period of a pendulum 6 m in length.

Solution:

$$T = 2\pi \sqrt{\frac{l}{g}}$$

$$= 6.28 \sqrt{\frac{6 \text{ m}}{9.8 \text{ m/sec}^2}}$$

$$= 6.28 \sqrt{0.61 \text{ sec}^2}$$

$$= 4.9 \text{ sec}$$

FIGURE 8-16. A pendulum clock is regulated by varying the length of the pendulum.

PROBLEMS

20. Determine the period of a pendulum 1 m long.

21. What is the period of a pendulum 0.5 m long?

22. The period of a pendulum is 1 sec. Find its length in meters.

23. The period of a pendulum is 4 seconds. If the pendulum is 4 m in length, determine the acceleration of gravity.

SUMMARY

Projectile motion includes all cases of bodies projected into the air. The horizontal and vertical motions of a projectile are independent of one another. Thus, a body thrown horizontally falls in accordance with the acceleration of gravity as does a body that has been dropped. When a body is projected at some angle with the horizontal, its velocity must be resolved into vertical and horizontal components. The vertical component (v_v) is used to find the time the body will spend in the air. The horizontal component (v_h) is constant and is used to find the horizontal distance traveled by the body.

Uniform circular motion results when a net force, called the centripetal force, always acts at a right angle to the direction in which a mass is moving. The centripetal force produces a constant centripetal acceleration. Both the centripetal force and the centripetal acceleration are always directed toward the center of the circle. The equation for centripetal force is $F_c = mv^2/r$.

The weight of a satellite provides the centripetal force needed to keep it in its orbital path. To put a satellite into orbit, the satellite must be given a certain minimum orbital velocity. Because weight increases with mass, this orbital velocity is almost the same for all satellites launched from the earth.

If a body moves back and forth over the same path, its motion is called vibrational motion. This type of motion is related to circular motion. Simple harmonic motion is a special kind of vibrational motion. SHM occurs when the acceleration of a body is directly proportional to its displacement. The frequency of a vibrating body is the number of vibrations per unit time. The unit for frequency is the hertz (Hz). The period is the time required for one vibration and is the reciprocal of the frequency. The amplitude of vibration is the maximum distance from the body's rest position.

QUESTIONS

1. A hunter standing on a high platform aims a rifle straight at a monkey who is hanging on a distant tree branch by one hand. The barrel of the rifle is parallel to the horizontal. Just as the hunter pulls the trigger, the monkey lets go of the branch and begins to fall. Will the bullet hit the monkey?

2. An airplane is flying at a constant speed in a straight line parallel to the horizontal, and the pilot drops a flare. Where will the plane be relative to the flare when the flare hits the ground?

3. What relationship must exist between an applied force and a moving mass if uniform circular motion is to result?

4. What constitutes one complete vibration of a pendulum?

5. Distinguish among the frequency, the period, and the amplitude of a pendulum.

6. How is simple harmonic motion distinguished from other types of vibrational motion?

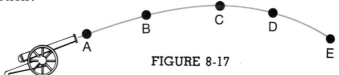

FIGURE 8-17

7. Consider the path of the ball in Figure 8-17.
   (a) At which point is the vertical velocity the greatest? (You may find two points.)
   (b) At which point is the horizontal velocity the greatest?
   (c) Where is the vertical velocity least?
   (d) Name the curve traveled by the ball.

PROBLEMS

1. A stone is thrown horizontally at 8 m/sec from a cliff 78.4 m high. How far from the base of the cliff will the stone strike the ground?

2. A bridge is 176.4 m above a river. If a lead fishing weight is thrown from the bridge with a horizontal speed of 22 m/sec, what horizontal distance will it travel before striking the water?

3. (a) If an object falls from rest from a height of 490 m, how long will it remain in the air? (b) If the object had a horizontal velocity of 200 m/sec when it began to fall, what horizontal distance will it travel?

4. A stone is thrown horizontally from the top of a cliff 122.5 m high. If the stone lands 40 m from the base of the cliff (a) how long did it take for the stone to fall to the base, and (b) with what horizontal velocity was the stone thrown?

5. Divers at Acapulco dive from a cliff that is 61 m high. If the rocks below the cliff extend outward for 23 m, what is the minimum horizontal velocity a diver must have to clear them?

6. A projectile is fired at an angle of 37° with the horizontal. If the initial velocity of the projectile is 1000 m/sec, what horizontal distance will it travel?

7. A golf ball is hit at an angle of 45° with the horizontal. If the initial velocity of the ball is 50 m/sec, how far will it travel horizontally before striking the ground?

8. A baseball is hit at 30 m/sec at an angle of 53° with the horizontal. An outfielder runs at 4 m/sec toward the infield and catches the ball. What was the original distance between the batter and the outfielder?

9. A projectile is fired at an angle of 30° with the horizontal and with a velocity of 78.4 m/sec. (a) Find the vertical and horizontal velocities of the projectile. (b) Make a table showing v_v and v_h at the end of each second. Do this for an 8-sec period. (c) Plot a graph of v_v vs t. Describe the curve obtained. (d) Plot a graph of v_h vs t. Describe the curve.

10. An athlete twirls a 7-kg hammer tied to the end of a 1.3-m rope about his head. The hammer moves at the rate of 1 rev/sec. (a) What is the centripetal acceleration of the hammer? (b) What is the tension in the rope?

11. A 0.5-kg mass is attached to a string 0.8 m long. It is swung in a horizontal circle. If the mass is moving at 4 rev/sec, what tension exists in the string?

12. What would be the period of a pendulum that is 9.8 m long?

13. How long must a pendulum be to have a period of 1.5 seconds?

PROJECTS

1. Tie a small mass on the end of a 1.5 m length of nylon cord. Pass the cord through a small tube and tie the spring scale to the other end of the cord. Hold the scale in one hand and the tube in the other. Twirl the mass about your head. Ask someone to time 10 revolutions. Use this data to verify the equation $F_c = mv^2/r$. The distance r is the distance from the edge of the glass tube to the mass.

2. Make a pendulum. Find its period by measuring the time needed for a certain number of swings (about 60 swings). Then calculate the acceleration of gravity in your location.

READINGS

De Santillana, Giorgio, *The Crime of Galileo*. Chicago, Ill., University of Chicago Press, 1955.

Drake, Stillman, "Galileo's Discovery of the Parabolic Trajectory." *Scientific American*, March, 1975.

March, Robert H., *Physics for Poets*. New York, McGraw-Hill Book Co., 1970, Chapter 4.

Roeder, John L., "Physics and the Amusement Park." *The Physics Teacher*, September, 1975.

At one time, gravity was thought to be a special force which pulls everything to the earth. However, in the 17th century, Sir Isaac Newton began to think that all objects might exert gravitational forces on all other objects. He found evidence to support this idea in the motions of heavenly bodies. From experience, we know that this parachutist is being pulled to the ground by the earth's gravitational force. But does the parachutist also exert a gravitational pull on the earth? If so, why is this force of attraction not easily observed?

UNIVERSAL GRAVITATION

chapter 9

Until Newton's time, gravitational force was thought to be a unique property of the earth. But Newton suspected that the earth was not unique among the heavenly bodies. He had already found that all motion follows three universal laws. Perhaps the gravitational force of the earth was only one example of a universal force which acts between any two bodies.

GOAL: You will gain knowledge and understanding of the law of universal gravitation and of some of the methods which scientists use to solve complex problems.

9:1 Kepler's Laws of Planetary Motion

The observations of Tycho Brahe and the calculations of Johannes Kepler provided the basis for Newton's theory of universal gravitation. Tycho Brahe (1546-1601) spent most of his life observing heavenly bodies. Night after night, for more than 20 years, he recorded the positions of the planets and the stars. Near the end of his life, Brahe hired an assistant named Johannes Kepler (1571-1630). Kepler did not have Brahe's patience for observation. But he was an excellent mathematician. Using Brahe's vast amount of data, Kepler formulated three laws of planetary motion.

1. The paths of the planets are ellipses.
2. An imaginary line from a planet to the sun sweeps out equal areas each second whether the planet is close to or far away from the sun.
3. If the radius of a planet's orbit about the sun is cubed and then divided by the planet's period (time for it to travel about the sun once) squared, the same number or constant (k) is always obtained. This constant is expressed as

$$\frac{r^3}{T^2} = k$$

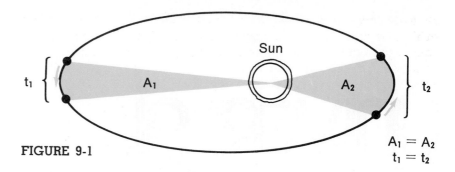

FIGURE 9-1

$$A_1 = A_2$$
$$t_1 = t_2$$

9:2 Universal Gravitation

Newton wondered if every body exerts a gravitational force on every other body.

Newton then reasoned that this universal gravitational force keeps the planets in their orbits.

Legend had it that while watching an apple fall from a tree, Newton recognized that the apple fell because an unbalanced force was acting on it. (Newton's second law of motion.) This force was gravity. Newton wondered if this special force was peculiar to the earth. Did other bodies also have it? Perhaps every body exerts a gravitational force on every other body. Newton looked for a way to describe this force and to determine its magnitude. He reasoned that if gravitational force is found throughout the universe, it might also be the force that keeps the planets in their orbits about the sun. Kepler's studies had

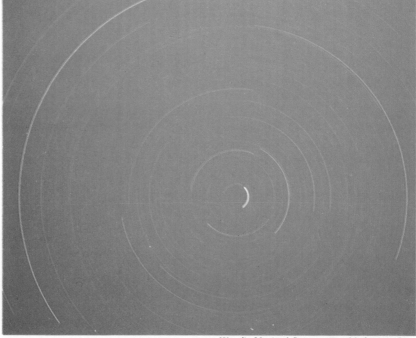

FIGURE 9-2. The circular motion of the earth is shown in this photo taken directly above the North Pole. As the earth turns on its axis, the stationary stars above the pole leave circular trails on the film.

Ward's Natural Science Establishment, Inc.

revealed two important facts about the planets. First, their orbits, while elliptical, are nearly circular. Thus, the force that causes the planets to move around the sun has to conform to the equation for circular motion, $F_c = mv^2/r$. Another form of this equation is

$$F_c = \frac{m4\pi^2 r}{T^2}$$

Secondly, Kepler had found that for all of the planets, r^3/T^2 gives the same number (k). Newton knew that this was no accident. It had to be the result of the force keeping the planets in their orbits. He rearranged $r^3/T^2 = k$ to read $T^2 = r^3/k$. The T in this equation represents the period of any planet as it orbits the sun. Thus, he could then substitute r^3/k for T^2 in the equation for the centripetal force acting on the planet.

Newton substituted Kepler's third law into the expression for centripetal force.

$$F_c = \frac{m4\pi^2 r}{T^2}$$
$$= \frac{m4\pi^2 r}{r^3/k}$$
$$= \frac{m4\pi^2 k}{r^2}$$

In this expression, $4\pi^2 k$ is considered to be a single factor. The value of each of its components is always the same. Thus, the $4\pi^2 k$ is called K. Then

$$F_c = \frac{mK}{r^2}$$

This result told Newton that the force between any planet and the sun varies inversely with the square of its distance (radius) from the sun. It also told him that the force varies directly with the mass of a planet.

Gravitational force varies inversely with the square of the distance between two bodies.

If the force between the sun and a planet depends on the mass of the planet, Newton reasoned that the force must also depend on the mass of the sun. After all, the planet is one mass and the sun is another. How can either mass tell which is which? If the sun exerts a force on the planet, then, by the third law of motion, the planet must exert an equal but opposite force on the sun. If the mass of a planet were suddenly doubled, the gravitational force between the planet and the sun would be doubled. If instead the mass of the sun were doubled, then the gravitational force between the sun and the planet would still be doubled. If the mass of both the planet and the sun were doubled, the gravitational force between the two would increase by a factor of four. ($2F \times 2F = 4F$) Thus, the gravitational force between any two bodies must increase as the product of their masses.

Gravitational force varies directly with the product of the masses.

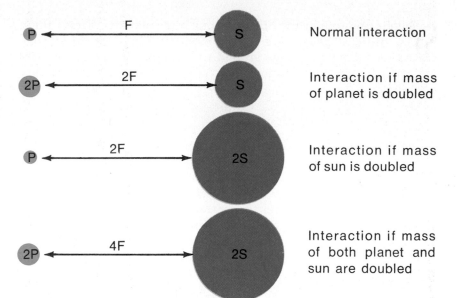

F   Normal interaction

2F   Interaction if mass of planet is doubled

2F   Interaction if mass of sun is doubled

4F   Interaction if mass of both planet and sun are doubled

FIGURE 9-3. The gravitational force between any two bodies increases as the product of their masses.

The law of universal gravitation gives the equation for the gravitational force between two bodies.

Newton assumed that the gravitational force between any two bodies acts in the same way as the force between a planet and the sun. From this assumption, he wrote the **law of universal gravitation.** This law states that *every body in the universe attracts every other body in the universe with a force that varies directly with the product of the masses and inversely with the square of the distance between the two masses.* This law is written

$$F = G\,\frac{m_1 m_2}{r^2}$$

The universal gravitational constant, G, is equal to 6.67 X 10^{-11} m³/kg-sec².

In the equation, m_1 and m_2 are the masses of the two bodies, r is the distance between the masses, and G is a universal constant. The value of G is 6.67 $\times$ 10^{-11} m³/kg-sec².

Example: Law of Universal Gravitation

Two trains, each of mass 3.0 $\times$ 10^5 kg, are located on adjacent tracks. Their centers are 9 m apart. What gravitational force exists between them?

Solution:

$$F = G\,\frac{m_1 m_2}{r^2}$$

$$= 6.67 \times 10^{-11}\ \text{m}^3/\text{kg-sec}^2\ \frac{(3.0 \times 10^5\text{kg})\,(3.0 \times 10^5\text{kg})}{(9\,\text{m})^2}$$

$$= 6.67 \times 10^{-11}\ \text{m}^3/\text{kg-sec}^2\ \frac{(9 \times 10^{10}\ \text{kg}^2)}{81\ \text{m}^2}$$

$$= 0.074\ \text{N}$$

FIGURE 9-4. Gravitational forces hold the stars in their relative positions in this spiral galaxy.

PROBLEMS

1. Two bodies are 2 m apart. One body has a mass of 80 kg. The second body has a mass of 60 kg. What is the gravitational force between them?

2. (a) What is the gravitational force between two 800-kg cars that are 5 m apart? (b) What is the gravitational force between them when they are 50 m apart?

3. Two ships are docked next to each other. Their centers of gravity are 40 m apart. One ship weighs 9.8×10^7 N. The other ship weighs 1.96×10^8 N. What gravitational force exists between them?

4. Two space capsules, each of mass 1600 kg, are put into orbit 30 m apart. (a) What gravitational force exists between them? (b) What is the initial acceleration given to each capsule by this force?

5. The mass of the moon is about 7.3×10^{22} kg. The mass of the earth is 6.0×10^{24} kg. If the centers of the two are 3.9×10^8 m apart, what is the gravitational force between them?

6. Use Newton's second law of motion to find the acceleration given to the moon by the force calculated in Problem 5.

7. The mass of an electron is 9×10^{-31} kg. The mass of a proton is 1.7×10^{-27} kg. They are about 1.0×10^{-10} m apart in a hydrogen atom. What force of gravitation exists between the proton and the electron of a hydrogen atom?

9:3 Newton's Test of the Inverse Square Law

Newton lacked the necessary equipment to make a direct test of the law of universal gravitation. That is, he could not measure the gravitational force between two small masses. However, Newton did know something about the moon and its orbit. Thus, to test the law, he used it to find if the gravitational force of the earth could keep the moon in orbit.

The moon is about 60 earth radii away from the earth. Gravitational force varies inversely with the square of the distance between two masses. Newton reasoned that the gravitational

Newton tested the law of universal gravitation indirectly by calculating to see if the earth's gravitational force could keep the moon in orbit.

FIGURE 9-5. High tides (a) and low tides (b) are caused by gravitational forces exerted on the earth by the moon and sun.

Roger K. Burnard

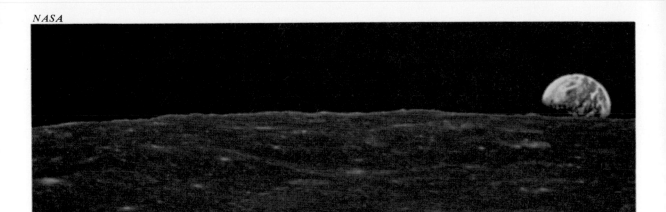

acceleration should vary in the same way. It is gravitational force that causes gravitational acceleration. Thus, the gravitational acceleration given to the moon by the earth should be only $1/(60)^2$ or $1/3600$ of the gravitational acceleration found at the earth's surface. This would be

$$9.8 \text{ m/sec}^2 \times \frac{1}{3600} = 0.0027 \text{ m/sec}^2$$

FIGURE 9-6. The moon is held in its orbit around the earth by the earth's gravitational field. Here you see an Earth rise photographed by an astronaut on the moon.

Newton knew the distance to the moon and its period. Thus, he could calculate the centripetal acceleration of the moon. Then he could see if it agreed with the predicted (by the inverse square law) gravitational acceleration at the point of location of the moon. The calculation is

$$a = \frac{v^2}{r}$$
$$= \frac{4\pi^2 r}{T^2}$$
$$= \frac{4(3.14)^2(3.9 \times 10^8 \text{ m})}{(2.3 \times 10^6 \text{ sec})^2}$$
$$= 0.0029 \text{ m/sec}^2$$

Thus, the actual centripetal acceleration of the moon was in close agreement with the acceleration predicted by the law of universal gravitation. This agreement was strong evidence that the theory of universal gravitation was correct.

9:4 The Cavendish Experiment

In 1798 the law of universal gravitation was confirmed by Henry Cavendish (1731-1810). The experimental arrangement

Cavendish tested the law of universal gravitation directly.

he used is shown in Figure 9-7. Cavendish attached a lead ball on each end of a long rod. He carefully suspended the rod from a wire. Then he placed two large lead balls close to the small ones as shown. The two small balls were attracted by the two large balls. This caused the wire to twist. Earlier, Cavendish had measured the force needed to twist the wire through given angles. Therefore, from the twisting of the wire, Cavendish was able to find the force between the lead masses. He found that the force exactly followed the law of gravitation.

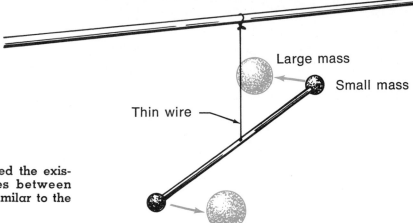

Large mass

Small mass

Thin wire

FIGURE 9-7. Cavendish verified the existence of gravitational forces between masses by using apparatus similar to the type shown.

Cavendish was also able to measure the masses of the balls and the distances between their centers. Substituting these values for force, mass, and distance into the law of gravitation, he solved for G. The value of G was found to be 6.67×10^{-11} m³/kg-sec².

9:5   The Law of Universal Gravitation and Weight

Because of the earth's large mass, the effect of its gravitational pull is noticeable.

The force that causes a body to fall toward the earth is the gravitational force between that body and the earth. This force is called weight. The weight of any body must follow the law of universal gravitation. The weight of any mass is

$$W = G \frac{m_b m_e}{r^2}$$

where m_b is the mass of the body, m_e is the mass of the earth, and r is the radius of the earth. (Gravitational force is always calculated by using the distances between the centers of two attracting bodies.)

Since W also equals mg, we can rewrite the equation above as

$$m_b g = G \frac{m_b m_e}{r^2}$$

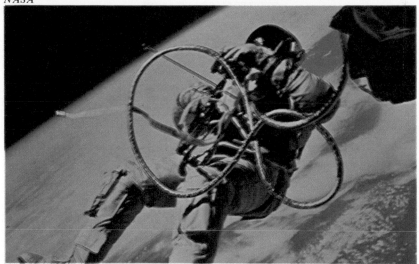

This reduces to

$$g = G\,\frac{m_e}{r^2}$$

Since G is a constant, this shows that only two factors affect the
acceleration of gravity, g. The first factor is the mass of the earth.
The second factor is the position of the mass in relation to the
center of the earth. Thus, the acceleration of gravity is the same
for all bodies near the earth's surface.

Because gravity causes weight,
all bodies close to the earth
are accelerated at the same
rate.

Figure 9-9 shows the change in a rocket's weight as the
distance between the rocket and the earth increases. The weight
of the rocket varies inversely with the square of its distance
from the earth's center.

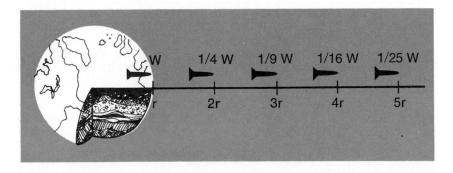

FIGURE 9-9. Variation of
gravitational force with
distance follows the in-
verse square law.

9:6   Gravitational Fields

The force of gravitation can act without a direct connection
between two bodies. The sun and the earth are millions of
kilometers apart. But the gravitational force of the sun keeps
the earth in its orbital path. In order to describe and predict the

The gravitational field concept
is used to describe the gravitational force at various
locations.

behavior of forces acting through a distance, the field concept has been developed. Essentially the field concept considers that a mass distorts the space around it, setting up a *gravitational field*. This field can interact with any mass placed in the field.

A gravitational field is plotted by placing a small test mass in the field and observing its behavior. If the earth's field is plotted, the force acting on the test mass is greater when the test mass is closer to the earth. According to the inverse square law, this is to be expected.

SUMMARY

Tycho Brahe observed and recorded the positions of the planets for more than 20 years. Then, Johannes Kepler analyzed Brahe's data and stated three laws of planetary motion. His third law states that the cube of any planet's radius is proportional to the square of its period.

For a time, gravitational force was thought to be a unique property of the earth. Newton wondered if all bodies exert gravitational forces on each other. He reasoned that if such a universal gravitational force exists, it might be the force that keeps planets in orbit. Therefore, he combined Kepler's third law, $r^3 = kT^2$, with the equation for centripetal force. The result showed that the force acting on a planet is inversely proportional to the square of its distance from the sun. He had assumed that this force was gravitational, and that all gravitational forces behave in the same way. Thus, he used his result to formulate the law of universal gravitation.

The law of universal gravitation states that every body in the universe attracts every other body with a force that varies directly with the product of the masses and inversely with the square of the distance between the masses. Newton tested this inverse square law by calculating the period the moon would have if its circular motion were caused by the earth's gravitational attraction. His calculated result agreed closely with the actual period of the moon.

In 1798 Henry Cavendish confirmed Newton's law of universal gravitation experimentally. He placed a large mass close to a small hanging mass and showed that the two masses do attract one another. He also showed that the force varied directly with the product of the masses and inversely with the square of the distance between them.

Using the law of universal gravitation, it can be shown that only two factors affect the acceleration of gravity (g). These are the mass of the earth and the distance from the center of the earth.

QUESTIONS

1. An imaginary line from a planet to the sun sweeps out equal areas in equal times. Does the planet move faster along its orbital path when it is close to or far away from the sun?

2. The radius of the earth is about 6400 km. A 7200 N spacecraft travels away from the earth. What would be the weight of the spacecraft at these distances from the earth's surface? (a) 6400 km, (b) 12 800 km, (c) 19 200 km, (d) 25 600 km, (e) 32 000 km.

3. The force of gravity acting on a body near the earth's surface is proportional to the mass of the body. Why doesn't a heavy body fall faster than a light body?

4. Two 1-kg masses are 1 m apart. What is the force of attraction between them?

5. The earth and the moon are attracted to each other by gravitational force. Does the more massive earth attract the moon with a greater force than the moon attracts the earth?

6. Astronomers have noticed that some stars wobble slightly as they move through space. They claim that this is evidence that these stars have a planet or system of planets orbiting around them. Why?

7. How did Cavendish demonstrate that a gravitational force of attraction exists between two small bodies?

PROBLEMS

1. Two lead spheres each have a mass of 5×10^5 kg. The spheres are located next to one another with their centers 5 m apart. What gravitational force do they exert on each other?

2. Two locomotives stand so that their centers are 10 m apart. Each weighs 1.96×10^5 N. What gravitational force exists between them?

3. A 1600 kg car is parked next to a 3200 kg truck. Their centers are 5 m apart. What gravitational force exists between them?

4. Use the following data to compute the gravitational force that the sun exerts on Jupiter.
    Mass of the earth $= 6 \times 10^{24}$ kg
    Mass of the sun $= 3.3 \times 10^5$ times the mass of the earth
    Mass of Jupiter $= 3 \times 10^2$ times the mass of the earth
    Distance between Jupiter and the sun $= 7.8 \times 10^{11}$ m

5. If a small planet were located 8 times as far from the sun as the earth's distance from the sun (1.5×10^{11} m), how many years would it take the planet to orbit the sun? ($r^3/T^2 = 3.35 \times 10^{18}$ m^3/sec^2; a year is 3.15×10^7 sec)

6. The radius of the moon's orbit about the earth is 60 times the radius of the earth. What is the gravitational acceleration of the moon toward the earth?

PROJECTS

1. Tycho Brahe presented quite a figure when he walked the streets in Denmark. He had bright red hair, brilliant blue eyes, and a nose of solid gold. Why was his nose made of gold?

2. Using two pins and a long string, draw an ellipse. Change the spacing of the pins to produce various ellipses. What happens if you put the pins very close together?

READINGS

Gamow, George, *Gravity*. New York, Doubleday and Co., Inc., 1962.

Gingerich, Owen, "Copernicus and Tycho." *Scientific American,* December, 1973.

Rutherford, F. J., et al, *The Project Physics Course*, text ed. New York, Holt, Rinehart and Winston, Inc., 1970, Chapters 7, 8.

Taylor, Langenberg, and Parker, "The Fundamental Physical Constants." *Scientific American*, October, 1970.

Weber, Joseph, "The Detection of Gravitational Waves." *Scientific American*, May, 1971.

Whipple, Fred L., *Earth, Moon and Planets* (Books on Astronomy Series), 3rd ed. Cambridge, Mass., Harvard University Press, 1969.

Wilson, Curtis, "How Did Kepler Discover His First Two Laws?" *Scientific American*, March, 1972.

Imagine that you have exerted great effort all day trying to remove a huge rock from your garden. Your muscles ache. You are very tired. In spite of all your efforts, the rock remains unmoved. You will say that you have worked hard all day. The physicist will say that you have done no work at all! According to the physicist, work is done only when a force causes an object to move some distance. This climber may have exerted great effort to move upward a distance of only a few meters. What can you say about the amount of work done by the climber?

WORK AND POWER

Work and power are familiar words. In everyday conversations, they are used in a very general sense. For example, you might tell a friend that you worked hard on your homework. In doing so, you might refer to your power of concentration. In physics, these words have very specific meanings. Let us take a close look at the concepts of work and power as they are viewed by scientists.

GOAL: You will gain knowledge and understanding of the concepts of work and power.

10:1 Work

When a person lifts a bag of groceries, pushes a lawnmower, or shovels snow, work is done. These examples of work have one thing in common—a force is exerted through a distance. A force does work on a body only if the body moves through a distance due to the force. **Work** is the product of the net force and the distance through which the body moves in the direction of the net force. As an equation, this becomes

$$\text{Work} = \text{Force} \times \text{Distance}$$
$$\text{or} \quad W = Fs$$

Work is a scalar quantity even though force and displacement are vectors. Note that this definition includes a force and a distance. If you push against a car for hours and do not move it, you may become very tired. But you have done no work on the car. A force must cause motion if work is to be done.

Work is the product of force and the distance through which the force acts.

139

(a)

(b)

FIGURE 10-1. (a) Work is not done when an object remains stationary, no matter how large the applied force. (b) Work is done only when a force causes an object to move some distance.

A joule is the MKS unit of work.

To calculate the work done by a force, use the equation $W = Fs$. Thus, if a person lifts a box that weighs 80 N to a height of 1.5 m, 80 N × 1.5 m or 120 N-m of work is done on the box. In the MKS system, the unit of work is the **joule** (jool). A joule is equal to a newton-meter. Therefore 120 N-m of work is called 120 joules of work or 120 J.

Example: Work

A person applies a force of 60 N for a distance of 20 m to push a desk across a floor. How much work is done?

Solution:

$$W = Fs$$
$$= (60 \text{ N}) (20 \text{ m})$$
$$= 1200 \text{ N-m}$$
$$= 1200 \text{ J}$$

PROBLEMS

1. A force of 800 N is needed to push a car across a lot. Two students push the car 40 m. How much work is done?

2. How much work is done to lift a 60-kg crate a vertical distance of 10 m?

3. A worker lifts a crate from one floor to the next in a warehouse. A force of 48 N is exerted through a distance of 40 m on the rope of a pulley system. How much work is done?

4. A package weighs 35 N. A person carries the package from the ground floor to the fifth floor of an office building, or 15 m upward. (a) How much work does the person do on the package? (b) The person weighs 750 N. How much total work is done?

5. In order to change a tire, a force of 80 N is exerted on the handle of a screw type bumper jack. The handle to which the steel shaft is attached has a radius of 0.5 m. The handle is turned through 30 rev. How much work is done?

6. (a) What is the weight of a 49-kg crate? (b) What work is done to lift the crate a distance of 10 m?

7. A worker carries cement blocks, weighing 150 N each, up a ladder onto a scaffold 8 m high. The worker carries them at a rate of 2 blocks per minute. How much work is done by the worker in (a) 10 min? (b) 1 hr?

8. The hammer of a pile-driver has a mass of 100 kg. The machine's engine lifts it to a height of 5 m every 10 sec. (a) How much does the hammer weigh? (b) How much work must the machine do to lift the hammer? (c) How much work does the machine do in 1 min?

9. A 50-kg student runs up a flight of stairs that is 6 m high. How much work is done?

10:2   Work and the Direction of Force

When work is done, the force that does the work is the net force. If a force is applied to an object at an angle with the direction of motion, the net force is the component of the force that acts in the direction of motion. For example, if you pull a bobsled across the snow, the force that is doing the work is the horizontal component (F_h) of the force in the rope. The vertical component (F_v) of the force in the rope is balanced by gravity. In Figure 10-2, a 100-N force (F) is applied to the handle of a lawnmower. The vertical component of the force is balanced by

In calculating work, use only the component of force that acts in the direction of motion.

Edwin L. Shay

FIGURE 10-2

1 division = 20 N

$\vec{F} = 100$ N

$\vec{F}_v$

25°

$\vec{F}_h$

$\vec{F}_h = F \cos 25°$

$= (100 \text{ N}) (0.906)$

$= 91 \text{ N}$

the upward push of the ground. The force that is doing the work is F_h.

The value of the horizontal component of a force F_h is found by multiplying the force F by the cosine of the angle between F and the horizontal. Thus,

$$W = F_h s$$
$$= F \cos \theta \, s$$

Example: Work—Force at an Angle to the Direction of Motion

A sailor pulls a boat along a dock. The rope is held at an angle of 60° with the horizontal and pulled on with a force of 250 N. (a) What horizontal force acts on the boat? (b) How much work is done if the sailor pulls the boat 30 m?

Solution:

$$\text{(a)} \; F_h = F \cos \theta$$
$$= (250 \text{ N}) (0.5)$$
$$= 125 \text{ N}$$
$$\text{(b)} \; W = F_h s$$
$$= (125 \text{ N}) (30 \text{ m})$$
$$= 3750 \text{ J}$$

PROBLEMS

10. A force of 600 N is applied to a metal box to pull it across a floor. The rope used to pull the box is held at an angle of 46° with the floor. The box is moved a distance of 15 m. How much work is done?

11. A person uses a rope to pull a 1000-kg boat 50 m along a wharf. The rope makes an angle of 45° with the horizontal. If a force of 40 N is used to move the boat, how much work is done?

12. A loaded sled weighing 800 N is pulled a distance of 200 m. To do this, a force of 120 N is exerted on a rope which makes an angle of 60° with the horizontal. How much work is done?

13. A cable attached to a small tractor pulls a barge through a canal lock. The tension in the cable is 2500 N. It makes an angle of 30° with the direction in which the barge is moving. (a) What force moves the barge along the lock? (b) If the lock is 200 m long, how much work is done to get the barge through the lock?

14. Because of friction, a force of 400 N is needed to drag a wooden crate across a floor. The rope tied to the crate is held at an angle of 56° with the horizontal. (a) How much tension is needed in the rope to move the crate? (b) What work is done if the crate is dragged 25 m?

FIGURE 10-3. The power needed to lift this cup of milk is about one watt.

10:3 Power

Power is the time rate of doing work. Power is an important concept in physics. It allows us to measure how fast work is done.

$$\text{Power} = \frac{\text{Work}}{\text{Time}}$$

Power is work per unit time.

In the MKS system, power is measured in watts. A **watt** is one joule per second. A machine that does work at a rate of one joule per second has a power of one watt. Since a joule is a newton-meter, a watt is a newton-meter per second. A watt is a relatively small unit of power. The power needed to lift a glass of water is one watt. Thus, power is often measured in kilowatts. A kilowatt is 1000 watts.

A watt is the MKS unit of power.

A kilowatt is 1000 watts.

FIGURE 10-4. The faster this elevator rises, the greater the power required to raise it.

Example: Power

A machine produces a force of 40 N through a distance of 100 m in 5 sec. (a) How much work is done? (b) What is the power of the machine in watts? (c) in kilowatts?

Solution:

$$(a) \quad W = Fs$$
$$= (40 \text{ N}) \ (100 \text{ m})$$
$$= 4000 \text{ J}$$

$$(b) \quad P = \frac{W}{t}$$
$$= \frac{4000 \text{ J}}{5 \text{ sec}}$$
$$= 800 \text{ watts}$$

$$(c) \quad \text{or, } P = \frac{800 \text{ watts}}{1000 \text{ watts/kilowatt}} = 0.80 \text{ kilowatts}$$

PROBLEMS

15. A box that weighs 1000 N is lifted a distance of 20 m straight up by a rope and pulley system. The work is done in 10 sec. What amount of power is used in (a) watts? (b) kilowatts?

16. A diesel engine lifts the 225-kg hammer of a pile driver 20 m in 5 sec. (a) How much work is done on the hammer? (b) What is the power of the engine in watts? (c) in kilowatts?

17. A hiker carries a 20-kg knapsack up a trail. After 30 minutes, he is 300 m higher than his starting point. (a) What is the weight of the knapsack? (b) How much work in joules is done on the knapsack? (c) If the hiker weighs 600 N, how much total work is done? (d) During the 30 min, what is the hiker's average power in watts? (e) in kilowatts?

18. An electric motor lifts a 2000-kg elevator 18 m in 40 sec. (a) How much work is done? (b) What is the power of the motor in watts? (c) in kilowatts?

19. A motor operates an endless conveyor belt. The motor produces a force of 500 N on the belt and moves it at the rate of 6.5 m/sec. What is the power of the motor in kilowatts?

SUMMARY

In physics, work is a product of force and distance. When work is calculated, the force used must be the component of the force acting on the object in the direction of motion. If the force is acting in the direction of motion, the work is equal to force times distance. If the force acts at some angle with the direction of motion, then the work is equal to force times the cosine of the angle times distance. When force is measured in newtons and distance in meters, work has the units newton-meters. A newton-meter is called a joule.

Power is the time rate of doing work. In the MKS system, the unit of power is the watt. A watt is a joule per second.

1. Define work.
2. What is a joule?
3. A person stands still and holds a heavy bag of groceries. Is work done?
4. What is power? What is the MKS unit of power?

1. A force of 60 N is needed to push a crate weighing 300 N across a waxed floor. How much work is required to push the crate 15 m?
2. The third floor of a house is 8 m above street level. How much work is required to move a 100-kg refrigerator up to the third floor?
3. A 50-kg mass is raised by a machine to a height of 20 m. Calculate the work done in (a) newton-meters, (b) joules.
4. Workers use a force of 1760 N to push a piano weighing 8800 N up a 20-m ramp. (a) How much work is done? (b) The piano is being moved from street level to the second floor of a building. The second floor is 4 m above street level. If the workers decide to lift the piano straight up by using ropes, how much work would they do?
5. A gardener applies a force of 150 N to push a wheelbarrow 60 m with a constant speed in 20 sec. (a) How much work is done? (b) What is the power in watts?
6. How much work does a 400-watt motor do in 5 min?
7. Calculate the wattage of a motor that does 11 250 J of work in 25 sec.
8. A loaded elevator weighs 1.2×10^4 N. An electric motor hoists the elevator 9 m in 15 sec. (a) How much work is done? (b) What is the power in watts? (c) in kilowatts?
9. A pump raises 30 liters of water per minute from a depth of 100 m. What is the wattage expended? (A liter of water has a mass of 1 kg.)
10. A horizontal force of 800 N is needed to drag a crate across a horizontal floor. A worker drags the crate by means of a rope held at an angle of 60°. (a) What force is applied to the rope? (b) How much work is performed in dragging the crate 22 m? (c) If the worker completes the job in 8 sec, what is the power in watts?

1. Can you do more work per second than a horse? Some people can, but only for a short time. To find out if you can, first measure the vertical height of a staircase in meters by measuring the rise of one stair and multiplying its height by the number of stairs. Then multiply your weight in newtons by the height of the staircase. This is the amount of work you must do every time you climb the staircase. Run up the stairs as fast as you can while someone times your climb. Calculate the work done per second. If it comes out higher than 750 J/sec, you can work faster than a horse. (To find your weight in newtons, multiply your weight in pounds by 4.5 N/lb.)

Fisher, John C., "Energy Crises in Perspective." *Physics Today*, December, 1973.
Kantrowitz, Arthur, "MHD Power Generator." *The Physics Teacher*, November, 1975.
Schmitt, Roland W., and Stewart, Peter J., "The Role of Industry in International Energy Programs." *Physics Today*, March, 1975.
Scientific American Editors, *Energy and Power* (Scientific American Books), text ed., San Francisco, W. H. Freeman and Co., 1971.
Young, Matt, "Solar Energy." *The Physics Teacher*, April, 1974.

Energy exists in many forms. All forms of energy are interchangeable. When energy changes forms, the total amount of energy remains the same. This relationship is known as the law of conservation of energy. For example, the potential energy of the water in a mill pond above this stream is converted to kinetic energy as it falls to the stream below. Part of the energy is converted to electric energy in a turbine. Part of the energy is transferred to special wheels which grind flour in this mill. What other examples of energy changes can you find here?

ENERGY AND ITS CONSERVATION

Many concepts in physics are easy to understand in terms of everyday experience. Matter, for example, can be seen and felt. It also occupies space. Energy, on the other hand, is a concept which cannot be seen or touched. It does not occupy space. However, we see evidence of energy every day.

GOAL: You will gain knowledge and understanding of energy and its conservation and of the relationship between energy and work.

11:1 Energy—The Capacity to Do Work

Energy is closely related to work. Energy always makes its presence known by doing work. The water that falls over a dam can do work. Therefore, it must have energy. Gravity makes the water move downward and gives it kinetic energy. The water has energy because work is done on it. If you stretch a bow, you are exerting a force through a distance or doing work on the bow. The bow then has potential energy. It can give this energy to an arrow by doing work on the arrow.

As energy does work, or as work is done on a system, energy changes form or place. You can store energy in a bow by doing work on it. But, that energy appears again as the kinetic energy of the arrow. If the arrow strikes a tree, it pushes the molecules of the tree. This makes the molecules move faster and thus raises the temperature. The work done on the molecules of the tree appears as heat energy. The heat energy in the tree is gradually lost to the atmosphere as the molecules of the tree do work and emit radiation. Energy never disappears. It simply moves around, often changing form as it does so.

Energy is the capacity to do work.

FIGURE 11-1. The potential energy of the water held back by this dam is converted to kinetic energy as the water falls over the dam. The energy of the falling water is converted to electric energy at this hydroelectric station.

The easiest way to measure energy is to measure the work that it does. **Energy** is defined as the capacity to do work. Some important facts about energy are

The unit of energy is the same as the unit of work.

1. Energy is the capacity to do work.
   (a) Energy has the same units as work.
   (b) Like work, energy is a scalar quantity.

Work causes energy exchanges.

2. Work is the means by which energy changes form. That is, every energy exchange is brought about by work.

Energy always exists as either potential or kinetic energy.

3. Regardless of its form, energy is always either potential or kinetic. Potential energy is stored energy or energy of position. Kinetic energy is the energy a body possesses by virtue of its motion.

11:2 Potential Energy

Potential energy is energy of position.

Potential energy is the energy a body has because of its position or state. A cement block resting on the ground has no potential energy. But as the block is lifted, it gains gravitational potential energy. If the block then falls toward the earth, it can do work. It might, for example, drive a stake into the ground by exerting a force on the stake through a distance.

Electric potential energy depends on the positions of charged particles in relation to one another.

There are other forms of potential energy. A stretched spring has electric potential energy due to the electric interactions between the molecules that make up the spring. A charged battery also has electric potential energy. If the negative plate has an

148

John Morgan

FIGURE 11-2. Electric potential energy of batteries can be converted to other forms of energy such as light energy, sound energy, and heat energy.

excess of electrons and the positive plate lacks electrons, the electrons have electric potential energy with respect to the positive plate. If the electrons are allowed to flow from the negative plate to the positive plate, they can do work. For example, they can operate a flashlight.

Chemical bonds store electric energy. In a chemical reaction, this energy can be released as bonding changes (potential energy changes) take place. Thus, the energy stored in coal or oil is actually electric potential energy.

It is also possible to produce magnetic potential energy. This change can be made by placing magnets close to one another. Electric motors run on this basis.

Matter itself can be considered a form of potential energy. Matter can be converted to energy during nuclear reactions.

Magnetic potential energy can be produced by placing magnets close together.

FIGURE 11-3. The electric potential energy stored in the molecules of the gas is converted to heat energy as the gas burns (a). The radiant energy from the sun is converted to heat energy in a solar house (b).

William Maddox

FIGURE 11-4. This rock has gravitational potential energy because of its position above the ground.

11:3   Base Levels

The potential energy a body has due to its position above the surface of the earth is called its gravitational potential energy. The potential energy a body releases to do work is equal to its change in potential energy as it falls from a higher to a lower level. This potential energy change is measured with reference to some arbitrary base for zero position (not necessarily the surface of the earth). Suppose a person on the third floor of a building drops a weight onto a nail also located on the third floor. The potential energy of the weight is measured with respect to the nail, not with respect to the surface of the earth. A base level is an arbitrary reference position and depends upon the situation.

11:4   Energy Units—Work Units

Energy, the capacity to do work, is measured in the same units as work (joules). Under ideal conditions, energy and work are completely interchangeable. For example, 200 joules of work are needed to lift a 20-N stone to the top of a 10-m wall. If the same stone falls back to the ground, it should be able to do 200 joules of work. The increase in the potential energy of a system is equal to the amount of work needed to place the system in its final position. That is

$$\text{Change in Potential Energy} = \text{Force} \times \text{Distance}$$
$$\Delta PE = Fs$$

The force needed to lift a body is equal to the weight (mg) of the body. Thus, when a body is lifted to a height h, the increase in gravitational potential energy is mgh.

$$\Delta PE = Fs$$
$$= (mg)\,h$$
$$= mgh$$

Gravitational potential energy depends on mass and height.

Example: Potential Energy

A 5-kg mass is lifted to a height of 5 m. What is its increase in potential energy?

Solution:

$$\Delta PE = Fs$$
$$= mgh$$
$$= 5\text{ kg} \times 9.8\text{ m/sec}^2 \times 5\text{ m}$$
$$= 245\text{ N-m}$$
$$= 245\text{ J}$$

We have shown that work is needed to increase the gravitational potential energy of a body. Work is related to all energy exchanges. When energy changes form or location the change is always brought about by work.

PROBLEMS

1. The 200-kg hammer of a pile driver is lifted 10 m. Find the potential energy of the system when the hammer is at this height.

William Maddox

FIGURE 11-5. The gravitational potential energy of this steel girder is increased as the crane lifts the girder above the ground.

2. A 60-kg shell is shot from a cannon to a height of 400 m. (a) What is the potential energy of the earth-shell system when the shell is at this height? (b) What is the change in potential energy of the system when the shell falls to a height of 200 m?

3. A person who weighs 630 N climbs 5 m up a ladder. (a) What work does the person do? (b) What is the increase in the potential energy of the earth-person system when the person is at this height?

4. Find the potential energy of a 10-kg mass when it is raised to a height of 20 m.

5. In order to charge the plates of a small storage battery, a hand-generator is cranked through a total distance of 250 m. (a) An average force of 120 N is applied to the crank as it is turned. What is the total work done to charge the plates? (b) If the work was done in one minute, what power was developed? (c) The storage battery is then used to power a 10-watt light bulb. For how long a time can the bulb be used before the battery must be recharged?

11:5   Kinetic Energy

Kinetic energy is energy of motion.

Kinetic energy is the energy a body possesses by virtue of its motion. In deriving an equation for kinetic energy, let us look at an example. Imagine that a body of mass m rests on a frictionless surface. A constant force F acts on it through a distance s. The force will accelerate the body in accordance with Newton's second law of motion,

$$F = ma$$

If we multiply both sides of this equation by s, the left side of the equation represents work done on the mass.

$$Fs = mas$$

The speed of a body starting from rest is $v^2 = 2as$. This can be rearranged to read, $as = v^2/2$. Substituting this expression into $Fs = mas$, we obtain

$$Fs = \frac{mv^2}{2}$$

Kinetic energy depends on mass and velocity.

This expression relates the work done on the mass to the resulting speed of the mass. The right-hand side of the equation states the amount of work a mass m moving with a velocity v can do as it is brought to rest. The energy the body has because of its velocity is equal to the work that was done to give the mass its velocity. The quantity $mv^2/2$ is called the kinetic energy (*KE*) of the body.

$$KE = \tfrac{1}{2}\, mv^2$$

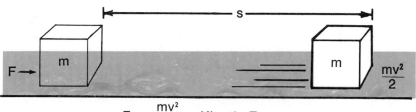

$$F_s = \frac{mv^2}{2} = \text{Kinetic Energy}$$

FIGURE 11-6. **The kinetic energy of a mass is equal to the work done on the mass to give it that kinetic energy. Therefore, the** speed of a body is dependent upon the amount of work done on it.

Example: Kinetic Energy

An 8-kg mass moves at 30 m/sec. What is its kinetic energy?

Solution:

$$KE = \tfrac{1}{2}\,mv^2$$
$$= \frac{(8 \text{ kg})\,(30 \text{ m/sec})^2}{2}$$
$$= 3600 \text{ J}$$

PROBLEMS

6. (a) A 10-kg mass moves with a speed of 20 m/sec. Find its kinetic energy. (b) If the 10-kg mass moves with a speed of 10 m/sec, what is its kinetic energy? (c) What is the ratio of the solution of (a) to the solution of (b)? Why?

7. What is the kinetic energy of a 1600-kg car which moves at (a) 30 km/hr? (b) 60 km/hr? (c) What is the ratio of (b) to (a)?

8. A baseball that weighs 4.9 N leaves a bat with a speed of 40 m/sec. Calculate the ball's kinetic energy in joules.

9. An alpha particle with a mass of 4.7×10^{-27} kg travels at 1.6×10^7 m/sec. What is the kinetic energy of the particle?

10. An electron with a mass of 9.0×10^{-31} kg moves through a vacuum with a speed of 2.5×10^8 m/sec. Find the electron's kinetic energy.

11. Consider a 5-kg mass located 10 m from the earth's surface. (a) What potential energy does the mass have? (b) How much potential energy does the mass lose if it falls 5 m? (c) What kinetic energy does the mass have after it falls 5 m? (d) What speed does the mass have after it falls the 5 m? (Assume that it starts from rest.)

11:6   Conservation of Energy

The **law of conservation of energy** states that the total energy of a system cannot change, unless work is done on the system. Within an isolated system, energy can change from one form to another, but the total amount of energy always remains the same.

The law of conservation of energy states that energy can neither be created nor destroyed.

FIGURE 11-7. Energy is never lost in a system. The kinetic energy of this monorail train is changed to other forms of energy as the train slows down.

Energy can never be "lost" by a system. The law of conservation of energy is one of the most useful tools of science.

As an example of the law of conservation of energy, consider a mass that weighs 100 N and is located 20 m above the surface of the earth. At this height the mass has ($Fs = 100$ N $\times$ 20 m) 2000 joules of potential energy. If the mass is allowed to fall freely for a distance of 10 meters its potential energy will be ($Fs = 100$ N $\times$ 10 m) 1000 joules. The mass loses half of its potential energy by falling 10 meters.

When the mass has fallen 10 meters its vertical velocity will be 14 m/sec. Its kinetic energy will be

KE = 0 J
PE = 2000 J   20 m

KE = 1000 J
PE = 1000 J   10 m

KE = 2000 J
PE = 0 J   0 m

$$KE = \frac{mv^2}{2}$$
$$= \left(\frac{W}{g}\right)\frac{v^2}{2}$$
$$= \frac{100 \text{ N} (14 \text{ m/sec})^2}{9.8 \text{ m/sec}^2 \times 2}$$
$$= 1000 \text{ J}$$

The loss of potential energy by the mass is, at all times, equal to its gain in kinetic energy. The transition of potential energy to kinetic energy occurs as the body falls. By the time the mass reaches the earth's surface, all of its potential energy has been changed to kinetic energy. Upon impact with the earth, the kinetic energy is changed to heat, and sometimes, to sound energy.

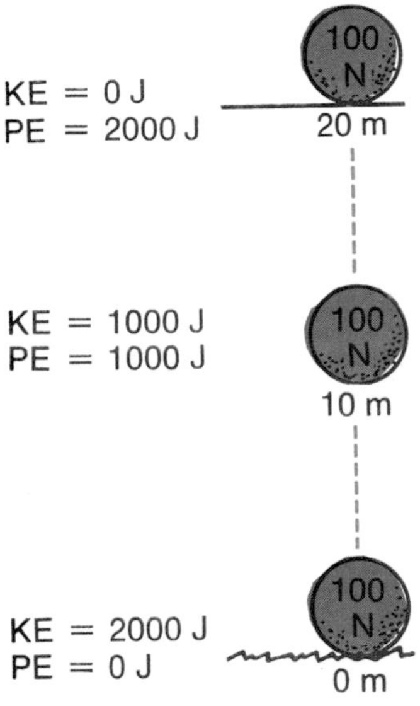

FIGURE 11-8. The loss of potential energy is equal to the gain of kinetic energy.

A decrease in potential energy causes an equal increase in kinetic energy.

The path an object follows as it is raised does not affect the potential energy of the object. A 200-N barrel 8 m above the ground has 1600 J of potential energy whether it is raised straight up to that height or it is pushed up an incline. The same is true for kinetic energy. The barrel's kinetic energy, neglecting fric-

154

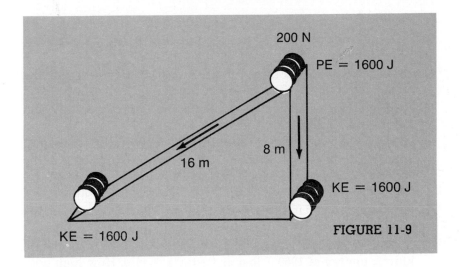

200 N

PE = 1600 J

8 m

16 m

KE = 1600 J

KE = 1600 J

FIGURE 11-9

tion, is 1600 J when it reaches ground level. This is true whether it falls straight down or rolls down the incline.

Example: Conservation of Energy

An object with a mass of 15 kg falls 8 m. (a) What is the kinetic energy of the object as it reaches the earth? (b) What is its speed just as it reaches the earth?

Solution:

(a) The kinetic energy of the object as it reaches the earth is equal to the potential energy the object possessed before it fell.

$$KE = PE$$
$$= mgh$$
$$= 15 \text{ kg} \times 9.8 \text{ m/sec}^2 \times 8 \text{ m}$$
$$= 1176 \text{ J}$$

(b) The speed can be found by using the equation for kinetic energy.

$$KE = \frac{mv^2}{2}$$
$$1176 \text{ J} = \frac{mv^2}{2}$$
$$v^2 = \frac{2 \times 1176 \text{ J}}{m}$$
$$v = \sqrt{\frac{2 \times 1176 \text{ J}}{15 \text{ kg}}}$$
$$= \sqrt{\frac{157 \text{ m}^2}{\text{sec}^2}}$$
$$= 12.5 \text{ m/sec}$$

PROBLEMS

12. A 15-kg mass moves with a speed of 12.5 m/sec. Calculate its kinetic energy.

13. An 8-kg mass drops 12 m. What is the kinetic energy of the mass just before it strikes the ground?

14. A 16-kg stone falls 40 m. Find the stone's kinetic energy just before it strikes the ground.

15. A block that weighs 98 N drops 64 m. (a) Find the potential energy of the block at its highest point. (b) What is the kinetic energy of the block just as it strikes the ground? (c) What speed does the block have as it strikes the ground?

16. An 8-kg hammer is thrown straight up. 784 J of work is done on the hammer. How high does the hammer rise?

17. A 10-kg mass is shot straight up in the air. The mass has a kinetic energy of 1960 J just as it starts to rise. How high does it rise before it stops?

18. A 5-kg mass receives 600 J of energy. What speed is given to the mass? Assume the mass starts from rest on a horizontal, frictionless surface.

19. A 10-kg mass slides 16 m along a 30° incline. (a) Calculate the speed acquired (neglect friction). (b) What is the kinetic energy of the mass?

20. A 5-kg mass is projected straight up with a speed of 15 m/sec. (a) What is the kinetic energy of the mass at the outset? (b) To what height does the mass rise?

11:7   Conservation of Matter and Energy

Energy is always conserved when it changes form. A given amount of potential energy always changes to an equal amount of another form of energy. For example, the electrons on a charged plate have potential energy that can be changed to heat energy as the electrons flow through a heater. Energy never disappears. It just changes form or location.

The law of conservation of matter states that matter can neither be created nor destroyed.

The law of conservation of matter parallels the law of conservation of energy. This law states that matter can neither be created nor destroyed. But, matter can change form. For example, when a piece of paper is burned, it is not destroyed. Instead, it is all transformed to ashes and gas.

Matter and energy are interchangeable.

Until recently, the law of conservation of energy and the law of conservation of matter were thought to be completely true. However, research in nuclear physics has shown that matter can be changed into energy. The amount of energy obtained from a certain amount of mass is

$$E = mc^2$$

In this equation, E represents the energy released, m is the quantity of mass converted into energy, and c is the speed of light. This equation was derived by Dr. Albert Einstein (1879–1955). Many experiments have shown that it is correct. The law of conservation of energy and the law of conservation of matter are now combined into the **law of conservation of mass-energy**. This law states that *the total amount of matter plus energy in the universe is a constant.*

FIGURE 11-10. All of the matter and energy present in the original forest area (a) still exist after the forest fire (b), but they have taken new forms.

The law of conservation of mass-energy was stated to account for this interchange of matter and energy. The sum of matter and energy is constant.

11:8 Elastic Collisions

An **elastic collision** is a collision in which the total kinetic energy of the bodies involved is exactly the same after the collision as it was before the collision. Strictly speaking, all collisions between objects larger than molecules are inelastic. In an **inelastic collision,** the total kinetic energy decreases. Therefore, the velocity of the objects involved in the collision also decreases. The loss in energy is accounted for by an increase in the heat energy content of the bodies that collide, by the generation of sound during the collision, or by both. The amount of energy lost in an inelastic collision varies. Remember that energy is not really lost. It merely changes form.

The collision between some large objects is very nearly elastic. Such a collision may be considered to be elastic. A collision between two billiard balls or two glass marbles moving across a smooth surface is nearly elastic.

In an elastic collision, the KE is constant.

In an inelastic collision, some KE changes to other forms of energy.

FIGURE 11-11. A golf ball collides with a hard surface. How can you tell if the collision is nearly elastic?

Momentum is conserved in all collisions.

The law of conservation of momentum holds for all collisions. Although kinetic energy decreases during an inelastic collision, there is no change in momentum. For example, consider a 1-kg block of putty sliding across a frictionless surface at 20 m/sec. This block of putty collides head-on with a 1-kg block of putty which is at rest. The two blocks of putty stick together and move off as one mass. According to the law of conservation of momentum, the total momentum of the two blocks stuck together is equal to the momentum of the original block of putty. The momentum of the original block is

$$mv = (1 \text{ kg}) (20 \text{ m/sec}) = 20 \text{ kg-m/sec}$$

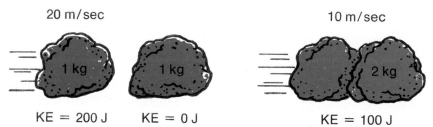

20 m/sec   10 m/sec

KE = 200 J   KE = 0 J   KE = 100 J

FIGURE 11-12. Kinetic energy is not conserved in an inelastic collision.

In order for the momentum to be conserved the two blocks stuck together must also have a momentum of 20 kg-m/sec. Thus, after the collision, the two blocks move with a velocity of 10 m/sec in the direction of the original velocity. If the velocity had been different, the law of conservation of momentum would have been violated. But the kinetic energy of the blocks of putty before and after the collision is not the same.

$$\left(\begin{array}{c} Original \ KE \\ \tfrac{1}{2} \ mv^2 = \dfrac{1 \text{ kg} (20 \text{ m/sec})^2}{2} \\ = 200 \text{ J} \end{array} \right) \neq \left(\begin{array}{c} Final \ KE \\ \tfrac{1}{2} \ mv^2 = \dfrac{2 \text{ kg} (10 \text{ m/sec})^2}{2} \\ = 100 \text{ J} \end{array} \right)$$

While momentum is conserved, half the kinetic energy is converted to another form of energy (such as heat). This collision is completely inelastic.

The behavior of bodies involved in an elastic collision can often be predicted. This is done by considering the laws of conservation of energy and conservation of momentum together. For example, suppose a billiard ball of mass m moves with a speed v. This ball collides head-on with a billiard ball of equal mass that is at rest. After the collision, if the two balls rolled off together at half the speed of the original billiard ball, the law of conservation of momentum would be satisfied. But, as was shown for the balls of putty, the total kinetic energy of the billiard balls would then be only half the kinetic energy before the collision. What actually happens in a collision of this type is that the first ball comes to a complete halt. The second ball (of equal mass) moves off at exactly the speed of the first ball before the collision took place. Thus momentum and kinetic energy are both conserved. The interesting thing about this is that we know what must happen in advance. The conservation laws tell us what will happen.

Many collisions are neither elastic nor completely inelastic. In such cases it becomes very difficult to predict what will happen during a collision.

In an elastic collision, the behavior of objects is predictable.

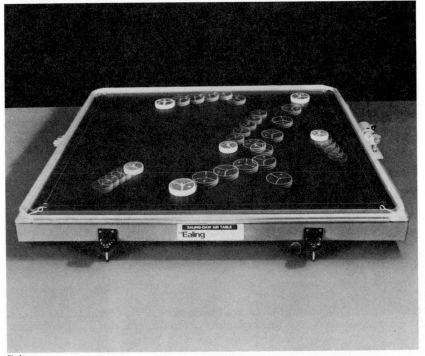

Ealing

FIGURE 11-13. The collisions of the pucks on this nearly frictionless air table are examples of nearly perfect elastic collisions.

PROBLEMS

21. Two bowling balls, each with a mass of 10 kg, roll together along a smooth ramp at 10 m/sec. They collide with a row of 10-kg bowling balls at rest. Collisions between bowling balls are very nearly elastic. (a) After the collision, can one bowling ball leave the opposite end of the row with a speed of 20 m/sec and satisfy the law of conservation of momentum? (b) If one bowling ball did leave the opposite end of the row at 20 m/sec, what kinetic energy would it possess? What was the total kinetic energy of the two balls before the collision? Would energy be conserved under these circumstances? (c) Two bowling balls leave the opposite end of the row at 10 m/sec. Is the law of conservation of momentum obeyed? Is the law of conservation of energy observed?

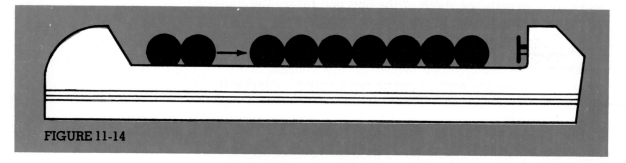

FIGURE 11-14

22. What happens if a single bowling ball with a mass of 10 kg moving at 10 m/sec collides with a row of stationary bowling balls? That is, will one bowling ball move away from the opposite end of the row at 10 m/sec? Or, will two balls move away from the opposite end of the row at 5 m/sec each?

23. A railroad car with a mass of 5×10^5 kg collides with a stationary railroad car of equal mass. After the collision, the two cars lock together and move off at 4 m/sec. (a) Before the collision, the first railroad car moved at 8 m/sec. What was its momentum? (b) What is the total momentum of the two cars after the collision? (c) Find the kinetic energies of the two cars before and after the collision. (d) Account for the loss of kinetic energy.

SUMMARY

Energy is the capacity to do work. It always exists as either potential energy or kinetic energy. Potential energy is the energy a body has because of its position or state. The potential energy of a body is measured from an arbitrary base level. The potential energy of a system is equal to the work done to place the system in its energy state. Kinetic energy is the energy a body has due to its motion. Kinetic energy and potential energy are interchangeable. The equation for kinetic energy is $KE = \frac{1}{2} mv^2$.

Energy has the same units as work (joules). Work must be done to increase the potential energy of a body or to change potential energy to kinetic energy. Work is always involved in an exchange of energy. As work is done, energy changes form or location.

The law of conservation of energy states that the total energy of a system cannot change unless work is done on the system. When energy changes from one form to another or from one place to another, it is always conserved. The law of conservation of mass-energy states that the total amount of matter plus energy in the universe is a constant.

An elastic collision is a collision in which the total kinetic energy of the bodies involved in the collision is the same after the collision as it was before the collision. In an inelastic collision, the total kinetic energy decreases. In an elastic collision, both momentum and kinetic energy are conserved. Because of this, the behavior of bodies involved in an elastic collision can often be predicted.

QUESTIONS

1. What type of energy does a wound-up watch spring possess? What form of energy does a running watch use? When the watch runs down, what has happened to the energy?

2. Describe the types of energy the earth-sun system possesses.

3. The earth is approximately 6.7×10^6 km closer to the sun in winter than in summer. The earth moves along its orbit faster in winter than in summer. Explain these two statements in terms of the earth's potential and kinetic energy.

4. A rubber ball is dropped from a height of 8 m. After striking the floor, it bounces to a height of 5 m. (a) If the ball had bounced to a height of 8 m, how would you describe the collision between the ball and the floor? (b) If the ball had not bounced at all, how would you describe the collision between the ball and the floor? (c) What happened to the energy lost by the ball during the collision?

5. A film was produced that centered around the discovery of a substance called "flubber." This substance could bounce higher than the height from which it was dropped. Explain why "flubber" is not likely to exist.

6. If "flubber" did exist, what changes would have to take place in the surface from which "flubber" bounced?

PROBLEMS

1. (a) How much work is needed to hoist a 98-N sack of grain to a storage room 50 m above the ground floor of a grain elevator? (b) What is the potential energy of the sack of grain at this height? (c) The rope being used to lift the sack of grain breaks just as the sack reaches the storage room. What kinetic energy does the sack have just before it strikes the ground floor?

2. A 1600-kg car travels at a speed of 12.5 m/sec. What is its kinetic energy?

3. A car has a mass of 1500 kg. What is its kinetic energy if it has a speed of 108 km/hr? (Convert km/hr to m/sec)

4. An archer puts a 0.3 kg arrow to his bowstring. An average force of 200 N is exerted to draw the string back 1.3 m. (a) Assuming no friction loss, with what speed does the arrow leave the bow? (b) If the arrow is shot straight up, how high does it rise?

5. A 1200-kg car starts from rest and accelerates to 72 km/hr in 20 sec. The average force needed to overcome friction during this period is 450 N. (a) What distance does the car move during its period of acceleration? (b) What force does the engine produce on the car during this time? (c) How much work does the engine do to accelerate the car?

6. A force of 400 N is applied in a direction straight up to a stone that weighs 32 N. To what height does the stone rise if the force is applied through a distance of 2 m?

7. (a) A 20-kg mass is on the edge of a 100-m high cliff. What potential energy does it possess? (b) The mass falls from the cliff. What is its kinetic energy just before it strikes the ground? (c) What speed does it have as it strikes the ground?

8. A steel ball has a mass of 4 kg and rolls along a smooth, level surface at 60 m/sec. (a) Find its kinetic energy. (b) At first, the ball was at rest on the surface. A force acted on it through a distance of 20 m to give it the speed of 60 m/sec. What was the magnitude of the force?

9. Calculate the amount of energy that is released if a kilogram of mass is destroyed completely. (The speed of light is 3.0×10^8 m/sec.)

10. A submarine's engines use energy at the rate of 3000 J/sec. How long can a kilogram of mass propel the sub before the sub will stop? (Assume that one year is equivalent to 3.0×10^7 sec.)

11. Calculate the amount of matter that is destroyed to produce 30.0 J of energy.

12. A steel ball with a mass of 5 kg rolls along a horizontal surface at 40 m/sec. (a) Find the kinetic energy of the ball. (b) A chute changes the direction of the ball so that it moves vertically. How high does it rise?

13. As shown, a bowling ball rolls down an incline. The surface of the incline is frictionless. (a) To what point does the ball rise on the opposite incline? (b) At what point in the diagram is the speed maximum? (c) At what point is the speed zero?

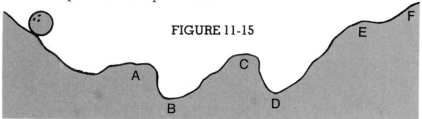

FIGURE 11-15

14. A railroad car with a mass of 1500 kg rolls along a level track at a speed of 12 m/sec. It collides with a stationary car of equal mass. (a) The two cars lock together and then move off. What is their new velocity? (b) How much energy is lost during the collision?

PROJECTS

1. Construct an experimental solar-heating system. You may be able to obtain glass tubing for this purpose from your chemistry department. Black plastic rubbish bags can serve as an energy-absorbing material. Bend the tubing in the flame of a Bunsen burner to form a continuous grill through which water can flow. Cover the grill with the black plastic, and place it inside a flat box. Place a sheet of glass over the box and connect either end of your glass tubing to a small tank. One end of the tubing should enter the top of the tank. The other should enter the bottom

of the tank. Fill the tank and tubing with water and place the entire system in sunlight. From time to time measure the temperature of the water in the tank. Consult Chapter 12, and learn how to calculate the heat energy being produced by your solar heater.

2. Many battery-operated toy cars are powered by small electric motors. Locate such a motor. Ask your physics teacher for the loan of a milliammeter or galvanometer. Connect the two wire leads from the motor to the meter. Then, twirl the shaft of the motor. Notice that the work you do to turn the motor is converted to electric energy.

Construct a small windmill to turn the shaft of the motor. This will provide a demonstration of wind-power.

READINGS

Bonner, et al, *Principles of Physical Science* (Physics and Physical Science Series). Reading, Mass., Addison-Wesley Publishing Co., Inc., 1971, Chapter 10.

Chester, Michael, *Relativity, an Introduction for Young Readers.* New York, W. W. Norton and Co., Inc., 1967.

Dirac, P. A. M., "The Evolution of the Physicists Picture of Nature." *Scientific American,* May, 1963.

Feinberg, Gerald, and Goldhaber, Maurice, "The Conservation Laws of Physics." *Scientific American,* October, 1963.

Gough, William, and Eastlund, Bernard J., "The Prospects of Fusion Power." *Scientific American,* February, 1971.

Haber-Schaim, Uri, et al, *PSSC Physics,* 4th ed. Boston, D. C. Heath and Co., 1976, Chapters 15, 16, 17.

Socolow, Robert H., et al, "Efficient Use of Energy." *Physics Today,* August, 1975.

The transfer of heat from one body to another can be observed in two ways. The transfer can cause either a temperature change or a change in state. The amount of heat transferred can be measured in terms of some physical effect which results. Examples of these effects are change in volume and electric resistance. From experience, you know that equal amounts of different substances at the same temperature may differ greatly in thermal energy. How might a large body of water affect the climate of adjacent land areas?

MEASUREMENT OF HEAT

Before the nineteenth century, heat was thought to be an invisible fluid called "caloric." It was also thought that a warm object contained more of this fluid than a cool object. "Caloric" could supposedly flow only from a warmer object to a cooler object. In this way, a cool object became warmer when placed close to a warm object.

GOAL: You will gain knowledge and understanding of heat and its measurement, temperature, heat exchange, and latent heat.

12:1 What is Heat?

By the middle of the nineteenth century, the caloric theory of heat was abandoned. It was replaced by the kinetic theory of heat. The kinetic theory states that all matter is made up of particles which are constantly in motion. Today, the accepted theory of heat is still the kinetic theory.

Heat is explained by the kinetic theory of heat.

In the kinetic theory, heat is associated only with internal energy. Internal energy is the kinetic and potential energy which comes from the motions and relative positions of the molecules of an object. External energy is the kinetic and potential energy of the object as a whole. For example, the external energy of a baseball in flight is due to its position above the earth and also to its motion. The internal energy of the baseball is a result of the kinetic and potential energies of its molecules. Internal energy is

Internal energy is the sum of the kinetic and potential energies of the particles of a substance.

External energy concerns the object as a whole.

165

Heat is internal energy which is transferred from one body to another.

what we mean when we speak of heat energy. **Heat** is the internal energy which is transferred from bodies of higher internal energy to bodies of lower internal energy. Heat can be used to do work. Work can be used to produce heat.

12:2 Temperature and Heat

Temperature refers to the average kinetic energy of an object's molecules.

Temperature and heat are two different quantities. While temperature is related to heat, it is not the same as heat. The **temperature** of a substance is a measure of the average kinetic energy of the molecules of the substance. Suppose you have two pans filled with boiling water. One pan is very large and the other is quite small. The temperature of the water in both pans is the same. But the water in the large pan would have much more heat energy than the water in the small pan. This difference exists because the water in the large pan has more mass. Placed in a cold room, the water in the large pan would transfer much more heat to the room than would the water in the small pan.

Heat is internal energy. Internal energy consists of both the kinetic and potential energy of the molecules of a substance. A substance can absorb heat and store it as potential energy rather than as kinetic energy. Then, there is no increase in temperature. However, there is a large increase in heat content.

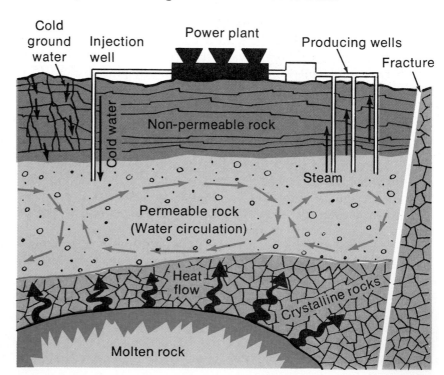

FIGURE 12-1. In some areas water is trapped and heated in layers of rock. Wells can be drilled into some of these layers to obtain steam. The steam can then be used to generate electricity.

FIGURE 12-2. This is a section of a geothermal field where 396 000 kilowatts of electric power are generated from underground steam.

Consider a 1-kg sample of water at 100° C. In order to become water vapor, water must absorb enough heat energy to separate its molecules into a gas. As the molecules are separated, their potential energies are increased. The heat energy is stored in the water vapor as potential rather than kinetic energy. In this case, there is no temperature change and the 1-kg sample of water vapor also has a temperature of 100° C. Thus, a 1-kg sample of water vapor at 100° C contains much more heat energy than does a 1-kg sample of water at 100° C. This energy can be reclaimed by condensing the water vapor. Steam at 100° C will condense and form water at 100° C inside a radiator. In this way, large amounts of heat energy can be obtained to heat rooms.

Heat energy can be used to change potential energy instead of kinetic energy. Then, there is no change in temperature.

FIGURE 12-3. Steam in a steam radiator (a) or from a teakettle (b), contains much more heat energy than water at the same temperature.

Craig Kramer

William Maddox

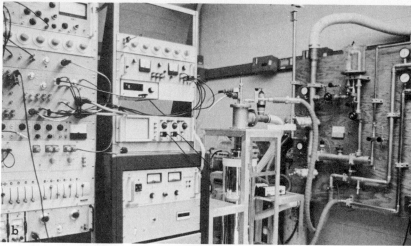

FIGURE 12-4. In low-temperature research, (a) materials are studied in insulated containers. (b) Temperatures are measured and regulated with devices whose electric resistance is very sensitive to changes in temperature.

Temperature is often measured with a mercury thermometer.

The use of mercury is limited to a short range of temperatures.

12:3 Thermometry

In scientific work, temperature is measured with a mercury thermometer. A column of mercury is sealed in a glass tube. An appropriate scale is placed on the tube. Changes in temperature cause the column of mercury to expand or contract. Mercury expands at a much greater rate per degree of temperature change than does glass. Therefore, the level of the mercury in the tube varies with the temperature.

Mercury and alcohol thermometers are common. However, their use is limited to a short range of temperatures. Mercury is limited by its freezing point ($-39°$ C) and its boiling point ($357°$ C). For low temperatures, either hydrogen or helium gas can be used.

FIGURE 12-5. Electric resistance varies with temperature. Based on this principle, this thermistor thermometer indicates temperature with great accuracy.

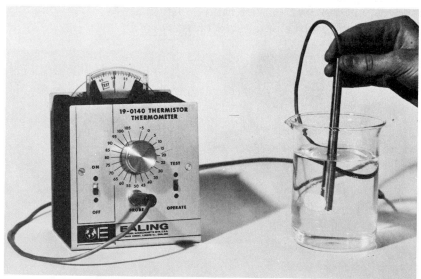

Bruce Charlton

For very high temperatures, devices that measure a property other than expansion usually are used. The temperature of incandescent substances can be estimated by analyzing the color of light the substance emits. Another means to determine high temperatures makes use of the fact that the electric conductivity of wire depends on the temperature of the wire. Platinum wire shows precise variation in electric conductivity with temperature. Thus, it is often used to measure temperature.

To measure very low or very high temperatures, devices other than a mercury thermometer are used.

12:4   The Celsius Temperature Scale

The **Celsius temperature scale** was devised by Anders Celsius (1701–1744). Two fixed temperatures were selected and marked on a scale. These were the freezing and boiling points of water. At fixed atmospheric pressure, these points are reproduced easily. On the Celsius scale, the freezing point of water is defined as 0°, and the boiling point of water is defined as 100°. There are 100 degrees between these two points. The Celsius degree is the basic unit of temperature in the metric system.

The Celsius degree is the basic MKS unit of temperature.

12:5   The Kelvin Temperature Scale

Temperatures do not appear to have an upper limit. The interior temperature of the sun ranges above $1.5 \times 10^7°$ C. Other stars may have even higher temperatures. However, temperatures do appear to have a lower limit. The random motion of molecules is thought to approach zero at $-273°$ C. At this temperature, the average kinetic energy of molecules is zero. Since the average kinetic energy is zero, the temperature must also be zero. Even so, molecules still have energy. They still have rotational motion as well as other forms of internal energy not related to temperature.

Lord Kelvin (1824–1907) devised a scale known as the **Kelvin temperature scale.** This scale extends the Celsius scale to absolute zero and places the zero-degree mark at that point. The size of a degree on the Kelvin scale is the same as that on a Celsius scale. The zero degree mark on the Kelvin scale corresponds to $-273°$ C. A temperature on the Celsius scale is converted to the Kelvin scale by adding 273°.

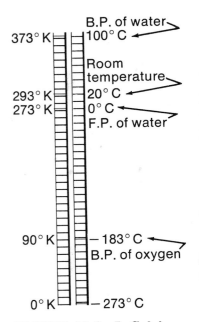

FIGURE 12-6. A Celsius temperature is 273° higher than its corresponding Kelvin temperature.

At $-273°$ C, the motion of molecules approaches zero.

Although temperatures have no apparent upper limit, $-273°$ C appears to be the lower limit.

Zero degrees Celsius equals 273° Kelvin.

Example: Converting Celsius to Kelvin Temperature

Convert 20° C to degrees Kelvin.

Solution:

$$°K = °C + 273°$$
$$= 20° + 273°$$
$$= 293° K$$

Example: Converting Kelvin to Celsius Temperature

Convert 50° K to degrees Celsius.

Solution:

$$°K = °C + 273°$$

Thus, $$°C = °K - 273°$$
$$= 50° - 273°$$
$$= -223° C$$

PROBLEMS

1. Convert 40° C to degrees Kelvin.

2. Convert 40° K to degrees Celsius.

3. Convert 273° C to degrees Kelvin.

4. Convert 273° K to degrees Celsius.

5. Convert 200° K to degrees Celsius.

6. Convert these Kelvin temperatures to Celsius temperatures:

(a) 100° K   (d) 323° K
(b) 22° K   (e) 400° K
(c) 373° K

7. Convert these Celsius temperatures to Kelvin temperatures:

(a) 100° C   (d) 20° C
(b) −100° C   (e) −23° C
(c) 300° C

12:6   The First Law of Thermodynamics

The first law of thermodynamics states that energy is conserved.

The first law of thermodynamics reasserts the law of conservation of energy. This law states that when mechanical energy, electric energy, or any other kind of energy is converted to heat, all energy is conserved. The heat, if converted to any other form of energy, develops exactly the same amount of energy as the amount of energy originally used to develop the heat.

FIGURE 12-7. Heat is converted directly to electricity in this thermocouple. More than 2 amperes of current are produced when the flame heats the junction of two dissimilar thermoelectric materials.

FIGURE 12-8. Special containers help to keep foods hot or cold by slowing down the process of heat transfer.

12:7 The Second Law of Thermodynamics

The quantity of heat a body supplies is not necessarily indicated by its temperature. Temperature serves chiefly to describe which way heat flows when two bodies of different temperatures are brought together. For example, a hot iron bar is placed in cold water. The heat travels from the metal bar into the water. The iron bar is "hot" because its molecules have a higher average kinetic energy than do those of the water. Collisions between the water molecules and the more energetic iron molecules impart energy to the water molecules. The energy spreads out into the entire system. However, the reverse process never occurs. The hot iron bar does not become hotter while the water becomes colder. This principle is the second law of thermodynamics. Heat flows from hot to cold. This law prohibits the transfer of energy from areas of low concentration to areas of high concentration.

The second law of thermodynamics sometimes is stated in terms of entropy. **Entropy** (EN truh pee) is the "unavailability" of energy. Dissipated energy cannot be retrieved without additional energy input. The entropy of the universe is always increasing.

The second law of thermodynamics states that heat flows spontaneously from a hotter to a colder body, but not vice versa.

Entropy is the randomness of a system.

12:8 Heat Units

The basic unit of heat in the metric system is the calorie. A **calorie** (cal) is the amount of heat needed to raise the temperature of one gram of water one Celsius degree. Since the calorie is a relatively small unit of heat, another unit called the kilocalorie (kcal) is often used. A kilocalorie is one thousand calories. A kilocalorie is the amount of heat needed to raise the temperature of one kilogram of water one Celsius degree. The increasing use of the joule as a unit of heat will be discussed in the next chapter.

The calorie is the basic unit of heat.

A kilocalorie is 1000 calories.

12:9 Specific Heat

The **specific heat** of a substance is the amount of heat needed to raise the temperature of a unit mass of that substance through one degree. In the metric system, specific heat (c) is expressed in calories per gram-Celsius degree or in kilocalories per kilogram-Celsius degree. For example, 0.2 calories of heat are needed to raise the temperature of one gram of aluminum through one Celsius degree. The specific heat of aluminum is 0.2 cal/g-C°. The specific heat of aluminum also could be written 0.2 kcal/kg-C°.

Table 12–1

SPECIFIC HEAT OF COMMON SUBSTANCES

Material	Specific Heat (cal/g-C°)	Material	Specific Heat (cal/g-C°)
Alcohol	0.594	Ice	0.50
Aluminum	0.22	Iron	0.107
Brass	0.09	Lead	0.030
Carbon	0.170	Silver	0.056
Copper	0.092	Steam	0.5
Glass	0.20	Water	1.0
Gold	0.030	Zinc	0.092

Less than one calorie of heat is needed to raise the temperature of one gram of most materials through one Celsius degree. Therefore, most specific heats are less than the specific heat of water. Copper requires only about 0.09 calories per gram for a temperature increase of one Celsius degree. One calorie of heat raises the temperature of one gram of copper by more than 10 Celsius degrees. Table 12-1 gives the specific heat of some common materials.

When the specific heat of a material is known, the amount of heat lost or gained by any given mass of that material as its temperature is changed can be calculated. The specific heat of water is 1 cal/g-C°. Thus, when the temperature of one gram of water is increased 1 C°, the heat absorbed by the water is 1 cal. When the temperature of 10 grams of water is raised 1 C°, the heat absorbed is 10 cal. When 10 grams of water are heated 5 C°, the heat absorbed is 50 cal. Thus, the quantity of heat gained or lost by a mass as it changes temperature is determined by the mass, change in temperature, and specific heat. This statement can be written

$$H = mc\Delta t$$

FIGURE 12-9. Water has a very high specific heat. Thus, a large body of water tends to moderate the climate of a coastal area. In this way, fruit crops in coastal areas are often protected from temperature extremes and resulting crop damage.

In this equation, H is the heat gained or lost, m is the mass involved, c is the specific heat of the mass, and Δt is the change in temperature.

Example: Heat Transfer

A 400-g block of iron is heated from 20° C to 50° C. How much heat is absorbed by the iron?

Solution:

$$H = mc\Delta t$$
$$= \left(400 \text{ g} \right) \left(0.107 \frac{\text{cal}}{\text{g-C}°} \right) \left(30 \text{ C}° \right)$$
$$= 1284 \text{ cal}$$

PROBLEMS

8. How much heat is absorbed by 250 g of water when it is heated from 10° C to 85° C?

9. How much heat is absorbed by 60 g of copper when it is heated from 20° C to 80° C?

10. A 38-kg block of lead is heated from −26° C to 180° C. How much heat does it absorb during the heating?

11. A 5-kg gold ingot is cooled from 120° C to −20° C. How much heat is given up by the ingot?

12. A 400-g glass coffee cup at room temperature (20° C) is plunged into hot dishwater (80° C). Later, the temperature of the cup reaches that of the dishwater. How much heat does the cup absorb?

13. Five kilograms of ice cubes are moved from the freezing compartment of a refrigerator into a home freezer. The refrigerator's freezing compartment is kept at $-4°$ C. The home freezer is kept at $-17°$ C. How much heat does the freezer's cooling system remove from the ice cubes?

14. A 250-kg cast-iron car engine contains 15 kg of water as a coolant. Suppose the engine's temperature is $35°$ C when it is shut off. The air temperature is $10°$ C. How much heat is given up by the engine and the water in it as they cool to the air temperature?

15. Steam enters one end of a turbine at $450°$ C. It leaves the other end at $175°$ C. How much heat does each kilogram of steam give up to the turbine as it passes through?

12:10   Conservation in Heat Transfer

According to the first law of thermodynamics, the heat lost by one substance is equal to the heat gained by another.

In an experiment, 100 g of water at $10°$ C are mixed with 100 g of hot water at $90°$ C. The container in which they are mixed is well insulated to prevent heat loss. The hot water gives up heat to the cold water. The temperature of the mixture when measured with a thermometer is $50°$ C. The temperature of the cold water has increased by 40 Celsius degrees. The temperature of the hot water has decreased by 40 Celsius degrees.

To heat 100 g of water through one Celsius degree requires 100 calories. Thus, to heat 100 g of water through 40 Celsius degrees requires 40×100 calories, or 4000 calories. The cold water gains 4000 calories of heat. Similarly, the 100 g of hot water is cooled through 40 Celsius degrees. As a result, the hot water gives up 40×100 calories, or 4000 calories of heat. The heat gained by the cold water is equal to the heat lost by the hot water. This relationship agrees with the first law of thermodynamics.

FIGURE 12-10. This student calorimeter (a) consists of a jacket, stirrer, inner vessel, a seal, and a lid. A twin-bridge calorimeter (b) is being used here to measure heat given off during nuclear decay.

Courtesy of Central Scientific Company

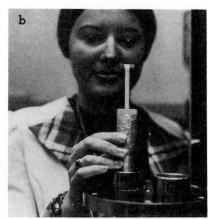

U.S. Energy Research and Development Administration

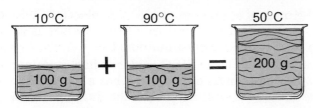

FIGURE 12-11. Heat lost by
the hot water is equal to
the heat gained by the cold
water.

To solve problems of heat transfer, assume that the heat lost
by one substance is equal to the heat gained by the second substance. Heat lost or gained by a substance is equal to $mc\Delta t$. This is
expressed

$$\text{Heat lost} = \text{Heat gained}$$
$$(mc\Delta t)_{\text{substance 1}} = (mc\Delta t)_{\text{substance 2}}$$

Example: Conservation in Heat Transfer

A 500-g block of iron at 100° C is placed in 500 g of water at
20° C. What is the final temperature of the iron and water mixture? (The specific heat of iron is about 0.11 cal/g-C°.)

Solution:

The temperature of the iron decreases. Its temperature
change (Δt) is ($100°$ C $- t_2$) where t_2 represents the final
temperature of the mixture. The temperature of the water
increases. Its temperature change is ($t_2 - 20°$ C). Hence,

$$\text{Heat lost by iron} = \text{Heat gained by water}$$
$$(mc\Delta t)_{\text{iron}} = (mc\Delta t)_{\text{water}}$$
$$(500 \text{ g}) (0.11 \text{ cal/g-C}°) (100° \text{ C} - t_2)$$
$$= (500 \text{ g}) (1 \text{ cal/g-C}°) (t_2 - 20° \text{ C})$$
$$55 (100° \text{ C} - t_2) = (500) (t_2 - 20° \text{ C})$$
$$5500 \text{ C}° - 55 t_2 = 500 t_2 - 10\,000 \text{ C}°$$
$$555 t_2 = 15\,500° \text{ C}$$
$$t_2 = 28° \text{ C}$$

PROBLEMS

16. A 200-g sample of water at 80° C is mixed with 200 g of water
at 10° C. Assume no heat loss to surroundings. What is the final
temperature of the mixture?

17. A 600-g sample of water at 90° C is mixed with 400 g of water
at 22° C. Assume no heat loss to surroundings. What is the
final temperature of the mixture?

18. A 400-g sample of alcohol at 16° C is mixed with 400 g of water
at 85° C. Assume no heat loss to surroundings. What is the
final temperature of the mixture?

19. A 100-g mass of brass at 90° C is placed in a glass beaker containing 200 g of water at 20° C. Assume no heat loss to the
glass or surroundings. What is the final temperature of the
mixture?

20. A 100-g mass of aluminum at 100° C is placed in 100 g of water at 10° C. The final temperature of the mixture is 25° C. What is the specific heat of the aluminum?

21. A 10-kg piece of zinc at 71° C is placed in a container of water. The water has a mass of 20 kg and has a temperature of 10° C before the zinc is added. What is the final temperature of the water and zinc?

12:11   Latent Heat and Change of State

The particle nature of matter implies that some force holds the molecules together. Otherwise its molecules would just drift apart, and an object would have no shape. The forces holding molecules together are called **cohesive forces.** They help to explain how a substance can absorb heat without an increase in temperature. For example, the specific heat of ice is 0.5 cal/g-C°. If a gram of ice at −10° C has 5 cal of heat added to it, the temperature of the ice becomes 0° C. This is the melting point of ice. Once the gram of ice is warmed to this temperature, it continues to absorb heat. Yet it shows no increase in temperature. The ice at 0° C absorbs 80 calories of heat to become water at 0° C. The 80 calories cause the ice to change state but do not change its temperature. The number of calories needed to change the state is called the **latent heat of fusion.** The latent heat of fusion of ice is 80 cal/g. Each substance has a characteristic latent heat of fusion.

As the ice melts, the heat it absorbs must be stored in some form other than the kinetic energies of its molecules. If the kinetic energies of the molecules were increased, the temperature of the ice would increase. But this does not happen. Instead, the absorbed energy is used to do work on the ice molecules and to help separate them. Since molecules attract one another, work is required to force them apart. As the molecules are forced apart, their potential energies are increased. The potential energy of

A cohesive force is that attractive force between molecules of the same kind.

FIGURE 12-12. Molecules of a solid behave as if they were held together by springs.

Latent heat of fusion is the number of calories required to change the state of a substance from a solid to a liquid.

The latent heat of fusion of ice is 80 cal/g.

Table 12–2			
LATENT HEAT OF FUSION OF COMMON SUBSTANCES			
Material	*Heat of Fusion (cal/g)*	*Material*	*Heat of Fusion (cal/g)*
alcohol	25.8	lead	5.6
copper	49.4	mercury	2.7
gold	15.0	silver	25.0
iron	59.1	water (ice)	79.8

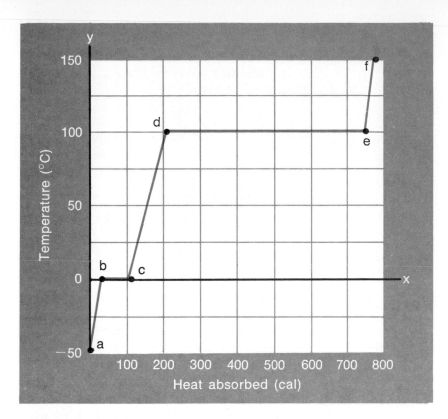

FIGURE 12-13. Graph of the heat absorbed by 1.0 g of ice as its temperature is raised from −50° C to 150° C. Notice that the slope of the graph is steeper from a to b and from e to f than it is from c to d. This is because the specific heats of ice and steam are less than the specific heat of water. What do the horizontal portions of the graph indicate?

From this graph, find the heat of vaporization and heat of fusion of water.

each molecule increases in relation to all the molecules about it. However, its kinetic energy content remains constant.

As the space between ice molecules increases, the cohesive forces decrease. This decrease allows each individual molecule more freedom of movement. Eventually the forces among molecules are reduced to the point where the molecules can slide easily over one another. Then the ice melts.

After the gram of ice has absorbed 80 calories of heat and has changed to water, the water may continue to absorb heat. The temperature of the water increases one Celsius degree for each calorie of heat it absorbs. As heat is added, the temperature continues to rise until the water reaches a temperature of 100° C. This temperature is the boiling point of water. After the boiling point is reached, any heat absorbed is used to change the water from the liquid state to the vapor state. The amount of heat needed to change one gram of a liquid at its boiling point to a vapor at the same temperature is known as the **latent heat of vaporization.** The latent heat of vaporization of water is 540 cal/g.

The latent heat of vaporization of water is considerably higher than the latent heat of fusion of ice. The result of this large energy input is that the gas molecules are much more free of forces between molecules than are liquid molecules. Each substance has a characteristic latent heat of vaporization.

Latent heat increases the potential energy between the molecules of a substance.

As molecules are separated, the cohesive force decreases. Eventually the solid changes to a liquid.

The latent heat of vaporization is the number of calories required to change the state of a substance from a liquid to a gas.

The latent heat of vaporization of water is 540 cal/g.

Molecules in a gas move more freely than molecules in a liquid or solid.

Table 12–3

LATENT HEAT OF VAPORIZATION OF COMMON SUBSTANCES

Material	Latent Heat of Vaporization (cal/g)	Material	Latent Heat of Vaporization (cal/g)
alcohol	204	lead	207
copper	1130	mercury	71
gold	411	silver	556
iron	1500	water	540

Example: Latent Heat of Fusion

Heat is applied to 100 g of ice at 0° C until the ice melts and the temperature of the resulting water rises to 20° C. How much heat is absorbed?

Solution:

First, find how much heat the ice absorbs to cause a change of state from solid ice to liquid water. Each gram requires 80 calories to bring about the change.

$$100 \text{ g} \times 80 \frac{\text{cal}}{\text{g}} = 8000 \text{ cal}$$

Next, find how much heat the water absorbs to raise its temperature from 0° C to 20° C.

$$H = mc\Delta t$$
$$= \left(100 \text{ g}\right)\left(1 \ \frac{\text{cal}}{\text{g-C}^\circ}\right)\left(20 \text{ C}^\circ\right)$$
$$= 2000 \text{ cal}$$

Total: 8000 cal + 2000 cal = 10 000 cal

Example: Latent Heat of Vaporization

A 100-g sample of water at 80° C is heated until it becomes steam at 130° C. How much heat is absorbed?

Solution:

First, find how much heat the water absorbs to raise its temperature to 100° C.

$$H = mc\Delta t$$
$$= \left(100 \text{ g}\right)\left(1 \ \frac{\text{cal}}{\text{g-C}^\circ}\right)\left(20 \text{ C}^\circ\right)$$
$$= 2000 \text{ cal}$$

Next, find how much heat the water absorbs at 100° C to become steam at 100° C. Each gram requires 540 cal to cause the change.

$$100 \text{ g} \times 540 \, \frac{\text{cal}}{\text{g}} = 54\,000 \text{ cal}$$

Finally, find how much heat the steam absorbs to raise its temperature from 100°C to 130° C. The specific heat of steam is 0.5 cal/g-C°.

$$H = mc\Delta t$$
$$= \left(100 \text{ g}\right)\left(0.5 \, \frac{\text{cal}}{\text{g-C}^\circ}\right)\left(30 \text{ C}^\circ\right)$$
$$= 1500 \text{ cal}$$

Total: 2000 cal + 54 000 cal + 1500 cal = 57 500 cal

PROBLEMS

22. How much heat is needed to change 50 g of ice at 0° C to water at 0° C?

23. How much heat is needed to change 50 g of water at 100° C to steam at 100° C?

24. How much heat is absorbed by 100 g of ice at −20° C to become water at 0° C? The specific heat of ice is 0.5 cal/g-C°.

25. A 200-g sample of water at 60° C is heated to steam at 140° C. How much heat is absorbed?

26. How much heat is needed to change 300 g of ice at −30° C to steam at 130° C?

27. How much heat is removed from 60 g of steam at 100° C to change it to 60 g of water at 20° C?

28. The specific heat of mercury is 0.033 cal/g-C°. Its latent heat of vaporization is 71 cal/g. How much heat is needed to completely vaporize a kilogram of mercury at 10° C? The boiling point of mercury is 357° C.

29. Years ago, a block of ice with a mass of about 20 kg was used daily in a home icebox. The temperature of the ice was 0° C when delivered. As it melted, how much heat in calories did a block of ice of this size absorb?

SUMMARY

Heat is the measure of internal energy transfer. Internal energy refers to the kinetic and potential energy possessed by the molecules of a body. External energy refers to the kinetic and potential energy possessed by the mass as a whole. Internal or thermal energy is due to the kinetic and potential energies of the molecules. Molecules have potential energy because they attract one another.

Temperature is a measure of the average kinetic energy of the molecules of a substance. It is not a measure of the thermal energy the body possesses. Scientists use either the Celsius or Kelvin temperature scales. A Kelvin degree is the same size as a Celsius degree.

The average kinetic energy of the molecules of a substance is zero at $-273°$ C, or $0°$ K. These temperatures are referred to as absolute zero.

The first law of thermodynamics restates the law of conservation of energy. It states that energy is conserved when thermal energy is changed to any other form.

The second law of thermodynamics requires that thermal energy may undergo transfer only from areas of high concentration to areas of low concentration.

A calorie is the quantity of heat needed to raise the temperature of one gram of water one Celsius degree. Specific heat is the quantity of heat needed to raise the temperature of one gram of a substance through one Celsius degree. Most specific heats are less than the specific heat of water.

The latent heat of fusion is the quantity of heat required to change a solid to the liquid state. The latent heat of vaporization is the quantity of heat needed to change a liquid to the gas state. The heat gained or lost when a substance changes state at its boiling point or melting point does not produce a temperature change.

QUESTIONS

1. How is heat described in terms of the kinetic theory?
2. Distinguish between heat and temperature.
3. Why are the readings of thermometers of different diameters the same under identical conditions?
4. Describe the Celsius temperature scale.
5. How is the Kelvin scale different from the Celsius scale?
6. A wheel is stopped by a friction brake. The brake gets hot, and the internal energy of the brake is increased. The kinetic energy of the wheel is decreased by the same amount as the increase in internal energy of the brake. The first law of thermodynamics would be satisfied if the hot brake were to cool and give back its internal energy to the wheel, causing it to resume rotation. This does not happen. Explain.
7. Ten grams of aluminum and ten grams of lead are heated to the same temperature. The pieces of metal are placed on a block of ice. Which metal will cause more ice to melt?
8. Would the water at the bottom of a high waterfall be warmer or colder than the water at the top of the same falls? Explain.
9. Will an ice cube lower the temperature of a glass of water or a glass containing an alcoholic beverage faster? Explain.

PROBLEMS

1. Convert these Celsius temperatures to Kelvin temperatures:
   (a) $50°$ C   (b) $150°$ C   (c) $-200°$ C   (d) $300°$ C
2. Convert these Kelvin temperatures to Celsius temperatures:
   (a) $50°$ K   (b) $150°$ K   (c) $273°$ K   (d) $300°$ K
3. How much heat in kcal is needed to raise the temperature of 50 kg of water from $4.5°$ C to $83°$ C?
4. How much heat in calories must be added to 50 g of aluminum at $20°$ C to raise its temperature to $120°$ C?
5. Suppose the same amount of heat needed to raise the temperature of 50 g of water through 100 C° is applied to 50 g of zinc. What is the temperature change of the zinc?
6. A copper wire has a mass of 165 g. An electric current runs through the wire for a short time and its temperature rises from $20°$ C to $38°$ C. What minimum quantity of heat is generated by the electric current?

7. A 500-g sample of water at 90° C is mixed with 500 g of water at 30° C. Assume no heat loss to surroundings. What is the final temperature of the mixture?

8. A 200-g sample of brass at 300° C is placed in a calorimeter cup which contains 260 g of water at 20° C. Disregard the absorption of heat by the cup and calculate the final temperature of the mixture. The specific heat of brass is 0.09 cal/g-C°.

9. A 100-g sample of tungsten at 100° C is placed in 200 g of water at 20° C. The mixture reaches equilibrium at 21.6° C. Calculate the specific heat of tungsten.

10. How much heat is added to 10 g of ice at −20° C to convert it to steam at 120° C?

11. A 40-g sample of chloroform is condensed from a vapor at 61.6° C to a liquid at 61.6° C. It liberates 2360 calories of heat. What is the latent heat of vaporization of chloroform?

12. A 50-g sample of ice at 0° C is placed in a glass beaker containing 400 g of water at 50° C. All the ice melts. What is the final temperature of the mixture? Disregard heat loss to the glass. (Recall that when ice melts it becomes water.)

13. A block of metal (mass = 500 g) absorbs 1200 cal of heat when its temperature changes from 20° C to 30° C. Calculate the specific heat of the metal.

PROJECTS

1. Make a convectional current demonstrator for your physics teacher. You will need two Erlenmeyer flasks, two 10-cm lengths of glass tubing, two two-hole stoppers to fit the flasks and a few drops of food coloring. Fit the two lengths of glass tubing into the tops of the stoppers. Fill both flasks with water and add coloring to one of the flasks. Fit one of the stoppers into the second flask and then quickly invert the second flask and place the remaining stopper in the first flask. Now heat the bottom flask and the warm, colored water will illustrate a convection current as it rises through one tube and clear water descends through the other tube.

2. Compare the temperature of boiling water with the temperature of a boiling solution of salt and water.

READINGS

Ashcroft, N. W., "Liquid Metals." *Scientific American,* July, 1969.

Bartlett, Albert A., "Thermal Patterns in the Snow." *The Physics Teacher,* February, 1976.

Bonner, et al, *Principles of Physical Science* (Physics and Physical Science Series). Reading, Mass., Addison-Wesley Publishing Co., Inc., 1971, Chapter 11.

Bryant, Lynwood, "Rudolf Diesel and His Rational Engine." *Scientific American,* August, 1969.

Ehrenberg, W., "Maxwell's Demon." *Scientific American,* November, 1967.

Joule, James, "The Mechanical Equivalent of Heat," in Morris H. Shames, ed., *Great Experiments in Physics.* New York, Holt, Rinehart and Winston, Inc., 1959, Chapter 12.

Mott, Sir Nevil, "The Solid State." *Scientific American,* September, 1967.

Thompson, Paul D., *Gases and Plasmas* (Introducing Modern Science Book Series). Philadelphia, Pa., J. B. Lippincott and Co., 1966.

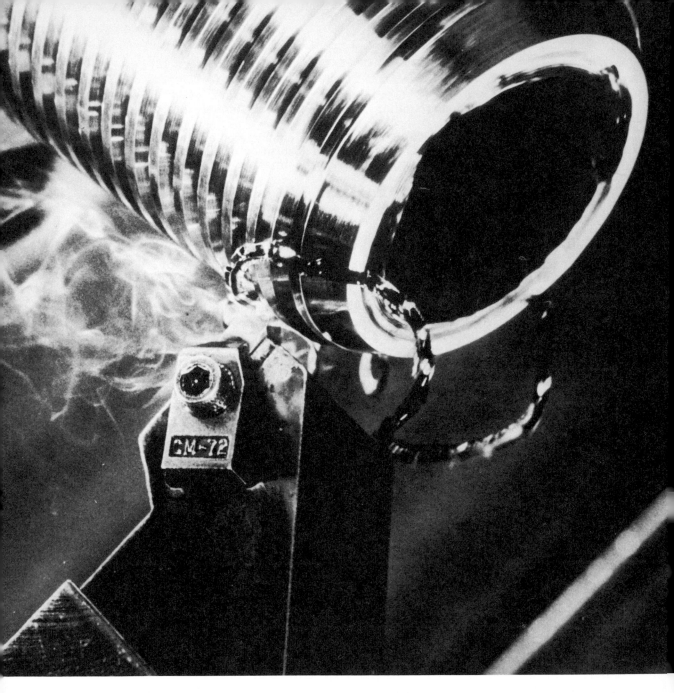

Heat can be added to an object by placing the object in contact with a warmer object. Heat can also be added to an object by doing work on the object. For example, when you strike a match, enough heat is produced to ignite the match. When you sand a piece of metal, you can feel the metal become hot. So much heat is produced as this steel rod is threaded that the metal begins to smoke. The amount of heat produced by work varies with the amount of work done. When is the production of heat in this way desirable? When is it not desirable?

HEAT AS ENERGY

Does a certain amount of work produce a certain amount of heat every time work is changed to heat? Does just so much electric energy produce just so must heat? Can that amount of heat be changed back to the original amount of electric energy?

GOAL: You will gain knowledge and understanding of the law of conservation of energy through a study of the mechanical equivalent of heat.

13:1 Mechanical Equivalent of Heat

The experiments described in this section were done in an attempt to find out if energy is conserved as it changes form. This question was very important to some scientists. They were beginning to suspect that energy can change from one form to another but that it can never be lost. This idea has now been confirmed by many experiments. It is known as the law of conservation of energy. The laws of conservation of energy and conservation of momentum are two of the most important of all scientific laws.

Heat is internal energy that is transferred from one place to another. It is difficult to measure heat because it so easily escapes from even the most sophisticated laboratory equipment. But, when experiments are done with care, it is found that so many joules of thermal energy always produce exactly the same number of joules of any other form of energy.

FIGURE 13-1. In this steam engine, heat energy is converted to mechanical energy.

Count Rumford performed the first experiments to determine the relationship between work and energy.

The first experiments designed to establish a relationship between work and heat were done by Count Rumford (1753–1814)*. At the time Count Rumford was Minister of War of Bavaria, he was also a leading scientist. For one of his projects, Rumford conducted experiments concerned with the caloric theory of heat. As we pointed out in Chapter 12, the caloric theory of heat considered heat to be a fluid that flowed from hot to cold. All of the Count's experiments failed to show the existence of any such thing as a caloric fluid.

One of the Count's most famous heat experiments took place while he was watching the boring of cannons at the arsenal in Munich. Cannons are made by pouring steel into large molds and then drilling, or boring, a hole down their centers. The drills were powered by two horses harnessed to long shafts. During the drilling, both cannon and drills became very hot due to friction. Rumford thought he could use this process to test the caloric theory. He ordered a cannon to be submerged in a large tub of water. He then had the cannon drilled while submerged and made frequent measurements of the temperature of the water. He found that as long as the drilling went on, heat was produced. This meant that if caloric fluid did exist, it could keep coming out of the cannon indefinitely. This finding was strong evidence that there can be no such thing as caloric fluid.

---

*Count Rumford was born Benjamin Thompson in 1753 in Woburn, Mass., the son of a poor farmer. Almost entirely self-educated, he became a superb scientist, a count of the Holy Roman Empire (the name by which he came to be known), Minister of War of Bavaria, and an English Knight.

Dick Smith

FIGURE 13-2. Count Rumford determined the mechanical equivalent of heat by comparing the amount of heat produced during the boring of cannons with the amount of work done by horses during this process.

There was a more important result of this experiment. A relationship was established between the work done by the horses and the heat produced by the friction between drills and cannon. Rumford found that while the horses worked, the temperature of the water increased steadily. If the horses worked eight hours, the temperature of the water increased just twice as much as it did if they worked four hours. The temperature increased by the same amount every hour that the horses worked. Rumford concluded that the heat added to the water was due to the work done by the horses. It was not the result of some mysterious fluid. This steady increase in heat shows that heat energy is related to the energy output of the horses in a very definite way.

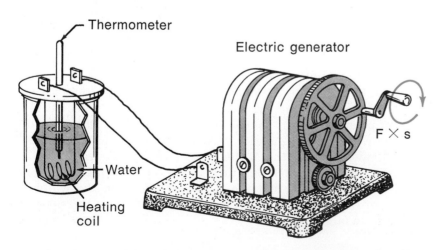

FIGURE 13-3. One of Joule's early experiments to investigate the relationship between the forms of energy. How many energy transformations do you observe in the figure?

FIGURE 13-4. This dental drill (a) is cooled with a water spray, and this lathe (b) is cooled with an oil spray to prevent a buildup of heat from friction.

One calorie of heat is always produced from 4.2 joules of work. This relationship is known as the mechanical equivalent of heat.

In 1830, James Prescott Joule (1818–1889) began a series of precise experiments. His aim was to establish the equivalence of the various forms of energy. In an early experiment, Joule carefully measured the work (Fs) required to drive an electric generator. Then he measured the heat produced by the electric current put out by the generator. He consistently found that every 4.2 joules of work used to turn the generator produced one calorie of heat. The 4.2 joules of work needed to produce one calorie of heat is called the **mechanical equivalent of heat.**

1 calorie = 4.2 joules

Joule performed many other experiments to measure the mechanical equivalent of heat. One of the best known is shown in Figure 13-5. The potential energy of a falling mass operates a pulley. The pulley turns a set of paddles submerged in a water-filled calorimeter. When the proper mass is used, the force it applies to the pulley turns the pulley smoothly and steadily. Then, the total potential energy of the mass is used to turn the paddles and not to accelerate the mass. In his experiment, Joule assumed that the work done by the paddles on the water was equal to the loss of potential energy (mgh) of the falling mass. The work done on the water by the paddles was converted to heat. As a result, the temperature of the water rose steadily. To cause a large change in the water temperature, Joule repeated the process several times. He found that the total work done on the water was equal to $N(mgh)$ where N is the number of times the mass was allowed to fall.

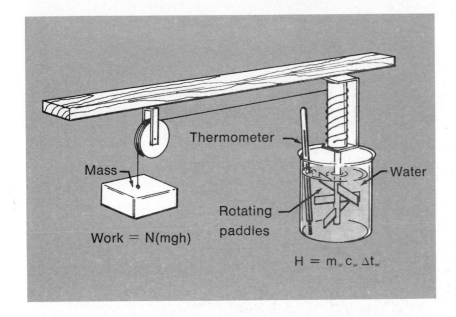

Mass

Thermometer

Work = N(mgh)

Rotating paddles

Water

$H = m_w c_w \Delta t_w$

FIGURE 13-5. Joule also determined the mechanical equivalent of heat by measuring the energy transferred to the water by falling masses. Joule made corrections for the kinetic energy of the masses hitting the floor, the amount of stretch of the string, and energy losses in the pulleys. Joule's experiments were instrumental in establishing the principle of the conservation of energy.

By measuring the change in water temperature, Joule found the heat produced. He knew the mass in grams and the specific heat of the water. Thus, the heat energy added to the water was $m_w c_w \Delta t_w$. He divided the total work done by the heat produced. Again, Joule found that every 4.2 joules of work produces one calorie of heat.

Joule established a definite relationship between heat and other forms of energy. Thus, it became possible to predict the quantity of heat that will be produced when other forms of energy are converted to heat.

A definite relationship exists between heat and other forms of energy.

Example: Mechanical Equivalent of Heat

When lifting a cement block from the ground to a platform, 630 J of work is done. The block falls off the platform. How much heat is produced when it strikes the ground?

Solution:

Assume that all the potential energy of the block is converted to kinetic energy as the block falls. Also assume that all the kinetic energy is changed to heat energy when the block strikes the ground. Then, the heat energy produced must be equal to the original potential energy of the block. This, in turn, is equal to the work done on the block. Since 1 calorie requires 4.2 J of work, the number of calories of heat developed by 630 J is

$$H = \frac{630 \text{ J}}{4.2 \text{ J/cal}} = 150 \text{ cal}$$

Example: Mechanical Equivalent of Heat

A 900-kg car moving at 20 m/sec is braked to a halt. How much heat is generated by the car's brakes?

Solution:

The car's braking system uses friction to convert the kinetic energy of the car to heat. This brings the car to a halt. First calculate the kinetic energy of the car.

$$KE = \frac{1}{2} mv^2$$
$$= \frac{900 \text{ kg} (20 \text{ m/sec})^2}{2}$$
$$= 1.8 \times 10^5 \text{ J}$$

The heat produced by this energy will be

$$H = \frac{\text{Energy}}{\text{Mechanical equivalent of heat}}$$
$$= \frac{1.8 \times 10^5 \text{ J}}{4.2 \text{ J/cal}}$$
$$= 42.9 \text{ kcal}$$

PROBLEMS

1. A 10-kg mass weighing 98 N falls 20 m. How much heat is generated when the mass strikes the ground?

2. How much heat does 1 J produce?

3. An iron object weighing 196 N falls 10 m. Assuming that the object absorbs all the heat produced when it strikes the earth, what is its temperature increase? (The specific heat of iron is 0.11 cal/g-C°.)

4. A mass weighing 30 N falls 1.5 m. It falls 10 times. All the work done by the falling mass is converted to heat. What temperature change does it bring about in 150 g of water?

5. An electric generator is connected to a 500 watt heater. It operates at 100% efficiency. (a) How many calories of heat does it produce each minute? (b) How much work is done each minute by the energy source turning the generator? (c) If the generator is turned by water falling over a dam 5 m high, what is the minimum amount of water that must pass through the electric generator each minute? (One liter of water weighs 9.8 N.)

6. A 0.02-kg bullet traveling at 700 m/sec becomes embedded in a tree. How many calories of heat are generated by the kinetic energy of the bullet?

7. How much heat could two of Count Rumford's horses generate in one hour? A horse can work at a rate of 750 J/sec.

13:2   The Joule as a Universal Unit of Energy

In the mid 19th century, Hermann von Helmholtz used mathematics to show that all forms of energy are equivalent. This was the first definite statement of the law of conservation of energy.

Because all forms of energy are equivalent, the same unit of measurement can be used for all forms of energy. This basic unit is the joule. The joule is used to measure electric energy, light energy, mechanical energy, and nuclear energy. Heat energy should also be measured in joules.

All forms of energy can be measured in joules.

When the temperature of one gram of water increases one Celsius degree, a scientist does not say that a calorie of heat is added to the water. Instead, it is said that 4.2 joules of energy are added to the gram of water. If the temperature of a kilogram of water decreases 5 Celsius degrees, 4.2 J/g-C° × 1000 g × 5 C° or 21 000 J of energy are given up by the water. The calorie is an old unit. It was put into use before the equivalence of all forms of energy was understood. Eventually, heat energy will be measured in joules.

U.S. Energy Research and Development Administration

FIGURE 13-6. Nuclear energy is being released in the form of heat energy by this radioactive pellet. The heat energy released has raised the temperature of the water in this beaker to its boiling point.

SUMMARY

Count Rumford did one of the first experiments which indicated that a given amount of work produces an equal amount of heat. James Joule performed a more precise series of experiments. They were designed to measure the quantity of energy needed to produce one calorie of heat. He found that 4.2 joules of work always produced one calorie of heat. It became clear that one calorie of heat is equal to 4.2 joules of energy.

Joule found evidence that thermal energy, work, and electrical energy are equivalent. This led to the formulation of the law of conservation of energy. Since all forms of energy are equivalent, they should all be measured in the same units. The joule is the basic unit of energy. All forms of energy are measured in joules.

QUESTIONS

1. The energy a person needs to live comes from food. This energy is chemical potential energy that is stored in the food. If a person's work output per day is less than his energy intake in food, what happens? If the person's work output is greater than his energy intake, what tends to happen?

2. Figure 13-7 shows the laboratory apparatus commonly used to find the mechanical equivalent of heat. Look at the apparatus carefully and explain how it is used.

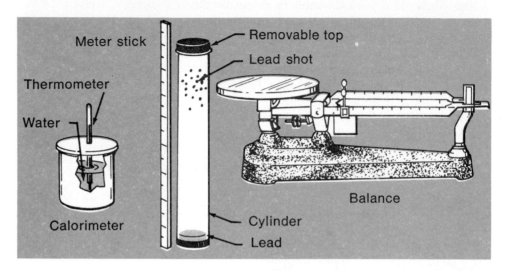

Meter stick

Thermometer

Water

Calorimeter

Removable top

Lead shot

Cylinder

Lead

Balance

FIGURE 13-7

PROBLEMS

1. In an experiment, 800 J of work is done against friction. How many calories of heat are produced?

2. A 20-kg mass falls 30 m. How much heat is produced when the mass strikes the ground?

3. A lead ball of mass m is dropped onto a sidewalk from a height of 20 m. Assume 75% of the heat generated remains in the ball. Calculate the temperature rise of the ball.

4. A 40-kg child slides down a playground slide. At the bottom of the slide the child is moving at 1 m/sec. The slide is 4 m long and inclined at 45°. How much heat in calories is shared by the slide and child?

5. A 1500-kg car moving 20 m/sec is brought to a halt by its brakes. How much heat is developed in the brakes? Assume all heat is absorbed by the braking system.

6. When the first transcontinental railroad was completed, a ceremony was held to drive the "final" spike. The spike was made of gold ($c = 0.03$ cal/g-C°) and had a mass of 200 g. What was the spike's change in temperature if it was driven by a hammer with a mass of 5.0 kg moving at 10 m/sec? (It took 6 blows to drive the spike.) Assume the heat is absorbed equally by the hammer and the spike.

7. How much heat is produced by a 150-watt soldering iron in 30 sec?

8. Victoria Falls is 108 m high. Calculate the difference in temperature between the water at the top of the falls and the water at the bottom of the falls.

9. A 50-kg child coasts down a hill on a 10-kg sled. The hill is 80 m long and falls 2 m for every 10 m of its length. The speed at the bottom of the hill

is 15 m/sec. (a) How much heat was produced by the friction between the sled runners and the snow when coasting down the hill? (b) The steel runners have a specific heat of 0.11 cal/g-C°. Assume that half the heat goes into the runners. What is the increase in temperature of the runners if they represent 2 kg of the sled's mass?

PROJECTS

1. Twist a piece of wire (a coathanger wire) back and forth until it breaks. Touch the broken end of the wire with a finger.
2. If you have a waterfall near your school, measure the temperature of the water at the top and the bottom of the falls. You will need a good thermometer for this.
3. Put some dry sand in an empty coffee can. Measure the temperature of the sand. Then cover the can and shake it for two or three minutes. Measure the temperature of the sand again.
4. Work is the means by which energy changes form or place. Mechanical energy can be changed to heat energy. Fill two mixing bowls half full of water. Measure the temperature of the water in each bowl. Then, using a mixer, beat the water in one of the bowls for a few minutes. Compare the temperatures of the water in the two bowls again. What kind of energy results from the work done on the water?

READINGS

Brown, Sanborn C., *Count Rumford*. New York, Doubleday & Co., Inc., 1962.

MacDonald, D. K. C., *Near Zero: The Physics of Low Temperature*. New York, Doubleday and Co., Inc., 1961.

Posin, Dan Q., *Doctor Posin's Giants*. New York, Harper and Row Publishers, Inc., 1961.

Sandfort, John F., *Heat Engines: Thermodynamics in Theory and Practice*. (Science Study Series). New York, Doubleday and Co., Inc., 1962.

Wheatley, John C., "Superfluid Phases of Helium Three." *Physics Today,* February, 1976.

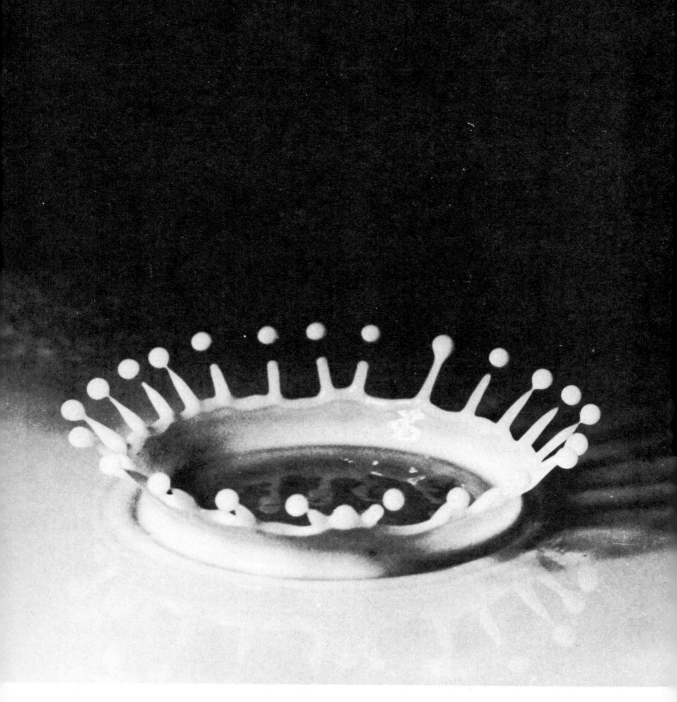

What is matter made of. Why does it behave the way it does? The kinetic theory attempts to explain the nature and behavior of the three common states of matter — solid, liquid, and gas. For example, it helps us understand how water can exist in all three states in nature. It also helps us understand how water changes from one state to another. Note the shapes formed by this splashing milk. Using the kinetic theory, how can you explain their formation?

KINETIC THEORY

Gold and silver are easily shaped and bent. In contrast, chalk breaks when an attempt is made to bend it. Water and alcohol mix readily with one another. However, water and salad oil separate into layers after mixing. In general, an increase in temperature causes materials to expand. Usually, gases expand more than liquids, and liquids expand more than solids with a given change in temperature. All of these properties can be understood if certain assumptions are made about matter.

GOAL: You will gain knowledge and understanding of the kinetic theory and will interpret some common physical phenomena in terms of this theory.

14:1 Assumptions of the Kinetic Theory

The **kinetic theory** of matter forms the basis of our understanding of heat. The three basic assumptions of the kinetic theory are
1. All matter is made up of very small particles.
2. These particles are in constant motion.
3. A mutual force of attraction acts between particles of the same kind. These forces are called **cohesive forces**. Cohesive forces are sometimes called van der Waals forces. Cohesive forces are strongest in solids, strong in liquids, and weak in gases.

There is much evidence to support these assumptions. For example, the evaporation of water gives us a clue to the nature of matter. Water placed in an open dish for a few days will slowly evaporate. Only if the water is made up of many tiny particles could water evaporate in this way.

The kinetic theory explains many aspects of the behavior of matter.

Cohesion is the attraction between particles of the same kind.

193

FIGURE 14-1. A model of Brownian motion. The time intervals between successive positions of the particles are the same.

Brownian motion provides evidence that particles are in constant motion.

William Maddox

FIGURE 14-2. Objects have shapes because forces hold their particles together in position.

The motion of particles can be detected by a method first used by the biologist Robert Brown in 1827. Brown suspended pollen grains in a drop of water. He then observed them under a microscope. He found that the grains moved in a strange zigzag way. This motion can be explained as follows. Water molecules constantly collide with pollen grains. Each time a grain is struck by water molecules in such a way that there is a net force acting on the grain, the grain changes its motion. Further evidence of the motion of particles is the detection of odors. The odor of perfume spreads throughout a room in a very short time. Therefore, perfume must consist of tiny particles which move very fast.

The third assumption of the kinetic theory follows from the first two assumptions. If matter is made of particles, some force must hold the particles together. Otherwise, objects would not have a shape. All materials would just drift apart. From experience, we know this does not happen. Thus, there must be forces holding the particles together.

14:2 Thermal Expansion of Matter

Most materials expand when heated and contract when cooled. The expansion of solids, liquids, and gases can be understood in terms of the kinetic theory. Consider a fluid. A **fluid** is any material which flows. Both gases and liquids are fluids. The particles of a fluid collide more often and more violently when the fluid is heated. At higher temperatures, the particles rebound greater distances after collisions. Thus, a fluid expands when heated.

Because liquids and gases flow, they are both considered to be fluids.

There is a second reason for the expansion of fluids. In fluids, the particles are free to move throughout the substance. Consider what happens when a particle passes a second particle. A force of attraction exists between the two particles. If the two particles pass each other at high speed, this force of attraction has less time to be effective. Suppose the temperature of a fluid is raised. Then, the particles move faster. When the particles

Cohesive forces are less effective on fast-moving particles. Thus, fluids expand when heated.

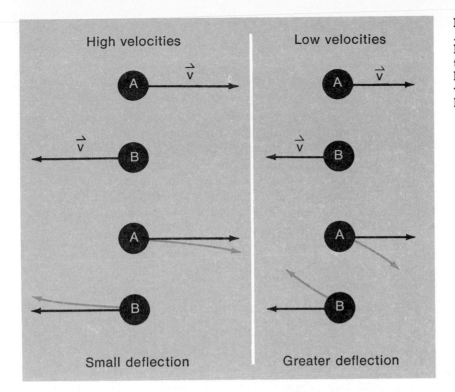

High velocities   Low velocities

Small deflection   Greater deflection

FIGURE 14-3. As molecule A passes molecule B at a high velocity, the attractive force between them is less effective than it is when the velocity of A is low.

move faster, the force of attraction between particles becomes less effective and the substance tends to expand. On the other hand, suppose the temperature of the fluid is lowered. Then, the particles move more slowly. When the particles move more slowly, the force of attraction between particles becomes more effective and the fluid contracts.

Fluids expand when heated and contract when cooled.

In solids, the particles are not free to move about. Instead, they vibrate about fixed positions. When the solid is heated, the particles vibrate more violently and move farther away from their

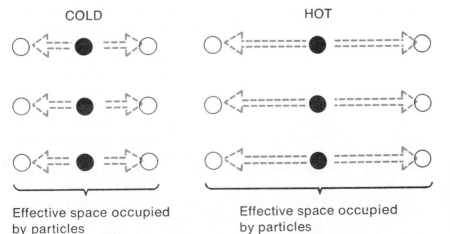

COLD   HOT

Effective space occupied by particles   Effective space occupied by particles

FIGURE 14-4. Molecules vibrate more vigorously and move farther from their fixed positions in hot solids than in cold solids.

A solid expands when heated because its particles move farther from their centers of vibration.

Convection currents in fluids are a result of the combined effects of gravity and difference in density.

centers of vibration. This motion causes expansion of the solid. You can observe evidence of expansion and contraction caused by heating and cooling every day. Telephone wires expand in the summer and sag. They contract in the winter and do not sag between poles. Sections of railroad track contract and have more spaces between them in the winter than in the summer. Water in a pan filled to the brim will expand and overflow when heated.

A practical application of the expansion and contraction of gases and liquids is found in systems for heating buildings. The air directly around a radiator expands as it is heated. In this way, it becomes less dense than the cool air above it. The warm air

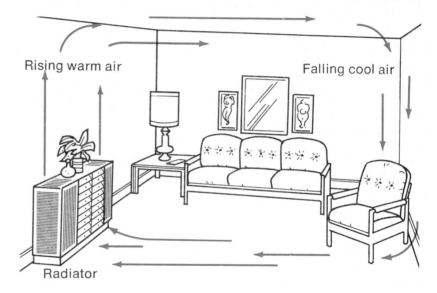

Rising warm air   Falling cool air

Radiator

FIGURE 14-5. The air in a room can be warmed by a radiator and circulated by convection currents.

FIGURE 14-6. The bimetallic strip in a thermostat completes and breaks an electric circuit as it cools and warms.

John Morgan

rises and the cool air moves in to take its place. This results in circulation of air. This kind of movement resulting from density difference and gravity is called a **convection current.** Through convection currents, air in a room may be quickly warmed.

Different materials expand at different rates. In general, the expansion rates of gases and liquids are larger than those of solids. Engineers must consider these different expansion rates in designing structures. Steel bars are often used to reinforce concrete. These bars must expand at the same rate as the concrete. Otherwise, the structure may crack on a hot day. Bridges must be built with special joints to allow for expansion and contraction with temperature changes. For a similar reason, a dentist must use filling materials that expand and contract at the same rate as a tooth.

Sometimes, different rates of expansion are useful. Engineers have taken advantage of these differences to construct a useful device called a **bimetallic** (by muh TAL ik) **strip**. A bimetallic

strip consists of two different metals. These strips are either welded or riveted together. Usually, one strip is brass and the other is iron. When heated, brass expands more than iron. Thus, when the bimetallic strip of brass and iron is heated, the brass strip becomes longer than the iron strip. In this case, the bimetallic strip bends with the brass on the outside of the curve. If the bimetallic strip is cooled, it will bend in the opposite direction. Then the bimetallic strip bends with the brass on the inside of the curve. In this way, the bimetallic strip can be used to make and break electric contacts.

Thermostats that are used in the home usually contain a bimetallic strip. The bimetallic strip is arranged so that it bends toward an electric contact as the room cools. When the room cools below the setting on the thermostat, the bimetallic strip

FIGURE 14-7. This bimetallic strip bends when heated. A coiled bimetallic strip is used to operate a thermostat.

A bimetallic strip consists of two metal strips that expand and contract at different rates. Thus, a bimetallic strip bends when heated or cooled.

FIGURE 14-8. To allow for changes in length with changes in temperature, small spaces have been left between the sections of this train rail.

bends enough to make electric contact with the switch which turns on the heater. As the room warms, the bimetallic strip bends the other direction. The electric contact is broken and the heater is switched off.

14:3 Surface Tension

The cohesive force between like molecules leads to an effect known as **surface tension**. A liquid is made up of molecules that attract each other. Beneath the surface of the liquid (Figure 14-9) each molecule is attracted equally in all directions by neighboring molecules. The result is that there is no net force acting on any of the molecules beneath the surface. At the surface, however, the molecules are attracted to the side and downward, but not upward. Thus, there is a net downward force acting on the top several molecular layers. This net force tends to increase the density of the surface layer. Thus, the net force causes the surface layers to act as a film. Water bugs can stand on the surface of quiet pools of water because of surface tension. The surface tension of water also supports an object such as a steel sewing

Surface tension results from the unbalanced force on the surface molecules of a liquid.

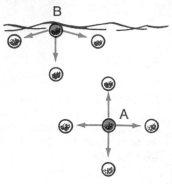

FIGURE 14-9. The net downward force on molecule B draws the surface molecules together.

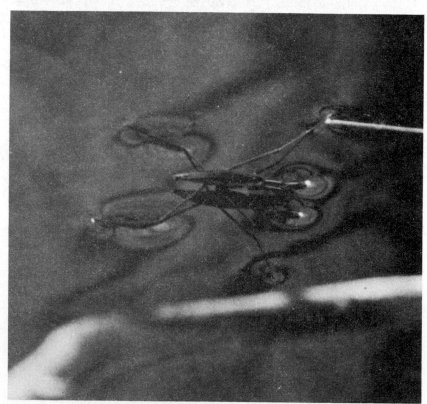

FIGURE 14-10. Bugs can stand on the surface of water because of surface tension.

Sharon Kurgis

FIGURE 14-11. Because of surface tension, water stands in droplets on these leaves.

needle even though the density of steel is seven times greater than that of water.

Surface tension also accounts for the tendency of unconfined liquids to form drops. The force pulling the surface molecules into the liquid causes the surface to become as small as possible. The shape that has the least surface for a given volume is a sphere. Notice that a small drop of water tends to form a sphere when placed on a smooth surface. However, the water droplet usually tends to flatten out. Liquid mercury has a much stronger cohesive force between its molecules than water does. Thus, small amounts of mercury form spherical drops even when placed on a smooth surface.

On the other hand, liquids such as alcohol or ether have very weak cohesive forces between their molecules. A drop of either of these liquids flattens when placed on a smooth surface. These two liquids also evaporate quickly because the forces between their molecules are weak. A liquid which evaporates quickly is called a **volatile** (VAHL uht uhl) liquid.

A force similar to cohesion is **adhesion**. Adhesion is the attractive force that often acts between the molecules of different substances. If a glass tube with a small bore is placed in water, the water will rise inside the tube. The water rises because the adhesive force between glass and water molecules is stronger than the force between water molecules. The water will rise in the tube until its weight counteracts the difference in forces. This phenomenon is called **capillary action**. A tube of small bore has a larger surface area per unit volume than a tube of large bore. Thus, the adhesive force is more effective in the tube of small bore. In this way, water rises higher in a small-bore tube than in one of large bore.

Oil rises in the wick of a lamp because of capillary action. Paint moves up through the bristles of a brush for the same reason. It is also capillary action that causes water to move up through the soil to the roots of plants.

A volatile liquid has weak cohesive forces between its molecules.

Adhesion is the attraction between molecules of different substances.

Capillary action occurs when adhesive forces are stronger than cohesive forces.

FIGURE 14-12. Because of capillary action, sap rises in these maple trees which are being tapped for maple syrup production.

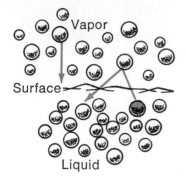

FIGURE 14-13. The vapor above a liquid slows the rate of evaporation.

The cooling effect of evaporation occurs because the molecules which escape from the liquid are those with the highest KE.

During condensation, a liquid absorbs a vapor molecule, and the average KE of the liquid increases.

FIGURE 14-14. The boiling point of water in a pressure cooker (a) and in an autoclave (b) can be raised well above 100° C by increasing the pressure inside the containers.

14:4 Vaporization

The molecules in a liquid state move about in a random way. Some are moving rapidly while others are moving slowly. The temperature of the liquid is a measure of the average speed of the molecules. Suppose a fast-moving molecule is near the surface of the liquid. If it is moving in a certain direction, it can break through the tightly-packed surface layers and escape from the liquid. Since there is a net downward cohesive force at the surface, only the faster moving or more energetic molecules can escape. Each time a molecule escapes from the liquid, the average kinetic energy of the molecules remaining in the liquid decreases. Thus, the temperature of the liquid is lowered. This effect is known as the cooling effect of evaporation.

The cooling effect of evaporation is easily demonstrated. Pour some rubbing alcohol into the palm of your hand. Alcohol molecules have weak cohesive forces with a resulting low surface tension. Alcohol molecules therefore evaporate easily. The cooling effect is quite noticeable.

The opposite process is also true. Vapor molecules near the surface of a liquid may fall on the surface and be absorbed by the liquid. This process is called **condensation** (kahn duhn SAY shuhn). Each time a vapor molecule is absorbed by the liquid, the average kinetic energy of the liquid is increased. Thus, the temperature of the liquid is increased. This effect is known as the warming effect of condensation.

An increase in pressure above a liquid makes it more difficult for a molecule to escape from the liquid. Thus, increased pressure means that the molecules need a higher kinetic energy to escape.

Mirro Aluminum Company

William Maddox

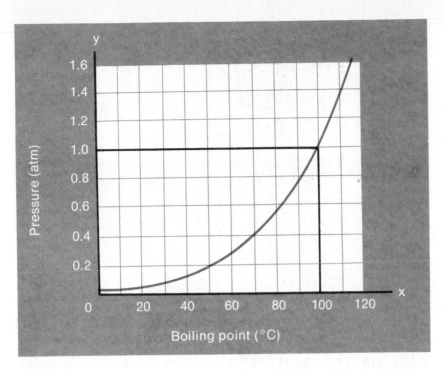

FIGURE 14-15. This vapor-
ization curve for water
shows how the boiling
point varies with pressure.

Under increased pressure, a liquid must reach a higher temperature before boiling takes place. When a liquid boils, fast moving
molecules form vapor pockets. Then the pockets of vapor leave
the liquid as a whole. At the boiling point, the pressure inside
these pockets is equal to the pressure above the liquid.

At normal atmospheric pressure, water boils at 100° C. If the
pressure above water is decreased, boiling occurs at lower temperatures. To demonstrate this (Figure 14-16), place a small container of warm water inside a bell jar. The bell jar is attached
to a vacuum pump. Slowly remove air from the jar with a
vacuum pump. As the pressure is lowered, the water boils, even
though its temperature is less than 100° C.

A pressure increase reduces
the chance for molecules to
escape from a liquid. Thus,
boiling occurs at higher temperatures when pressure is
raised.

A pressure decrease makes it
easier for molecules to escape.
Thus, boiling occurs at lower
temperatures when pressure is
lowered.

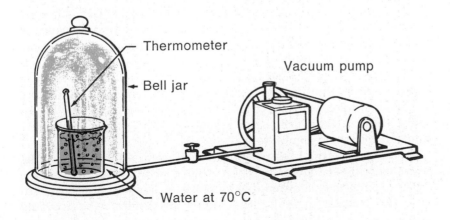

FIGURE 14-16. Water boils
at low temperatures when
the pressure is decreased.

FIGURE 14-17. Ice crystals (a) have an open lattice structure. Fluorite (b) forms an octehedron and potassium chloride (c) forms a cube.

Optovac, Inc.

Optovac, Inc.

14:5 The Solid State

When a liquid freezes, the particles of the liquid are no longer able to move about freely. As the particles of a liquid slow down, the cohesive forces between them become more effective (Section 14:2). This causes the particles to assume more stable positions. The particles in a solid do not stop moving completely. Instead, each particle vibrates about a set position. The position of each particle is affected by the cohesive forces around it. Particles of the same material have similar cohesive attractions for one another. Therefore, the particles in a solid often take a uniform arrangement in relation to one another. In this way crystals are formed. Examples of materials with interesting crystal structures are snowflakes and diamonds.

In a solid, each particle vibrates about a set position.

As a liquid freezes, its particles usually fit more closely together than they do in the liquid state. Water is an exception. Because of the crystalline structure, water particles in the solid state take up more space than they do as a liquid. Thus, water expands as it freezes. If water contracted as it froze, ice would have a higher density than water and would sink in water. Lakes and rivers would freeze from the bottom up. In summer, the water above the ice would act as an insulator. Many lakes and rivers would never thaw completely.

The crystalline structure of some solids is a result of similar cohesive forces between particles.

Unlike most liquids, water expands as it freezes.

An increase in the pressure on the surface of a liquid forces the particles closer together. Then the cohesive forces become stronger. For most liquids, an increase in surface pressure will raise the freezing point of the liquid. In general, the freezing

FIGURE 14-18. The expansion and contraction of water as it freezes and melts can cause extensive road damage.

point of a liquid increases as the pressure on the liquid increases. Again, water is the exception. Because water expands as it freezes, an increase in pressure prevents this expansion. The freezing point of water is lowered as the pressure on its surface is increased. Ice skaters make use of this knowledge. Increased pressure from the skate blades causes the ice under the blades to melt. The water that forms acts as a lubricant to make skating easier and faster.

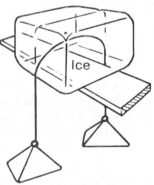

FIGURE 14-19. Because of pressure, ice melts under the blades of this skater and a wire can melt its way through a block of ice.

203

FIGURE 14-20. (a) The nose cone material of a reentry vehicle is tested with plasma. (b) Plasma from the sun extends millions of kilometers into space.

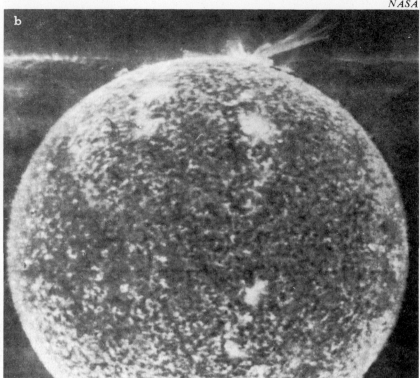

Courtesy of AVCO Corporation

14:6 Plasma

Plasma is the fourth state of matter.

We have studied the three common states of matter—solid, liquid, and gas. There is a fourth state of matter called **plasma.** There is very little plasma on the earth. However, more than 99 percent of the universe is made up of plasma. Stars and much of the space between planets consist of plasma.

In the plasma state, the particles have charges. Atoms have lost one or more of their electrons as a result of energetic collisions. An atom which has lost electrons has a net positive charge and is a positive ion. The electrons are negative particles. Gas that contains more than 5 percent ions is called plasma. By this definition, fluorescent lamps contain plasma.

Plasma is gas that is more than 5% ions.

Ideal plasma, such as the plasma found in stars, consists of electrons and bare nuclei. The plasma then contains a swirling mass of positive ions and electrons. Although the ions themselves are charged, the plasma as a whole has no charge. It contains as many positive charges as negative charges. The main difference between a gas and a plasma is that a plasma can conduct an electric current. A gas cannot conduct an electric current.

A plasma as a whole has no net charge.

Because a plasma contains ions, it can conduct an electric current.

The surface of the sun consists of a glowing mass of plasma at temperatures in excess of 6000° C. Plasma is not limited to the sun's surface. Plasma from the sun extends for millions of miles into space. The earth is actually inside the sun's sphere of plasma. This plasma is mainly hydrogen plasma that leaves the sun and makes up the solar wind. The solar wind speeds by the earth at a rate of 1 500 000 km/hr.

At the extreme temperatures in a star, hydrogen plasma fuses to form helium nuclei. This process is called **nuclear fusion**. Nuclear fusion is the source of all the sun's radiant energy. A small part of this radiant energy reaches the earth.

An example of nuclear fusion is the combining of hydrogen nuclei to form helium nuclei.

In about 10 billion years, the sun will run out of hydrogen fuel. Then, its helium will collapse under gravitational forces and higher temperatures will result. At these higher temperatures a new series of fusion reactions will take place. Heavier elements will then be formed. Vast amounts of energy will be released. This event may result in enough radiant pressure to cause a violent explosion. The sun could become a **nova**. A nova is a large bright star which lasts for a few days or weeks and then fades away.

A nova is a large bright star which lasts for only a few days or weeks.

A nova leaves behind a very dense central core called a **neutron star**. Neutron stars result from the gravitational collapse of the original star. Usually they are only a few kilometers wide and have densities 10^{14} times that of the sun. The neutrons are formed as electrons and protons are pressed together during the collapse. Neutrons have no charge. Therefore, they can be compacted much more than normal nuclei. The density of the star becomes huge.

A neutron star results when a star collapses.

Since momentum is always conserved, a neutron star must maintain a constant angular momentum. Therefore, the mass that collapses into the center of the star must rotate faster and faster as it nears the center. This high rate of rotation causes neutron stars to emit radio waves with great regularity. For this reason, some neutron stars are also called **pulsars**. The first detection of a pulsar led astronomers to believe that they had detected signals from outer space.

Pulsars are neutron stars which emit radio pulses at extremely regular rates.

Stars of huge mass create neutron stars of unbelievable density. These stars are called **black holes**. The gravitational field of a black hole is so great that not even light can leave the star. In order to escape from a black hole, an object would have to be traveling faster than the speed of light. Black holes cannot be "seen." Instead, they are detected by their effects on nearby stars.

Black holes are neutron stars of huge density. They cannot be "seen" because of their extremely large gravitational field.

14:7 Electric Resistance and Superconductivity

The transfer of electric energy from place to place requires the use of conductors. Good conductors have low resistance to electron flow. Metallic solids such as copper and aluminum are good conductors.

Under normal conditions, all electric conductors show some resistance to electron flow. Thus, some of the energy developed by an electric generator must be used to force electrons through conducting wires. The energy used in this way does not appear as electric energy.

One theory that attempts to explain electric resistance is based on the kinetic theory and its assumption that the particles of a substance are in constant motion. In Figure 14-21, electrons are shown as flowing through the crystalline lattice of a metallic conductor. Suppose nothing hinders the movement of the electrons through the space between the atoms that make up the lattice. In this case, the electrons would move through the conductor without any resistance. In reality, these particles vibrate as they occupy positions in the lattice. Thus, they often move toward the center of the lattice. In this way they hinder the flow of electrons through the conductor. According to the kinetic theory, vibration of atoms in the lattice results in resistance in electric conductors.

FIGURE 14-21. Vibration of particles in a lattice causes resistance to electron flow through the lattice.

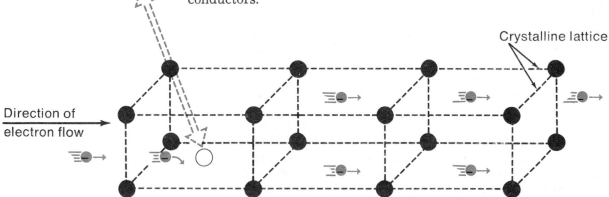

Crystalline lattice

Direction of electron flow

From this explanation, it follows that temperature should affect the electric resistance of a conductor. If the solid is heated, its particles will vibrate more energetically. Then they will move farther away from their centers of vibration. Thus, the particles will hinder the electron flow more effectively. In this way, the electric resistance of a wire increases as it is heated. Conversely, cooling a conductor slows the vibration of the particles. Then they interfere less with the electron flow. In this way, the electric resistance of a wire decreases as it is cooled.

When the temperature of certain conductors is reduced to near absolute zero, the particles in the lattice do not vibrate enough to interfere with the electrons. Thus, at very low temperatures, these conductors have zero electric resistance. This property is known as **superconductivity**. When electrons flow through a super-

FIGURE 14-22. Resistance to electron flow in a lattice can result in the production of heat. This principle is used in the operation of an electric hot plate.

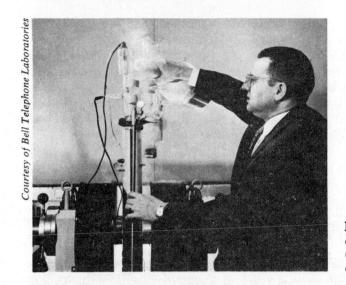

Courtesy of Bell Telephone Laboratories

FIGURE 14-23. A metallurgist pours liquid nitrogen into the apparatus to cool it to -196° C (77° K). He is studying the conductivity of a tin alloy at this temperature.

conductor, there is zero energy loss. A current introduced into a superconductive circuit will flow around the circuit indefinitely.

Some materials are superconductors at temperatures higher than absolute zero. A few materials become superconductive at about 20° K. Much research is being done to develop materials that will be superconductors at still higher temperatures. Such materials could lead to large increases in available electric energy.

When certain conductors are cooled to near absolute zero, they become superconducting.

14:8   Studying the Unobservable

We have used the assumptions of the kinetic theory to explain different behaviors of matter. Scientists have not yet been able to construct a device that will allow us to directly observe the behavior of particles that make up matter.

The kinetic theory appears to be correct because it consistently provides a good explanation of the behavior of matter. Some scientists call this testing process an "if—then" process. *If* matter is made up of particles that attract one another, *then* liquids should display surface tension. We do observe surface tension in liquids. Thus, the theory passes the test. *If* any uniform substance is made up of similar particles, *then* solids should assume regular crystalline arrangements just as marbles in a jar assume a regular arrangement. Solids do form crystalline arrangements, and the theory again passes a test.

The "if—then" process is an inference process. It is useful whenever we want to study behavior that we cannot observe directly. For example, we cannot observe directly the planetary systems orbiting distant stars. The light from a star interferes

The kinetic theory has been tested and observable phenomena consistently agree with the predictions of the kinetic theory.

with any dim light which might be reflected from any of its orbiting planets. But *if* there are planets near a star, *then* the star should wobble a bit from the gravitational attraction of its planets as it moves through space. Some stars do wobble slightly. Their wobbling is evidence that the planets we cannot observe directly are really there. In the same way, the inference process has been applied to the unobservable atom. Thus, we have been able to learn indirectly much about atomic structure.

SUMMARY

The kinetic theory helps us understand the behavior of matter. The three basic assumptions of this theory state that matter is made up of minute particles, that these particles are constantly in motion, and that they have a mutual force of attraction. The force of attraction between like molecules is called cohesive or van der Waals forces. The force of attraction between unlike molecules is called adhesion. Adhesion is responsible for capillary action of many liquids.

The kinetic theory accounts for the thermal expansion of matter, surface tension, capillary action, the cooling effect of evaporation, crystalline structure of solids, the resistance of electric conductors and many other phenomena.

The three common states of matter on the earth are solid, liquid, and gas. The fourth state of matter is plasma. Plasma is very rare on the earth. However, it makes up a large part of the universe including stars. The ideal plasma consists of free electrons and atomic nuclei stripped of all orbiting electrons. While plasma is made up of charged particles, plasma as a whole is neutral. Plasma can conduct electricity.

Some things cannot be studied directly. Thus, it becomes necessary to study them indirectly. These things are often studied by an "if—then" process. This process is an inference process.

QUESTIONS

1. How do forest fires sometimes destroy metal sections of railroad tracks?
2. Why does the pressure inside a container filled with a gas increase if its temperature increases?
3. If two baseballs collide in midair, much of their kinetic energy is changed to heat, and the balls become warmer but move more slowly. Why do two molecules of a gas not lose energy in the same way when they collide?
4. A razor blade is much denser than water. Yet, it can be made to float on the surface of water. Explain.
5. Denver, Colorado, has the highest altitude of any major city in the United States. Why are pressure cookers widely used in Denver?
6. A drop of water, a drop of mercury, and a drop of naphtha (lighter fluid) are placed on a smooth, flat surface. The water and the mercury take a definite shape. The naphtha spreads out over the surface. What does this tell you about the cohesive forces between naphtha molecules? Explain why naphtha vaporizes readily.
7. Use your answer to Question 6 to explain why naphtha has a low freezing point.
8. In what way does a plasma differ from a gas? What portion of the universe consists of plasma?
9. How is a neutron star formed?

10. What is a "black hole" in space? Explain why black holes cannot be seen.
11. Why does the resistance of electric conductors increase when they are heated?
12. Does a power company make more money in the summer or the winter? Explain.
13. Explain why electric companies do not use superconductors to transmit power to their customers.

PROBLEMS

1. New 20-m lengths of railroad track are installed on a winter day when the temperature is $0°$ C. A meter of steel expands 1×10^{-5} m when the temperature increases 1 C°. If summer temperatures reach $35°$ C, what minimum distance must be left between each length of track?
2. A meter of brass expands at the rate of 2×10^{-5} m/C°. What is the increase in the length of a 50-m brass rod if it is heated from $20°$ to $50°$ C?
3. An icicle 0.80 m long is heated from $-30°$ C to $-10°$ C. If a meter of ice expands at a rate of 5×10^{-5} m/C°, what is the new length of the icicle?
4. Using the vaporization curve of Figure 14-15, state the pressure under which water will boil at:
   (a) $80°$ C   (b) $60°$ C   (c) $45°$ C   (d) $20°$ C
5. Assume that a quasar converts 5×10^5 kg of mass to radiant energy each second. Using the equation $E = mc^2$, find the energy in joules released each second by the quasar. (Recall that $c = 3 \times 10^8$ m/sec.)
6. A 100-watt light bulb produces about 15 J of radiant energy each second. How many 100-watt light bulbs would be needed to produce the same radiant energy as the quasar of Problem 5?
7. A major manufacturer of light bulbs can produce 10 000 light bulbs per day. How many years would it take for this manufacturer to produce enough light bulbs to equal the brilliance of the quasar of Problem 5?

PROJECTS

1. Bring a "lava-lamp" to class and turn it on. Observe the "lava." Explain why the lava takes the shape of spheres as it rises.
2. Place a double-edged razor blade carefully on the surface of some water in a saucer. Explain why it is possible for the razor blade to float.
3. Put some water in a dish and place a toothpick on the water. Now remove the toothpick and rub a little soap on one of its ends. Put the toothpick back on the surface of the water. Explain your observations.

READINGS

Holden, Alan, *The Nature of Solids*. New York, Columbia University Press, 1968.

Knight, Charles and Nancy, "Hailstones." *Scientific American*, April, 1971.

Lifshitz, Eugene M., "Superfluidity." *Scientific American*, June, 1958.

Long, Chris, "Superconducting Ring Fluxmeters." *The Physics Teacher*, December, 1975.

Posin, Dan Q., *Doctor Posin's Giants*. New York, Harper and Row Publishers, Inc., 1961.

Smith, Robert A., "Introduction to the Structure of Matter." *The Science Teacher*, December 1969.

Topper, David R., "20th Century Quasars and 17th Century Stars." *The Physics Teacher*, September, 1975.

Trout, Verdine E., "Surface Tension." *The Science Teacher*, October, 1957.

The construction and handling of a parade balloon requires an understanding of the properties of gases. Before this balloon of constant volume was constructed, its volume was carefully planned. Knowing the exact volume of the balloon, engineers then calculated the mass of an air-helium mixture needed to inflate the balloon to capacity at a given temperature. What factors must be taken into consideration in filling this balloon at different times of the year?

THE GAS LAWS chapter 15

Gas particles are distributed evenly throughout an enclosed container. Therefore, the volume of a gas is the volume of the container that encloses it. Three quantities are necessary to describe the condition of any given sample of a gas. These quantities are temperature, pressure, and volume. A change in one of these quantities always results in a change in at least one of the others.

GOAL: You will gain knowledge and understanding of the gas laws and will become familiar with some of their applications.

Three quantities describe the condition of a gas — temperature, pressure, and volume.

15:1 Standard Pressure

Pressure is defined as force per unit area. Pressure units are force units divided by area units, such as N/m^2. Standard atmospheric pressure at sea level is 1.01×10^5 N/m^2 or one **atmosphere** (atm). Ten atmospheres (10 atm) indicates a pressure of (10) $(1.01 \times 10^5$ $N/m^2)$, or 1.01×10^6 N/m^2. One tenth of an atmosphere (0.1 atm) indicates a pressure of $(0.1)(1.01 \times 10^5$ $N/m^2)$, or 1.01×10^4 N/m^2.

There are several ways to measure atmospheric pressure. The most common method relates atmospheric pressure to the height of the column of mercury that it supports. Figure 15-1a shows a glass tube, 1000 mm in length, completely filled with mercury. The tube is inverted and placed in a dish of mercury. The mercury in the tube falls until the column of mercury reads 760 mm. A vacuum, or zero pressure, is created in the tube above the mercury. The pressure on the mercury in the dish is atmospheric pressure. The difference in the pressures supports the column of mercury. Normal atmospheric pressure supports a column of mercury 760 mm (76 cm) high. Thus, standard atmospheric pressure is referred to as 760 millimeters (mm) of mercury.

Pressure is force per unit area.

Normal atmospheric pressure (1 atmosphere) supports a 760 mm-high column of mercury.

211

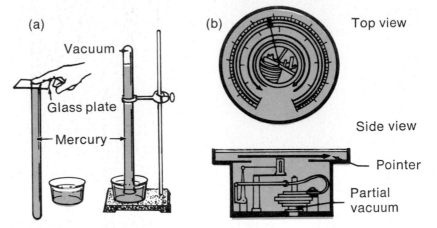

(a)

Vacuum

Glass plate

Mercury

(b)   Top view

Side view

Pointer

Partial
vacuum

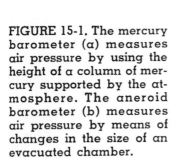

FIGURE 15-1. The mercury barometer (a) measures air pressure by using the height of a column of mercury supported by the atmosphere. The aneroid barometer (b) measures air pressure by means of changes in the size of an evacuated chamber.

An increase in air pressure causes the pressure on the mercury in the dish to increase. Thus, the height of the mercury column in the tube must also increase. A decrease in air pressure causes the height of the mercury column in the tube to decrease. Therefore the height of mercury in the tube is a measure of atmospheric pressure.

A mercury barometer is large and awkward to handle. For this reason an aneroid (AN uh royd) barometer (Figure 15-1b) is often used to measure pressure. An aneroid barometer consists of a metal "can" that contains a vacuum. When the air pressure changes, the top of the can is displaced slightly. A needle is attached to the top of the can. Because the top of the can moves when air pressure changes, this needle can be used to indicate the air pressure. The scale of the barometer is usually calibrated in millimeters of mercury.

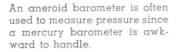

An aneroid barometer is often used to measure pressure since a mercury barometer is awkward to handle.

15:2 Boyle's Law

Figure 15-2a shows a gas-filled cylinder. A 1-kg mass rests on the piston. This mass exerts a force on the piston which in turn exerts pressure on the gas. Gas molecules collide with the underside of the piston. These collisions produce an upward pressure on the piston. Even a small sample of gas has a large number of molecules. Thus, many collisions take place between the gas molecules and the piston in any given instant. The fact that there are many collisions guarantees (statistically) that the number of collisions taking place at any given instant is constant. Therefore, the upward pressure on the underside of the piston is constant.

In Figure 15-2b, two 1-kg masses are placed on the piston. Now the piston produces twice the pressure on the gas as it did in Figure 15-2a. Molecular collisions account for the gas pressure on the underside of the piston. In this case, twice as many

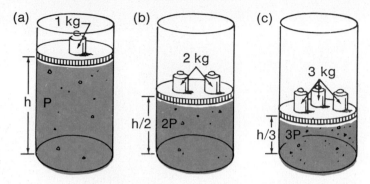

FIGURE 15-2. The volume of a gas decreases as the pressure applied to it increases.

collisions per second must act on the underside of the piston before equilibrium is regained. Twice as many collisions per second will occur if the piston sinks to half its previous distance from the bottom of the cylinder. With the piston in this new position, the distance each molecule travels between collisions is reduced to one-half its former value. With only half the distance to travel, the molecules strike the underside of the piston twice as often. These collisions result in twice as much pressure on the piston.

Following this line of reasoning, three times the pressure on the top of the piston pushes the piston down to one-third its original height (Figure 15-2c). Four times the pressure pushes the piston down to one-fourth its original height. Thus, the kinetic theory predicts **Boyle's law:** *the volume occupied by a gas varies inversely with the applied pressure.* Therefore, the product of volume and pressure is a constant.

Boyle's law states that the volume and the pressure of a gas are inversely related.

$$PV = k$$

If P_1 = initial pressure, V_1 = initial volume, P_2 = new pressure, and V_2 = new volume, then

$$P_1V_1 = k \text{ and } P_2V_2 = k$$

Since k is a constant, substitute $k = P_2V_2$ into the first equation.

$$P_1V_1 = P_2V_2$$

Example: Boyle's Law

Under a pressure of 2×10^5 N/m², a confined gas has a volume of 2.6 m³. The pressure acting on the gas is increased to 5×10^5 N/m². The temperature of the gas remains unchanged. What is the volume of the gas?

Solution:

$$P_1V_1 = P_2V_2$$

$$V_2 = \frac{P_1V_1}{P_2}$$

$$= \frac{(2 \times 10^5 \text{ N/m}^2)(2.6 \text{ m}^3)}{5 \times 10^5 \text{ N/m}^2}$$

$$= 1.0 \text{ m}^3$$

Joe Jacques

FIGURE 15-3. The pressure on the air in the lungs of a scuba diver increases as the diver swims deeper into the water. Why must scuba divers avoid rising to the surface of the water too rapidly?

PROBLEMS

1. Pressure acting on 60 m³ of a gas is raised from 1 atm to 2 atm. The temperature is kept constant. What new volume does the gas occupy?

2. Pressure acting on 8.0 m³ of a gas is 20 atm. The pressure is reduced steadily until the volume of the gas is 20 m³. What is the new pressure acting on the gas (a) in atm? (b) in N/m²?

3. A gas occupies a volume of 20.0 liters under a pressure of 1 atm. The pressure is increased to 4 atm. What is the volume of the gas?

4. A volume of 50 m³ of neon gas is compressed until its volume becomes 12.5 m³. The original pressure acting on the gas was 2.0×10^5 N/m². What is the final pressure acting on the gas?

5. An inflated balloon occupies a volume of 2 liters. The balloon is tied with a string and weighted with a heavy stone. What is its volume when it reaches the bottom of a pond 20.8 m deep? Note: One atmosphere of pressure supports a column of water 10.4 m high. Assume the pressure acting on the balloon before it submerges is 1 atm.

6. A helium-filled balloon occupies a volume of 16 m³ at sea level. The balloon is released and rises to a point in the atmosphere where the pressure is 0.75 atm. What is its volume?

7. A helium-filled balloon occupies a volume of 2 m³ at sea level. The balloon then rises to a height in the atmosphere where its volume is 6 m³. What is the pressure at this height?

8. A diver works at a depth of 52 m in fresh water. A bubble of air with a volume of 2 cm³ escapes from his mouthpiece. What is the volume of the same bubble as it breaks the surface of the water? (See note in Problem 5.)

15:3 Charles' Law

Boyle's law assumes that the temperature of a gas remains constant. We will now consider the relationship that exists between the temperature and volume of a gas.

Jacques Charles (1746–1823) discovered that, at constant pressure, all gases expand the same amount for a given temperature change. Charles kept a gas at 0° C under a pressure of 1 atm. He increased its temperature to 1° C and the gas expanded 1/273 of its original volume. He increased the temperature to 2° C. Its volume increased 2/273 of the first volume. At 273° C, the volume was twice the volume at 0° C. Charles obtained similar results when he reduced the temperature of the gas below 0° C. For each Celsius degree below 0° C, the gas reduced 1/273 of its original volume. The discovery has startling implications. In theory, it means that at −273° C a gas would have zero volume. However, a substance does not remain a gas as its temperature is lowered. A point is reached when a phase change occurs and the gas becomes a liquid. Then, a further decrease in temperature causes the liquid to follow a different rate of contraction.

Figure 15-4 plots the volume of a gas against its temperature. The volume of the gas at 0° C is the basic volume. Today, in the laboratory, it is possible to measure most of the data needed to plot such a graph. However, in Charles' day, it was not possible to attain temperatures much below −20° C. Charles extended the line of the graph down to temperatures below −20° C to see what lower limits might be possible. Extending a graph beyond measurable points is called extrapolation. Although extrapolation is not based on precise data, it can provide useful information.

Figure 15-4 indicates that the lowest possible volume of a gas occurs at −273° C. This leads to the conclusion that −273° C is

Charles found that the volume change of a gas per degree Kelvin is 1/273 of its volume at 0°C and 1 atm pressure.

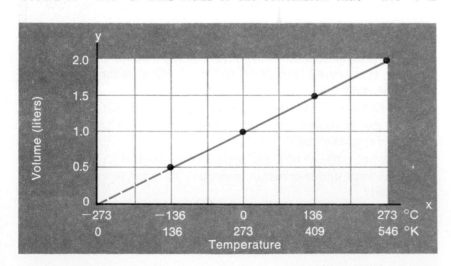

FIGURE 15-4. A graph of the temperature of a gas versus its volume. The straight line indicates that the volume varies directly as the temperature. The constant of proportionality, taken from the slope of the graph, is $\triangle y / \triangle x$. What is the numerical value of the slope of this graph?

the lowest possible temperature. Lord Kelvin chose this point as zero on what is called the Kelvin temperature scale. The temperature $-273°$ C or $0°$ K is called absolute zero.

Through his work with gases, Charles accomplished two things. He postulated the point of absolute zero and found the relationship between the temperature and the volume of a gas. **Charles' law** states that, *under constant pressure, the volume of a gas varies directly with its Kelvin temperature.*

$$\frac{V_1}{V_2} = \frac{T_1}{T_2}$$

In calculations using Charles' law, temperature must be expressed in Kelvin degrees.

Charles' law states that, at constant pressure, the volume and the temperature of a gas are directly related.

When using Charles' law, temperatures must be Kelvin temperatures.

Example: Charles' Law

A volume of 22.0 m³ of nitrogen gas at 20° C is heated under constant pressure to 167° C. What is the new volume of the nitrogen gas?

Solution:

First, change the Celsius temperatures to Kelvin temperatures.

$$T_1 = 20° \text{ C} = 20° + 273° = 293° \text{ K}$$
$$T_2 = 167° \text{ C} = 167° + 273° = 440° \text{ K}$$

Then,

$$\frac{V_1}{V_2} = \frac{T_1}{T_2}$$
$$V_2 = \frac{V_1 T_2}{T_1}$$
$$= \frac{22.0 \text{ m}^3 \times 440° \text{ K}}{293° \text{ K}}$$
$$= 33.0 \text{ m}^3$$

PROBLEMS

9. A volume of 30.0 m³ of argon gas is kept under constant pressure. It is heated from 20° C to 293° C. What is the new volume of the gas?

10. Thirty liters of oxygen gas are kept under constant pressure. The gas is cooled from 20° C to −146.5° C. What is the new volume of the gas?

11. At 60° C, 0.02 m³ of a gas is heated to double its volume. The gas is kept under constant pressure. To what temperature is it heated?

12. A volume of 4 m³ of a gas is kept under constant pressure. Its temperature is increased from 40° C to 140° C. What is the new volume of the gas?

15:4   The General Gas Law

By combining Boyle's law and Charles' law, an equation can be derived which relates pressure, temperature, and volume of a gas.

$$\frac{P_1 V_1}{T_1} = \frac{P_2 V_2}{T_2}$$

This equation is called the **general gas law.** It holds for all gases at moderate pressures. Under high pressures or low temperatures, the law is modified. The general gas law reduces to Boyle's law if the temperature is constant. If the pressure is kept constant, it reduces to Charles' law. If the volume is kept constant, the pressure varies directly with the temperature.

The general gas law relates temperature, pressure, and volume of a gas.

The general gas law reduces to Boyle's law if T is kept constant. It reduces to Charles' law if P is kept constant.

Example: The General Gas Law

Twenty liters of gas are kept under a pressure of 1 atm at a temperature of 273° K. The gas temperature is lowered to 91° K. The pressure is increased to 1.5 atm. What is the new volume?

Solution:

$$\frac{P_1 V_1}{T_1} = \frac{P_2 V_2}{T_2}$$

$$V_2 = \frac{P_1 V_1 T_2}{P_2 T_1}$$

$$= \frac{(1 \text{ atm}) (20 \text{ liters}) (91° \text{ K})}{(1.5 \text{ atm}) (273° \text{ K})}$$

$$= 4.4 \text{ liters}$$

FIGURE 15-5. The weather balloon carrying a variety of measuring devices will rise and drift until the air pressure outside the balloon is so much lower than the gas pressure inside the balloon that the balloon bursts. This scientist uses measurements obtained in this way to learn more about the atmosphere at the South Pole.

Ian Whillans, Institute of Polar Studies, Ohio State University

PROBLEMS

13. Ten cubic meters of hydrogen gas are confined in a cylinder under a pressure of 1 atm at a temperature of 91° K. The volume is kept constant but the temperature is increased to 182° K. What pressure does the gas exert on the walls of the container?

14. Two hundred liters of gas at 0° C are kept under a pressure of 1 atm. The temperature of the gas is raised to 273° C. The pressure is increased to 2 atm. What is the final volume?

15. Fifty liters of gas are kept at a temperature of 200° K and under a pressure of 15 atm. The temperature of the gas is increased to 400° K. The pressure is decreased to 7.5 atm. What is the volume of the gas?

16. One hundred liters of gas are kept under a pressure of 1 atm and at a temperature of 27° C. The pressure on the gas is increased to 4 atm. The temperature is increased to 327° C. What is the new volume of the gas?

SUMMARY   Pressure is force per unit area and is expressed as newtons per square meter. Standard atmospheric pressure is usually measured by the height of the column of mercury that it supports. Standard pressure supports a column of mercury 760 millimeters high.

Boyle's law states that the volume of a gas varies inversely with the applied pressure, provided the temperature remains constant. Charles' law states that the volume of a gas varies directly with its Kelvin temperature, provided the pressure remains constant. The general gas law combines Boyle's law and Charles' law. Kelvin temperatures must always be used in calculations involving gas laws.

QUESTIONS

1. What is standard atmospheric pressure?
2. State Boyle's law.
3. State Charles' law.
4. State the general gas law.
5. Use the general gas law to explain what happens if a gas is heated while its volume is kept constant.
6. The molecules of a gas produce a greater pressure on the walls of a container if the gas is heated. Explain why.
7. Charles' experiments with gases indicated the possible location of absolute zero. Explain.

PROBLEMS

1. Convert to atmospheres: (a) 380 mm of mercury (b) 5.05×10^5 N/m².
2. A bubble of air with a volume of 0.05 cm³ escapes from a pressure hose at the bottom of a tank. The tank is filled with mercury to a height of 6.84 m. What is the volume of the air bubble as it reaches the surface of the mercury? Assume the pressure at the surface which acts on the bubble is 1 atm. The pressure at the bottom of the tank is the pressure due to the mercury plus the pressure at the surface.
3. Pressure acting on 50 cm³ of a gas is reduced from 1.2 atm to 0.3 atm. (a) What is the new volume of the gas? (b) The gas is kept at 0° C

while the pressure is reduced. If the gas resumes its original volume, to what temperature in degrees Celsius is the gas cooled?

4. Pressure acting on a volume of 50 m³ of air is 1.01×10^5 N/m². The air is at a temperature of $-50°$ C. The pressure acting on the gas is increased to 2.02×10^5 N/m². Then the gas occupies a volume of 30 m³. What is the temperature of the air at this new volume?

5. Two cubic meters of a gas at 30° C are heated at constant pressure until the volume is doubled. What is the final temperature of the gas?

6. A cubic meter of gas at standard temperature and pressure is cooled to 91° K. The pressure is not changed. What volume does the gas occupy?

7. A cubic meter of gas at standard temperature and pressure is heated to 364° C. The pressure acting on the gas is kept constant. What volume does the gas occupy?

8. A volume of 10 m³ of carbon dioxide at 27° C is heated to 177° C. The pressure on the gas is kept constant. What is the new volume?

9. A volume of 500 cm³ of air at 0° C is under a pressure of 1.01×10^5 N/m². The pressure acting on it is increased to 2.02×10^5 N/m², and it is heated to 273° C. What volume does the gas occupy?

10. At 40° K, 10 m³ of nitrogen is under 4.00×10^5 N/m² pressure. The pressure acting on the nitrogen is increased to 2.0×10^6 N/m². Its volume remains constant. To what temperature does the nitrogen rise?

11. A balloon contains 200 m³ of helium while on the surface of the earth. Atmospheric pressure is 1.0 atm. Temperature is 20° C. The balloon expands freely and rises to a height where the pressure is only 0.67 atm and the temperature is $-50°$ C. What is the new volume of the balloon?

PROJECTS

1. Ask your school secretary for an empty duplicating fluid can with a cap. Wash the can carefully to remove all traces of duplicating fluid. Put about five centimeters of water in the can and WITH THE CAP REMOVED bring the water to a boil. When steam is coming out of the can, turn off the flame and then screw the cap on tightly. Watch the can for several minutes. Explain your observations.

2. To make a barometer you need a bottle with a narrow neck, a one-hole stopper, and a meter of glass tubing. Bend the tubing over the flame of a Bunsen burner so that it forms a "V" with one leg about 30 cm long and the other about 70 cm long. Keep an angle of about 30° between the legs of the tubing. Fill the bottle with water and add a few drops of food coloring. Place the short end of the glass "V" into the stopper. Put the stopper in the bottle, and invert the bottle. The water should rise halfway in the long leg of the tube. Make a netting from string and hang up your barometer.

   Calibrate your barometer. Take readings from the school barometer. Mark these on a strip of cardboard placed behind the long tube. Weather reports are good sources of barometer readings also. Keep in mind that a barometer of this sort is very sensitive to temperature changes. Thus, it should be kept where the temperature is constant.

READINGS

Bonner, et al, *Principles of Physical Science* (Physics and Physical Science Series). Reading, Mass., Addison-Wesley Publishing Co., Inc., 1971, Chapter 12.

Gamow, George, *One, Two, Three—Infinity* (Science and Mathematics Series). New York, Bantam Books, Inc., 1971.

Hall, Marie, "Robert Boyle." *Scientific American,* August, 1967.

Waves are probably familiar to you. You may have seen them at the beach. You may have observed them traveling along a rope or a metal spring. There are other waves which you have probably observed but not recognized as being waves. All waves have one property in common. All waves transfer energy. What evidence of energy transfer by waves have you observed recently?

WAVES AND ENERGY TRANSFER

There are only two methods by which energy can be transferred between two points. The first method involves the transfer of matter. A falling weight can drive a stake into the ground. Electrons moving through a wire can transfer energy from one place to another.

The second method of energy transfer involves wave motion. All waves transfer energy. Sound waves transfer the energy of a vibrating string of a guitar to your ear. Light waves bring energy from the sun to the earth. Radio waves carry energy from a radio station to your home. Water waves can do tremendous amounts of damage during storms. Waves are a means of transferring energy.

16:1 All Waves Follow the Same Rules

The behavior of all types of waves follows the same general rules. For example, when a water wave is reflected from a barrier, the angle at which the wave is reflected is the same as the angle at which the wave approaches the barrier. Sound waves, light waves, and all other waves are reflected from barriers in exactly the same way. By learning the general rules of wave behavior, you can understand the behavior of all waves.

GOAL: You will gain knowledge and understanding of the general properties of waves.

Energy can be transferred by particles or by waves.

FIGURE 16-1. Different kinds of waves are reflected from barriers according to the law of reflection — the angle of incidence is equal to the angle of reflection.

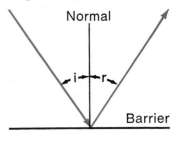

FIGURE 16-2. Scientists are studying ways to preserve shore lines. In an attempt to reduce wave damage to this shore, discarded tires have been joined together to form a wave barrier.

16:2 Mechanical and Electromagnetic Waves

Mechanical waves need a medium.

Mechanical waves need a material medium through which they can travel as they transfer energy. Some examples of mechanical waves are water waves, sound waves, and the waves that travel along a spring or rope. The behavior of most mechanical waves can readily be observed.

Electromagnetic waves do not need a medium.

Electromagnetic waves make up a large and important family of waves. They need no medium to travel through as they transfer energy. Some examples of electromagnetic waves are light waves, radio waves, and X rays. We know that electromagnetic waves are both magnetic and electric in nature, but we cannot observe them directly. An important reason for studying observable mechanical waves is to gain an understanding of electromagnetic waves.

16:3 Transverse and Longitudinal Waves

In a transverse wave, particles vibrate at right angles to the direction of the wave.

There are two general types of waves—transverse waves and longitudinal waves. A **transverse wave** causes the particles of a medium to vibrate perpendicularly to the direction of the wave itself. A water wave is an example of a transverse wave. As a water wave moves forward, it causes water to vibrate up and down. The direction in which the water particles vibrate is perpendicular to the direction of the water wave. Figure 16-3 a shows a transverse wave. The wave moves along the spring. But, the spring vibrates perpendicularly to the motion of the wave.

In a longitudinal wave, particles vibrate parallel to the wave direction.

A **longitudinal wave** causes the particles of a medium to vibrate parallel to the direction of the wave. Figure 16-3 b shows a longitudinal wave. Note that the vibratory motion of the spring is parallel to the direction in which the wave is moving. A sound wave is an example of a longitudinal wave.

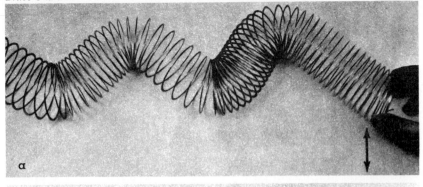

Although the particles of a medium vibrate in response to a passing wave, they do not move along with the wave. The float on a fishing line will bob up and down as waves from a passing motorboat go by, but the float does not move with the wave. After a wave has passed through the spring of Figure 16-3, each coil is where it was before the wave arrived.

A medium vibrates in response to a wave but does not move with the wave.

16:4 Pulses and Waves

A pulse is a single disturbance traveling through a medium (Figure 16-4 a). A pulse can be produced by applying a single sideways movement to one end of a spring. Any point which is undisturbed before the pulse arrives will be undisturbed after

A pulse is a single disturbance in a medium.

(a)

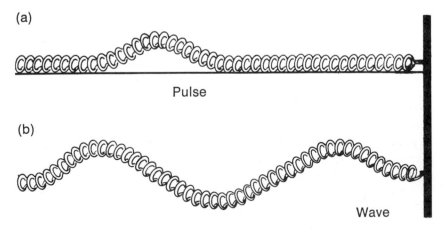

Pulse

(b)

Wave

FIGURE 16-4. Waves and pulses in a long spiral spring.

the pulse passes. Suppose a series of pulses are produced at regular intervals. Then a wave is formed as shown in Figure 16-4b. When a wave passes, a given point vibrates regularly in response to the wave.

A wave is a series of pulses at regular intervals.

16:5   Wave Characteristics

There are several characteristics common to all waves. The positions and motions of points along the wave indicate the phase of the wave. Points that have the same displacement and are moving in the same direction at the same time are said to be in phase. Points *C* in Figure 16-5 are in phase. Points which have opposite displacements and are moving in opposite directions are said to be 180° out of phase. Points *C* and *T* are 180° out of phase.

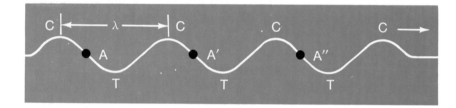

FIGURE 16-5. Points labeled *C* represent wave crests; points labeled *T* represent wave troughs.

Wavelength is the linear distance between corresponding points on consecutive waves.

The **wavelength** (λ) of a wave is the linear distance between corresponding points on consecutive waves. Points *C* of the diagram are crests. Points *T* are troughs. The wavelength of the wave is the distance from one *C* to the next *C*, or one *T* to the next *T*. Points *A* and *A'* are also one wavelength apart. However, points *A* and *A''* are two wavelengths apart.

Frequency is the number of waves which pass a given point per unit time.

The **frequency** of a wave is the number of wavelengths that pass a given point per second. Frequency is measured in hertz (1 hertz = 1 wave/sec).

The velocity of a wave is the product of its frequency and wavelength.

If the wavelength and the frequency of a wave are both known, the **speed** of the wave can be calculated. To do this, multiply the frequency by the wavelength. To understand why the speed of a wave can be found in this way, consider the following example. Each car of a train is 20 meters long. The number of cars that pass a given point each second can be counted. If two cars pass per second, the speed of the train must be 40 m/sec. The length of one railroad car compares to the wavelength of a wave. The number of cars that pass each second is the frequency. The length of each railroad car multiplied by the number of cars per second gives the speed of the train. In the same way, the speed of a wave is frequency times wavelength. The equation is,

$$v = f\lambda$$

Wavelength can be measured in any convenient unit of length.

Example: The Speed of a Wave

Transverse waves traveling along a rope have a frequency of 12 hertz. They are 2.4 m long. What is the speed of the waves?

$$v = f\lambda$$
$$= 12/\text{sec} \times 2.4\,\text{m}$$
$$= 28.8\,\text{m/sec}$$

16:6   Sound Waves

The frequency of a wave is the same as the frequency of the source of the wave. Waves in a spring can be generated by hand. In such a case, the frequency of the wave is determined by the person generating the wave. Sound waves are caused by vibrating objects. Therefore, the frequency of a sound wave is the same as the frequency of the vibrating object.

A vibrating object moves back and forth. As the object moves forward, it compresses the air on one side. When the object moves in the opposite direction, it rarefies the air on this same side. This process continues as the object swings to the other side of the rest (equilibrium) position (Figure 16-6). The positions of greatest compression and rarefaction correspond to the crests and troughs of a transverse wave. Sound waves are longitudinal waves. Sound waves cause particles of the medium to vibrate in the same direction as the movement of the wave.

Sound waves are longitudinal waves generated by vibrating objects.

The frequency of the sound wave is equal to the frequency of the vibrating object.

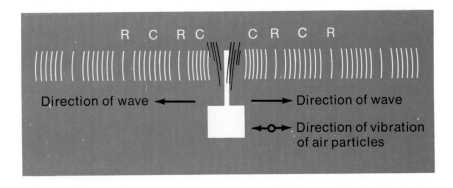

FIGURE 16-6. Sound waves are generated by vibrating objects.

The **period** of a wave is the time required for one wave to pass a given point. The frequency of the wave determines its period. For example, if the frequency of a wave is 10 hertz, ten waves pass a given point per second. Then the time for one wave to pass a given point is 0.1 sec. Thus, the period of a wave is the reciprocal of its frequency.

The period of a wave is the reciprocal of its frequency.

$$T = \frac{1}{f}$$

Example: The Period of a Wave

A sound wave has a frequency of 250 hertz. What is the period of the sound wave?

Solution:

$$T = \frac{1}{f}$$

$$= \frac{1}{250 \text{ hertz}}$$

$$= 0.004 \text{ sec}$$

PROBLEMS

1. Sound waves traveling through air have a frequency of 250 hertz. The sound waves are 1.3 m in length. What is the speed of sound in air?

2. A radio wave has a frequency of 3×10^7 hertz. It is 10 m long. What is the speed of the radio wave?

3. Water waves in a small tank are 6 cm long. They pass a given point at the rate of 4.8 waves per second. What is the speed of the water waves?

4. What is the period of the waves in Problem 3?

5. Microwaves are electromagnetic waves. They travel through space at the rate of 3.0×10^8 m/sec. A microwave has a wavelength of 0.20 m. (a) What is the frequency of the microwave? (b) What is the period of the microwave?

6. A sound pulse is directed toward a vertical cliff 660 m from the source. A reflected pulse is detected 4 sec after the pulse is produced. (a) What is the speed of sound in air? (b) The sound pulse has a frequency of 500 hertz. What is its wavelength? (c) What is the period of the pulse?

7. The speed of sound waves in air is 330 m/sec. A sound wave has a frequency of 500 hertz. (a) What is its wavelength as it travels through air? (b) What is its period?

8. An Angstrom unit is 10^{-10} m. A typical light wave has a wavelength of 5800 Å. (a) What is the length of the light wave in meters? (b) The speed of light is 3.0×10^8 m/sec. What is the frequency of the wave?

16:7   Energy and the Amplitude of a Wave

The amplitude of a wave is its maximum displacement from rest position.

The energy content of a wave is characterized by the wave's amplitude. The **amplitude** of a wave is its maximum displacement from the rest or equilibrium position. Figure 16-7 shows two waves traveling along identical ropes. The two waves have the

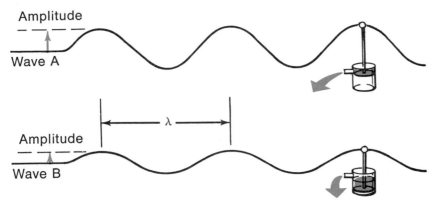

same frequency, velocity, and wavelength. But, their amplitudes are different. The source that generates wave A has the same frequency as the source that generates wave B. But the source that generates wave A puts more energy into the wave. This produces a wave of greater amplitude.

Since wave A has more energy input and a greater amplitude than wave B, wave A transfers more energy. Wave A can do more work than wave B. Suppose that water pumps are attached to each rope. The pumps lift water and transform the wave energy into useful work. Wave A can do more work per unit time than wave B.

The energy content of a wave depends on its amplitude.

16:8   Wave Speed in a Medium

The speed at which waves travel through a medium depends on the properties of that medium. Figure 16-8 shows two waves produced at different times in the same medium. The wavelengths and the frequencies of the waves are different. But their speeds are the same. Wave A has a high frequency and a short wavelength. Wave B has a low frequency and a long wavelength. In both cases, the product of the frequency and the wavelength results in the same speed. It makes no difference what

The speed of a wave depends on the medium.

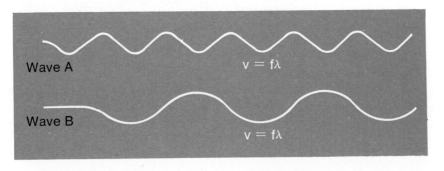

FIGURE 16-8. The speed of a wave depends on the medium in which the wave travels. The product of frequency and wavelength gives the speed.

frequency wave is produced in the medium. The only result of a change in frequency is that the wavelength changes to keep the speed of the wave constant in the medium. The amplitude of the wave also has no effect on its speed. An increase in amplitude of a wave causes it to transfer more energy. But an increase in amplitude does not change the speed of the wave. The medium determines the speed of the waves that pass through.

The speed of light in a vacuum is 3.0×10^8 m/sec. All electromagnetic waves move through space at this speed. In the same way, all sound waves move through air at about 330 m/sec. If all sound waves did not travel at the same velocity in air, musical instruments could not exist. Notes from the same instrument would overtake each other or fall behind their proper sequence. This would produce noise, not music. Fortunately all sound waves do have the same speed in air. Thus, we are able to enjoy music.

All electromagnetic waves travel at 3.0×10^8 m/sec in a vacuum. All sound waves travel at about 330 m/sec in air.

16:9   Behavior of Waves at Boundaries

Transverse waves are easier to draw and visualize than longitudinal waves. Therefore, transverse waves will be used as examples to discuss wave behavior. However, these rules of wave behavior apply to both transverse and longitudinal waves.

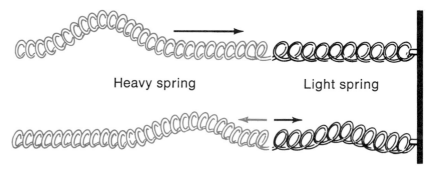

Heavy spring   Light spring

FIGURE 16-9. A pulse reaching a boundary between two media is partially reflected and partially transmitted.

The part of a wave reflected at a boundary depends on the difference between the two media.

When a wave traveling through a medium reaches the boundary of a new medium, part of the wave will be reflected. The other part of the wave will be transmitted into the new medium. The part that is reflected depends on the difference between the two media. If the difference between the two media is slight, the amplitude of the reflected wave is small. This indicates that most of the energy is transmitted.

Consider a spring that is attached to a rigid object, such as a wall. The two media, the spring and the wall, are different from each other. Thus, when the pulse reaches the spring-wall boundary, most of the pulse is reflected. In theory, a small amount of the energy of the pulse does enter the wall. Figure 16-10 shows

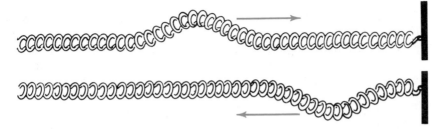

FIGURE 16-10. The pulse that is reflected from the rigid wall returns inverted. Notice that the amplitude of the reflected pulse is nearly equal to the amplitude of the incident pulse.

When a wave is reflected from a more rigid medium, the reflected portion is inverted.

that the amplitude of the reflected pulse is almost equal to the amplitude of the incident pulse. But the pulse is inverted upon reflection from the rigid wall. When a wave is reflected at the boundary of a more rigid medium, it undergoes inversion (180° change in phase).

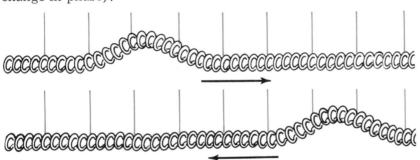

FIGURE 16-11. A pulse reflected from an open-ended boundary returns erect.

When a wave is reflected from a less rigid medium, the reflected wave is erect.

Now consider a spring that is supported by light threads (Figure 16-11). As in Figure 16-10, when a pulse reaches the end of the spring, it passes into a different medium. In this case, the new medium is air. The large difference in the two media causes nearly total reflection of the pulse. Because the pulse is reflected from the boundary of a medium less rigid than the one from which it came, the reflected pulse is erect (no change in phase). When a wave is reflected from the boundary of a less rigid medium, the reflected wave is erect.

In all cases there is a reflected wave at a boundary. The amount of reflected energy depends on the difference in the properties of the two media. A pulse passing from a less rigid medium into a more rigid medium produces a reflected pulse that is inverted. A pulse entering a less rigid medium from a more rigid medium produces a reflected pulse that is erect.

PROBLEMS

9. A long spring passes along the floor of a room and out a door. A pulse is sent along the spring. After a while, an inverted pulse of almost the same amplitude returns along the spring. Is the spring attached to the wall in the next room or is it lying loose on the floor?

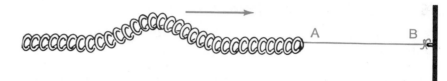

FIGURE 16-12

10. A pulse is sent along a spring (Figure 16-12). The spring is attached to a light thread which ends at a wall. (a) Describe the behavior of the pulse when it reaches A. (b) Is the reflected pulse from A erect or inverted? (c) Describe the behavior of the transmitted pulse when it reaches B. (d) Is the reflected pulse from B erect or inverted?

FIGURE 16-13

11. (a) Describe the behavior of the pulse in Figure 16-13 when it reaches boundary A. (b) Describe the behavior of the transmitted pulse when it reaches boundary B.

12. A light wave leaves a lamp and approaches a glass window. (a) Describe the behavior of the light wave as it is reflected from the surface of the window. (b) Part of the wave enters the window glass and travels through the glass. It is partly reflected again when it reaches the next surface of the glass. Describe the wave that is reflected from this surface.

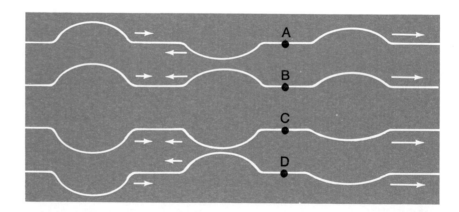

FIGURE 16-14

13. The left side of Figure 16-14 shows a pulse. The right side shows the transmitted pulse and reflected pulse. Describe the boundaries A, B, C, and D.

14. To obtain waves of a longer wavelength, is wave frequency along a rope increased or decreased?

16:10   The Transmitted Wave

The speed at which a wave travels through a medium depends on the medium. When a wave passes into a new medium, it has a different speed. The wave in the new medium is generated directly by the wave in the old medium. Thus, the frequency of the wave in the new medium is exactly the same as the frequency of the wave in the old medium. Because the speed of the transmitted wave changes and the frequency remains the same, the wavelength must change. This is true because $v = f\lambda$. Figure 16-15

When a wave passes into a new medium, its speed changes.

The wave must have the same frequency in the new medium as in the old medium. Thus, the wavelength adjusts so that $v = f\lambda$.

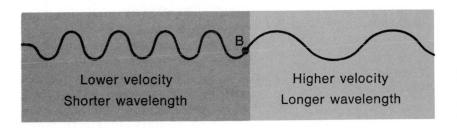

Lower velocity

Shorter wavelength

Higher velocity

Longer wavelength

FIGURE 16-15. The speed and wavelength of a wave change when the wave enters a new medium.

shows a wave passing into a new medium. Since the speed in the new medium is greater, the wavelength is longer. Conversely, if the wave were to pass from the medium on the right to the medium on the left, its speed would be slower in the new medium. Thus, its wavelength would decrease.

16:11   Interference

Suppose two or more waves travel through the same medium at the same time. When the waves meet, their displacements are superimposed. This process is called **interference**. Waves can interfere constructively or destructively.

Figure 16-16 shows the constructive interference of two equal pulses. When pulse a and pulse b meet, a stronger pulse $(a + b)$

When two or more waves meet, their displacements add. This process is called interference.

Constructive interference occurs when two pulses combine to produce a pulse of greater amplitude.

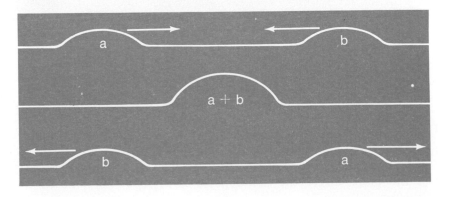

FIGURE 16-16. Constructive interference of two equal pulses.

FIGURE 16-17. Destructive interference of two equal pulses.

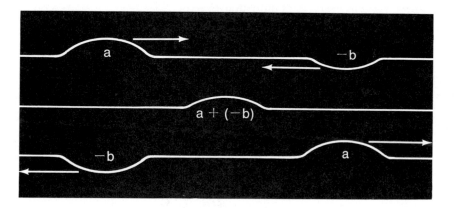

is formed. For an instant, the amplitude of this stronger pulse is the algebraic sum of the amplitudes of the two pulses. Note that once the two pulses have passed through each other, they are completely unaffected and retain their original form.

Figure 16-17 shows the destructive interference of two equal but opposite pulses. When pulse a and pulse b meet, a weaker pulse $(a + (-b))$ is formed. For an instant, the sum of the displacements is zero and the medium is completely undisturbed. At that instant, the combined amplitude is zero. The pulses are not affected permanently by their momentary union. An important characteristic of waves is their ability to pass through one another and not change permanently in any way.

If the pulses that meet are unequal in amplitude, their combined amplitude cannot equal zero (Figure 16-18).

Destructive interference occurs when two pulses combine to produce a pulse with smaller amplitude than either of the original amplitudes.

After two pulses pass through one another, they return to their original form.

FIGURE 16-18. Interference of two pulses with the same wavelength but different amplitudes.

16:12 Nodes

A node is a point in a medium that never undergoes a displacement as waves pass through each other in the medium.

Suppose two pulses have identical shapes but opposite displacements and move toward each other in a medium. When they meet, there will be a point in the medium that is completely unaffected at all times. The point that never undergoes a displacement is called a **node**. A nodal point is shown in Figure 16-19. Notice parts b, c, and d of the diagram. The amplitude of the part of the pulse above the nodal point is always the same as the

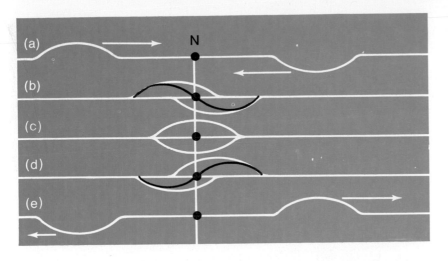

FIGURE 16-19. The nodal point is undisturbed during the meeting of two equal and opposite pulses or waves.

amplitude of the part below the nodal point. Cancellation always takes place at the nodal point during the crossing of the two pulses.

When a wave moving in one direction meets an identical wave moving in the opposite direction, the same process occurs. Nodal points appear all along the path of the waves. Between these nodal points the waves interfere constructively and destructively. Because of the two interfering waves, the medium appears to be vibrating in segments. The result is called a **standing wave.**

A standing wave is the result of identical waves moving in opposite directions.

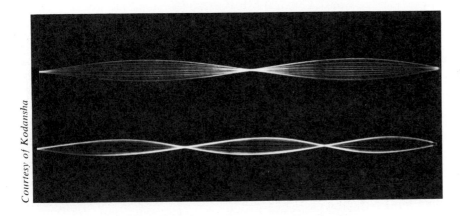

Courtesy of Kodansha

FIGURE 16-20. Standing waves in a string.

16:13 Ripple Tanks

A ripple tank is a shallow, rectangular tank with a glass bottom. When it is filled with water to a depth of one or two centimeters, waves can be produced so that their behavior can be studied. By placing a bright light above the tank, the shadows of the waves can be observed on a screen below the tank.

To produce straight waves along the surface of the water, dip a ruler into the water at the end of the tank. Waves are produced

Ripple tanks are used to study wave behavior.

Eduquip Inc.

FIGURE 16-21. The ripple tank is a useful device for demonstrating wave behavior. Several types of waves and pulses can be generated. This photograph shows two circular waves. The image of the waves is shown on the white paper below the tank.

with a wave generator in most ripple tanks. A ripple tank is useful for observing wave behavior.

16:14 The Law of Reflection

Waves are reflected from a barrier at the same angle at which they approach it. The **law of reflection** states that *the angle of incidence is equal to angle of reflection.*

The law of reflection states that the angle at which a wave approaches a barrier is equal to the angle at which the wave is reflected.

FIGURE 16-22. Reflection of a wave pulse by a barrier. A ray indicates the direction in which the pulse is moving. The angle which the incident ray makes with the normal to the surface is equal to the angle the reflected ray makes with the normal.

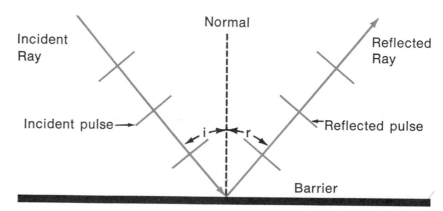

Incident Ray

Normal

Reflected Ray

Incident pulse →

← Reflected pulse

i r

Barrier

Figure 16-22 shows a pulse sent toward a barrier. The direction of the pulse is shown by a line drawn at a right angle to the wave front. This imaginary line is called a **ray**. Wave behavior is often shown by ray diagrams. Ray diagrams show only the directions of the waves. They do not show the actual waves. The use of ray diagrams in the study of light is known as ray optics.

16:15 Refraction of Waves

The speed of a wave depends on the medium through which the wave travels. As a wave travels from one medium into a new medium, the speed of the wave changes.

The behavior of waves as they move from one medium into another can be observed in a ripple tank. The water above a glass plate placed in the tank is more shallow than the water in the rest of the tank. It acts like a different medium.

The speed of waves is greater in deep water than in shallow water. To verify this, place the edge of the glass plate parallel to the advancing wave fronts. Observe the decrease in the wavelength of the waves as they pass into the shallow water. Waves in the shallow water are produced by waves in the deep water. Thus, their frequency is exactly the same as the frequency of the waves in the deep water. Because $v = f\lambda$, the decrease in the wavelength of the waves indicates a lower speed.

When wavefronts approach a boundary parallel to that boundary (Figure 16-23a), they continue straight into the new medium. When wavefronts approach the boundary at an angle (Figure 16-23b), their direction is changed. This change in the direction of waves at the boundary between two different media is known as **refraction.**

Refraction is the change of wave direction at the boundary between two media.

Sargent-Welch Scientific Company

FIGURE 16-23. (a) Straight waves enter a different medium (shallow water) head-on. Notice the change in wavelength. (b) The straight waves enter the shallow water at an angle. Notice that the change in media causes the waves to bend at the boundaries of the barrier. This is refraction.

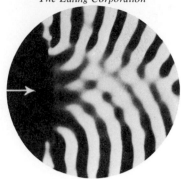

FIGURE 16-24. Straight waves hit the barrier from the direction of the arrow. Notice the bending of the waves beyond the barrier.

Diffraction is the bending of a wave around an object in its path.

FIGURE 16-25. Waves are diffracted at two openings in the barrier. At each opening, circular waves are formed. The circular waves interfere with each other. Points of constructive interference are indicated by dashed lines.

FIGURE 16-26. Changing the frequency of the wave changes the pattern produced by interference. The nodal lines are much closer together in (a) than in (b). The central line of wave maxima is present in both (a) and (b).

16:16 Diffraction of Waves

Diffraction is the bending of a wave around obstacles placed in its path. Diffraction may be observed in a ripple tank by placing a small barrier in the path of straight waves. The waves bend around the edges of the barrier. They meet a short distance beyond the barrier. Thus, the barrier does not cast much of a "shadow."

Create a diffraction pattern by placing three straight barriers as shown in Figure 16-25. Make the spaces between the barriers smaller than the wavelength of the approaching waves. The diffraction of the waves around the edges of the openings causes each opening to produce new circular waves. The circular waves from the two openings interfere with one another. Along the points marked by dashed lines, wave crests are superimposed. At these points the water is displaced doubly from its normal position. These points of reinforcement all lie along the same line. Between these lines of reinforcement are areas where a crest and a trough are superimposed. Destructive interference occurs and the water remains undisturbed. These undisturbed points lie in definite lines, called **nodal lines.**

The frequency of waves in the ripple tank can be varied. Thus, waves of different wavelengths can be sent toward the barriers. Each wavelength produces a diffraction pattern. By comparing the diffraction patterns for several different wavelengths, two facts are learned.

1. Different wavelengths produce similar diffraction patterns, but the lines of reinforcement are in slightly different places.
2. Regardless of the wavelength of the wave, the central line of reinforcement always falls in the center of the pattern.

Different waves pass through one another but do not change each other. Suppose several waves of different wavelengths are sent toward a barrier at the same time. Each wave produces its own independent diffraction pattern. A very strong central line of reinforcement is caused by these simultaneous diffraction patterns.

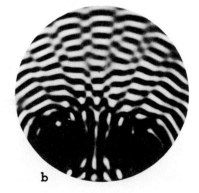

a   b

To both sides of the central line is a cluster of lines of reinforcement. Each cluster has one line for each wavelength which falls on the barrier.

It is difficult to produce several wavelengths at once when using a ripple tank. The pattern that results is hard to analyze. A clearer pattern can be obtained by using light waves (Chapter 20).

16:17 The Doppler Effect

The Doppler effect is the change in the observed frequency of waves when a wave source and an observer are in relative motion. The wave source and the observer must move toward or away from each other. Figure 16-27 shows that the wavelength of the waves is shorter in front of the moving source and longer behind the moving source. Notice that the circular waves are closer together in front of the swimming ducks than behind them. In the same way, the sound or light waves ahead of a moving source are closer together. Thus, they reach an observer more frequently.

In the case of sound waves, a sound of higher frequency is heard when a source is moving toward a listener. The sound is higher in pitch because of the higher frequency. When the source passes the listener and moves away, a lower frequency is heard. This lower frequency appears as a sudden drop in pitch. This effect can be observed by a person standing beside a highway or race car track.

The Doppler effect is the change in the observed frequency of a wave when a source and an observer are in relative motion.

FIGURE 16-27. The ducks swimming on the surface of the water provide examples of the Doppler effect. The wavelength of the waves ahead of the ducks is noticeably shorter than the wavelength of the waves behind the ducks. The speed of the ducks can be determined by the difference in wavelength.

William Maddox

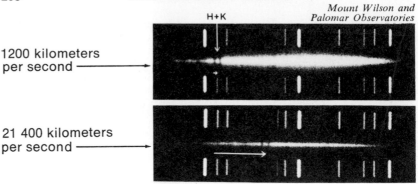

Mount Wilson and Palomar Observatories

H+K

1200 kilometers per second

21 400 kilometers per second

FIGURE 16-28. Astronomers use the Doppler shift of spectral lines to calculate the speed of a star. The arrows indicate the shift of the H and K lines of calcium. Notice how the lines are farther to the right in the lower photograph.

The Doppler shift in the wavelength of light coming from distant stars indicates an expanding universe.

The Doppler effect also explains why stars that are moving away from the earth display light of longer wavelengths than they should. This is known as the "red shift" because the longer wavelengths of light are red. The wavelengths observed coming from a star will show a shift towards the red, but they may not be red. The shift towards the longer wavelengths indicates that the stars are moving away from the earth. Astronomers have found that no matter in what direction they look, they find stars that display "red shift." This means that stars are moving away from our solar system and from each other. The "red shift" is evidence that the universe is expanding. Consider what would happen if you put small stars all over a small balloon and then blew up the balloon. The stars would move away from each other because the balloon would expand.

SUMMARY

Waves are a means of transferring energy. Because all waves follow the same rules of behavior, it is possible to study waves in general. Mechanical waves such as sound waves, water waves, and waves in a spring require a medium. Electromagnetic waves do not require a medium. Light and radio waves are examples of electromagnetic waves.

Transverse waves cause the particles of a medium to vibrate perpendicularly to the direction in which the wave is moving. Longitudinal waves cause a medium to vibrate parallel to the direction of the wave's motion.

There are several characteristics common to all waves. Points of a wave that have the same displacement and are moving in the same direction are said to be in phase. The wavelength (λ) of a wave is the linear distance between corresponding points on consecutive waves. The frequency of a wave is the number of waves that pass a given point per second. The velocity of a wave is its frequency multiplied by its wavelength ($v = f\lambda$).

Sound waves are generated by vibrating objects. A sound wave has the same frequency as the object that produces the wave. If an object vibrates in air, the air on each side of the object is compressed and rarefied. The vibrations of the air particles are passed along through the air.

The period (T) of a wave is the time needed for a full wave to pass a given point. The period is the reciprocal of the frequency. The energy of a wave is proportional to its amplitude. The speed of a wave depends on the properties of the medium through which the wave is traveling. All waves of the same kind travel in a given medium at the same speed.

When waves reach the boundary of a medium, they are partly reflected and partly transmitted. When the new medium is more rigid than the old medium, the reflected wave will be inverted (180° change in phase). When the new medium is less rigid than the old medium, the reflected wave will be erect (no change in phase). In both cases, the part of the wave that is reflected depends on how different the two media are. Large reflections occur at the boundary of two very different media.

When a wave passes into a new medium it will have a new velocity. Since $v = f\lambda$, and v changes, the wavelength must also change. The frequency cannot change because the wave in the new medium is generated by the wave in the old medium.

When waves meet, their displacements add. This is called interference. After the waves pass through one another, they are unaffected. Suppose two equal pulses, having opposite displacements, move toward each other in a medium. When they meet there will be a point, called a node, that never undergoes a displacement.

When waves are reflected from boundaries, the angle of incidence equals the angle of reflection. This statement is the law of reflection. The change in the direction of a wave at the boundary between two media is known as refraction. Diffraction is the bending of a wave around obstacles in its path.

The change in the frequency of a wave received by an observer when the wave source and the observer are in relative motion is called the Doppler effect.

QUESTIONS

1. How many general methods of energy transfer are there? Give two examples of each.
2. There are many kinds of waves. Why is it possible to learn the rules of wave behavior of all kinds of waves without an extensive study of each?
3. Distinguish between a mechanical wave and an electromagnetic wave.
4. How does a transverse wave differ from a longitudinal wave? Give an example of each.
5. If a pulse is sent along a rope, how does the rope behave at any given point after the pulse has passed?
6. A pulse differs from a wave. How?
7. Distinguish between the wavelength, frequency, and period of a wave.
8. Write an equation used to find the velocity of a wave.
9. What does the amplitude of a wave represent?
10. An instructor sends waves along a spring of fixed length. Can the speed of the waves in the spring be changed? How can the frequency of a wave in the spring be changed?
11. The top of a drum vibrates at a frequency that cannot be changed without altering the drum itself. Therefore, all sound waves coming from the drum must have the same frequency. If the drum is hit harder, what is different about the sound waves?
12. When a wave reaches the boundary of a new medium, part of the wave is reflected and part is transmitted. What determines the amount of reflection?
13. A pulse reaches the boundary of a medium more rigid than the one from which it came. Is the reflected pulse erect or inverted?
14. A pulse reaches the boundary of a medium less rigid than the one from which it came. Is the reflected pulse erect or inverted?

15. A light wave is reflected from the surface of a pond. Is the reflected wave erect or inverted?

16. When a wave passes into a new medium, what remains the same? What changes?

For Questions 17–21, sketch the result of wave a and wave b (a) when they meet, and (b) when they pass one another.

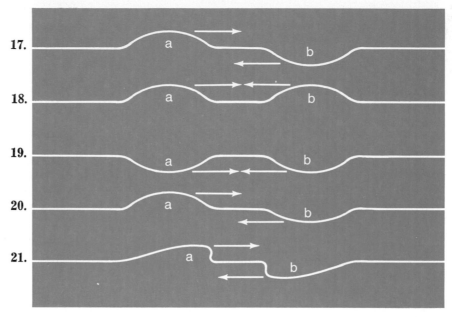

17.

18.

19.

20.

21.

FIGURE 16-29

22. In Questions 17–21: (a) In which diagrams do the pulses produce constructive interference when they meet? (b) In which diagrams do the waves produce destructive interference?

23. In Questions 17–21, in which diagrams are nodes formed as the pulses pass through one another?

24. List three different means of changing the direction of a wave.

25. State the law of reflection.

26. What is diffraction?

27. Name two facts about the diffraction patterns produced by waves of different wavelengths as they pass through the same pair of openings.

28. How do the waves in front of a moving source differ from the waves behind a moving source?

29. Contrary to popular belief, a tidal wave (tsunami) usually takes the form of a very fast-moving shallow wave that moves across the ocean's surface. A tidal wave could pass under a ship and hardly be noticed. Why does such a wave cause so much damage when it reaches land? (Hint: Consider the energy form of the wave at all times.)

PROBLEMS

1. What is the wavelength of a sound wave that has a frequency of 50 hertz?

2. An ocean wave has a wavelength of 10 m. A wave passes by every 2 sec. What is the speed of the wave?

3. A sonar signal (sound wave) of frequency 1000 hertz has a wavelength of 1.5 m in water. (a) What is the speed of sound in water? (b) What is the period of the sound wave in water? (c) What is the period of the sound wave in air?

4. A sound wave in a steel rail has a frequency of 500 hertz and a wavelength of 10 m. What is the speed of sound in steel?

5. A light wave has a wavelength of 4.0×10^{-7} m. The frequency of the wave is 7.5×10^{14} hertz. What is the speed of light?

6. Waves of frequency 2 hertz are generated along a spring. The waves have a wavelength of 0.45 m. (a) What is the speed of the waves along the spring? (b) What is the wavelength of the waves along the spring if their frequency is increased to 6 hertz? (c) If the frequency is decreased to 0.5 hertz, what is their wavelength?

7. Determine the frequency of a microwave 6 cm in length. (A microwave is an electromagnetic wave. It travels through space at a speed of 3.0×10^8 m/sec.)

8. What is the period of the microwave in Problem 7?

9. A gamma ray has a period of 10^{-24} sec. (a) What is the frequency of the gamma ray? (b) What is the wavelength of the gamma ray in meters? (A gamma ray is an electromagnetic wave. It travels through space at a speed of 3.0×10^8 m/sec.)

PROJECTS

1. Using a toy "slinky," generate both transverse and longitudinal waves. Notice changes in the speed of the waves as you change the tension in the spring. Keeping the tension of the spring constant, observe the changes in wavelength as you vary the frequency at which the wave is generated.

2. Tape a paper cup to each end of a long piece of string. Use this as a telephone. For good results, keep the string fairly taut and talk with your lower lip against the edge of the cup.

3. Take a needle and thread. Put the thread through the needle. Then, hold the needle gently on a turning record. Hold the string near your ear. You should hear sound.

4. If you have a pitch pipe, tie a string or light rope to it. The rope should be about 1 m long. Whirl the pitch pipe rapidly around your head. Notice the Doppler effect.

READINGS

Bascom, Willard, *Waves and Beaches: The Dynamics of the Ocean Surface.* New York, Doubleday and Co., Inc., 1964.

Bergeisk, Willem, *Waves and the Ear.* New York, Doubleday and Co., Inc., 1960.

Greenewalt, Crowford H., "How Birds Sing." *Scientific American,* November, 1969.

Griffin, Donald R., *Echoes of Bats and Men.* New York, Doubleday and Co., Inc., 1959.

Linde, Ronald K., and Crewdson, Richard C., "Shock Waves in Solids." *Scientific American,* May, 1969.

Stickney, Sue Ellen, and Englert, Thad J., "The Ghost Flute." *The Physics Teacher,* December, 1975.

Strong, C. L., "The Amateur Scientists: How to Build a Ripple Tank to Examine Wave Phenomenon." *Scientific American,* October, 1962.

Light has intrigued people for ages. It has long been known that light is produced by some objects, while other objects can only reflect light which originates in some other place. Under some conditions, white light can be spread out to form bands of color. Light also travels at a very high speed, even through a vacuum. Many theories have been developed to explain these fascinating properties of light. Based on your observations of the properties of light, what do you think light is?

THE NATURE OF LIGHT

Many facts about light were known long ago. For example, people knew that light travels in straight lines. They also knew that light striking a barrier at a certain angle is reflected at the same angle but in a different direction. Through the ages, many theories were developed by scholars to explain the true nature of light. However, the true nature of light was not discovered until the century in which we live.

GOAL: You will gain knowledge and understanding of the wave and particle properties of light, the illumination of a surface by a point light source, and methods used to measure the speed of light.

17:1 Light—An Electromagnetic Wave

The sun is a source of huge quantities of radiation. Radiation is also emitted from incandescent lamps, fluorescent lamps, and flames. Some of this radiation can stimulate the retina of the human eye. It is called **light.** But much of the radiation that comes from these sources is not detected by the eye and has other names. Some of these other names are infrared waves, ultraviolet waves, and radio waves. These waves can be detected by other means.

A **luminous body** is a body that emits light waves. An **illuminated body** reflects light waves. The sun is a luminous body. The moon is an illuminated body. The word luminous refers only to bodies that emit light waves. All warm bodies emit radiation, but not all emit visible light. The radiation that a hot stove gives out cannot be seen but can be detected by other means.

Electromagnetic waves require no medium. Light is an electromagnetic wave. But light waves represent only one small portion

Light is electromagnetic radiation capable of stimulating the retina of the eye.

A luminous body emits light. An illuminated body reflects light.

Light waves, like all electromagnetic waves, do not need a medium.

243

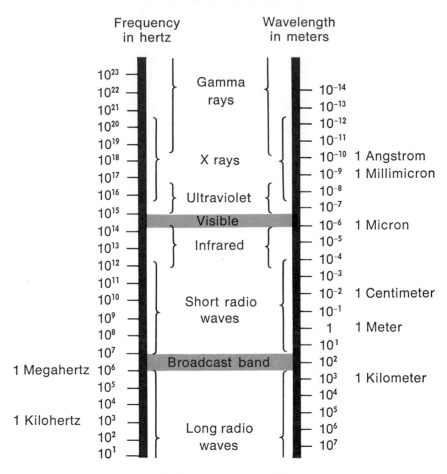

FIGURE 17-1. A chart of the electromagnetic spectrum. Electromagnetic waves of different frequencies are detected by different means. Note that the visible spectrum is only a very small portion of the whole electromagnetic spectrum.

Light waves make up only a small part of the electromagnetic spectrum.

of electromagnetic radiations. Figure 17-1 shows the known spectrum (array) of electromagnetic waves. Note that light waves account for only a small part of this spectrum.

All electromagnetic waves travel at the same speed in space. However, they differ in frequency, and therefore, in wavelength. Figure 17-1 shows the frequencies and wavelengths of various electromagnetic waves.

An electromagnetic wave has both electric and magnetic properties. An electric field and a magnetic field are associated with the wave. These fields vibrate in planes perpendicular to each other and perpendicular to the direction of the wave.

17:2   Transmission and Absorption of Light

Many materials transmit light without distorting the rays. Objects can be seen clearly through glass, quartz, air, and some other materials. These materials are called **transparent materials.** Other matter, such as smoked glass, transmits light but distorts the rays during transmission. These materials are called **translucent.** Materials such as brick transmit no light. They absorb or reflect all light that falls on them. These materials are called **opaque.**

17:3   The Speed of Light

The speed of light is difficult to measure. However, the methods used to measure the speed of light are easily understood. The first rough measurement of the speed of light was made by the Danish astronomer Olaf Roemer (1644–1710). About 1676 Roemer was studying one of the moons of Jupiter. While the earth was in position E_1 (Figure 17-2) he observed the moon move behind Jupiter. Later the moon emerged from the other side of Jupiter. Carefully, Roemer timed several of these eclipses. He then made a table which predicted when eclipses of the moon would take place during the next few months. At first, Roemer's table was fairly accurate. But as the months passed, an error of increasing size gradually appeared. The eclipses were occurring later than predicted. But after six months, the error began to get smaller. At the end of twelve months the table was once again accurate. Roemer at once understood the source of error. He had

Roemer made the first calculation of the speed of light using data from astronomical observations.

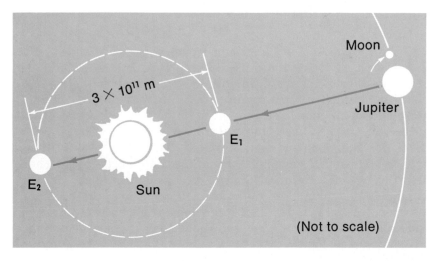

FIGURE 17-2. Roemer's method of measuring the speed of light.

made the table while the earth was at position E_1. As the earth followed its orbit around the sun, it moved farther from Jupiter. Jupiter, however, moved only a short distance along its orbit. The error occurred because the light from Jupiter's moon had to travel a greater distance to reach the observer on the earth as the months went by. At position E_2, the earth was 3×10^{11} m farther from Jupiter than it was at position E_1. At position E_2, the eclipse began about 1000 seconds later than predicted (in Roemer's table). Roemer assumed that this 1000 seconds was the time needed for the light coming from Jupiter's moon to traverse the diameter of the earth's orbit. Therefore, the speed of light must be

$$v = \frac{s}{t} = \frac{3 \times 10^{11}\,\text{m}}{1000\,\text{sec}} = 3 \times 10^8\,\text{m/sec}$$

Michelson made an accurate land measurement of the speed of light.

The first accurate land measurement of the speed of light was made by the American scientist Albert Michelson (1852–1931). Michelson timed the flight of a beam of light on a round trip between two mountains. To do this he used a rotating octagonal mirror (Figure 17-3). A pulse of light was sent from the source

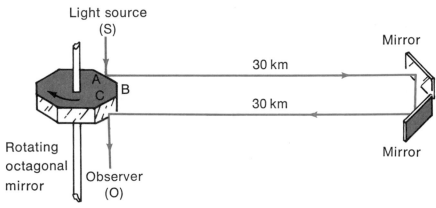

FIGURE 17-3. Michelson's method of measuring the speed of light.

S to the mirror A. The light then traveled the path shown. For the observer O to see the pulse, mirror B had to move into the exact position of mirror C in just the time it took the light to travel the path. The time required for B to move into position C was just one-eighth of the time needed for one revolution of the mirror. In practice, the octagonal mirror was turned by an electric motor. Starting from rest, the speed of the motor was adjusted until the light reflected from C was at maximum brightness. Then, with the rate of rotation of the mirror known, the speed of light was calculated. Michelson obtained a value of 3×10^8 m/sec for the speed of light in air. The following problems will help you understand the reasoning behind Michelson's method of measuring the speed of light.

PROBLEMS

1. The octagonal mirror in Figure 17-3 makes 625 rev/sec. What time is required for one revolution?

2. (a) For the octagonal mirror of Problem 1, what time is needed for B to move into position C? (b) Using Figure 17-3, find the total distance the light travels in this time.

3. Use the solutions to Problem 2 to find the speed of light in (a) km/sec, and (b) m/sec.

4. The speed of the motor is increased until the mirror is rotating at the rate of 1250 rev/sec. Will an observer see the pulse of light? Explain.

5. What steps can an observer take to be sure that the octagonal mirror does not rotate at some multiple of the proper number of rev/sec?

17:4   Light Travels in a Straight Line

Light appears to travel in a straight line. For example, when the air contains many dust particles, the path of light coming from a flashlight can be seen. The light forms a "beam" of light. Also, an opaque object casts a sharp shadow when light falls on it. This is further evidence that light travels in straight lines.

Even a small beam of light consists of a very large number of individual waves of many different wavelengths. The waves travel together in a straight line. This fact helps to explain much of the behavior of light. Since light travels in straight lines in the direction of the waves, lines can be used to represent the direction of the light waves. These lines are called **rays**. This way of studying light is called ray optics.

Since light travels in straight lines, the direction of light waves can be represented by rays.

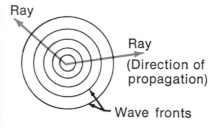

FIGURE 17-4. (a) The fact that light travels in straight lines can be observed in beams of light reflected from fog and dust in the air. (b) A ray diagram showing the direction of propagation of a circular wave. Circular waves are progagated from a common center. Rays for circular waves are perpendicular to the wave fronts.

Ray

Ray
(Direction of propagation)

Wave fronts

b   Circular waves

Official U.S. Coast Guard Photo

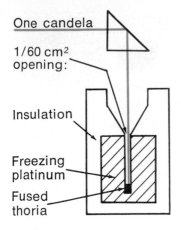

One candela

1/60 cm² opening:

Insulation

Freezing platinum

Fused thoria

FIGURE 17-5. The standard light source contains glowing thoria. The brightness of all other light sources is defined in terms of light emitted by this standard.

The luminous intensity of a light source is the amount of light that the source gives out.

The candela is the unit for luminous intensity.

Luminous flux is the flow of light from a source.

The lumen is the unit for luminous flux. It is a power unit.

17:5 Illumination by a Point Source

The light that comes from a light source consists of many short bursts of light emitted randomly by the atoms that make up the source. Since even a small light source consists of many billions of atoms, the net result is a smooth flow of light away from the source in all directions.

The **luminous intensity** (I) of a light source is measured by comparing it with the international unit, the **candela** (cd). At first, the unit for luminous intensity was called a candle. This was an actual candle made to meet certain specifications. However, even carefully made candles have an unsteady light intensity. Thus, a candle was not a good reference device.

At present, the standard source of luminous intensity is one sixtieth of a square centimeter of fused thoria. At the temperature of freezing platinum, thoria is incandescent and emits a steady flow of light energy. One candela is defined to be the luminous intensity of this source.

The amount of light that a source gives out, its luminous intensity, depends on the amount of energy being put into the source. It also depends on how efficiently the source converts the energy input to light energy. Incandescent lamps are very inefficient sources of light. A fluorescent lamp produces about four times more light per watt than a typical lightbulb. It is clear that a homeowner can reduce electric costs by using fluorescent lamps rather than incandescent lamps.

The flow of light energy from a source is called the **luminous flux.** The unit of luminous flux is called the **lumen.** Rate of energy flow is power. Thus, the lumen is a power unit.

In order to define the lumen, standards must be set up as to the area that light passes through and the intensity of the light. Imagine a hollow sphere with a radius of one meter. At the center

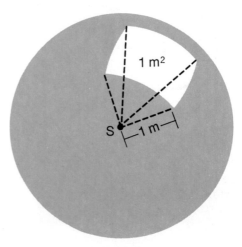

FIGURE 17-6. The lumen is the unit of luminous flux and is a measure of the rate of flow of light energy from a source.

1 m²

S ⊢—1 m—⊣

William Maddox

of the sphere is a point light source of one candela intensity. A point light source is a very small light source that sends out light uniformly in all directions. Now, imagine four radii leaving the point source, each to form a corner of the surface of one square meter. The angle defined by the four radii is a unit solid angle. The luminous flux through any surface that would cap this unit solid angle at any point back to the source would be one lumen. If the four radii were all one meter in length, the surface area would be one square meter. The light energy flowing through that area would be one lumen. The lumen is therefore the rate at which light from a one-candela source passes through a solid angle of unit size.

The surface area of a sphere is $4\pi r^2$. The sphere of one meter radius must have a total surface area of $4\pi (1\,\text{m})^2$ or $4\pi\,\text{m}^2$. The rate at which light crosses the entire surface is accordingly 4π lumens. Thus, the total energy flow from a one-candela source is 4π lumens. A two-candela source would emit 8π lumens, a three-candela source, 12π lumens, and so on. The energy flow in lumens from a light source is directly proportional to the intensity of the source.

Illuminance (E) is the rate at which light energy falls on a unit area some distance from a light source. Illuminance is measured in lumens/m². One lumen/m² is the illuminance of a surface located one meter from a one-candela source. A surface one meter from a 10-candela source receives illuminance of 10 lumens per square meter.

FIGURE 17-7. The illuminance of a surface varies directly with the intensity of the light source.

Illuminance is the rate at which light falls on a surface of unit area.

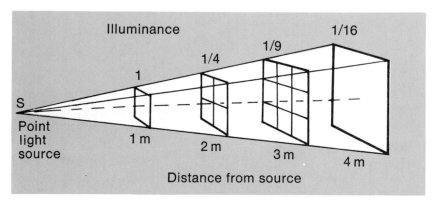

Illuminance

1/16

1/9

1/4

1

S

Point light source

1 m

2 m

3 m

4 m

Distance from source

FIGURE 17-8. The illuminance of a surface varies inversely as the square of its distance from a light source.

Light from a point source radiates in all directions. Therefore, it spreads out with distance. Surfaces far from a light source receive less illumination than surfaces closer to the source. Figure 17-8 shows that the amount of illumination received by a surface varies inversely with the square of its distance from the source. A given amount of light energy falls on one square meter of a surface one meter away from a source. This same amount of energy spreads out to cover an area of four square meters on a surface two meters from the source. Hence, the illumination of the surface two meters from the source is only one fourth that of the surface one meter from the source. In the same way, the source provides one ninth the illumination to a surface three meters away.

There are two ways to increase the illuminance of a surface. The luminous intensity of a light source can be increased. Or, the distance between the source and the surface can be decreased. Thus, the illuminance of a surface varies directly with the intensity of the light source and inversely with the square of its distance from the source. Let I represent the luminous intensity of the source in candelas. Let E represent the illuminance of the surface in lumens/m². Then, the illuminance of any surface can be expressed as,

Illuminance varies directly with the source intensity and varies inversely with the square of distance from the source.

$$E = \frac{I}{d^2}$$

Example: Illumination

A student's desk top is 2.5 m below a 150-candela incandescent lamp. What is the illumination of the desk top?

Solution:

$$E = \frac{I}{d^2}$$
$$= \frac{150 \text{ candela}}{\left(\dfrac{1 \text{ candela}}{\text{lumen}}\right) (2.5 \text{ m})^2}$$
$$= 24 \text{ lumens/m}^2$$

PROBLEMS

6. Find the illumination 4 m below a 32-candela source of light.

7. A lamp is moved from 30 cm to 90 cm above the pages of a book. Compare the illumination of the book before and after the book is moved.

8. The intensity of illumination on a surface 3 m below a 150-watt incandescent lamp is 10 lumens/m². What is the intensity of the lamp in candelas?

9. A light produces an illumination of 18.0 lumens/m² on a road 5 m below the point of its suspension. What is the intensity of the light source in candelas?

10. A public school law requires a minimum illumination of 160 lumens/m² on the surface of each student's desk. An architect's specifications call for classroom lights to be located 2 m above the desks. What must be the minimum intensity of the lights?

11. A screen is placed between two lamps of different intensities. The illumination is 20 lumens/m² on both sides of the screen. The smaller lamp has an intensity of 20 candelas and is located 1 meter from the screen. The larger lamp is 2.5 meters from the screen. What is the intensity of the larger lamp?

17:6   Color and Light

Sunlight or white light from a lamp is dispersed into an array of different colors when it passes through a glass prism. White light is a combination of many colors of light. Each color corresponds to a different wavelength. Red light waves have the longest wavelengths. Violet light waves have the shortest wavelengths. When white light passes through a prism, these wavelengths are separated. Note in Figure 17-9 that red and violet light are at opposite ends of the spectrum.

Color is a property of light. A shirt is red because it reflects red light. When white light falls on the shirt, the pigments in the dye of the shirt absorb most of the light. However, the pigments do not absorb wavelengths in the red region of visible light. These wavelengths are reflected to the eye and the shirt looks red. Suppose that only blue light falls on the red shirt. The pigments in the dye would absorb all the blue light. No light would be reflected from the shirt. Thus, it would appear to be black. Black is the absence of color or light.

White light is composed of many colors.

FIGURE 17-9. White light, when passed through a prism, is separated into a band of different colors.

Red and violet make up opposite ends of the visible light spectrum.

The color of an object depends on which wavelengths of light the object reflects.

James M. Jackson

FIGURE 17-10. The pigments in the surface of this hot air balloon absorb some wavelengths of white light but reflect others to your eye. Thus, you see red, orange, blue, and green areas in this balloon.

17:7 Light—Waves or Particles?

The nature of light was a subject of much debate during Newton's lifetime.

During Newton's lifetime a debate arose concerning the nature of light. Newton thought that light consists of minute particles. The Dutch scientist Christian Huygens (1629–1695) thought that light consists of waves. Both theories had strong arguments in their favor.

Newton reasoned that light consists of particles because of the way light reflects from a surface. Newton knew that when a beam of light strikes a surface, the angle of reflection is equal to the angle of approach. A particle is also reflected in this way. A basketball bounces away from a gym floor at the same angle that it hits the floor.

But Huygens pointed out that waves act in the same way. When waves fall on a surface, the angle of reflection is equal to the angle of incidence. Since particles and waves are reflected from surfaces in the same way, the question of the nature of light remained.

Diffraction is the bending of waves around barriers placed in their path. Because waves bend around the edges of obstacles, they behave as shown in Figure 17-11. The waves pass through an opening in the barrier. As they pass through they bend around the two edges and form new circular waves. The wave spreads out to both sides of the opening. Particles do not seem to act this way. In Figure 17-12a, a compressed air gun shoots pellets at a steel plate. The plate has a small circular opening in its center. The pellets cut a sharp, well defined image of the opening on a paper screen some distance from the plate. The pellets travel straight through the hole. No bending takes place at the edges. In Figure 17-12b, light seems to behave like the pellets. A street lamp casts a sharp image of a window onto the wall of a room. Thus, it appears that light is not diffracted in the manner of waves and that, therefore, Newton was right. Light must consist of particles.

The Ealing Corporation

FIGURE 17-11. Waves are diffracted at openings.

FIGURE 17-12. (a) Particles are not diffracted as they pass through openings. (b) Light does not seem to be diffracted at large openings.

(a) Particles

(b) Light

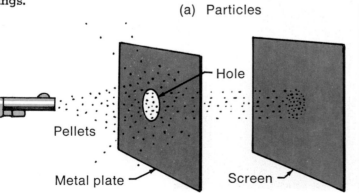

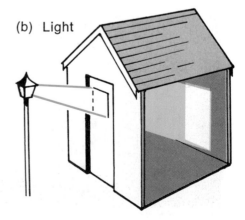

The Italian physicist Francesco Grimaldi (1618–1663) did not agree with the idea that light casts sharp shadows. He said that if the edges of a shadow are examined closely, they appear to be slightly blurred. Light does bend around obstacles if only slightly. Grimaldi suggested that the diffraction was hardly noticeable because the light waves were very small. If the light rays had short wavelengths, then observable diffraction would take place only when the waves passed through very small openings.

During the 18th century, Thomas Young tested Grimaldi's hypothesis. Young postulated that if light is diffracted as it passes through narrow openings, it should form a pattern like the one in Figure 17-14. Therefore, he passed light through very small openings. This was done by making two narrow slits in a screen. The pattern formed was similar to the pattern formed by the diffrac-

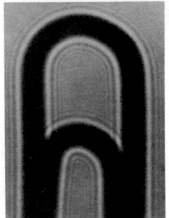

FIGURE 17-13. Diffraction pattern produced by a paper clip.

Light shining through a window appears to cast a well-defined image. But light is actually diffracted, or bent, when it moves past a barrier.

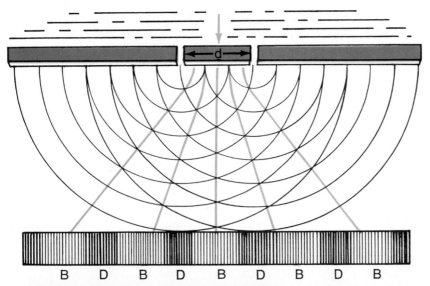

B   D   B   D   B   D   B   D   B

FIGURE 17-14. If the two slits are small compared to the wavelength of the waves, an interference pattern is produced. Note the equal spacing between the bright bands.

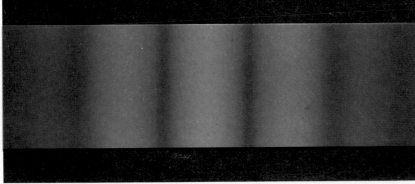

Courtesy of Kodansha

tion and interference of water waves. In this case, lines of constructive interference resulted in bright spots on a screen some distance from the slits. Between the bright spots were dark spots where destructive interference caused the light waves to cancel. Young concluded that since light can be diffracted and exhibits interference, it must consist of waves.

17:8 Interference in Thin Films

The diffraction of light is not the only evidence in favor of the wave theory of light. Other evidence is found in the colorful pattern often seen in soap films, soap bubbles, and oil-slicks. If a soap film is held vertically, its weight makes it thicker at the bottom than at the top (Figure 17-15). In fact, the film changes

FIGURE 17-15. Each color is reinforced where the soap film is 1/4, 3/4, 5/4, etc., of the wavelength for that color. Since each color has a different wavelength, a series of color bands are seen reflected from the soap films.

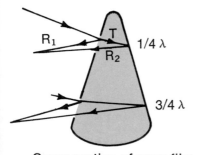

Cross section of soap film

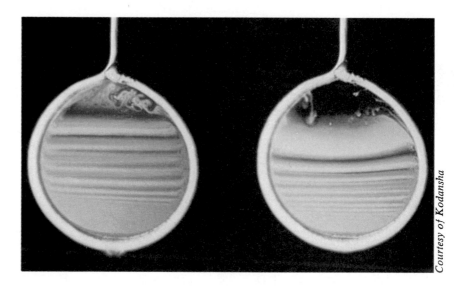

Courtesy of Kodansha

gradually in thickness from top to bottom. When a light wave strikes the film, part of it is reflected (R_1) and part is transmitted (T). The transmitted wave travels through the film to the inner surface. Again, part of the wave is reflected (R_2). If the thickness of the film is ¼ of the wavelength of the wave ($\lambda/4$), the "round-trip" path length in the film is $\lambda/2$. It would appear that the wave returning from the inner surface would arrive back at the outer-surface just one-half wavelength (180°) out of phase with the first reflected wave and that the two waves would cancel. However, when a wave is reflected from a more dense medium, it undergoes inversion. Thus, the first reflected wave (R_1) is inverted upon reflection. The second reflected wave (R_2), returning from the boundary of a less dense medium, is not inverted. The wave reflected from the inner surface arrives back at the first surface in phase with the first reflected wave. Thus, reinforcement occurs.

Different colors of light have different wavelengths. Since the thickness of the film changes, the $\lambda/4$ requirement for different colors is met at intervals down the film. Thus, white light falling on the film results in a rainbow of color.

When a point is reached where the thickness is $3\lambda/4$ for the first color, the first color reappears. This point again gives a $\lambda/2$ path difference. Any odd multiple of quarter wavelengths such as $\lambda/4$, $3\lambda/4$, or $5\lambda/4$ satisfies the conditions for reinforcement for a given color. If the film is $\lambda/2$ thick, or any multiple thereof, the returning wave cancels the wave reflected from the outer surface. There is no reflected wave for the wavelength at that point.

17:9 Polarization of Light

In Figure 17-16, waves sent along a rope pass through a slot. Under these circumstances, waves can be sent along the rope only if the waves are generated in the plane of the slot. Each slot per-

Waves oriented to a particular plane are plane polarized.

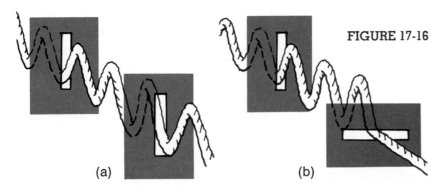

FIGURE 17-16

(a)   (b)

mits only those waves that are oriented in the direction of the slot to pass through. The waves are said to be **polarized** to a particular plane, or plane polarized.

FIGURE 17-17. The arrows show that unpolarized light vibrates in many planes. Plane polarized light vibrates in only one plane. Polarized light from the first polarizer is absorbed by the analyzer.

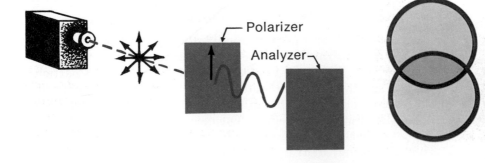

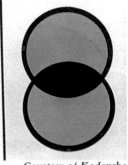

Courtesy of Kodansha

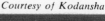
Courtesy of Kodansha

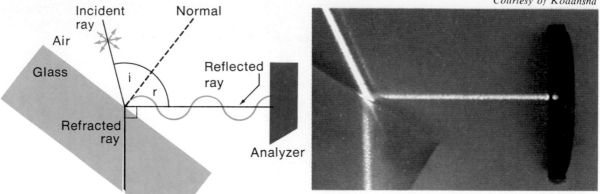

FIGURE 17-18. Light becomes polarized when it is reflected from a smooth surface such as glass or water.

Light can be polarized by passing it through a polaroid filter.

Light can be polarized by reflection.

The polarization of light gives evidence that light is a transverse wave.

The photoelectric effect is the ejection of electrons from a metal surface when light falls on it.

A beam of light contains a huge number of waves vibrating in every possible plane. All the waves can be resolved into vertical and horizontal components. Thus, it averages out as if half of the waves vibrate vertically and half vibrate horizontally. If a filter (polarizer), such as polaroid sunglasses, is placed in front of the beam of light, only those waves that vibrate parallel to the permitted plane pass through. Thus, half of the light rays are eliminated. Suppose a second sheet of polaroid material (analyzer) is placed in the path of the polarized light. If its permitted plane is perpendicular to the light that passed through the polarizer, almost no light will pass through.

Light can also be polarized by reflection. Look at the light reflected from a tank of water through a piece of polaroid material. Rotate the polaroid and continue to observe the reflected light. Note that the light brightens and dims. Try various angles of reflection. There will be one angle at which no light is able to pass through the polaroid. This angle is the angle of polarization. At this angle, the light which is reflected from the water is completely polarized.

The fact that light can be polarized supports two ideas. First, light consists of waves. Particles would be unaffected by a polarizer. Secondly, light waves are transverse waves. Longitudinal waves would not be affected by a polarizer. For example, sound waves cannot be polarized.

17:10   The Dual Nature of Light

Beyond all doubt, the diffraction, interference, and polarization of light demonstrate the wave properties of light. Now consider an effect that shows just as clearly that light consists of particles.

Light which falls on a metal surface, such as zinc or cesium, ejects electrons from the metal. This ejection of electrons is called the **photoelectric effect.** The electrons leave the metal with a kinetic energy that is independent of the intensity of the light. This means that light energy is not distributed evenly. Instead,

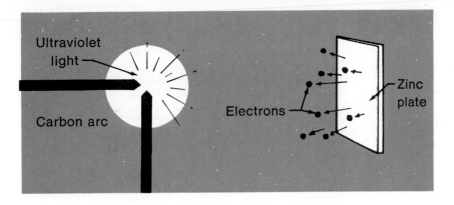

FIGURE 17-19. Apparatus to demonstrate the photo-electric effect.

it is concentrated in small packages or bundles of energy. This is definitely not a property of waves but is a property of particles.

We have still not answered our question about the nature of light. Does light consist of waves or is it made up of particles? We can avoid the problem if we reword the question about light. Instead of asking if light is waves *or* particles, let us look at the possibility that light behaves as *both* waves and particles.

The **quantum theory of light** was proposed by Max Planck (1858–1947) and fostered by Neils Bohr and Albert Einstein. The quantum theory attempts to explain the dual nature of light. According to the quantum theory, light is emitted from a source in discrete packages. These packages are called **photons**. Each photon is related to a light wave of specific frequency. The energy of a photon is proportional to its wave frequency, in accordance with the formula proposed by Max Planck,

$$E = hf$$

In the equation, E is the energy in joules. The symbol h is Planck's constant 6.6×10^{-34} J-sec, and f is the frequency of the photon.

The photoelectric effect supports the particle theory of light.

The quantum theory of light attempts to explain the fact that light behaves as both waves and particles.

Photons are small bundles of energy.

Each photon corresponds to a specific wave frequency. The ratio of energy to frequency is Planck's constant.

Example: Energy of a Photon

A photon of red light has a frequency of 5.0×10^{14} hertz. How much energy does the photon have?

Solution:

$$E = hf$$
$$= (6.6 \times 10^{-34} \text{ J-sec}) \ (5.0 \times 10^{14} \text{ hertz})$$
$$= 3.3 \times 10^{-19} \text{ J}$$

SUMMARY

Electromagnetic radiation that can stimulate the retina of the eye is called light. White light is a combination of many colors of light. Each color has a different wavelength. The speed of light is 3×10^8 m/sec in air or a vacuum. Light travels in straight lines.

The standard of luminous intensity is the candela. The candela is often called a candle. The rate at which light energy flows from a light source is called the luminous flux. The unit of luminous flux is the lumen. Illuminance is the rate at which light energy falls on a unit area some distance from the source. Illuminance is measured in lumens/m². The illumination received by a surface varies inversely with the square of its distance from a light source. It also varies directly with the luminous intensity of the source.

Light waves may be reflected, refracted and diffracted. If light falls on two narrow slits diffraction will cause the light waves to interfere and produce a diffraction pattern. Light can also produce interference effects when falling on thin films of soap or oil.

Waves are said to be plane polarized if only waves oriented in one direction (plane) are present. One method of polarizing light is to let light fall on a very fine grating such as found in polaroid sunglasses. Light can also be polarized by reflection.

The diffraction, interference, and polarization of light all clearly indicate that light is a wave. The photoelectric effect just as clearly indicates that light consists of particles. Thus, light has both wave and particle properties. The quantum theory attempts to explain this dual nature of light. It states that light is emitted from a source in discrete packages called quanta, or photons. The energy of a photon is equal to its frequency multiplied by Planck's constant, or $E = hf$.

QUESTIONS

1. What determines whether an electromagnetic wave is a light wave?
2. Electromagnetic waves differ from mechanical waves. How?
3. Distinguish among transparent, translucent, and opaque.
4. Of what does white light consist?
5. Why does a red shirt look red?
6. Is black a color? Why does an object appear to be black?
7. Distinguish between a luminous body and an illuminated body.
8. In what unit is the intensity of a light source measured?
9. In what unit is the illumination of a surface measured?
10. To what is the illumination of a surface by a light source directly proportional? To what is it inversely proportional?
11. Explain why the reflection of light cannot be used as evidence that light is either waves or particles.
12. What theory of light does the diffraction of light support?
13. What theory of light does the polarization of light support?
14. The polarization of light indicates that light waves are what kind of waves?
15. The photoelectric effect supports what theory of light?
16. To what is the energy of a photon proportional?
17. If light is a wave, why is there no apparent diffraction when light goes through large openings?

PROBLEMS

1. An observer uses a 10-sided mirror to measure the speed of light. Maximum brightness occurs when the mirror is rotating at 2000 rev/sec. The total path of the light pulse is 15 km. What is the speed of light?
2. Assume that the sun is 1.5×10^8 km from the earth. Calculate the time required for light to travel from the sun to the earth.
3. A radar signal is reflected from the moon. It is detected after a 2.58 sec time lapse between sending and receiving. How far away is the moon?
4. The light year is a unit of distance used by astronomers. It is the distance light travels in one year. (a) Calculate this distance in kilometers.

(b) The nearest star is approximately four light-years away. How far in kilometers is this star from the earth?

5. A 64-candela point source of light is 3 m above the surface of a desk. What is the illumination of the desk's surface in lumens per square meter?

6. A 100-candela point source of light is 2 m from screen A and 4 m from screen B. How does the illumination of screen B compare with the illumination of screen A?

7. The illumination of a tabletop is 20 lumens/m². The lamp providing the illumination is 4 m above the table. What is the intensity of the lamp?

8. Two lamps illuminate a screen equally. The first lamp has an intensity of 100 candelas and is 5 m from the screen. The second lamp is 3 m from the screen. What is the intensity of the second lamp?

9. A polaroid filter is placed over the light detecting surface of a light meter. The meter is then exposed to the sun on a clear day. The meter reads 500 lumens/m². What actual illumination falls on the meter?

10. If the sun is 1.5×10^8 km away, what is the intensity of the sun as a light source? (Use the answer to Problem **9** and scientific notation.)

11. (a) Calculate the illumination of a screen when it is located at the following distances from a 400-candela source: 5 m, 10 m, 15 m, 20 m, 25 m. (b) Make a table to show the distances in the first column and the corresponding illuminations in the second column. (c) Use graph paper to plot illumination versus distance. Plot the distance on the x axis. (d) Draw the curve that best fits these points. What is the resulting curve called? What does it indicate?

12. A radio wave has a frequency of 10^8 hertz. Planck's constant is 6.6×10^{-34} J-sec. What energy is associated with the radio wave's photons?

13. A gamma-ray photon has a frequency of 10^{20} hertz. What energy is associated with this photon?

14. Which has more energy, the radio wave or the gamma ray?

15. How thick is the first point near the top of a soap-film wedge that will reinforce light of wavelength 3.0×10^{-7} m?

PROJECTS

1. Fold a small piece of paper in half. Using a pair of scissors, snip slits along the folded edge of the paper in two or three places. Unfold the paper and look through the slits at a bright light source. You may need to pull the slits apart slightly.

2. If you can find a pair of old or broken polaroid sunglasses, remove the lenses. Holding one lens in your hand, rotate the second lens above it.

3. Locate a prism. Rotate the prism in the sunlight until a spectrum appears.

READINGS

Brotherton, Manfred, *Masers and Lasers: How They Work, What They Do.* New York, McGraw-Hill Book Co., 1964.

Carroll, John M., *The Story of the Laser,* rev. ed., New York, E. P. Dutton and Co., Inc., 1970.

Crewe, Albert V., "A High-Resolution Scanning Microscope." *Scientific American,* April, 1971.

Feinberg, Gerald, "Light." *Scientific American,* September, 1968.

Jaffe, Bernard, *Michelson and the Speed of Light.* New York, Doubleday and Co., Inc., 1960.

Metelli, Fabio, "The Perception of Transparency." *Scientific American,* April, 1974.

Things are not always what and where they appear to be. You may have great difficulty finding your way out of a maze of mirrors at a carnival. A coin dropped in a swimming pool may not be located exactly where you think it is. A puddle may appear to exist at some distance down a perfectly dry highway on a hot summer day. These are examples of reflection and refraction. What examples of reflection and refraction do you find in this lake scene?

REFLECTION AND REFRACTION

In our study of the nature of light, we found that light behaves both as waves and as particles. We also found that light travels in straight lines and at a very high speed. Let us now study some specific behaviors of light. What happens when light is bounced off a barrier? How does light behave when it passes from one medium into another medium?

18:1 The Law of Reflection

When a light ray is incident upon a surface, the angle of incidence is equal to the angle of reflection. Both of these angles are measured from a normal (perpendicular) to the surface at the point of incidence. The incident ray, the reflected ray, and the normal all lie in the same plane.

18:2 Diffuse and Regular Reflection

When a beam of light strikes most surfaces, the rays reflect in many directions. Most surfaces do not reflect light in a regular manner because they are not smooth. A painted wall or a page of a book appear to be smooth. Actually their surfaces are rough and have many small projections. Rays of light strike different parts of these projections. Each ray reflects according to the law of reflection and the rays are scattered in many different directions (Figure 18-2a).

GOAL: You will gain knowledge and understanding of reflection and refraction, the effects which result from these phenomena, and the relationship between refraction and the speed of light in a medium.

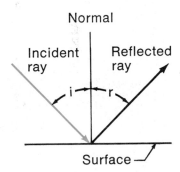

FIGURE 18-1. The law of reflection: The angle of incidence is equal to the angle of reflection.

Light reflected from an uneven surface is scattered in different directions.

261

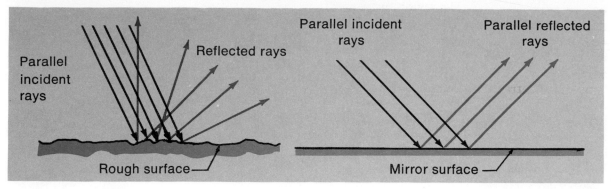

FIGURE 18-2. When parallel light rays strike an uneven surface, they are reflected randomly. When parallel light rays strike a mirror surface, they are reflected as parallel rays.

If a beam of light falls on a very smooth surface, the rays reflect in a regular way. Figure 18-2b shows a beam of parallel rays reflecting from a smooth, flat surface. Since each ray follows the law of reflection, the reflected rays are also parallel. The rays are arranged in the same order after they leave a smooth surface as they were before they approached the surface.

Refraction is the bending of light as it enters a new medium.

FIGURE 18-3. Comparison of the refraction of light at a boundary to the deflection of a car at the boundary of mud and pavement. Light is refracted toward the normal as it enters a more dense medium.

18:3   Refraction of Light

Light travels at different speeds in different media. For this reason, light may bend as it moves from one medium to another. The bending of light at the boundary between two media is called **refraction**.

An incident ray is a ray that falls on the boundary between two media. Once the ray enters a new medium, it is a refracted ray. The angle between the incident ray and a normal to the surface at the point of incidence is the **angle of incidence**. The angle between the refracted ray and the same normal is the **angle of**

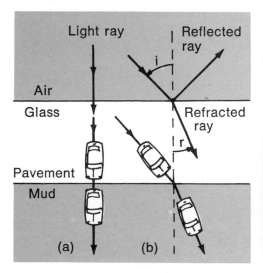

Courtesy of Kodansha

refraction. Refraction occurs only when the incident ray strikes the boundary between the two media obliquely. When the angle of incidence is zero (the ray is perpendicular to the surface), there is no refraction. Then the ray passes straight into the new medium.

Figure 18-3 shows a ray of light as it passes from air into glass at different angles of incidence. Part of the ray is reflected and part is transmitted. Notice that as the ray enters a medium in which it travels more slowly, the refracted ray bends toward the normal. The angle of refraction is smaller than the angle of incidence.

In Figure 18-4, a light ray passes from glass into air at different angles. A ray perpendicular to the surface is not refracted. Rays that strike the surface obliquely are refracted. They bend away from the normal. When a light ray passes into a medium in which it travels faster, the light ray refracts away from the normal. **Optical density** is the property of a medium that determines the speed of light in that medium. If a medium is optically dense, it slows light more than a medium which is less optically dense.

Figures 18-3 and 18-4 compare the refraction of light to a car entering or leaving a patch of mud. When the car enters the mud at an angle (Figure 18-3b), its right wheel enters the mud before its left wheel does. The right wheel slows down. The result is that the car swings to the right or toward the normal. In Figure 18-4b, the car leaves the mud at an angle. The right wheel leaves the mud first and speeds up. The left wheel is still held back. Therefore, the car swings to the left or away from the normal. Keep this car analogy in mind until the behavior of light at various surfaces becomes more familiar to you.

The angle of incidence is measured from the normal to the incident ray. The angle of refraction is measured from the normal to the refracted ray.

Light is refracted only when it hits a boundary at an angle.

Light bends toward the normal if its speed is reduced as it enters the new medium; light bends away from the normal if its speed increases as it enters the new medium.

Optical density of a medium determines the speed of light in that medium.

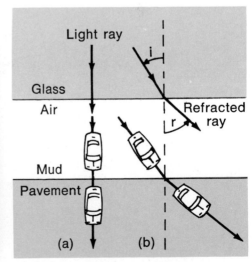

FIGURE 18-4. Light is refracted away from the normal as it enters a less dense medium.

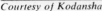
Courtesy of Kodansha

PROBLEM

1. Find the path of the incident light ray through and beyond the medium in each case.

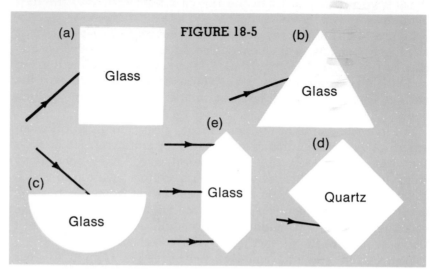

FIGURE 18-5

18:4   Snell's Law

Rays of light that travel from air into glass, or any other medium more optically dense than air, are refracted toward the normal. As the angle of incidence increases, the angle of refraction increases (Figure 18-3). But, the angle of refraction does

Table 18–1

INDICES OF REFRACTION

Medium	n
Vacuum	1.00
Air	1.00*
Water	1.33
Alcohol	1.36
Quartz	1.46
Polyethylene	1.52
Crown Glass	1.52
Flint Glass	1.61
Diamond	2.42

*Index of refraction of air is 1.0003 which is higher than that of vacuum which is 1.0000. However, for practical purposes they are the same.

France Actuelle

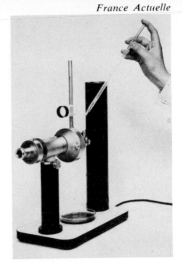

not vary directly with the angle of incidence. Still, the way in which the angle of refraction becomes larger as the angle of incidence is made larger suggests that a definite relationship exists.

The relationship between the angle of incidence and the angle of refraction was discovered by the Dutch scientist Willebrord Snell (1591–1626). **Snell's law** states that *a ray of light bends in such a way that the ratio of the sine of the angle of incidence to the sine of the angle of refraction is a constant.*

For a light ray passing from air into a given medium, the ratio between these sines is called the index of refraction (n) for that medium. Snell's law can be written

$$n = \frac{\sin i}{\sin r}$$

In this equation, i is the angle of incidence, r is the angle of refraction, and n is the index of refraction of the medium. Note that this equation applies only to a ray traveling from air to another medium.

In general, for a ray traveling from any medium to another medium, Snell's law can be written

$$n_1 \sin i = n_2 \sin r$$

In this equation, n_1 is the index of refraction of the incident medium and n_2 is the index of refraction of the second medium.

FIGURE 18-6. This refractometer is used to measure the amount of sugar in honey. The index of refraction of honey changes as the amount of dissolved sugar varies.

Snell's law states that the ratio of the sine of the incident angle to the sine of the refracted angle is a constant.

Example: Snell's Law

A ray of light traveling through air is incident upon a sheet of crown glass at an angle of 30°. What is the angle of refraction?

Solution:

Find the index of refraction from Table 18-1. Find the sine of 30° from Table A-1 in Appendix A. Using $n = \sin i/\sin r$,

$$\sin r = \frac{\sin i}{n} = \frac{0.5}{1.52} = 0.32$$

angle of refraction $= 19°$

PROBLEMS

2. Light is incident upon a piece of crown glass at an angle of 45°. What is the angle of refraction to the nearest degree?

3. A ray of light passes from air into water at an angle of 30°. Find the angle of refraction to the nearest degree.

4. Light is incident upon a piece of quartz at an angle of 45°. What is the angle of refraction to the nearest degree?

5. A ray of light is incident upon a diamond at 45°. (a) What is the angle of refraction? (b) Compare this solution to the solution for Problem 2. Does glass or diamond bend light more?

6. A ray of light travels from air into a liquid. The ray is incident upon the liquid at an angle of 30°. The angle of refraction is

22°. (a) What is the index of refraction of the liquid? (b) Look at Table 18-1. What might the liquid be?

7. In the example on page 265, a ray of light is incident upon crown glass at 30°. The angle of refraction is 19°. Assume the glass is rectangular in shape. Construct a diagram to show the incident ray, the refracted ray, and the normal. Continue the ray through the glass until it reaches the opposite edge. (a) Construct a normal at this point. Measure the angle at which the refracted ray is incident upon the opposite edge of the glass. (b) Did you measure this angle or use a geometric proof to find its value? (c) Assume the material outside the opposite edge is air. What is the angle at which the ray leaves the glass? (d) Is the ray refracted away from the normal or toward the normal?

18:5 Index of Refraction and the Speed of Light

Refraction occurs because the speed of light depends on the medium in which the light is traveling. The index of refraction of a medium is a measure of the amount of bending (refraction). In this section, the relationship between the index of refraction and the speed of light in a medium will be derived.

Figure 18-7 shows the behavior of two parallel rays of light that are incident upon a glass plate from air. The rays are refracted toward the normal. Consider the wave front CB as it approaches the glass plate. After a time interval, the wave front reaches position DA. Since the speed of the wave is slower in the glass, point C on ray y travels only distance CD. Point B on ray x travels distance BA. This causes the wave front to turn.

Point B on ray x travels to A in the same time that point C on ray y travels to D. Therefore, the ratio of BA to CD is the same as the ratio of the speed of light in vacuum v_v to the speed of light in glass v_g.

$$\frac{BA}{CD} = \frac{v_v}{v_g}$$

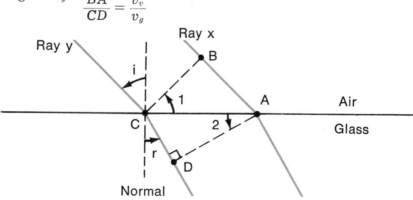

FIGURE 18-7. Index of refraction.

Angle 1 in Figure 18-7 is equal to the angle of incidence of the ray. Angle 2 is equal to the angle of refraction of the ray (corresponding sides mutually perpendicular). The sine of angle 1 is BA/CA. The sine of angle 2 is CD/CA. Using Snell's law, the index of refraction is

$$n_{glass} = \frac{\sin i}{\sin r} = \frac{\sin 1}{\sin 2} = \frac{BA}{CD} = \frac{v_v}{v_g}$$

Thus, the index of refraction of any substance is the speed of light in a vacuum divided by the speed of light in the medium.

The index of refraction of a medium is the ratio of the speed of light in a vacuum to the speed of light in the medium.

The speed of light in air is assumed to be the same as the speed of light in a vacuum. Because this speed has a special significance, it is assigned the symbol c. The index of refraction for any substance is

$$n_s = \frac{c}{v_s}$$

where v_s represents the speed of light in the medium.

The index of refraction of many substances can be found by measurement. The speed of light in a vacuum, 3×10^8 m/sec, is known. Therefore, it is possible to calculate the speed of light in many substances.

Example: **Speed of Light in a Medium**

The index of refraction of water is 1.33. Calculate the speed of light in water.

Solution:

$$
\begin{aligned}
v &= \frac{c}{n} \\
&= \frac{3 \times 10^8 \text{ m/sec}}{1.33} \\
&= 2.25 \times 10^8 \text{ m/sec}
\end{aligned}
$$

PROBLEMS

8. Use Table 18-1 to find the speed of light in (a) alcohol, (b) quartz, and (c) polyethylene.

9. The speed of light in a plastic is 2.0×10^8 m/sec. What is the index of refraction of the plastic?

10. The speed of light in a glass plate is 196 890 km/sec. Find the index of refraction of the glass.

18:6   Total Internal Reflection

When a ray of light passes from a dense medium into air, it is bent away from the normal. In other words, the angle of refraction is larger than the angle of incidence. The fact that the angle

In total internal reflection no light rays are transmitted into the new medium.

of refraction must be larger than the angle of incidence leads to an interesting phenomenon known as **total internal reflection**. Total internal reflection occurs when light falls on the surface of a less optically dense medium at an angle so great that it cannot produce a refracted ray. Figure 18-8 is such an occurrence. Ray

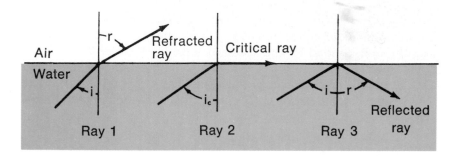

FIGURE 18-8. Total internal reflection.

1 is incident upon the surface of the water at angle i_1. Ray 1 produces the angle of refraction, r_1. Ray 2 is incident at such a large angle (i_c) that the refracted ray lies along the surface of the water. The angle of refraction is 90°. The incident angle which causes the refracted ray to lie right along the boundary of the substance (angle i_c) is peculiar to the substance. It is known as the critical angle of the substance. Any ray which falls upon the surface of the water at an angle greater than the critical angle (ray 3) cannot be refracted. All of the light is reflected.

Total internal reflection causes some curious effects. Suppose an underwater swimmer looks at the surface of the water. The legs of a second swimmer, seated on the edge of the pool, may

FIGURE 18-9. Examples of total internal reflection at air-glass interfaces.

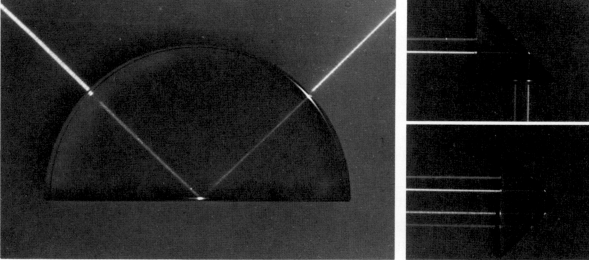

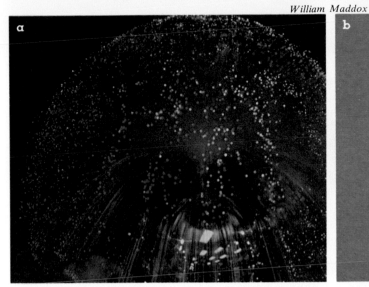

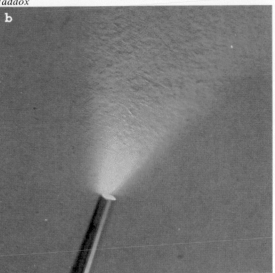

appear to be high in the air. Total internal reflection also has some very practical uses. It is important in the design of binoculars. It has also given rise to a field of optics known as **fiber optics**. Fiber optics promises to contribute much to the field of communications.

18:7 Effects of Refraction

Many interesting effects are caused by the refraction of light. The puddle-effect, the apparent shift in the position of objects immersed in liquids, and the lengthening of the day are examples.

The puddle-effect can be observed along highways in summer. A driver looking down the road sees what looks like a puddle of water. But, the puddle disappears as the car approaches. This happens because the air next to the surface of the road is heated sooner than the air above it. This heated air expands. As the distance above the road increases, the air gradually becomes cooler.

FIGURE 18-10. Total internal reflection can be observed in the fiber optics display (a) and can be put to practical use in medical instruments which contain their own light source (b).

Fiber optics is an example of the practical application of total internal reflection.

The puddle effect is due to the gradual change in air density above a warm surface.

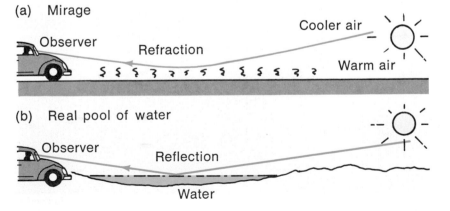

FIGURE 18-11. (a) Refraction of light in air of differing densities produces the same effect as (b) reflection of light from a pool of water.

FIGURE 18-12. Because of the refraction of light, the handle of the spoon in this glass of water appears bent.

As a result, the density of the air gradually increases. Therefore, the index of refraction of the air also increases with distance above the road. As a ray of light moves toward the road, it passes through air of increasingly lower index of refraction. The ray bends in the manner shown in Figure 18-11. To an observer, the refracted light looks like light reflected from a puddle.

An object viewed in a liquid is not where it appears to be. As a result of the refraction of light, an object may appear to be much closer to the surface of the liquid than it really is. This same effect makes a spoon placed in a glass of water appear broken.

Light travels at a slightly slower speed in air than it does in the near vacuum conditions of outer space. As a result, sunlight is refracted by the atmosphere. In the morning, this causes sunlight to reach the earth before the sun actually comes up. In the evening, the sunlight is bent over the horizon after the sun has actually set. Thus, daylight is extended in the morning and evening because of the refraction of light.

18:8   Dispersion of Light

White light is dispersed into an array of colored light when it passes through a prism.

When a beam of light from the sun or a light bulb falls on the surface of a glass prism, the light disperses. The light emerges from the prism as an array of different colors. Early scientists thought that the colors were produced somehow inside the glass.

FIGURE 18-13. White light, when directed through a prism, is dispersed into a band of light of different colors.

Photo by Eric Lessing, Magnum

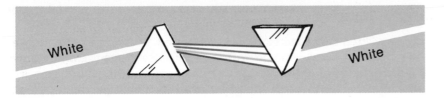

Sir Isaac Newton disproved this assumption. Newton allowed a beam of sunlight (white light) to fall on a prism. Then he allowed the emerging colored light to fall on a second, inverted prism. The colored light rays recombined to form white light once again. Newton was the first to understand that white light is made up of many colors of light.

All electromagnetic waves travel through space at the speed of light, 3×10^8 m/sec. But, in all other media, these waves travel more slowly, and waves of different frequencies travel at slightly different speeds. Therefore the index of refraction is slightly different for each wavelength of light. When white light falls on a prism, the waves of each color bend by different amounts and the light disperses.

As light emerges from a prism, the various colors are in a distinct arrangement. Red light is refracted the least by the prism because red light has the fastest speed in the glass. Violet light is always refracted the most because violet light has the slowest speed in the glass.

Red light has the longest wavelength and the highest speed for visible light in a medium. Violet light has the shortest wavelength and the lowest speed.

The array of different colors that emerges from a prism is called a spectrum. If the prism is placed between the light source and a screen, the spectrum produced by the source will fall on the

A visible spectrum is a display of color formed when a light beam of multiple wavelengths is bent and spread by passing through a prism.

William Maddox

FIGURE 18-15. This rainbow is a result of the dispersion of white light by water droplets in the air.

271

screen. Then this spectrum can be studied. It is found that different light sources produce different spectra. Light from an incandescent solid produces all visible wavelengths of light. When this light passes through the prism, a **continuous spectrum** is seen. Sunlight passing through a prism or through raindrops will cause a spectrum of this sort, commonly called a rainbow.

A rainbow shows the various components of white light.

SUMMARY
Light rays follow the law of reflection. This law states that the angle of incidence is equal to the angle of reflection. The law of reflection explains both diffuse reflection from a rough surface and regular reflection from a smooth surface.

Refraction is the bending of a light ray at the boundary between two media. Refraction occurs only when the incident ray strikes the boundary obliquely.

Snell's law states that when a light ray passes from air into a more optically dense medium at an angle, the ratio of the sine of the angle of incidence to the sine of the angle of refraction is a constant. The ratio (n) is called the index of refraction. The index of refraction is also equal to the speed of light in a vacuum divided by the speed of light in the medium.

The refraction of light accounts for the dispersion of light by a prism. Light waves of different frequencies are refracted by slightly different amounts. Thus, when white light falls on a prism, waves of each color bend by different amounts. A spectrum of colored light is produced.

QUESTIONS
1. How does regular reflection differ from diffuse reflection?
2. If a light ray does not undergo refraction at a boundary between two media, what is its angle of incidence?
3. How does the angle of incidence compare with the angle of refraction when a light ray passes obliquely from air into glass?
4. How does the angle of incidence compare with the angle of refraction when a light ray leaves glass and enters air?
5. State Snell's law.
6. Write two equations for finding the index of refraction of a medium. To do this, use two different sets of symbols.
7. What is the "critical angle" of incidence?
8. Explain the "puddle-effect."
9. Explain how white light is dispersed by a prism.
10. Which travels fastest in glass: red light, green light, or blue light?
11. What type of spectrum is the spectrum of sunlight?

PROBLEMS
1. A ray of light strikes a mirror at an angle of 53° to the normal. (a) What is the angle of reflection? (b) What is the angle between the incident ray and the reflected ray?
2. A ray of light incident upon a mirror makes an angle of 36° with the mirror. What is the angle between the incident ray and the reflected ray?
3. In each of the diagrams of Figure 18-16, a ray of light is incident upon the surface of a glass prism. Trace the diagrams on a separate sheet of paper. Extend each ray to show how it travels through the prism and beyond.

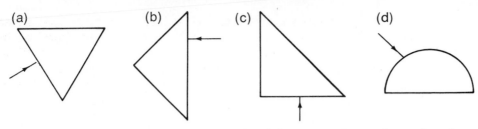

(a)　　(b)　　(c)　　(d)

FIGURE 18-16

4. A ray of light is incident at an angle of 60° upon the surface of a piece of glass ($n = 1.5$). What is the angle of refraction?

5. A light ray strikes the surface of a pond at an angle of incidence of 36°. At what angle, to the nearest degree, is the ray refracted?

6. Light is incident at an angle of 60° on the surface of a diamond. Find the angle of refraction.

7. A light ray is incident at an angle of 45° on one surface of a 10-cm glass cube ($n_g = 1.5$). At what angle with the normal does the ray emerge from the other side of the cube?

8. By what amount is the emergent ray of Problem 7 shifted from the path of the incident ray?

9. The index of refraction of water is 1.33. What is the speed of light in water?

10. What is the speed of light in diamond?

11. The speed of light in a clear plastic is 1.90×10^8 m/sec. A ray of light enters the plastic at an angle of 22°. At what angle is the ray refracted?

PROJECTS

1. Obtain a small piece of window glass. Place masking tape around the sides to prevent cutting yourself on any sharp edges. Place the piece of glass between a burning candle and a beaker of water. Adjust the position of the glass until the reflected image of the candle appears to be located in the beaker of water. Measure the distance between the glass and the candle. Then measure the distance between the glass and the beaker. Compare the distances.

2. Place a pencil in a glass of water. Using a protractor determine the angle of incidence and the angle of refraction. Using these, find the index of refraction of water.

3. Why is the lettering on the front of some vehicles such as ambulances, printed backwards?

4. Place two mirrors at right angles to each other. Place a small object in front of the mirrors and locate the images. Explain why you can see three images in only two mirrors.

READINGS

Connes, Pierre, "How Light Is Analyzed." *Scientific American,* September, 1968.

Corballis, Michael C., and Beale, Ivan L., "On Telling Left from Right." *Scientific American,* March, 1971.

Fichtel, Carl, et al, "High-Energy Gamma-Ray Astronomy." *Physics Today,* September, 1975.

Jenkins, F. A., and White, H. E., *Fundamentals of Optics,* 3rd ed. New York, McGraw-Hill Book Co., 1957.

Kapany, Narinder S., "Fiber Optics." *Scientific American,* November, 1960.

Mirrors reflect light. In contrast, lenses transmit light. Mirrors and lenses may be curved or flat. Both produce images. The characteristics of the images depend on the shape of the mirrors and lenses which produce them. Images may be right side up or upside down. They may also be larger or smaller than the original object. This glass of water acts like a lens. What other common objects act like mirrors or lenses? What are some practical uses of mirrors and lenses?

MIRRORS AND LENSES

We have studied the behavior of light when it is reflected off a surface. We have also studied light as it moves from one medium into another. These properties of reflection and refraction have many practical uses. Mirrored surfaces are based on reflection. Eyeglasses and magnifying glasses are based on refraction. Microscopes and cameras make use of both mirrors and lenses. Let us look at the way in which different mirrors and lenses reflect or transmit light. In this way, we can better understand how they can be used in everyday life.

GOAL: You will gain knowledge and understanding of mirrors and lenses with various shapes, and of the images they form.

19:1 Plane Mirrors

The regular reflection of light rays enables us to see the images of objects in mirrors. In Figure 19-1a, object A is illuminated by a light source. A large number of the light rays that fall on object A are reflected in all directions. Thus, object A can be seen from any direction. If some of the rays that leave A fall on a mirror, they will be reflected from the mirror. Since the surface of the mirror is smooth, the rays are reflected in a regular way. Looking at the mirror produces an effect similar to looking at A. Because the directions of the rays are changed as they are reflected from the mirror, the image of A appears to be behind the mirror.

One interesting effect of mirror-images is the apparent reversal of the image from left to right. In Figure 19-1b an observer looks into the mirror. The right arm of the object is seen as the left arm of the image. This effect is due to the change in direction of the light rays as they are reflected from the mirror.

A plane mirror reflects light rays in the same order that they approach it.

The image in a plane mirror is reversed left to right.

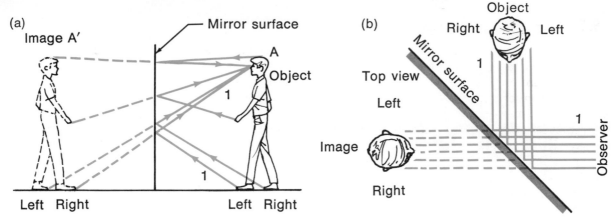

(a) Image A'
Mirror surface
A
Object
1
Left Right
Left Right

(b)
Object
Right   Left
Mirror surface
1
Top view
Left
Image
Right
1
Observer

FIGURE 19-1. Formation of an image in a plane mirror. The image is the same size as the object and is the same distance behind the mirror as the object is in front of it. The image is also erect but reversed right for left.

The image is the same size as the object and the same distance behind the mirror as the object is in front of the mirror.

Suppose an object is located at point P (Figure 19-2a). Light rays extend in every direction from point P. The rays that strike the mirror at points M_1 and M_2 are reflected to the eye of an observer. By extending the two reflected rays behind the mirror, point P' is located. Triangles PBM and $P'BM$ are congruent. Point P' appears to be as far behind the mirror as point P is in front of the mirror. If the same method is used to locate a second point next to P, the eye will also interpret that point to be as far behind the mirror as it is in front of the mirror. Thus points all along the image appear to have the same relation to each other as do their corresponding points on the object. The image will be the same size as the object.

In summary, the image observed in a plane mirror is the same size as the object. It is as far behind the mirror as the object is in front of the mirror. It also appears to be reversed.

FIGURE 19-2. Ray diagram for finding an image in a plane mirror. Two rays from the object are traced to the point behind the mirror at which they intersect.

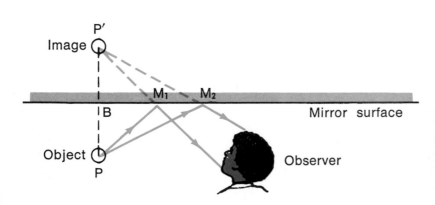

P'
Image
M₁   M₂
B
Mirror surface
Object
P
Observer

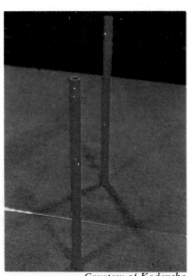

Courtesy of Kodansha

19:2 Converging Mirrors

Figure 19-3 represents a number of small plane mirrors. They are arranged to form an arc of a circle. When parallel rays of light are sent to the mirrors, they follow the law of reflection. The rays converge at point *F*, or the **focal point** of the mirror. Converging mirrors focus light rays in this way.

Figure 19-4 represents a spherical mirror. Although three dimensions are needed to show a curved mirror, try to picture a spherical mirror. This mirror is a **spherical concave mirror.** It may be thought of as an infinite number of plane mirrors arranged in a spherical fashion (Figure 19-3). Since it is a portion of a sphere, a spherical mirror has a geometric center or vertex, *A*

The focal point (F) of a converging mirror is the point where parallel rays of light meet after being reflected from the mirror.

A concave mirror is a converging mirror.

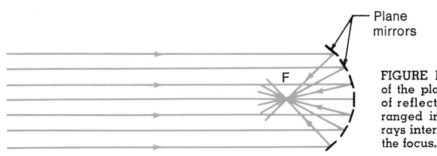

Plane mirrors

FIGURE 19-3. Each ray striking one of the plane mirrors follows the law of reflection. If the mirrors are arranged in the proper curve, all the rays intersect at a single point called the focus.

(Figure 19-4). A radius perpendicular to a tangent to this point passes back to the **center of curvature** of the mirror, *C* (Figure 19-4). This radius is called the **principal axis.**

It is important to remember two rules concerning concave mirrors. Any light ray that approaches the mirror parallel to the principal axis is reflected through the point halfway between the center of curvature, *C*, and the vertex *A*. This halfway point is

FIGURE 19-4. The focus of a concave spherical mirror is located halfway between the center of curvature and the center of the mirror surface. Rays reflected by this spherical mirror converge at the focus.

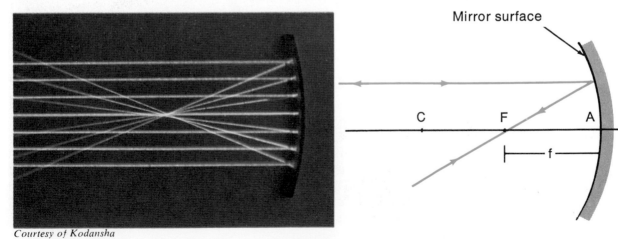

Mirror surface

Courtesy of Kodansha

the focal point, F. This point is a result of the law of reflection. Any ray that approaches the mirror on a path that passes through F will be reflected from the mirror parallel to the principal axis.

If the principal axis of a small concave mirror is pointed at the sun, all rays that fall on the mirror are parallel to each other and to the principal axis. Rays from the sun travel more than 1.5×10^8 km to reach the mirror. Any rays leaving the sun that are not parallel to the principal axis would be far from the mirror by the time they travel this distance. To determine the focal point, allow light from a fairly distant source to fall on the concave mirror. Move a piece of paper toward and away from the mirror to find the sharpest point of focus. This is the focal point. The distance from the focal point to the vertex of the mirror is the **focal length** (f) of the mirror.

The principal axis is an imaginary line extending from the geometric center of a spherical mirror to its center of curvature (C).

The focal length (f) is the distance from F to A.

19:3   Spherical Aberration

In a truly spherical mirror, rays that approach the mirror parallel to the principal axis are not all reflected through F. Those rays that strike the mirror along its outer edge miss F slightly. This effect is called **spherical aberration** (ab uh RAY shuhn). Because of spherical aberration, parabolic mirrors are used to focus light instead of spherical mirrors.

Spherical aberration occurs because rays that strike a spherical mirror along its outer edge are not reflected through F.

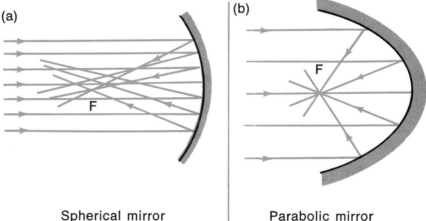

(a) Spherical mirror

(b) Parabolic mirror

FIGURE 19-5. In a concave spherical mirror, some rays converge at other points than the focus. A parabolic mirror focuses all rays at a sharp point.

A parabolic mirror can be used for cooking. A cooking pot is placed at F of a large concave mirror. The concentrated sunlight provides an intense source of heat. Parabolic mirrors are also used to produce parallel beams of light. Imagine that a light source is placed at F. The light rays that leave F reflect from the mirror as a parallel beam of light. Flashlights and car headlights send out parallel beams of light in this way.

19:4   Real and Virtual Images

The image seen in a plane mirror appears to be behind the mirror. Light rays do not pass through the image seen in a plane mirror. This image cannot be cast upon a screen. Thus, it is called a **virtual image**.

When a concave mirror reflects the sun's rays, the reflected rays meet at the principal focus of the mirror. Thus they produce an image of the sun at this point. A bright point of light that falls on a piece of paper placed at the principal focus of a concave mirror is a very small image of the sun. This image is actually where it appears to be and can be cast upon a screen. Thus, it is called a **real image.**

An image is virtual when light rays do not pass through it.

An image is real when light rays actually do meet to reproduce the object.

19:5   Images Formed by Converging Mirrors

In this section "ray diagrams" will be drawn. The diagrams will show how converging mirrors cause real images to appear outside the mirrors. They will also aid in locating the image.

Figure 19-6 shows how a concave mirror forms an image. Consider a point that is farther from the mirror than C. This point is said to be "beyond C." When light falls on an object, light rays

Ray diagrams can be used to locate images graphically.

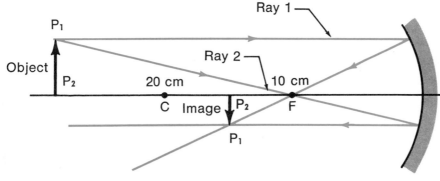

FIGURE 19-6. Finding the real image formed by a concave spherical mirror when the object is located beyond the center of curvature (C) of the mirror.

are reflected in all directions. Therefore rays can be drawn from the object to the mirror in any direction.

To construct a ray diagram, first select a point on the object, P_1. Draw two rays from this point to the mirror. Draw ray 1 parallel to the principal axis. Ray 1, therefore, reflects through F. Draw ray 2 so that it passes through F on its way to the mirror. This ray reflects parallel to the principal axis. The two rays from P_1 converge beyond F. If two rays are drawn from point P_2 in the same way, they meet at point P_2 on the image. Other points on the object send out rays that meet at corresponding points on the image. In this way, the image is formed. The object is placed

In a ray diagram, ray 1 is drawn parallel to the principal axis and then is reflected through F; ray 2 is drawn through F and then is reflected parallel to the principal axis.

with one end on the principal axis. A ray goes straight to the mirror and straight back. Thus, the bottom of the image is also located on the principal axis.

Figure 19-6 shows an object that is beyond C. The image is between C and F. It is real because the rays actually do come together to form an image at this point. It is also inverted and smaller than the object. Figure 19-6 also shows that when an object is placed in the position of the image, its image is formed in the position of the object. Thus, if the object is between C and F, the image will be beyond C. It will be inverted, larger than the object, and real.

As the object is moved in toward C from beyond C, the image position also approaches C. The image and the object meet at C. In this case, the image is inverted, real, and the same size as the object. If the object then is moved between C and F, the image moves out beyond C. Object and image positions are interchangeable (Figure 19-10a, b, c).

Suppose the object distance and the focal length of the mirror are given. The position of the image can then be calculated from the mirror equation below. Let d_o be the distance from the object to A; d_i the distance from the image to A; and f the focal length of the mirror.

The mirror equation can be used to locate the image.

$$\frac{1}{d_o} + \frac{1}{d_i} = \frac{1}{f}$$

Also, the size of the image is to the size of the object as the image distance is to the object distance. The ratio of the image size to the object size is called the magnification of the mirror.

$$\frac{d_i}{d_o} = \frac{S_i}{S_o}$$

Example: Real Image From a Converging Mirror

An object 2 cm high is 30 cm from a concave mirror. The focal length of the mirror is 10 cm. (a) What is the location of the image? (b) What is the size of the image?

Solution:

(a) $\quad \dfrac{1}{d_o} + \dfrac{1}{d_i} = \dfrac{1}{f}$

$\dfrac{1}{30\text{ cm}} + \dfrac{1}{d_i} = \dfrac{1}{10\text{ cm}}$

$\dfrac{1}{d_i} = \dfrac{1}{10\text{ cm}} - \dfrac{1}{30\text{ cm}}$

$= \dfrac{2}{30\text{ cm}}$

Thus, $d_i = 15$ cm

(b) $\dfrac{d_i}{d_o} = \dfrac{S_i}{S_o}$

$S_i = \dfrac{S_o d_i}{d_o}$

$= \dfrac{(15\text{ cm})(2\text{ cm})}{30\text{ cm}}$

$= 1$ cm

PROBLEMS

Needed: a compass, a metric ruler, a sharp pencil.

1. Use a compass and ruler to solve the example in Section 19:5 by constructing a ray diagram. The problem states that the focal length of the mirror is 10 cm. Focal length is always half the radius of curvature, so the radius of the mirror is 20 cm. Draw to scale if necessary.

2. An object is 15 cm from a concave spherical mirror of 20-cm radius. Locate the image from (a) a graph, (b) the mirror equation.

3. An object 3 cm high is 10 cm in front of a concave mirror of 12-cm radius. Locate the image from (a) a graph, (b) the mirror equation. (c) What is the height of the image?

4. An object 1.5 cm in height is 12 cm from a concave mirror of 12-cm radius. Locate the image from (a) a graph, (b) the mirror equation. (c) What is the height of the image?

5. An object 3 cm high is 12 cm from a concave mirror of 6-cm radius. Locate the image from (a) a graph, (b) the mirror equation. (c) What is the height of the image?

6. An image of an object is 30 cm from a concave mirror of 20-cm radius. Locate the object.

7. An image of an object is 30 cm from a concave mirror of 20-cm focal length. Locate the object.

19:6   Virtual Images in a Converging Mirror

The object in Figure 19-7 is located between F and the mirror. It is 5 cm in front of a mirror of 10-cm focal length. To locate the image of the object, construct the same two rays used in previous examples. Ray 1 leaves the object and follows the path it would have followed if it had started at F. This ray is reflected parallel to the principal axis. Ray 2 approaches the mirror parallel to the principal axis. It is reflected through the focal point. Note that

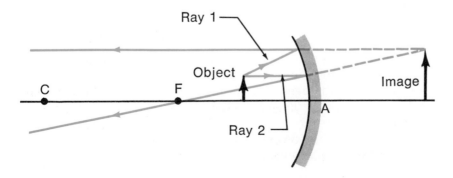

FIGURE 19-7. Finding the virtual image formed by a concave spherical mirror when the object is located between the mirror and F.

rays 1 and 2 diverge when reflected. Hence, the rays cannot come together to form a real image. On the other side of the mirror the rays are traced back to their apparent origin. The image is virtual, erect, and larger than the object.

A negative image distance indicates a virtual image.

When an object is placed between the vertex and the focal point of a concave mirror, the image distance is negative. Thus, the image is located behind the mirror and is a virtual image.

Example: Virtual Image From a Converging Mirror

Find the location of the image in Figure 19-7 if the object is 5 cm in front of a concave mirror of focal length 10 cm.

Solution:

$$d_o = 5 \text{ cm}, f = 10 \text{ cm}$$

$$\frac{1}{d_o} + \frac{1}{d_i} = \frac{1}{f}$$

Solving this equation for d_i yields,

$$
\begin{aligned}
d_i &= \frac{d_o f}{d_o - f} \\
&= \frac{(5 \text{ cm})\,(10 \text{ cm})}{5 \text{ cm} - 10 \text{ cm}} \\
&= \frac{50 \text{ cm}^2}{-5 \text{ cm}} \\
&= -10 \text{ cm}
\end{aligned}
$$

PROBLEMS

8. An object is 4 cm in front of a concave mirror of 12-cm radius. Locate the image.

9. An object is 6 cm in front of a concave mirror of 10-cm focal length. Find the image.

10. An object is 10 cm from a concave mirror of 16 cm focal length. (a) Locate the image. (b) The object is 4 cm high. What is the height of the image?

19:7 Diverging Mirrors

A convex mirror is a diverging mirror.

A convex mirror is a spherical mirror which is reflective on its outer surface. For example, the inside of a spoon is a concave mirror. The outer side of the spoon is a convex mirror. Convex mirrors can only cause rays to diverge. Hence, convex mirrors never form real images. The focal point (F) of a convex mirror is behind the mirror. The focal length (f) of a convex mirror is negative.

Images formed by diverging mirrors are always virtual, erect, and smaller than the object.

The image seen in a convex mirror is always virtual, behind the mirror, erect, and smaller than the object. Figure 19-8 shows how

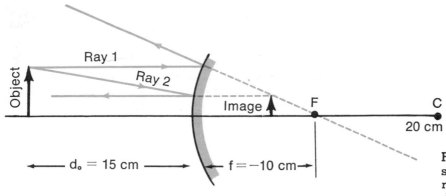

FIGURE 19-8. Convex spherical mirrors cause reflected light rays to diverge.

a convex mirror forms a virtual image. Follow the paths of the two principal rays. Ray 1 approaches the mirror parallel to the principal axis and is reflected. The path of the reflected rays, extended behind the mirror (dotted lines), passes through F. Ray 2 approaches the mirror on a path that, if extended behind the mirror, would pass through F. Ray 2's reflected ray is parallel to the principal axis. The two reflected rays when traced back to their point of apparent intersection behind the mirror indicate an erect, smaller, virtual image.

Divergent mirrors are used when a large field of view is needed. Some uses are rear-view mirrors on vehicles and mirrors used in stores to watch for shoplifters.

FIGURE 19-9. Examples of diverging mirrors are a lawn sphere (a) and a rear view mirror (b).

William Maddox

Courtesy of Kodansha

FIGURE 19-10. Formation of images in curved mirrors.

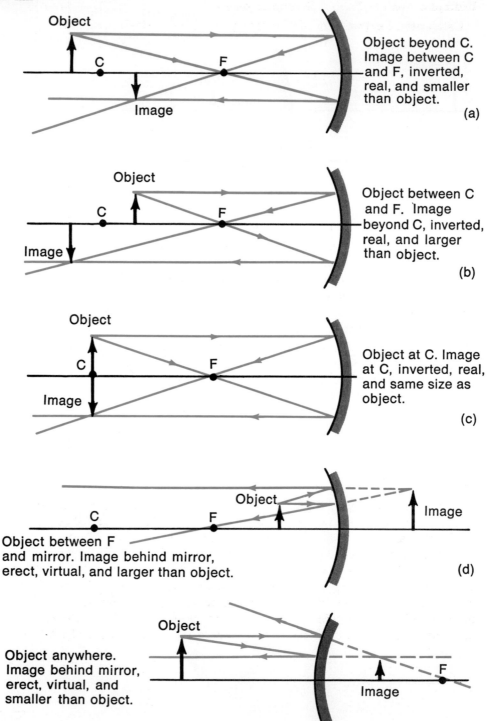

Object beyond C. Image between C and F, inverted, real, and smaller than object.

(a)

Object between C and F. Image beyond C, inverted, real, and larger than object.

(b)

Object at C. Image at C, inverted, real, and same size as object.

(c)

Object between F and mirror. Image behind mirror, erect, virtual, and larger than object.

(d)

Object anywhere. Image behind mirror, erect, virtual, and smaller than object.

(e)

Example: Image From a Diverging Mirror

Calculate the position of the image in Figure 19-8. Use the mirror equation.

Solution:

$$d_o = 15 \text{ cm}, \quad f = -10 \text{ cm}$$

$$\frac{1}{d_o} + \frac{1}{d_i} = \frac{1}{f}$$

$$\begin{aligned}
d_i &= \frac{d_o\,(f)}{d_o - f} \\
&= \frac{(15 \text{ cm})\,(-10 \text{ cm})}{15 \text{ cm} - (-10 \text{ cm})} \\
&= \frac{-150 \text{ cm}^2}{25 \text{ cm}} \\
&= -6 \text{ cm}
\end{aligned}$$

PROBLEMS

11. An object is 20 cm in front of a convex mirror of -15-cm focal length. Locate the image.

12. A convex mirror has a focal length of -12 cm. An object is placed 60 cm in front of the mirror. Locate the image.

13. A mirror used to watch for shoplifters in a department store has a focal length of -40 cm. A person stands in an aisle 6 m from the mirror. Locate the person's image.

14. Shiny lawn spheres placed on pedestals are convex mirrors. One such sphere has a focal length of -20 cm. A robin sits in a tree 10 m from the sphere. Locate the robin's image.

19:8   Lenses

Lenses are an essential part of telescopes, eyeglasses, cameras, microscopes, and other optical instruments. A lens is usually made of glass. But some are made of transparent plastic. Many precision optical instruments use quartz lenses.

The two main types of lenses are converging lenses and diverging lenses. A **converging lens** is thickest at its middle and becomes thinner at the edges. A **diverging lens** is thinnest at its middle and becomes thicker at the edges. Figure 19-11 shows the cross sections of a converging and a diverging lens. Because the

A converging lens is thick in the center and thin at the edges.

A diverging lens is thin in the center and thick at the edges.

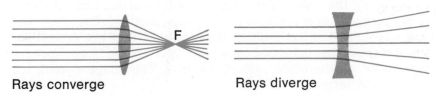

Rays converge   Rays diverge

FIGURE 19-11. Converging and diverging lenses.

A convex lens is a converging lens. A concave lens is a diverging lens.

surfaces of converging lenses are convex, they are often called convex lenses. Likewise, diverging lenses are called concave lenses because their surfaces are concave. A converging lens refracts light rays so that they converge. A diverging lens refracts light rays so that they diverge.

19:9 Converging Lenses

The focal point of a converging lens is the point where rays that approach the lens parallel to the principal axis meet after being refracted by the lens.

The principal axis of a lens is a perpendicular line to the mid-point of the lens. Light rays that approach a converging lens parallel to the principal axis will, upon refraction, converge at a point. This point is called the focal point (F) of the converging lens. The distance from the focal point to the lens is the focal length (f).

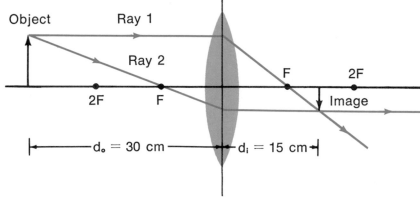

FIGURE 19-12. Finding the real images formed by a converging lens when the object is located beyond the principal focus (F) of the mirror.

The focal length of a lens depends on its shape and its index of refraction.

Symmetrical lenses, such as the one in Figure 19-12, have a focal point on each side of the lens. The focal length of a converging lens depends on two factors. These are the shape of the lens and the index of refraction of the lens material. An important position along the principal axis of a lens is twice the focal length $(2F)$.

In Figure 19-12 an object is placed at a distance greater than $2F$. To locate the image, draw two principal rays. Draw ray 1 parallel to the principal axis. It refracts and passes through F on the other side of the lens. Ray 2 passes through F on its way to the lens. Upon refraction, ray 2 leaves the lens parallel to the principal axis. The two rays converge between F and $2F$. The point where the rays converge is the image location. Rays selected at other points on the object would converge at corresponding points along the image. The image is real, inverted, and smaller.

Suppose an object is placed at the image position. The image appears at the old object position because light rays are reversible. Thus, if the object is located between F and $2F$, the image appears beyond $2F$ on the other side of the lens. The image is real, inverted, and larger.

Craig Kramer

FIGURE 19-13. This camper is using a converging lens to start a fire in this pile of leaves and paper.

If an object is placed at 2F, the image appears at 2F on the other side of the lens. It is real, inverted, and the same size as the object.

It is not necessary to draw a lens when making ray diagrams for lens problems. A straight line can be drawn instead. To find the size and location of the image mathematically, use these lens equations.

$$\frac{1}{d_o} + \frac{1}{d_i} = \frac{1}{f}$$
$$\frac{S_o}{S_i} = \frac{d_o}{d_i}$$

The lens equations can be used to find the size and location of an image.

Note that these equations are the same as those used with mirrors. The equations are derived on page 290.

The lens equations are exactly the same as the mirror equations.

Example: Real Image From a Converging Lens

In Figure 19-12 the object is 30 cm from a converging lens of 10-cm focal length. Use the lens equation to locate the image.

Solution:

$$\frac{1}{d_o} + \frac{1}{d_i} = \frac{1}{f}$$
$$d_i = \frac{d_o f}{d_o - f}$$
$$= \frac{(30 \text{ cm}) (10 \text{ cm})}{30 \text{ cm} - 10 \text{ cm}}$$
$$= 15 \text{ cm}$$

PROBLEMS

15. Use the graphical method to find the image position of an object 30 cm from a convex lens of 10-cm focal length. (Let 1 cm equal 2 cm.)

16. An object 1 cm high is 15 cm from a convex lens of 10 cm focal length. Find the distance and size of the image (a) graphically, (b) mathematically.

17. An object 3 cm high is 10 cm in front of a convex lens of 6 cm focal length. Find the image distance and height.

18. An object 1.5 cm high is 12 cm from a convex lens of 6 cm focal length. Find the height and position of the image (a) graphically, (b) mathematically.

19. An object 3 cm high is 12 cm from a convex lens of 3 cm focal length. Locate the image.

20. An image is 12 cm from a convex lens of 4 cm focal length. Locate the object.

21. An image is 10 cm from a convex lens of 8 cm focal length. Locate the object.

19:10   Virtual Images Formed by a Converging Lens

If an object is placed between a converging lens and its focal point, the rays do not meet on the other side of the lens. Instead, the image appears on the same side of the lens as the object. As Figure 19-14 shows, the image is erect, larger, and virtual.

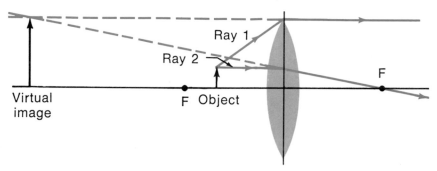

Ray 1

Ray 2

F

Virtual image   F   Object

FIGURE 19-14. Finding the virtual image formed by a converging lens when the object is placed between the lens and the principal focus (F).

If an object is placed between a converging lens and its focal point, a virtual, enlarged image is produced.

To understand how a converging lens forms a virtual image, look at Figure 19-14. The object is between F and the lens. Ray 1 is drawn from the tip of the object to the lens. It follows the same path it would have followed if it had started at F. Therefore, ray 1 is refracted in a way that it leaves the lens parallel to the principal axis. Ray 2 is drawn parallel to the principal axis. When refracted, ray 2 travels through the focal point on the other side of the lens. Note that when rays 1 and 2 leave the other side of the lens they diverge. Therefore, they cannot join to form a real image. However, if the two rays are traced back to their apparent origin, a larger virtual image is seen on the same side of the lens as the object. This image is magnified. A convex lens used in this way is a magnifier.

Example: Virtual Image From a Converging Lens

An object is 4 cm from a converging lens of 6 cm focal length.
(a) Locate its image. (b) What kind of image is formed?

Solution:
  (a) Solve the lens equation for d_i. Then

$$d_i = \frac{d_o f}{d_o - f}$$
$$= \frac{(4 \text{ cm}) (6 \text{ cm})}{4 \text{ cm} - 6 \text{ cm}}$$
$$= -12 \text{ cm}$$

FIGURE 19-15. A converging lens can be used as a magnifying glass.

  (b) Since the image distance is negative, the image is virtual.
It is on the same side of the lens as the object.

PROBLEMS

22. The focal length of a convex lens is 20 cm. A newspaper is 6 cm from the lens. Find the image distance.

23. A magnifying glass has a focal length of 12 cm. An object is placed 4 cm from the lens. (a) Locate the image. (b) The object is 2 cm high. How high is the image?

24. An object is 8 cm from a lens. What focal length must the lens have to form a virtual, erect image 16 cm from the lens?

19:11   Diverging Lenses

All images seen through diverging lenses are virtual and erect. Figure 19-16 shows how a concave lens forms these images. Ray 1 approaches the lens parallel to the principal axis. Upon refraction, ray 1 appears to originate at the focal point. Ray 2 passes through the center of the lens. Ray 2 is refracted as it enters the lens. It is refracted again as it leaves the lens. The two refractions cancel and ray 2, in effect, passes straight through the lens. Notice that the two rays are divergent and appear to originate at i.

Images formed by diverging lenses are always virtual and erect.

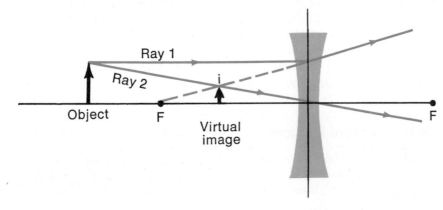

FIGURE 19-16. Formation of a virtual image by a diverging lens.

19:12   Derivation of the Lens Equation

Triangles APO and DGO are similar triangles (Figure 19-17).

$$\frac{S_o}{S_i} = \frac{AP}{DG} = \frac{OP}{OG} = \frac{d_o}{d_i}$$

and,

$$\frac{S_o}{S_i} = \frac{d_o}{d_i}$$

Also, triangles FGD and FOB are similar triangles. Hence,

$$\frac{OF}{GF} = \frac{BO}{DG} = \frac{d_o}{d_i}, \text{ so } \frac{OF}{GF} = \frac{d_o}{d_i}$$

Since $OF = f$ and $OG = d_i$ then,

$$\frac{OF}{GF} = \frac{f}{d_i - f} = \frac{d_o}{d_i}$$

or,

$$fd_i + fd_o = d_i d_o$$

Dividing both sides of this equation by $fd_o d_i$ yields,

$$\frac{1}{d_o} + \frac{1}{d_i} = \frac{1}{f}$$

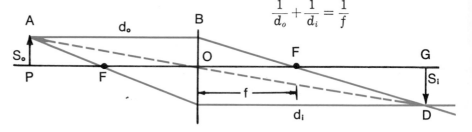

FIGURE 19-17. Diagram for derivation of lens equation.

19:13   Chromatic Aberration

Light is refracted when it falls on a lens. Upon passing through a medium, such as glass, different wavelengths of light refract at slightly different angles. Thus, the light that passes through a lens is slightly dispersed. Any object observed through a lens appears ringed with color. This effect is called **chromatic aberration**. It also limits the sharpness of an image on the film of a camera.

The chromatic aberration of a lens cannot be eliminated. But, it can be corrected. The lens can be coated with a material having a different index of refraction than the lens. The new material disperses light but in an opposite way from the lens. Hence the dispersion caused by the lens is cancelled. A lens prepared in this way is called an achromatic lens.

19:14   Optical Devices

For normal vision, the lens of the eye must focus the image of an object on the retina. If the shape of the lens of the eye is distorted, additional lenses (eyeglasses) are needed to adjust the

John Morgan

image distance to focus on the retina. The eye lens of a nearsighted person is too wide. Thus, images are formed in front of the retina. Concave lenses correct this defect by diverging the light rays so that the image distance is greater. Then, the image will focus on the retina. The eye lens of a farsighted person is not wide enough. The image in this case is formed behind the retina. Convex lenses correct this defect by converging the light rays. Then, the image distance is shorter and the image will be focused on the retina.

Most **microscopes** use two converging lenses. An object is placed close to the lower lens, called the **objective lens**. This lens produces a real image. The real image is located between the second lens called the **eyepiece** and its focal point. The eyepiece produces a greatly magnified virtual image of the real image.

FIGURE 19-18. A contact lens has been added to the lens of this eye to cause light rays from an object to form an image on the retina.

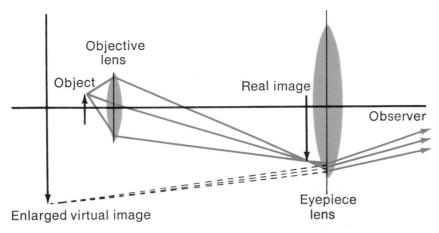

FIGURE 19-19. The compound microscope uses an objective lens of short focal length to form the first real image. The eyepiece lens of longer focal length forms a virtual image of the first real image.

A **refracting telescope** also uses two converging lenses. However, the objective lens of a telescope has a longer focal length than does the objective lens of a microscope. The objective lens of a telescope forms a real, inverted image of a star or other distant object. This image is located between the focal point of the eyepiece and the eyepiece itself. The viewer sees an enlarged, virtual, and inverted image.

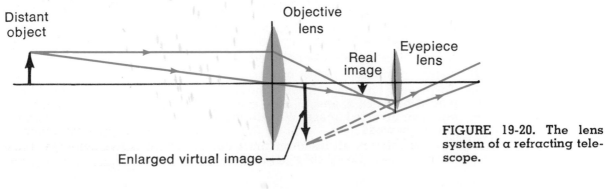

FIGURE 19-20. The lens system of a refracting telescope.

SUMMARY   The image in a plane mirror is the same size as the object. The image is as far behind the mirror as the object is in front of the mirror. Also it is reversed from left to right.

The focal point of a spherical mirror is halfway between the center of curvature of the mirror and the center of the mirror. The distance from the focal point to the center of the mirror is the focal length of the mirror. The radius from the center of the mirror to the center of curvature is called the principal axis. Spherical mirrors have an inherent defect called spherical aberration. Spherical aberration results when light rays falling on the outer edges of the mirror do not pass through the focal point.

A virtual image is not actually where it appears to be and cannot be cast upon a screen. A real image is where it appears to be and can be cast upon a screen. All erect images are virtual images. All inverted images are real images. Concave mirrors can form real, inverted images. If an object is closer to a concave mirror than its focal point, then a virtual image of the object will appear behind the mirror. Convex mirrors always produce virtual images.

Lenses that are thinner at their outer edges than in the middle are called converging or convex lenses. Lenses which are thicker at their outer edges are called diverging or concave lenses. Chromatic aberration is a lens defect caused by the dispersion of light as it passes through the lens.

The position of an image can be calculated by using the lens equation. To use this equation, two quantities must be known. These quantities are the distance of an object from a curved mirror or lens and the focal length of the mirror or lens.

QUESTIONS

1. Describe the image of an object seen in a plane mirror.
2. An object is located beyond the center of curvature of a spherical concave mirror. Locate and describe the image of the object.
3. Locate and describe the image produced by a concave mirror when the object is located at the center of curvature.
4. An object is located between the center of curvature and the principal focus of a concave mirror. Locate and describe the image of the object.
5. How does a virtual image differ from a real image?
6. An object produces a virtual image in a concave mirror. Where is the object located?
7. Describe the image seen in a convex mirror.
8. Describe the properties of a virtual image.
9. What factor, other than the curvature of a lens, determines the location of its focal point?
10. Locate and describe the image produced by a convex lens if an object is placed some distance beyond $2F$.
11. Name an inherent defect of a concave spherical mirror.
12. Name an inherent defect of lenses.
13. To project an image from a movie camera onto a screen, the film is placed between F and $2F$ of a converging lens. This arrangement produces an inverted image. Why do the actors appear to be erect when the film is viewed?
14. Convex mirrors are used on the front of school buses. Why are these mirrors used? Could they be dangerous?

1. An object is 20 cm from a concave mirror of 8 cm focal length (16 cm radius). Locate the image (a) graphically, (b) mathematically.
2. An object 3 cm high is placed 25 cm from a concave mirror of 15 cm focal length. Find the location and height of the image (a) graphically, (b) mathematically.
3. An object is 30 cm from a concave mirror of 15 cm focal length. (a) Locate the image. (b) The object is 1.8 cm high. How high is the image?
4. An object is 8 cm from a concave mirror of 12 cm focal length. Locate the image.
5. A convex mirror has a focal length of −16 cm. How far behind the mirror does the image of a person 3 m away appear?
6. An object is 8 cm in front of a concave mirror of 30 cm focal length. Locate the image.
7. How far behind the surface of a convex mirror of −6 cm focal length does an object 10 m from the mirror appear?
8. A convex lens has a focal length of 25 cm. An object is placed 40 cm from the lens. Where is the image?
9. An object is 40 cm from a convex lens of 10 cm focal length. Find the position of the image (a) graphically, (b) mathematically. (c) The object is 3 cm high. How high is the image?
10. An object is 25 cm from a convex lens of 12.5 cm focal length. Locate the image.
11. To develop a sharp image on a screen, the convex lens of the projector is moved until the film is 21 cm from the lens. The focal length of the lens is 20 cm. (a) How far is the screen from the lens? (b) How many times larger is the image on the screen than the picture on the film?

1. Some shaving and makeup mirrors are concave mirrors. You can use such a mirror to observe how real and virtual images are formed. Best results will be obtained if you use the mirror in a dark room and use a small candle as the object.
2. A magnifying glass is a converging lens. Take such a glass and a small candle into a dark room and use it to produce real images on the walls of the room. Can you produce a virtual image with the lens?
3. Place a pair of mirrors so that they are facing one another. Put a coin between the two mirrors. Look at the reflections in each mirror.
4. Place the two mirrors together so that their edges are perpendicular. Look at yourself in the two mirrors.
5. Hold one magnifying glass in front of another and look at distant objects through both lenses. Vary the relative positions of the magnifying glasses and the distance from your eye. You should be able to use the lenses as a simple telescope.

Cain, Gregory, "Extraterrestrial Life: An Introduction to Physical Science." *The Physics Teacher*, October, 1975.
Javan, Ali, "The Optical Properties of Materials." *Scientific American*, September, 1967.
Southall, James P. C., *Mirrors, Prisms and Lenses: A Test-Book of Geometrical Optics*, 3rd ed. New York, Dover Publications, Inc., 1964.
Wald, George, "Eye and Camera." *Scientific American*, August, 1950.

Light, like other waves, bends around edges. This bending of light can produce some interesting effects. This photograph was taken with a special filter which has cross-hatched lines. Light bending around the edges of these lines produced this star effect around the light sources. Note the bands of color in the rays spreading out from these light sources. Hold a comb having closely-space teeth between your eye and a light source. What causes the unusual light effect which you observe?

DIFFRACTION OF LIGHT

We have learned that light travels in straight lines. In most cases, this appears to be so. When light passes through a large opening, the shadow that is cast looks quite sharp. However, when light passes through a small opening, the edges of the shadow cast look blurred. This blurring effect can be understood if we think of light as bending around barriers. The bending of light as it passes the edge of a barrier is called **diffraction**. Diffraction can be explained in terms of the wave nature of light.

GOAL: You will gain knowledge and understanding of the interference and diffraction of light waves, and of the methods used to measure wavelength.

Diffraction occurs when light bends around the edges of a barrier.

20:1 Diffraction and Interference

Light waves are diffracted as they pass through narrow slits. Figure 20-1 shows the arrangement used by Thomas Young to show the diffraction of light waves. Young placed a barrier with a single slit in front of a light source. Any wave that falls on a narrow slit is diffracted. Another barrier with two narrow slits was placed between the first barrier and a screen. The single slit acts as a source of new uniform waves that strike the double slit at the same time. The double slit acts as two sources of new waves. The two waves interfere constructively at points where crests overlap. They interfere destructively where a crest and a trough

An interference pattern is set up when light falls on two narrow slits that are close together.

meet. In Figure 20-1 the semicircles represent wave crests moving outward from the sources. Midway between the crests are the troughs.

The solid lines in the diagram pass through points of constructive interference where crests meet crests. These lines are called **antinodal lines.** They trace the paths where the light is very bright. At points where the antinodal lines fall on the screen, bright bars of light appear.

Antinodal lines pass through points where waves interfere constructively.

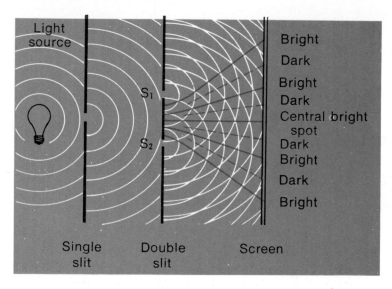

FIGURE 20-1. Formation of a diffraction pattern from an incandescent light source. The single slit acts as a source of uniform waves. The double slit produces the interference.

Nodal lines pass through points where waves interfere destructively.

The dotted lines in Figure 20-1 pass through points of destructive interference. These lines are called **nodal lines.** These lines trace paths where the light waves cancel each other and light is, in effect, absent. Dark spots appear at the points where nodal lines fall on the screen. Note that a bright spot of light appears on the screen directly opposite the midpoint between the two slits. On both sides of this central bright spot are other spots of light. These spots correspond to the other lines of reinforcement.

When white light is used as the source for a double-slit diffraction pattern, the light is dispersed into a continuous spectrum. A white light source emits several hundreds of wavelengths at the same time. Thus, many wavelengths approach the slits together. However, one of the basic rules of wave behavior is that waves can pass right through each other without changing one another. Each wavelength of light produces its own interference pattern. This pattern is not affected by the other patterns around it.

When white light passes through a double-slit, a continuous spectrum is produced.

Every wavelength of light gives its own interference pattern, independent of any others that may be forming.

Each wavelength produces a bright line at the center of the pattern. The addition of all wavelengths at the central bright line produces a line of white light. On both sides of the central bright line, the bright lines for each color do not fall in exactly the same

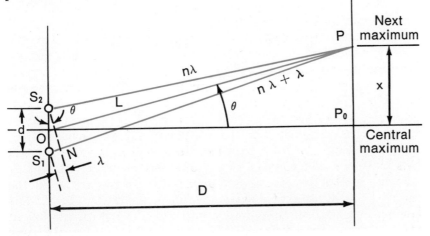
Courtesy of Kodansha

FIGURE 20-2. Double-slit interference pattern for white light.

places. Each wavelength produces a pattern that is slightly different from that of the other wavelengths. Thus, white light is
separated into a continuous spectrum of colors on each side of the
central bright line.

20:2 Measuring the Wavelength of a Light Wave

Interference can be used to measure the wavelengths of light
waves. Look at Figure 20-1. This figure shows the pattern produced by only one of the wavelengths from a light source. Choose
a line of reinforcement other than the central line. Select any
point along one of these lines where two crests come together.
Count the wavelengths back to S_1. Then from the same point,
count the wavelengths back to S_2. The difference is always a
whole number of wavelengths. For the first line of reinforcement
to both the right and the left of the central line, the path difference is one wavelength. For the second line of reinforcement, the
path difference is two wavelengths. For the third line, the difference is three wavelengths, and so on. Any point on a line of reinforcement is always a whole number of wavelengths farther
from one slit than the other. Thus, waves arrive at that point in
phase and reinforce each other.

From the use of interference patterns, wavelengths of light can be determined.

In double-slit interference, each point on a line of rein-forcement is a whole number of wavelengths farther from one slit than from the other.

FIGURE 20-3. Schematic diagram for analysis of double-slit interference.

Along the first line of reinforcement, the path difference is always one wavelength. Thus, the distance to the first bright line where this wavelength falls on the screen is just one wavelength farther from S_1 than from S_2. This situation is shown in Figure 20-3. Here, P_0 is the central bright line. P is the point where the next bright line of light appears on the screen. L is the distance from the center of the two slits to P, and x is the distance from the central bright line to P.

During an actual trial, a group of bright lines appears on the screen at P. Each of these represents one wavelength of light emitted by the source. These lines are called first-order lines. First-order lines can be seen both to the right and to the left of the central bright line. Some distance away, a second group of lines can be found. These lines are called second-order lines.

The distance between the two slits is marked d in Figure 20-3. The distance from the central line to the bright line of reinforcement is x. The distance from S_1 to P is one wavelength longer than the distance from S_2 to P. Thus, in right triangle S_1NS_2, the side S_1N equals the wavelength, λ. This triangle is similar to triangle PP_0O. These triangles are similar because the sizes of their angles are equal. Therefore, the ratios of corresponding sides of these similar triangles are the same.

$$\frac{x}{L} = \frac{\lambda}{d}$$

First-order lines appear to both sides of the central bright line. They are located one wavelength farther from one slit than from the other.

FIGURE 20-4. Wavelengths of light waves can be determined from interference patterns. A grating containing many slits spaced 0.002 cm apart was used to produce these interference patterns for (a) white light, (b) red light, and (c) blue light. Note the differences which result from differences in wavelengths.

Courtesy of Kodansha

Solving this equation for λ, we obtain the equation

$$\lambda = \frac{xd}{L}$$

By using interference patterns, the wavelengths of light waves can be measured with considerable accuracy. It is not unusual for wavelength measurements to be accurate to six digits. In addition to wavelengths, the speed of light is also known. Frequencies of light waves are then calculated by using the relationship

$$c = f\lambda$$

Example: Wavelength of Light

Red light falls on two small slits 1.9×10^{-4} cm apart. A first-order line appears 22.1 cm to the left of the central bright line on a screen opposite the slits. The distance from the center of the slits to the first-order line is 60 cm. What is the wavelength of the red light?

Solution:

$$x = 22.1 \text{ cm}, d = 1.9 \times 10^{-4} \text{ cm}, L = 60 \text{ cm}$$

$$\lambda = \frac{xd}{L}$$

$$= \frac{(22.1 \text{ cm}) (1.9 \times 10^{-4} \text{ cm})}{(60 \text{ cm})}$$

$$= 7.0 \times 10^{-5} \text{ cm}$$

PROBLEMS

1. Violet light falls on two small slits 1.9×10^{-4} cm apart. A first-order line appears 13.2 cm from the central bright spot on a screen opposite the slits. The distance from the center of the slits to the first-order violet line is 60 cm. What is the wavelength of the violet light?

2. Yellow light of wavelength 6.0×10^{-5} cm is used instead of the violet light of Problem 1. The distance from the center of the slits to the first-order line for the yellow light is measured and found to be 58 cm. How far from the central bright spot on the screen is the first-order yellow line?

3. Green light falls on a pair of slits 1.9×10^{-4} cm apart. A first-order line appears 28.4 cm to the left of the central bright line. The distance between the center of the slits and the first-order line is 100 cm. What is the wavelength of the light?

4. Blue light falls on a pair of slits 0.02 cm apart. A first-order line appears 0.184 cm from the central bright line on a screen opposite the slits. The distance from the midpoint between the slits to the first-order line is 80 cm. What is the wavelength of the blue light?

5. When the screen of a two-slit arrangement is replaced with a photographic plate, electromagnetic waves outside the visible region can be detected. An ultraviolet source produces a line on the film 0.072 cm from the central bright line. The slits are 0.02 cm apart and arranged so that the midpoint between them is 40 cm from the line appearing on the plate. What is the wavelength of the ultraviolet light?

20:3 Single-Slit Diffraction

A diffraction pattern results when light passes through a single narrow slit.

When light passes through one narrow slit, a diffraction pattern appears on a distant screen. This single-slit diffraction pattern differs from the double-slit pattern. The spacing between the bright lines lacks the regularity found in a double-slit diffraction pattern. Also, the central bright band is much larger and brighter than when two slits are used.

To observe single-slit diffraction, fold a small piece of paper and make a cut along its folded edge with a pair of scissors. Unfold the paper and peer through the slit at a light source. You will see a diffraction pattern. You can vary the width of the slit by pulling on the opposite edges of the paper. Observe the effect of the change in slit width on the diffraction pattern.

Monochromatic light is light of one wavelength.

Figure 20-5 shows how a single slit can cause a diffraction pattern. Here, **monochromatic** (mahn uh kroh MAT ik) **light** falls on a slit. Monochromatic light is light of only one wavelength. Because the slit is very narrow, all points of the wave along the slit are in phase. The diffraction pattern falls on a screen placed some distance from the slit. P_0 is the wide central bright band on the screen. P is a dark band. L is the distance from the center of the slit to P_0 and w is the slit width. L is so much larger than w that all rays falling on w are, in effect, the same distance from P_0. It follows that the band at point P_0 is very bright because all waves arriving at that point from w are in phase. Point P, however, is

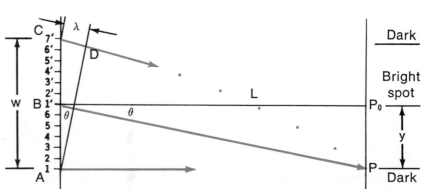

FIGURE 20-5. Schematic diagram for analysis of single-slit diffraction.

exactly one wavelength farther from point 7' on the slit than it is from point 1 on the slit. Therefore, point P is one-half wavelength farther from point 1' than it is from point 1. Hence, waves from points 1 and 1' arrive 180° out of phase at point P and cancel. The same is true for points 2 and 2', points 3 and 3', and so on down the slit. Therefore, no light is observed at point P. In our example, we used only six points along the slit. In reality, there are an infinite number of points acting in this way.

In Figure 20-5, triangles ADC and BP_0P are similar. Because L is so large when compared to w, you can approximate the corresponding sides of similar triangles. That is, BP and L are very nearly equal. Thus, in the equation showing the equality between ratios of corresponding sides of the similar triangles,

$$\frac{BP}{y} = \frac{w}{\lambda}$$

we can substitute L for BP so that

$$\frac{L}{y} = \frac{w}{\lambda}$$

Solving for λ, we obtain the equation

$$\lambda = \frac{yw}{L}$$

If w is very small, the bright central band will be large. If w is one wavelength, then $\lambda/w = 1$. In the language of trigonometry, $\sin \theta = 1$, and θ is 90°. The bright band will then spread over 180° and no dark lines will be observed on the screen.

a

b

c

FIGURE 20-6. These diffraction patterns for (a) red light, (b) blue light, and (c) white light were produced with a slit of width 0.02 cm.

With other slit widths, second-order dark bands will appear on the screen below the point P. In keeping with our explanation of the first-order dark bands, second-order bands appear where angle θ is large enough to cause CD to equal 2λ. When CD is equal to 3λ or some other multiple of λ, another dark band will appear.

Example: Single-Slit Diffraction

Monochromatic orange light falls upon a single slit of width 0.01 cm. The slit is located 100 cm from a screen. If a first-order dark band is observed 0.6 cm from the center of the central bright band, what is the wavelength of the orange light?

Solution:

$$\lambda = \frac{yw}{L}$$
$$= \frac{(6.0 \times 10^{-1}\,\text{cm})\,(1 \times 10^{-2}\,\text{cm})}{1 \times 10^2\,\text{cm}}$$
$$= 6.0 \times 10^{-5}\,\text{cm}$$

PROBLEMS

6. Monochromatic green light falls on a slit 0.01 cm wide and produces a first-order dark band 0.55 cm from the center of the central bright band on a screen 100 cm away. Find the wavelength of the green light.

7. Violet light of wavelength 4×10^{-5} cm falls on a slit 0.015 cm wide. The screen is located 80 cm from the slit. How far from the central band will the first-order dark band appear?

8. Yellow light from a sodium vapor lamp falls upon a single slit 0.0295 cm wide. A screen 60 cm away reveals a first-order dark band located 0.120 cm from the center of the bright central band. What is the wavelength of the yellow light?

9. Light of wavelength 4.8×10^{-5} cm passes through a single slit and falls on a screen 120 cm away. What is the width of the slit if the center of the first-order dark band is 0.5 cm away from the center of the bright central band?

20:4   Resolving Power of Lenses

When the light from two objects that are close together falls on a lens, the light is diffracted. The lens acts in the same way as a slit. It causes the diffracted light from the two objects to overlap. As a result, the width of a lens limits its ability to distinguish between the two images. To reduce the effects of diffraction, a wide lens must be used. In the case of the objective lens of a microscope, this is not possible. In a microscope, diffraction is reduced

A wide lens reduces the overlapping of light from objects that are close together. Thus, wide lenses resolve images better than narrow lenses.

by using light of a shorter wavelength. This produces the same effect as a wider lens. For this reason, biology classes often use blue or violet lamps when working with microscopes.

SUMMARY

When light falls on two very narrow slits which are close together, it is diffracted as it passes through each of the slits. The new, circular waves interfere with each other both constructively and destructively. The interference causes alternating dark and bright spots to appear on a screen some distance from the slits.

The diffraction pattern obtained by using double slits can be analyzed geometrically to obtain the wavelengths of the light passing through the slits. When the wavelength of light is known, the frequency of the light can be calculated from the relationship $c = f\lambda$.

Narrow single slits will also cause diffraction patterns to appear on a screen some distance from the slit. In a similar way, lenses diffract light. In microscope lenses, this effect can be reduced by using light of very short wavelengths.

QUESTIONS

1. Explain why the central bright line resulting from the diffraction of light by a double slit cannot be used to measure the wavelength of light waves.
2. Using a compass and a ruler, construct a diagram of the interference pattern that results when waves 1 cm in length fall on two slits which are 2 cm apart. The slits may be represented by two dots spaced 2 cm apart and kept to one side of the paper. Draw a line through the central line of reinforcement and through all other lines of reinforcement. Draw dotted lines where crests meet troughs and produce nodal lines.
3. If you are using light of a known wavelength in a double-slit experiment, how can you find the distance between the slits?
4. More accurate measurements of light waves can be made if the lines obtained for each wavelength are as far apart as possible. We know that $\lambda = xd/L$. How can the value of x be increased?
5. From the measurement of the wavelength of a light wave, how can we find the frequency as well?
6. How does a single-slit diffraction pattern differ from the pattern obtained by using two slits?
7. What happens to a single-slit diffraction pattern when the width of the slit approaches the wavelength of the light falling on it?
8. How do lenses make it difficult to distinguish between two objects that are very close together?

PROBLEMS

1. Light falls on a pair of slits 1.9×10^{-4} cm apart. The slits are 80 cm from a first-order bright line. The first-order line is 19 cm from the central bright line. What is the wavelength of the light?
2. Two slits are 5.0×10^{-4} cm apart. They form a first-order bright line 11.2 cm from the central bright line on a screen opposite the slits. The distance from the center of the slits to the first-order line is 100 cm. What is the wavelength of the light falling on the slits?
3. Light of wavelength 4×10^{-5} cm falls on a pair of slits. First-order bright lines appear 4.0 cm from the central bright line. The first-order lines are 200 cm from the center of the slits. How far apart are the slits?

4. A good diffraction grating has 2500 lines per centimeter. What is the distance, d, between two lines in the grating?

5. Using the grating of Problem 4, a red line appears 16.5 cm from the central bright spot on a screen opposite the grating. The distance from the center of the grating to the red line is 100 cm. What is the wavelength of the red light?

6. What is the frequency of light waves of wavelength 4.6×10^{-5} cm?

7. Calculate the wavelength of a gamma ray of frequency 6.0×10^{24} Hz.

8. Light of frequency 6.0×10^{14} Hz falls on a pair of slits that are 2.0×10^{-4} cm apart. The center of the slits is 50 cm from the screen. How far from the central bright line will the first-order bright lines appear?

9. Light falls on a single slit 0.01 cm wide and develops a first-order dark band 0.59 cm from the center of the central bright band on a screen 100 cm away. Calculate the wavelength of the light.

10. Light that falls on the slit described in Problem 9 develops a first-order dark band 0.48 cm from the bright central band. (a) Calculate the wavelength of the light. (b) Compare the distance between the central bright band and the first-order dark band with the wavelength of the light in this problem and in Problem 9 as well. What relationship exists? Can the wavelengths of the light waves be read directly from the screen in an arrangement of this sort?

11. When light of wavelength 4.0×10^{-5} cm falls on a single slit, the two first-order dark bands are located 0.043 cm from the bright central band. If the slit is 86 cm from the screen, what is its width?

12. Sound waves of frequency 550 Hz fall on a window 1.2 m wide. The window is in the exact center of one wall of a theater 24 m $\times$ 12 m. The window is 12 m from the opposite wall along which is a row of seats filled with people. The theater is acoustically prepared to prevent the reflection of sound waves and the speed of sound is 330 m/sec. Two people in a row along the wall hear no sound. Where are they sitting?

PROJECTS

1. Diffraction is not difficult to observe. Hold a sheet of paper up to a light and look at the edge of the sheet. You should see diffraction fringes along the edge.

2. Keeping the fingers on one of your hands snugly together, hold the hand up to a light. In several places, narrow slits are left between your fingers. Look at a light source through one of these slits. You should see diffraction lines. If not, try squeezing your fingers together to adjust the width of the slit.

3. Place two combs together. Hold one of the combs upside down with respect to the other. Look through the teeth of the combs at a light source and slowly move one comb across the other. Explain your observations.

4. In practice, two slits are seldom used to measure the wavelengths of light waves because two slits do not allow very much light to pass onto a screen or photographic plate. Usually glass plates with thousands of openings or lines per centimeter are used. These plates are called diffraction gratings. To show that several slits produce the same interference pattern as two slits, use a piece of paper and a compass. Make two points on the paper near the center of one side of the paper about a centimeter apart. Using the compass, draw semicircles that represent waves leaving the slits. Make ½ cm divisions between waves. Draw several waves for each point across the paper. Mark the central line of reinforcement and

the first- and second-order lines of reinforcement for this wavelength. Now make a third point 1 cm to the side of the original pair of points and repeat the process. (a) Do the points of reinforcement fall in the same places? (b) Would several points or slits develop the same pattern as just two?

Connes, Pierre, "How Light Is Analyzed." *Scientific American,* September, 1968.

Haber-Schaim, Uri, et al, *PSSC Physics,* 4th ed. Boston, D. C. Heath and Co., 1976, Chapters 6, 8.

Murchie, Guy, *Music of the Spheres.* Boston, Mass., Houghton Mifflin Co., 1960.

Tomer, Darrel W., "Strobphotography." *The Science Teacher,* May, 1960.

Weinberg, Steven, "Light as a Fundamental Particle." *Physics Today,* June, 1975.

Williams, Dudley, "Infrared Radiation." *The Physics Teacher,* November, 1963.

READINGS

Light from luminous objects can be classified as either natural or artificial light. Luminous objects are objects which produce their own light. Most natural light comes from our sun. Some sources of artificial light are incandescent lamps, neon signs, and even fireworks. Here you see natural light from the sun shining down through the water. You also see a diver using an artificial-light source to illuminate the area under study. How does light originate in these sources?

THE ORIGIN OF LIGHT

The work of Michael Faraday and others led James Clerk Maxwell to develop a theory about the origin of electromagnetic waves. Maxwell's theory, based on mathematics, predicted that any accelerated charged particle should generate an electromagnetic wave. Note that the theory says the charged particle must be accelerated, not just moving.

21:1 Charged Particles Generate Light

By the year 1855, the German physicist Heinrich Hertz verified Maxwell's theory. Hertz actually generated and detected an electromagnetic wave. To generate the wave, he caused electrons to accelerate back and forth in a wire loop. The radio waves coming from the loop were detected by a second wire loop on the other side of his laboratory. It was known that radio waves differ from light waves only in their wavelengths and frequencies. Thus, it became clear that light waves must also be developed by accelerating charged particles.

Today Maxwell's theory includes all electromagnetic waves. Electromagnetic waves, including light waves, are generated by the acceleration of charged particles. Light waves usually are produced by the acceleration of electrons within an atom.

GOAL: You will gain knowledge and understanding of the origin of light, the means by which atoms can be excited, spectra, and the laser.

The acceleration of charged particles produces electromagnetic waves.

The charged particle must be accelerating and not just moving.

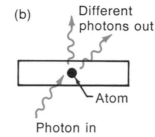

(a)

High speed electrons

Gas

High voltage

Photons

(b)

Different photons out

Atom

Photon in

(c)

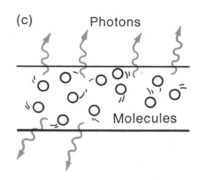

Photons

Molecules

FIGURE 21-1. Photons are emitted by atoms which have been excited. Atoms can be excited in three ways: (a) electron excitation, (b) photon excitation, and (c) thermal excitation.

FIGURE 21-2. (a) Brilliant colors of fireworks result from thermal excitation of atoms. (b) The light from neon signs results from electron excitation.

21:2   The Excitation of Atoms

An electron can be given energy to raise it from a lower energy level to a higher energy level within an atom. When this happens, the atom is said to be excited. Excited atoms remain excited for only a fraction of a second. Then the electron drops from the higher energy level to its normal energy level. However, energy is absorbed by the atom when its electron is raised to a higher energy level. By the law of conservation of energy, this energy must be accounted for. When the electron returns to its lower energy level, electromagnetic radiation is emitted. The energy content of the radiation is exactly equal to the energy absorbed by the atom when its electron was raised to a higher energy level. This process is the origin of light waves.

John Morgan   *Rich Brommer*

21:3   Means by Which Atoms Are Excited

Atoms can be excited in three ways. These are thermal excitation, electron collision, or photon collision. Thermal excitation takes place when two atoms collide. As a fast moving atom collides with another atom, it transfers energy to that atom. The added energy can raise an electron to a higher energy level within the atom. The atoms in a hot material move very fast. Thus, collisions take place more often and with more energy in a hot material than in a cool material. Therefore, a hot material emits more light as a result of thermal excitation than does a cool material. Heating a substance often causes it to glow or give off light. The filament of a light bulb and a glowing coal give out light in this way.

When an electron collides with an atom, it often causes an electron to move to a higher energy level within the atom. When this electron returns to its lower energy level, it emits radiation. The light from fluorescent lamps and neon signs is produced in this way. To make electrons flow through the tubes at a high speed, a high voltage is placed across the terminals of the tube. As the electrons pass through the tube, many collisions occur between the atoms and the electrons. Thus, the atoms are excited and emit light. Neon and fluorescent lamps are highly efficient because almost all of the electric energy input is used to produce light. On the other hand, incandescent lamps produce more heat than light. A 30-watt fluorescent lamp produces more light than a 100-watt incandescent lamp.

When a photon collides with an atom, a photon of radiation enters an atom and its energy is absorbed. The energy of the photon raises an electron to a higher energy level. When the electron returns to its normal energy level, one or more photons leave the atom. The reflectors on car bumpers contain atoms which are easily excited by photons. When light from another car shines on the reflector, its atoms are excited and emit light. The sticker then glows.

An atom absorbs energy when an electron moves to a higher energy level. The atom is then said to be excited.

An electron emits energy as it drops to a lower energy level.

An atom can be excited upon collision with another atom.

An atom can be excited upon collision with an electron.

William Maddox

FIGURE 21-3. The paint in this poster fluoresces because of photon excitation.

An atom can be excited upon collision with a photon.

21:4   Fluorescence and Phosphorescence

Atoms are easily excited in fluorescent and phosphorescent substances. A fluorescent substance differs from a phosphorescent substance. The difference is in the time it takes for excited atoms to return electrons to normal energy levels. Most electrons are very unstable in higher than normal energy levels. They return at once to their normal levels. Fluorescent materials emit light only while being excited. A reflector gives out light only while it is being flooded with external light. The reflector is fluorescent. A

Fluorescent materials emit light only when light strikes them.

Phosphorescent materials continue to emit light after the external light source is removed.

FIGURE 21-4. The fluorescent screen in this TV set emits light when bombarded by electrons. In this way, a picture is formed on the screen.

fluorescent lamp emits light only while electrons pass through the lamp. After the current passing through the lamp stops, a fluorescent lamp no longer glows.

In a TV picture tube, electrons are shot at a fluorescent screen. Wherever an electron strikes, excitation causes the atoms to emit light. The amount of light that comes from any part of the screen is governed by the number and energy of electrons that strike that part of the screen. A picture is formed on the screen by the varying amount of light emitted from different parts of the surface of the tube.

A doctor's fluoroscope works like the TV picture tube, with one difference. The fluoroscope uses X rays instead of electrons to bombard the screen and excite atoms. The X rays pass through the patient and fall on the fluorescent screen. Fewer X rays get through bones than flesh. The result is a picture of the bone structure only.

In phosphorescent materials, electrons in higher than normal energy levels have greater stability. After excitation occurs, electrons return to their normal levels. But they could return at once, within a few minutes, or in several hours. Some small statuettes may be held under a lamp for a short time and made to glow for a long time afterward. They glow because they are painted with a phosphorescent substance.

FIGURE 21-5. This flying disc glows in the dark because it contains a phosphorescent material.

John Morgan

21:5 Allowed Transitions

The absorption of energy by electrons within an atom is discrete. This means that an electron will absorb energy only if it is exactly the amount of energy needed for it to move from one energy level to another. Otherwise it will not absorb the energy by changing energy levels. A similar idea would be a ballplayer trying to throw a baseball straight up and having the ball refuse to leave the player's hand because it was not given the right amount of energy to raise it to an intended height. In the same way, atoms can emit energy in discrete packages. This indicates that energy itself is quantized, or comes in packages. The energy levels within each element are unique to that element. Figure 21-6 shows a group of energy levels for a typical atom.

An electron makes transitions only between exact energy levels.

Energy is quantized.

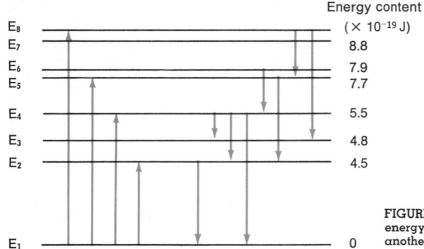

FIGURE 21-6. Each line represents an energy transition from one level to another.

The electrons in an atom make only certain transitions between energy levels. These transitions are called allowed transitions. To understand why electrons occupy only certain levels, a wave model of the atom is helpful. The wave model assumes that as an electron moves about the nucleus, it follows a path that is a whole number multiple of its wavelength. The electron then continually reinforces itself and its energy remains constant. At any level that does not provide for a path length that is a whole number multiple of the wavelength, the wave will interfere with itself. As a result, the electron would lose energy. Theory and experiment strongly indicate that an electron occupies only the energy levels in which it can keep a constant energy. Thus, when an electron moves from one energy level to another, it moves only between exact levels.

A wave model of the atom is useful in explaining energy levels.

When an electron returns from a higher energy level to a lower energy level, once again only certain transitions are allowed. As Figure 21-6 shows, these transitions need not be the same transitions as those that increased the energy of the atom. Therefore, any fluorescent material can be flooded with light of one color and emit light of a different color. The atoms in TV color screens are excited by electron collision. The color each screen gives out depends on the favored down-transitions of its electrons.

Each element has its own set of allowed transitions. Thus, under normal conditions, each element emits only certain wavelengths of light. For this reason, every element has its own spectrum.

21:6   Emission Spectra

If an element in its gaseous state is heated until it becomes incandescent, it emits only a limited number of wavelengths. The group of wavelengths emitted by an element is always the same and is called the **emission spectrum** of that element. Each element's spectrum is different from all other spectra. Thus, the spectrum can be used as a sort of "fingerprint" of the element. To analyze a substance, a sample of the substance is heated in an electric arc until it becomes a gas and gives off light. From the wavelengths that are present, the composition of the substance can be determined.

The emission spectrum of each element is unique to that element and serves to identify it.

One way to observe the spectra of elements is shown in Figure 21-7. A glass tube containing neon gas is equipped with electrodes at both ends. When a high voltage is applied to the tube,

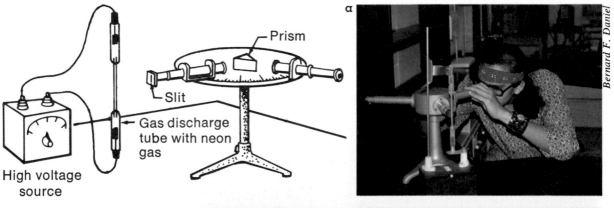

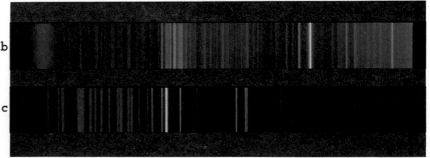

Bernard F. Daniel

FIGURE 21-7. (a) Observing emission spectra of (b) hydrogen and (c) neon.

Courtesy of Kodansha

electrons pass through it and cause the neon atoms to emit light. The light passes through a slit and then through a prism. Each wavelength of light forms an image of the slit, or lines, that can be observed by looking at the prism through a telescope. Each line corresponds to a particular wavelength of neon. Suppose a different gas such as helium, argon, or nitrogen is contained in the tube, and you want to find out which gas the tube contains. Each gas emits light of characteristic wavelengths. Thus the gas is easily identified by noting the lines present in the spectrum.

The arrangement shown in Figure 21-7 is called a spectroscope. The spectrum that passes through a spectroscope is often photographed. When this is done, the lines on the photograph indicate both the elements present in a substance and their relative amounts. If the substance being examined contains a large amount of any particular element, the lines on the photographic plate that correspond to the element are stronger. By comparing the strengths of the lines, the percentage composition of the substance can be determined.

Official U.S. Navy photo

FIGURE 21-8. Through spectra, Dr. George R. Carruthers was the first person to detect molecules in outer space.

21:7 Absorption Spectra

Another method to detect the nature of a substance is by the use of **absorption spectra.** To obtain an absorption spectrum, white light, such as that from the sun, is sent through a gas and then into

The identity of an element can also be determined by observing the wavelengths that it absorbs.

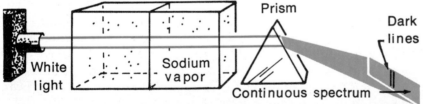

FIGURE 21-9. Producing the absorption spectrum of sodium.

a prism. The result is a continuous spectrum that has several dark lines along its length. These lines show that some wavelengths are missing from the continuous spectrum. By comparison, it is found that the lines of the emission spectrum of the gas and the dark

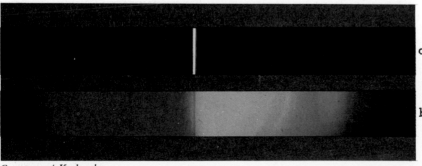

Courtesy of Kodansha

FIGURE 21-10. (a) The emission spectrum of sodium and (b) the absorption spectrum of sodium.

lines occur at the same wavelengths. Gaseous elements absorb the same wavelengths that they emit. An atom that emits blue light absorbs blue light easily. White light, sent through an unknown gas, produces a continuous spectrum with missing lines. The wavelengths of the missing lines indicate the composition of the gas.

21:8   Fraunhofer Lines

While examining the spectrum of sunlight, Fraunhofer noticed some dark lines. The dark lines he found in the sun's spectrum are known as Fraunhofer lines. To account for these lines, he assumed that the sun has an atmosphere of hot gaseous elements.

Courtesy of Kodansha

FIGURE 21-11. Fraunhofer lines in the absorption spectrum of the sun.

As light leaves the sun, it passes through these gases. As a result, the gases absorb light at their characteristic wavelengths. Thus, these wavelengths are missing from the sun's spectrum. By comparing the missing lines with the known lines of the various elements, the makeup of the sun is determined. The same method can be used to find the composition of the stars.

21:9   Lasers and Masers

Light emitted by atoms of an incandescent source is random. Each atom emits light of different wavelengths at different times and in different directions. Such light is incoherent light. **Coherent light** consists of light waves of the same wavelength joined together in phase to produce an intense beam of light. Once scientists thought that a coherent light source could not be developed. Today lasers produce coherent light.

The word **laser** is an acronym. It stands for *Light Amplification by the Stimulated Emission of Radiation.* The first laser was a short ruby (Al_2O_3) rod containing about 0.1 percent chromium atoms as an impurity. The operation of the laser depends upon an interesting property of excited atoms. When an atom is excited, an electron is in a higher than normal energy level. What happens if the electron is in this high energy state when a photon enters the atom? Suppose this incident photon has the same wavelength as the photon that the electron will emit when it makes its down-transition. When the photon strikes the atom, it stimulates the electron to make its down-transition. Then, two photons will leave the atom in phase.

Often a photon of the proper wavelength enters an atom and stimulates the emission of radiation. A small bit of material contains many excited atoms that are at the same energy level. But the effect is usually not large enough to be noticed. A photon that has been amplified can lose its excess energy to the next atom it enters if the next atom is not in the excited state. In a laser, most of the atoms are in the excited state. Thus, the photons are likely to increase their energy each time they enter a new atom. This energy increase can produce an intense beam of coherent light.

Figure 21-14 shows one laser arrangement. A ruby rod is flooded with X rays. X rays are high energy photons. The flooding of the rod is called **pumping**. Pumping excites a great number of atoms in the rod. A mirror is placed at each end of the rod. The mirror on one end partly transmits and partly reflects. The mirror on the other end reflects only. When a photon enters an excited atom, it stimulates the electron to make its down-transition. Thus, the

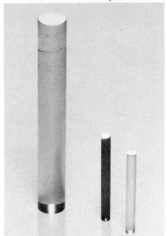

Optovac, Inc.

FIGURE 21-12. Ruby rods with reflective ends are used to make lasers.

Pumping or flooding a laser with X rays puts atoms in their excited states.

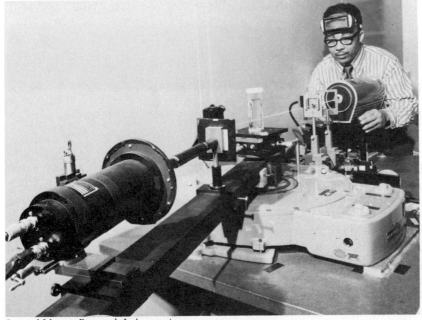

General Motors Research Laboratories

FIGURE 21-13. This scientist is using a laser in the measurement of the mass and the size of particles in a plastic.

(a) Unexcited chromium atoms (solid circles) are arranged in a regular pattern within the crystalline structure of a ruby rod.

(b) The ruby rod is flooded or "pumped" with X rays to raise most of the atoms to the excited state (open circles).

(c) During the down-transitions of the electrons, energy in the form of red light is emitted. Photons of red light not parallel with the edges of the rod pass out of the rod.

(d) Photons parallel with the edges of the rod stimulate down-transitions in adjacent atoms and thus produce more photons of the same frequency.

(e) The light travels back and forth between the mirrored ends of the rod, causing an avalanche of down-transitions.

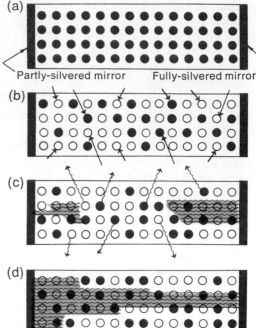

(a)

Partly-silvered mirror　　Fully-silvered mirror

(b)

(c)

(d)

(e)

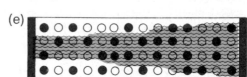

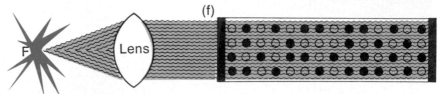

(f)

(f) The light bursts forth from the partially silvered mirror, producing an extremely intense flash of light.

FIGURE 21-14. Lasing action in a ruby rod. The entire process takes less than one millionth of a second.

photon is amplified. This takes place in many atoms at the same time. The amplified photons pass on to other excited atoms. Thus photon intensities continue to increase. The photons are reflected by the two mirrors. They repeat the process back and forth between the two mirrors. In a short time, there is an avalanche of down-transitions. A short burst of intense, coherent light leaves the end of the ruby rod. This beam may be diffracted by a pair of slits. The diffraction pattern shows that laser light is coherent. The laser beam may be focused with a lens to provide an even more intense and accurately placed spot of coherent light.

FIGURE 21-15. Ruby laser beam piercing a sheet of tantalum. The beam is a million times brighter than the sun and melts the tantalum metal at 5500° C.

Several solids and gases can also be made to "lase." Helium and neon gas can emit continuous laser beams. The radiation emitted does not have to be in the visible region. Masers emit radiation in the microwave region. Masers are very useful in communications. The word maser is also an acronym. It stands for *Micro*wave *A*mplification by the *S*timulated *E*mission of *R*adiation.

FIGURE 21-16. The hologram is a photographic recording of tiny interference fringes and contains all the optical data about a 3-dimensional scene. With a laser beam, a virtual image of the 3-dimensional scene is reconstructed in space.

Baush & Lomb, Inc.

SUMMARY   James Clerk Maxwell developed a theory about the origin of electromagnetic waves. This theory predicted that any accelerated charged particle should generate an electromagnetic wave. Heinrich Hertz confirmed Maxwell's theory experimentally by accelerating electrons in a wire loop and detecting the resulting electromagnetic waves. Light waves are electromagnetic waves. Thus, light waves must be produced by accelerating charged particles.

An electron can be raised from a lower to a higher energy level within an atom. When this happens, the atom is said to be excited. When the electron returns to its normal energy level, electromagnetic radiation is emitted. Often this radiation is light.

An atom can be excited by thermal excitation, electron collision, or photon collision. Thermal excitation occurs when atoms or molecules collide. Electron collisions occur as high speed electrons pass through a gas and strike atoms of the gas. During a photon collision a photon enters an atom and its energy is used to raise an electron to a higher energy level.

A material is fluorescent if its electrons return to their normal energy levels immediately. A material is phosphorescent if its electrons can remain in higher energy levels for some time. Fluorescent materials emit light only while their atoms are being excited. Phosphorescent materials can glow for hours after their atoms have been excited.

The electrons within an atom can exist only in definite energy levels. Thus, the electrons can only make energy transitions between these discrete levels. Electrons will absorb energy if it is the amount needed to move the electron between energy levels. Thus, gases absorb the same wavelengths of light that they emit.

Different light sources produce different spectra. Light from an incandescent solid produces a continuous spectrum. The gaseous form of an element produces an emission spectrum that contains only a limited number of wavelengths. Each element has a unique spectrum which can be used to identify that element.

If white light is sent through a gas, the gas will absorb the same wavelengths that it would characteristically emit. If the emergent white light is passed through a prism, the wavelengths unique to the elements which make up the gas will be missing from the resulting spectrum. As a result, this spectrum will have dark lines in it. This kind of spectrum is called an absorption spectrum. The dark lines which appear in the absorption spectrum of the sun are called Fraunhofer lines.

A laser is capable of producing coherent light. Coherent light consists of light of the same wavelength joined together in phase. A laser can produce a very intense beam of light.

QUESTIONS
1. What is an excited atom?
2. Name three methods by which an atom can be excited.
3. Why does a hot material emit light?
4. A TV picture tube is coated with a fluorescent material rather than a phosphorescent material. Explain.
5. Why do different fluorescent materials emit different colored light when illuminated with the same ultraviolet light source?
6. The electrons within an atom absorb energy only in discrete amounts. Explain why electrons make transitions between specific energy levels only.
7. Make a diagram of a laser. Explain its operation.
8. Can a laser put out more energy than is put into it? Explain.

9. What type of spectrum is emitted by a gaseous element?
10. What are absorption spectra?

PROBLEMS

In previous chapters we studied two important equations that can tell us a great deal about photons.

$E = hf$ (Where h is Planck's constant 6.6×10^{-34} J-sec.)
$c = f\lambda$ (Where c is the speed of light, 3×10^8 m/sec.)

Use these equations and the theory presented in this chapter to solve the following problems.

1. Calculate the frequency of the photon emitted when an electron makes the down-transition E_5 to E_2 in Figure 21-6.
2. What is the wavelength of the photon emitted by the down-transition E_5 to E_2?
3. What will be the frequency of the photon emitted by the down-transition E_4 to E_1 (Figure 21-6)?
4. What is the wavelength of the photon of Problem 3?
5. At what rate must electrons be made to vibrate in a wire if the wire is to emit radio waves 10 m in length?
6. A visible light wave in the red region is emitted from an atom. The wave has a wavelength of 6.6×10^{-7} m. (a) What is its frequency? (b) What time is required for the electron to vibrate within its atom?

PROJECTS

1. Turn on a TV set. While the set is on, run a vacuum cleaner. Watch the picture on the TV set. What does this tell you about the current in the vacuum cleaner?
2. Stretch a piece of cloth tightly and place it in front of a laser. Turn on the laser and observe the pattern on a wall. CAUTION: *Do this only under your instructor's supervision.*
3. Collect some fluorescent and phosphorescent objects and arrange a display in the physics lab.
4. Take a shiny needle or pin and hold it in bright sunshine. Look at the pin through a prism. You should be able to see a few dark Fraunhofer lines in the sun's spectrum.

READINGS

Ashkin, Arthur, "The Pressure of Laser Light." *Scientific American,* February, 1972.

Chapline, George, and Wood, Lowell, "X-Ray Lasers." *Physics Today,* June, 1975.

Klein, Arthur H., *Masers and Lasers.* Philadelphia, Pa., J. B. Lippincott and Co., 1963.

Miller, Stewart E., "Communication by Laser." *Scientific American,* January, 1966.

Park, Robert L., "Inner-Shell Spectroscopy." *Physics Today,* April, 1975.

Schnopper, Herbert W., and Delvaille, John P., "The X-Ray Sky." *Scientific American,* July, 1972.

Stambler, Irwin, *Revolution in Light Lasers and Holography.* New York, Doubleday and Co., Inc., 1972.

You know static electricity as the shock you receive when you touch an object after shuffling your feet across a carpet. Static electricity causes a balloon to stick to the wall after you have rubbed the balloon on a sweater. Lightning is still another example of static electricity. What other effects of static electricity have you observed? How does static electricity differ from current electricity?

STATIC ELECTRICITY

For thousands of years, it has been known that an electric charge can build up on some objects. You are familiar with this kind of electricity in everyday life. Sometimes you get a shock when you touch a doorknob after shuffling your feet across a rug. Your clothes may cling together after they have been run through a dryer. A closer look at the structure of an atom will help to explain what is happening in each of these cases.

GOAL: You will gain knowledge and understanding of static charges and the forces between them, and will be introduced to the concept of an electric field.

22:1 Micro-structure of Matter

Models of the atom place the protons and neutrons in its center or nucleus. The protons have a positive electric charge. The charge is exactly the same on each proton. Neutrons are neutral and have no electric charge. Located outside the nucleus of the atom is a "cloud" of electrons. Each electron has a negative charge equal in magnitude but opposite in sign to the charge of a proton. The magnitude of the charge is the same on all electrons and protons. The charge on an electron or proton is the elementary unit of charge. Usually, an atom contains the same number of electrons as protons. Then, the atom is electrically neutral. Electric charges appear when this balance is disturbed.

The proton is firmly "locked" in the nucleus of the atom. It can be dislodged only by methods used in nuclear physics. The electron is the mobile particle of the atom. Thus, all electric phenomena are due to the movements of electrons.

The nucleus of an atom contains protons (positively charged) and neutrons (no charge).

About the nucleus is a "cloud" of electrons (negatively charged).

Electron movements cause electric phenomena.

22:2 Charging Bodies Electrically

Because an electron can be moved easily, negative and positive charges can be produced on objects. A neutral body contains the same number of electrons as protons. By moving electrons about, it is possible to add electrons to a neutral body. Electrons are

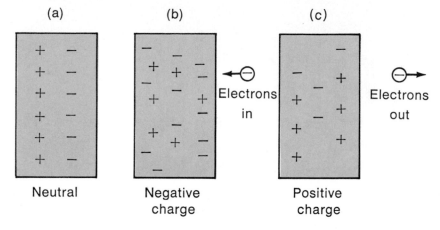

FIGURE 22-1. Objects become charged through a gain or loss of electrons. (a) The neutral object has equal numbers of electrons and protons. (b) The negative object has excess electrons. (c) The positive object is deficient in electrons.

then in excess, and the body has a net negative charge. If electrons are taken away from a neutral body, the body has a net positive charge. The body then contains an excess of protons. In both cases, the protons remain in the nucleus and the electrons move. When a body is charged by adding or removing electrons, the charge stays on the body, at least for a short time. The body has a static charge. Static means "at rest."

To illustrate, rub a glass rod with a piece of silk. Electrons leave the glass and move onto the silk. The glass rod then has a net positive charge while the silk has a negative charge.

If two glass rods are rubbed with a silk cloth, both have a positive charge. Then one of the rods may be suspended and the second rod brought close to it. The suspended rod will be repelled. Thus, two positively charged bodies repel one another. In the same way, two rubber rods can be charged negatively by rubbing them with fur or wool. If one of the rubber rods is suspended, it is repelled by the second rubber rod. Thus, two negatively charged bodies repel one another. However, if the negatively charged rubber rod is brought close to the suspended, positively charged rod, attraction occurs. There are three important facts about static electric charges.

1. Electric charges are of two distinct kinds, positive and negative.
2. Like charges repel. Unlike charges attract.
3. Charges exert forces through a distance.

From PSSC PHYSICS, D.C. Heath & Company, Lexington, 1965

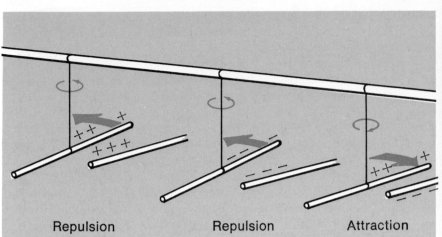

Repulsion   Repulsion   Attraction

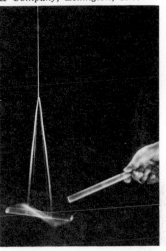

FIGURE 22-2. A charged rod, when brought close to another suspended rod, will attract or repel the suspended rod.

Electroscopes are used to detect the presence of static charges.

22:3   Electrostatic Demonstrations

Many demonstrations support the theory that static charges are due to the transfer of electrons. The device in Figure 22-3 is an electroscope. Its rod is insulated from the ground by a glass flask. Electrons do not flow easily through glass. Thus, charges placed on the rod will stay on the rod. Hanging from one end of the metal rod are two leaves of silver or aluminum foil. When a charged rod is brought close to the top of the electroscope, the leaves diverge. A negatively charged rod repels the mobile electrons down into the leaves. Then, both leaves have a negative charge. Thus, the leaves repel each other (Figure 22-3a). A positively charged rod attracts the electrons into the top of the electroscope. Thus, both leaves have a net positive charge. Again, repulsion takes place (Figure 22-3b). In both of these cases, when the rod is removed, the electrons at once redistribute themselves and the leaves fall.

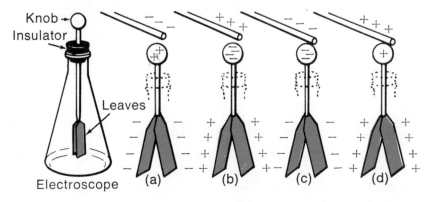

FIGURE 22-3. Electroscope with accompanying diagrams of possible charge distributions.

A negatively charged rod brought into contact with the top of the electroscope repels electrons from the knob down to the leaves. The top of the electroscope then has a net positive charge and draws electrons from the negative rod. The electroscope then gains an overall excess negative charge. When the negative rod is removed, the leaves remain in a diverged position for some time (Figure 22-3c).

When a positively charged rod is brought into contact with the top of the electroscope, an overall excess positive charge develops. The rod produces this excess positive charge by drawing electrons from the electroscope (Figure 22-3d).

A negatively charged rod is brought close to two insulated metal spheres that are touching. Electrons are repelled from the sphere nearest the rod onto the sphere farthest away. If the

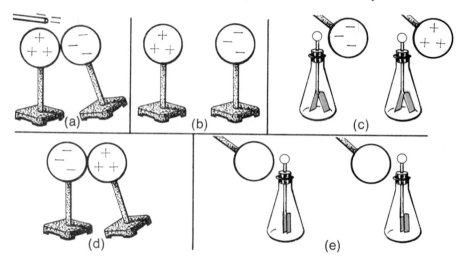

FIGURE 22-4. The use of metal spheres to transfer charges.

spheres are then separated, one is charged negatively and the other positively. Each sphere, when brought close to the knob of an electroscope, causes the leaves to diverge. The two spheres are charged equally and oppositely. To demonstrate this, touch the spheres together. The excess electrons flow from the negative sphere onto the positive sphere. The result is that both spheres become neutral. To show that the spheres no longer bear a charge, again bring them close to the knob of an electroscope. The uncharged spheres do not affect the leaves.

22:4   Charged Bodies Attract Neutral Bodies

In demonstrations of static electricity, rubber rods or glass rods are often used. The false idea that static charges are induced only on glass or rubber can develop. In fact all substances contain

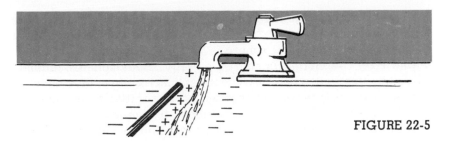

FIGURE 22-5

electrons, and all substances can gain a static charge. For example, a charged rubber rod held near a stream of water pulls the stream to one side (Figure 22-5). The negative rod repels electrons from the side of the stream closest to it to the other side of the stream. Thus the surface of the stream nearest the rod becomes positive. Then the positive water is attracted to the negative rod and the stream of water bends.

In the same way, a comb can be used to pick up small bits of paper even though the paper is neutral. A comb run through hair gains a negative charge. The negatively charged comb repels electrons from the side of the paper closest to it. This side of the paper is then positive, and the comb attracts it. The paper is drawn to the comb. But almost at once, the paper is repelled by the comb. This occurs because the negative comb gives electrons to the positive side of the paper. Soon the paper itself becomes negative. The two negative bodies then repel.

Any substance can be given a static charge.

22:5 Grounding

Suppose an insulated metal sphere is charged negatively and then touched to a second sphere. The charged sphere repels electrons from the surface it is touching. Then it feeds electrons onto

FIGURE 22-6. A charged sphere (a) shares charges equally with a neutral sphere of equal size (b). It gives much of its charge to a larger neutral sphere (c), and gives virtually all of its charge to a grounded object (d).

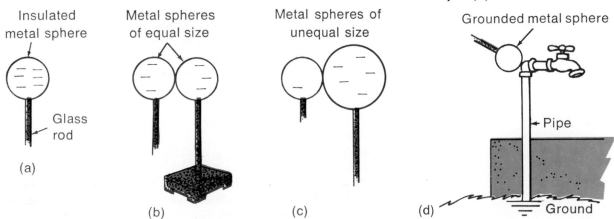

FIGURE 22-7. Lightning rods protect buildings by conducting electrons directly to the earth.

Grounding allows a charged body to feed all of its excess charge into the earth.

the now positive side of the second sphere. What happens to the charge on the first sphere? This depends upon the size of what it is touching. If the metal sphere is touched to a second sphere of equal size, the charge is shared equally. Both spheres indicate they are charged when held near an electroscope. But they do not indicate as intense a charge as the one initially possessed by the first sphere. If the sphere is touched to a much larger sphere, it does not stop feeding the charge into the larger sphere until both spheres have the same charge per unit of surface area. In other words, the size of the charge on the small sphere is greatly reduced. An electroscope is affected only slightly, if at all, by either sphere.

Now consider what happens if the sphere is touched to the earth. The sphere tries to share its charge with the earth itself. In effect, the sphere feeds all of its charge into the earth and becomes neutral. The earth is so large that no net charge develops on the earth. Both bodies are neutral. Touching a charged body to the earth is called **grounding**.

22:6   Conductors and Insulators

Materials which do not conduct electricity well are insulators.

All materials can be charged electrostatically. But, not all materials conduct electrons well. A rubber rod can be charged, but its charge does not move along the rod. Therefore, rubber or glass rods are used for electrostatic experiments. The failure of such materials to conduct electricity makes them good insulators.

Metals are good electric conductors.

All metals are good conductors of electricity. The atoms of a metallic solid are packed closely together. As a result, the outermost electrons of the atoms in metals are almost as close to the attractive force of the positive nuclei of surrounding atoms as they are to the attractive force of their own nuclei. Many of the outermost electrons leave their atoms and move about the metal. This effect is prominent in metals such as gold, silver, and copper which have only one electron in their outermost levels. The large number of free electrons in metals are often referred to as the electron gas. These electrons are easily moved back and forth through the metal. Thus, metals are good electrical conductors. Gold and silver are the best conductors but are very expensive. Copper and aluminum are the most suitable conductors for commercial use.

A metal rod can be charged by rubbing it with fur or wool. But, as a good conductor, the metal quickly sends its excess charge to ground through the person holding the rod. The body is also a good conductor. In order to maintain a charge on metal, it must be placed on an insulating support.

22:7 Concentration of Charge

Electrons repel electrons. Therefore, any charged body distributes its charge over its outer surface. It is on this outer surface that the electrons can get farthest from each other. The electrons distribute themselves in such a way as to bring about equilibrium over the surface. Therefore, any pointed or angular surface of a body must have a high concentration of charge to establish equilibrium. Charge per unit area along a pointed surface increases as the body narrows (Figure 22-8). This increase is due to the decrease in surface area along the point. More charges are needed in less area to push against the repulsive force of the larger areas. The concentration becomes extreme at the tip.

Electrons are distributed over the outer surface of a charged body.

As a body narrows, charge per unit surface area increases.

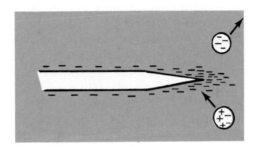

FIGURE 22-8. Electrons are concentrated around sharper surfaces of an object. They become so concentrated on pointed surfaces that they can leak off the object.

The charge can become so intense that it causes the electrons in the air molecules around the point to repel to the side farthest from the point. Thus, the sides of the molecules that face the point have a positive charge. At once the molecules are attracted to the point. When the molecules touch the point they gain electrons and become negatively charged. Then the molecules are repelled from the point. A point does this so efficiently that it causes the rapid discharge of the entire body of which it is a part. To prevent loss of charge from devices designed to hold static charges, the surfaces are rounded. For example, there is a knob on an electroscope and metal spheres are used to hold charges.

A pointed surface readily leaks static charge.

22:8 Electric Potential Energy

When a mass is raised to a height above the surface of the earth, the earth-mass system has energy it previously did not have. If the mass falls back to the earth, this energy can be used to do work. The system has energy because the earth and the mass attract one another. Work is done to lift the mass from the surface of the earth against the attractive force. This work is reclaimed as the mass returns to the surface of the earth.

Suppose charges are separated so that one body has an excess of electrons and another body lacks electrons. The situation is exactly like the one just described. Electrons are forced away from the positive plate and through some distance onto the negative plate. Work is done to separate the charge. The work is reclaimed when the charge moves back to the positive plate. While on the negative plate, the electrons have potential energy with respect to the positive plate. When the electrons flow from the negative plate to the positive plate, the flow is an electric current. Therefore, electric currents deliver energy.

Electric potential energy is more complex than gravitational potential energy. The gravitational force between the earth and a mass is always attractive. Electric forces are both attractive and repulsive. Also, the gravitational force acting on a unit mass near the surface of the earth is almost the same everywhere on the earth. The electric force acting on a unit charge depends on the number of electrons about the charge. Still, gravitational potential energy and electric potential energy are similar. In both cases, work is done to create the potential energy. Also, in both cases the same amount of work is done when the potential energy is used.

In order to have electric potential energy, it is not necessary to have both a negatively charged body and a positively charged body. Electrons always flow from areas of higher concentration to areas of lower concentration. Thus, if a wire connects two negatively charged bodies, electrons flow from the body of higher electron concentration to the body of lower electron concentration. Likewise, electrons flow from a negatively-charged body to a neutral body or from a neutral body to a positively-charged body. When a wire connects two bodies having different concentrations of electrons, electrons flow from the higher concentration to the lower.

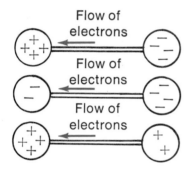

FIGURE 22-9. Electrons always flow from an area of higher electron concentration to an area of lower concentration.

Bodies with different concentrations of electrons have a difference in potential between them. This means that the two bodies are a source of potential energy. The difference in potential depends on the concentration of electrons on each. Difference in potential is measured in **volts** (V).

22:9   Electric Circuits

An electron flow takes place if two bodies having a difference in potential are connected by a conductor. This flow is an electric current. To be useful, the current must be maintained. The only way to maintain a current is to maintain a charge on the two bodies that are at different potentials. To maintain a potential difference, some device must pump the electrons back to the body with higher electron concentration as soon as they arrive at the body with lower concentration. Several devices can pump electrons. Voltaic cells (batteries) and generators are the most common.

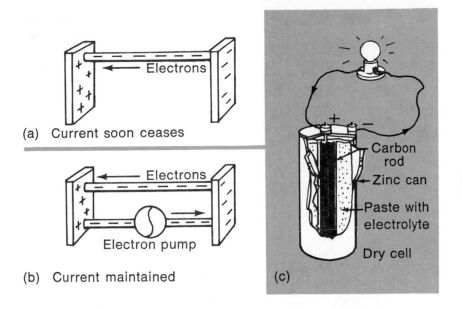

(a) Current soon ceases

(b) Current maintained

(c)

FIGURE 22-10. (α) Electrons flow from the negative to the positive plate. (b) A generator pumps electrons back to the negative plate. Thus, the current continues to flow. (c) A diagram of an ordinary battery.

A flashlight battery is actually a single cell consisting of a zinc plate and a carbon rod. They are separated by a paste containing an oxidizing agent. The chemical reaction between the oxidizing agent and the zinc causes the plates to maintain an electric charge. Essentially, this is the same as burning any fuel to provide energy. Remember that devices do exist which can provide two constantly charged plates that can be used to form an electric circuit.

22:10   The Coulomb

The quantity of electric charge that exists on a charged body is measured in coulombs. This is analogous to measuring water in liters. A liter of water may be defined as consisting of so many molecules of water. In much the same way, a **coulomb** (coul) is defined as the electric charge on 6.25×10^{18} electrons or protons. This definition came from early experiments in which electric charge was measured in terms of the amount of silver deposited on a plate during silver-plating. The existence of electrons and protons was not established until later. Then it became possible to find the number of electrons or protons in one coulomb.

The coulomb is the charge found on 6.25×10^{18} electrons or protons. The charge on a single proton or electron is $1/6.25 \times 10^{18}$ or 1.60×10^{-19} coulomb. This value is the elementary unit of charge. It is not possible to visualize quantities of these magnitudes. Think of a coulomb as a certain quantity of charge just as a liter of water is a certain quantity of water.

The coulomb is the amount of charge found on 6.25×10^{18} electrons.

22:11 Coulomb's Law

Electric forces are important in holding together the particles that make up atoms and in holding atoms together. The behavior of electric forces is the key to understanding atomic structure.

In 1785, Charles Coulomb (1736–1806) measured the force between two small charged spheres. He used a very sensitive torsion balance (Figure 22-11). The force needed to twist the wire through any given angle was first carefully measured. Then the

Coulomb's law describes the force between two charged bodies.

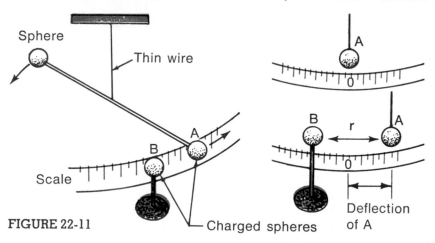

FIGURE 22-11

rod was suspended from the wire. A charged sphere, B, was touched to sphere A so that the two spheres, being equal in size, shared the charge equally. Coulomb varied the distance, r, between A and B and observed the deflection of A from its rest position. The deflection caused the wire to twist. Coulomb measured the angle of twist and used it to find the force between the two spheres. He then related this force to the distance beween the spheres.

After a series of measurements, Coulomb touched A with his finger and grounded it. Then he touched B to A a second time. The charges on both A and B became half their former charge. He repeated the process. The spheres then had one-fourth their former charge. After a number of careful experiments, Coulomb formed a conclusion. Coulomb's law states that the force between two charged bodies varies directly with the product of their charges and inversely with the square of the distance between them. Coulomb's law is expressed as

The electric force between two charged bodies varies directly with the product of their charges.

The electric force varies inversely with the square of distance between two charged bodies.

$$F \propto \frac{qq'}{r^2}$$

The charges on the bodies, q and q', are separated by a distance r. Note that this expression is similar to the one for gravitational force.

In general, electricity is measured in MKS units. When charge is expressed in coulombs, distance in meters, and force in newtons, the equation used to calculate electric forces is

$$F = K\frac{qq'}{r^2}$$

The constant K is found by measuring the force F (in newtons) between two known charges q and q' (in coulombs) that are a known distance (in meters) apart. The constant turns out to be

$$K = 9.0 \times 10^9 \frac{\text{N-m}^2}{\text{coul}^2}$$

Example: Coulomb's Law—Like Charges

A positive charge of 6.0×10^{-6} coul is 0.03 m from a second positive charge of 3.0×10^{-6} coul. Calculate the force between the charges.

Solution:

$$F = K\frac{qq'}{r^2}$$
$$= \left(9.0 \times 10^9 \ \frac{\text{N-m}^2}{\text{coul}^2}\right) \frac{(6.0 \times 10^{-6} \text{ coul}) (3.0 \times 10^{-6} \text{ coul})}{(0.03 \text{ m})^2}$$
$$= \left(9.0 \times 10^9 \ \frac{\text{N-m}^2}{\text{coul}^2}\right) \frac{(18 \times 10^{-12}) \text{ coul}^2}{9 \times 10^{-4} \text{ m}^2}$$
$$= 180 \text{ N}$$

The positive force between the charges indicates repulsion.

A positive force between charges indicates repulsion.

Example: Coulomb's Law—Unlike Charges

What force exists between a positive charge of 1.5×10^{-5} coul and a negative charge of 6.0×10^{-6} coul when they are separated by 5 cm?

Solution:

$$F = K\frac{qq'}{r^2}$$
$$= \left(9.0 \times 10^9 \ \frac{\text{N-m}^2}{\text{coul}^2}\right) \frac{(1.5 \times 10^{-5} \text{ coul}) (-6.0 \times 10^{-6} \text{ coul})}{(0.05 \text{ m})^2}$$
$$= -324 \text{ N}$$

The negative force between the charges indicates attraction. Note the large forces involved between electric charges given in millionths of a coulomb.

A negative force indicates attraction.

Coulomb's law is useful when working with atomic and subatomic particles. It helps to explain the forces that exist between electrons, protons, and the other particles within the atom. Atomic and subatomic particles are very close to point charges. Coulomb's law applies accurately to them. When two fairly large charged bodies are close together, Coulomb's law applies only with modification.

PROBLEMS

1. Two positive charges of 6.0×10^{-6} coul are separated by 0.5 m. What force exists between the charges?

2. A negative charge of 2.0×10^{-4} coul and a negative charge of 8.0×10^{-4} coul are separated by 0.3 m. What force exists between the two charges?

3. What is the force between a positive charge of 0.0008 coul and a negative charge of 0.0003 coul separated by 0.7 m?

4. Determine the force between two positive charges of 1 coul each separated by 1 m.

5. A negative charge of 6.0×10^{-6} coul exerts an attractive force of 64.8 N on a second charge 0.05 m away. What is the magnitude of the second charge?

6. A positive charge of 2.0×10^{-6} coul is 0.06 m from a second positive charge of 4.0×10^{-6} coul. Find the force between the two charges.

7. Suppose the bodies of Problem 6 each have a mass of 5 g (0.005 kg) and are somehow made free to move in a frictionless medium. What is the instantaneous acceleration of the masses upon release?

22:12   Electric Fields

A charged body can exert a force on a second charged body through a distance with no medium existing between the two. The electric field concept is used to describe the behavior of any charged body when it is near another charged body. The electric field is not, in itself, an explanation of electric forces.

The electric field concept is used to explain the behavior of a charged body in the presence of a second charged body.

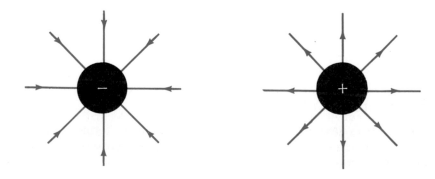

FIGURE 22-12. Lines of force are drawn perpendicularly away from the positive body and perpendicularly into the negative body.

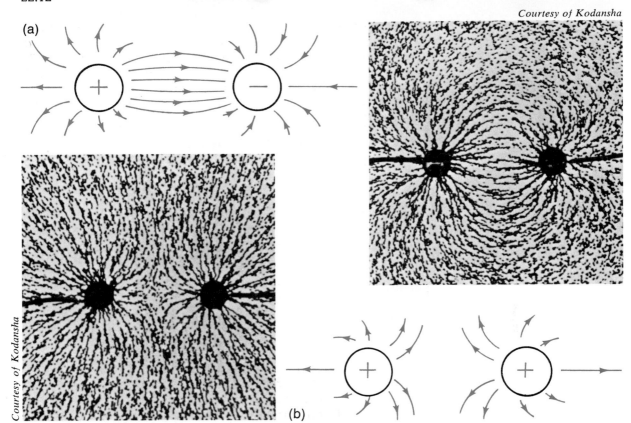

Courtesy of Kodansha

(a)

(b)

Courtesy of Kodansha

FIGURE 22-13. Lines of force between unlike charges (a), and between like charges (b).

To plot an electric field, a small positive test charge is placed at different points within the field. Its behavior is studied. The force on the positive test charge is always found to be toward a negatively charged body and away from a positively charged body. Figure 22-12 shows vectors representing the forces acting on a test charge in two situations. In all cases the vectors are perpendicular to the charged body. For this reason, the field about a charged body is sometimes described by drawing lines of force about and perpendicular to the charged body. These lines represent the force field, but they do not actually exist. Note that the lines get farther apart as the distance from the charged body increases. This increased spacing indicates a weakening of the field with distance in accord with Coulomb's law.

Figure 22-13 shows the patterns taken by the lines of force when the fields between charged bodies are plotted. Lines of force serve only to describe the behavior of a positively charged test body placed in the field. The direction of an electric field is the direction of the force on a positive charge placed in the field. This direction is always away from a positive charge and toward a negative charge. Electric fields run from positive to negative.

The direction of an electric field is always away from a positive charge and toward a negative charge.

22:13   Electric Field Intensity

A positive test charge placed at some point in an electric field is under a force that is proportional to the product of the field intensity, E, and the magnitude of the charge, q. As an equation this is written $F = Eq$. The intensity (strength) of the field at a given location is

Electric field intensity is electric force per unit charge.

$$E = \frac{F}{q}$$

F is in newtons, q is in coulombs, and E is in newtons per coulomb.

Example: Electric Field Intensity

A positive test charge of 4.0×10^{-5} coul is placed in an electric field. The force acting on it is 0.6 N. What is the magnitude of the electric field intensity at the point where the charge is placed?

Solution:

$$E = \frac{F}{q}$$
$$= \frac{0.6 \text{ N}}{4.0 \times 10^{-5} \text{ coul}}$$
$$= 1.5 \times 10^4 \text{ N/coul}$$

Note: If the charge is negative, the field intensity is still measured the same way. However, the charge experiences a force in the opposite direction.

PROBLEMS

8. A positive test charge of 8.0×10^{-5} coul is placed in an electric field. It experiences a force of 4.0×10^{-3} N. What is the intensity of the field at this point?

9. Suppose the test charge of Problem 8 is located in the field of a charge considered to be a point charge. It is moved to a distance twice as far from the charge. What force does the field exert on it?

10. A negative charge of 2.0×10^{-8} coul experiences a force of 0.06 N when in an electric field. What is the magnitude of the field intensity at the point where the charge is located?

11. A positive test charge of 5.0×10^{-4} coul is in an electric field which exerts a force of 5.0×10^{-4} N on it. What is the magnitude of the electric field at the point of the charge?

22:14   The Electric Field Between Two Parallel Plates

The electric field between two charged plates is uniform.

Point charges are used chiefly in the study of the structure of matter. But the field that exists between two charged parallel

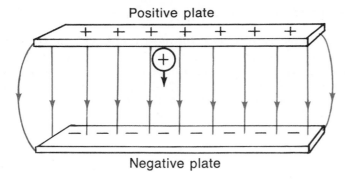

Positive plate

Negative plate

FIGURE 22-14. Diagram of electric field between two parallel plates of opposite charge. The lines of force are drawn from the positive plate to the negative plate.

plates has more practical uses. The field is uniform in the region between two such plates, except at the very edges of the plates. A test charge would find the same force at any point in the space between the plates.

SUMMARY

The atoms of a material usually contain as many electrons as protons and are electrically neutral. The negative electrons are located outside the nucleus and are easily moved. The positive protons are firmly locked in the nucleus. The positive and negative charges balance.

Because an electron can be moved easily, negative and positive charges can be produced on objects. A body may be charged negatively by adding electrons to it. A body may be charged positively by removing electrons from it. All electric phenomena are due to the movement of electrons.

Bodies that have like electric charges repel each other. Bodies that have unlike electric charges attract each other. A charged body brought near a neutral body will induce a charge on the neutral body and then attract it. If a charged body is touched to the earth, the body will give its charge to the earth. The body is then said to be grounded.

The distribution of charge on a body is related to the shape of the body. Any pointed surface will have a high concentration of charge. The charge on a point can become so intense that it causes the rapid discharge of the body of which it is a part. Thus, the surfaces of devices designed to hold charge are rounded.

Work must be done to separate charge. The work is then stored as electric potential energy on the bodies that bear the charge. If a conductor is connected between the bodies, electrons will flow from the negative body to the positive body in the form of an electric current. The electrons will deliver their potential energy as they flow to the positive body.

The coulomb is the standard for electric charge. One coulomb is the charge on 6.25×10^{18} electrons or protons. The charge on a single electron or proton is 1.60×10^{-19} coulomb. Coulomb's law states that the force between two charged bodies varies directly with the product of their charges and inversely with the square of the distance between the charges.

A charged body can exert a force on a second charged body through a distance. The electric field concept is used to describe the behavior of a charged body when it is near another charged body. Electric fields are directed away from positive charges and toward negative charges. When two charged bodies of opposite sign are near each other, the electric field is said to run from positive to negative. Electric field intensity is measured in newtons per coulomb.

QUESTIONS

1. List the three major particles of the atom. State the electric charge of each.

2. Explain how a body is charged (a) positively, (b) negatively, and (c) neutrally.

3. Explain how the leaves of an electroscope are made to diverge by the near presence of a rod (a) charged positively, (b) charged negatively.

4. A charged body can attract a neutral body. Describe how a negatively charged rod attracts a neutral bit of paper.

5. Why does a charged body lose its charge when it is touched to the ground?

6. A charged rubber rod placed on a table maintains its charge for some time. Why does the charge not "ground" immediately?

7. Name three good conductors of electricity.

8. What is the best shape for an object designed to maintain a static charge?

9. Draw a simple electric circuit.

10. Define the coulomb.

11. What is the charge on a single electron or proton?

12. State Coulomb's law.

13. Diagram the field between (a) two like charges, and (b) two unlike charges.

14. How is the direction of an electric field determined?

PROBLEMS

1. A positive charge of 1.8×10^{-6} coul and a negative charge of 1.0×10^{-6} coul are 0.04 m apart. What is the force between the two particles?

2. Two negative charges of 5.0×10^{-5} coul are 0.2 m from each other. What force acts on the particles?

3. A positive charge of 1.5×10^{-5} coul and a negative charge of 1.5×10^{-5} coul are separated by 15 cm. Find the force between the two particles.

4. What force exists between two negative charges of 1.2×10^{-3} coul separated by 1 m?

5. The common isotope of hydrogen contains a proton and an electron separated by about 5.0×10^{-11} m. Use 1.6×10^{-19} coul as the elementary unit of charge to determine the force of attraction between the two particles.

6. The mass of a proton is approximately 1.7×10^{-27} kg. The mass of the electron is approximately 9.0×10^{-31} kg. (a) Use Newton's law of universal gravitation to calculate the gravitational force between the electron and proton in the hydrogen atom. (b) Compare this solution to the solution of Problem 5. How many orders of magnitude greater is the electric force between the two particles than the gravitational force between the two particles?

7. Two pith balls, 1 g each, have equal charges (Figure 22-15a). One pith ball is suspended by an insulating thread. The other charge is brought to within 3 cm of the suspended ball ($r = 0.03$ m). The suspended pith ball is deflected from its rest position until the thread forms an angle of 30° with the vertical. At this angle, the ball is in equilibrium. Equilibrium exists because F_E and mg add vectorially to yield the equilibrant of T. Calculate (a) mg, (b) F_E, and (c) the charge on the pith balls.

8. Charges of 6.0×10^{-6} coul exist on the three charges in Figure 22-15b. Find the magnitude of the resultant force on A.

(a) mg   (b)   FIGURE 22-15

9. A charge of 2.0×10^{-4} coul is placed in the electric field around a larger body which has a negative charge. The force acting on the charge is 8×10^{-4} N. (a) What is the intensity of the electric field at the position of the test charge? (b) Is the field directed toward or away from the larger body?

10. What net force acts on a test charge of 4.0×10^{-3} coul when it is in an electric field at a point where the field intensity is 20 N/coul?

11. What charge exists on a test charge that experiences a force of 1.0×10^{-8} N at a point where the electric field intensity is 2.0×10^{-4} N/coul?

12. A positive test charge of 3.0×10^{-4} coul is placed between a pair of parallel plates. One is positive and the other is negative. The force acting on the test charge is 0.9 N. (a) What is the intensity of the field at the location of the charge? (b) The charge is moved 2 cm closer to the positive plate. What force acts on it?

PROJECTS

1. Rub a balloon briskly through your hair and place it on the ceiling.

2. Make an electroscope using an empty glass jar, a nail, and two strips of aluminum foil. Charge a plastic object by rubbing it through your hair or your clothing. A comb usually works well. Hold the charged object next to the electroscope.

3. Tear a piece of paper into tiny pieces. Charge a comb by rubbing it through your hair. Place the comb close to the paper bits. Can you explain what happens? Bring the charged comb close to a thin stream of smoothly running water.

4. Glue a short piece of a wooden rod to the center of the inside bottom of an aluminum pie plate. Find an old phonograph record and place it on a table or desk. Rub the record with a piece of wool or fur. Place the pie plate on the record and touch briefly the edge of the plate with one finger. Remove the pie plate by means of its wooden handle and place it near an electroscope. The plate should carry a strong charge. This device is called an electrophorus.

READINGS

Dunsheath, Percy, *Giants of Electricity*. New York, Thomas Y. Crowell Co., 1967.

Loeb, Leonard B., "The Mechanism of Lightning." *Scientific American*, February, 1949.

Moore, A. D., "Electrostatics." *Scientific American*, March, 1972.

Posin, Dan Q., *Doctor Posin's Giants*. New York, Harper and Row Publishers, Inc., 1961.

Schrieffer, J. Robert, and Soven, Paul, "Theory of the Electronic Structure." *Physics Today*, April, 1975.

It takes a power failure to make us realize how much we depend on current electricity in our daily lives. We use electric current to improve the quality of our lives and also to provide some forms of recreation. What is current electricity? How is it produced? How is it used in industry, in our homes, in the city, and on the farm?

ELECTRIC CURRENTS

Electric currents serve many useful purposes. Many modern devices such as radios and TV sets operate by means of electric currents. Perhaps the most important aspect of electric current is its ability to transfer energy. The large amount of potential and kinetic energy of the water at Niagara Falls is of no use to a factory a hundred kilometers away unless it can be transferred to that factory. Electric currents provide the means to transfer large quantities of energy over great distances with little loss.

GOAL: You will gain knowledge and understanding of electric current, electric units, the elements of an electric circuit, and the concepts of electric energy and potential difference.

The major purpose of electric current is to transfer energy.

23:1 Difference in Potential

The magnitude and direction of any field is measured by placing a standard unit in the field and measuring the force that acts on it. For example, the earth's gravitational field close to the earth has an intensity of 9.8 N/kg. That is, the earth exerts a force of 9.8 N on each kilogram near its surface. The intensity of the gravitational field on the moon is 1.6 N/kg.

To lift 1 kg of mass 1 m above the surface of the earth requires a force of 9.8 N acting through a distance of 1 m. This means that 9.8 N-m or 9.8 J of work are done on the mass to lift it 1 m. The mass then has 9.8 J of potential energy. Thus, the difference in potential between a point on the surface of the earth and a point 1 m above the surface of the earth is 9.8 J/kg. The difference in potential between two points in a field is the work needed to move a unit of whatever is affected by the field between the two points. Note that the potential difference is found by multiplying the field intensity by the distance moved.

The potential difference between two points in a field is the work required to move a unit charge between the two points.

$$\text{Potential difference} = \text{Field intensity} \times \text{Distance}$$
$$9.8 \, \text{J/kg} = 9.8 \, \text{N/kg} \times 1 \, \text{m}$$

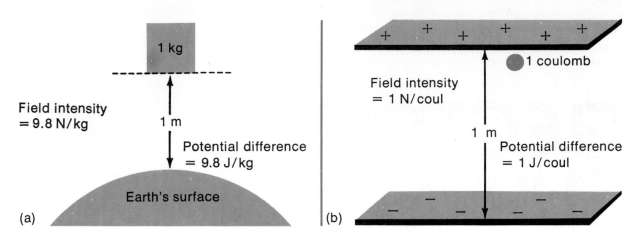

FIGURE 23-1. Gravitational potential difference (a) and electric potential difference (b) are both found by multiplying field intensity by distance moved.

The potential difference between two points in an electric field is measured in joules per coulomb, or volts.

Potential difference is found by multiplying electric field intensity by the distance a charge is moved against the field.

Electric fields affect electric charges. To measure the intensity of an electric field we place a standard charge in the field and measure the force acting on it. Thus, electric field intensity (Chapter 22) is measured in newtons per coulomb.

Suppose that a coulomb of charge is placed in an electric field. If the field produces a force of 1 N on the charge, the field intensity is 1 N/coul. If a force of 1 N is applied to the charge and moves it 1 m against the field, 1 N-m or 1 J of work is done on the charge. But, the coulomb of charge has gained 1 J of potential energy. Thus, the difference in potential between the two points a meter apart is a joule per coulomb. A joule per coulomb is called a **volt**. Note that the potential difference (V) is found by multiplying the field intensity (E) by the distance (d). The same method is used to find gravitational potential difference. Thus, for electric potential difference

$$\text{Potential Difference} = \text{Field Intensity} \times \text{Distance}$$
$$V = Ed$$

In practice, electric fields are usually more intense than 1 N/coul. Also parallel plates are closer together than 1 m. The example shows a typical situation.

Example: Potential Difference Between Parallel Plates

Two parallel plates are 0.03 m apart. The electric field intensity between them is 3000 N/coul. What is the difference in potential between the plates?

Solution:

$$
\begin{aligned}
V &= Ed \\
&= 3000 \text{ N/coul} \times 0.03 \text{ m} \\
&= 90 \text{ N-m/coul} \\
&= 90 \text{ J/coul} \\
&= 90 \text{ volts}
\end{aligned}
$$

Example: Electric Field Intensity Between Two Parallel Plates

A voltmeter shows a difference in potential of 50 volts between two parallel metal plates. The plates are 0.05 m apart. What is the field intensity?

Solution:

$$V = Ed$$

$$E = \frac{V}{d}$$

$$= \frac{50 \text{ volts}}{0.05 \text{ m}}$$

$$= \frac{50 \text{ J/coul}}{0.05 \text{ m}}$$

$$= \frac{50 \text{ N-m/coul}}{0.05 \text{ m}}$$

$$= 1000 \text{ N/coul}$$

PROBLEMS

1. The electric field intensity between two charged metal plates is 800 N/coul. The plates are 0.5 m apart. What is the difference in potential between them?

2. The field intensity between two plates is 2000 N/coul. What is the difference in potential between one parallel plate and a point halfway to a second parallel plate 0.06 m way?

3. A voltmeter reads 500 volts when placed across two parallel plates. The plates are 0.02 m apart. What is the field intensity between them?

4. Two plates are 0.008 m apart. The potential difference between them is 200 volts. What is the field intensity between the plates?

5. What voltage is applied to two metal plates 0.05 m apart if the field intensity between them is 2500 N/coul?

23:2   Work and Energy

A difference in potential of 1 volt between two plates means that 1 J of work must be done to transfer 1 coul of charge between the plates against the electric field. To transfer 1 coul of charge through a potential difference of 100 volts against the field, 100 J of work must be done on the charge. To transfer 2 coul of charge between the 100-volt difference in potential, 200 J of work must be done on the charge. The work done to move a charge against an electric field is given by the expression

$$W = Vq$$

The work done on the charge is stored as electric potential energy. Suppose 1 coul of charge flows back between the plates

The work done in moving a charge against an electric field is equal to the product of charge and potential difference.

Work done to move a charge is stored as electric potential energy.

under the influence of the electric field. It delivers exactly the same energy that was used to move it against the field. Thus, to move 1 coul of charge through a potential difference of 100 volts, 100 J of work are exerted on the charge. When the charge returns through the field, it delivers 100 J of energy. Suppose the charge passes through an electric motor on its return through the field. Then it would deliver 100 J of energy to the motor. The motor would then be able to do 100 J of work.

Example: Work Done to Move a Charge Against an Electric Field

(a) What work is done on a 5 coul charge to transfer it through a potential difference of 90 volts? (b) What is the potential energy of the charge as a result of the transfer?

Solution:
(a)
$$W = Vq$$
$$= 90 \text{ J/coul} \times 5 \text{ coul}$$
$$= 450 \text{ J}$$

(b) By the law of conservation of energy, the potential energy is equal to the work done on the charge. Thus,
$$PE = 450 \text{ J}$$

PROBLEMS

6. (a) What work does a generator do to transfer 1 coul of charge through a potential difference of 110 volts? (b) What is the potential energy of 1 coul of charge after the transfer takes place?

7. What work is done by the chemical energy of a dry cell to transfer 5 coul of negative charge from its positive plate to its negative plate? The dry cell is rated at 1.5 volts.

8. How much work does the chemical energy of a 90-volt battery do to transfer 30 coul of charge between its plates?

9. A generator transfers 50 coul of charge through a potential difference of 110 volts. (a) What work does the generator do to transfer this charge? (b) The generator accomplishes this work in 5 sec. How much work does it do per sec? (c) What power does the generator deliver in watts? (d) What is the power of the generator in kilowatts?

23:3   The General Plan of an Electric Circuit

Electric energy is produced by changing an available, natural source of energy to electric energy. In Figure 23-2, the kinetic energy of falling water turns a waterwheel (turbine). The wheel

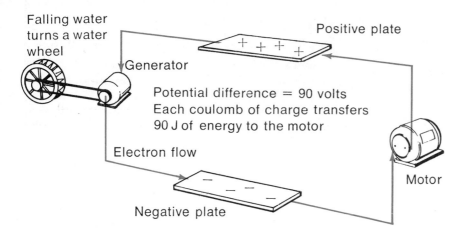

Falling water turns a water wheel

Generator

Positive plate

Potential difference = 90 volts
Each coulomb of charge transfers
90 J of energy to the motor

Electron flow

Negative plate

Motor

FIGURE 23-2. Simple diagram of production and use of electric current.

gains kinetic energy. Then, the kinetic energy of the wheel is transferred to the generator by a belt. When the generator turns, electrons are pulled from the positive plate and pushed onto the negative plate. Recall that electrons are attracted by a positive plate and repelled by a negative plate. The generator forces the electrons to move from the positive to the negative plate. The energy of the source is being used to do work on the electrons and charge the two plates. The concentration of charge on the two plates constitutes electric potential energy. The potential energy stored on the plates is equal to the work done on the generator by the falling water.

A generator forces electrons from a positive plate to the negative plate and gives them electric potential energy.

If a wire is connected between the two plates, electric current appears in the wire. Electrons begin to move from the negative plate to the positive plate through the wire. The electrons are said to "fall back through the field" because the situation is similar to a weight falling through the earth's gravitational field to the surface of the earth.

If an electric motor is connected between the two plates, the electric potential energy given up by the electrons as they move from the negative plate to the positive plate will be used to make the motor turn. The electric energy is converted to the kinetic energy of the turning motor.

Electric potential energy can be changed to the kinetic energy of a spinning motor as electrons return to the positive plate.

If the difference in potential between the two plates is 90 volts, the generator must do 90 joules of work on every coulomb of charge that it transfers from the positive plate to the negative plate. Thus, every coulomb of charge that moves from the negative plate back to the positive plate through the motor delivers 90 joules of energy to the motor.

In practice the two plates are not necessary. The wires themselves can act as plates. Note that electricity serves as a way to transfer the kinetic energy of falling water to the kinetic energy of a turning motor.

23:4 The Ampere and Electric Power

Power is the rate of doing work. It is measured in J/sec. Suppose the current flowing through the motor in Figure 23-2 is 3 coul/sec. Then a potential difference of 90 volts supplies the motor with 90 J/coul × 3 coul/sec, or 270 J/sec, or 270 watts. Thus, to find electric power, multiply the voltage (V) by the electron current flow (i). The unit for current is the ampere. One **ampere** (A) is equal to a flow of 1 coul/sec. The equation for electric power is

$$P = Vi$$

In this equation, P is the power in watts, V is the potential difference in volts, i is the current in amperes.

Electric current is measured in amperes.

Electric power is the product of current and potential difference.

Example: Electric Power

A 6-volt battery delivers 0.5 A of current to an electric motor connected across its terminals. (a) What is the power of the motor? (b) What energy does the motor use in 5 min?

Solution:

(a) $\qquad P = Vi$
$\qquad\qquad = 6 \text{ J/coul} \times 0.5 \text{ coul/sec}$
$\qquad\qquad = 3 \text{ J/sec}$
$\qquad\qquad = 3 \text{ watts}$

(b) Three watts is equal to 3 joules/sec. Thus,

Energy used $= 3 \text{ J/sec} \times 300 \text{ sec}$
$\qquad\qquad\quad = 900 \text{ J}$

PROBLEMS

10. The current through a light bulb connected across the terminals of a 120-volt outlet is 0.5 A. At what rate does the bulb use electric energy?

11. A 90-volt battery causes a current of 2 A to flow through a lamp. What is the power of the lamp in watts?

12. A toaster connected to a 120-volt source uses 4 A of current. What power in watts does the toaster use?

13. A light bulb uses 1.2 A when connected across a 120-volt source. What is the wattage of the bulb?

14. What current flows through a 75-watt light bulb connected to a 120-volt outlet?

15. The current through a motor connected to a 60-volt battery is 2 A. What energy in joules does the motor use in 5 min?

16. A lamp is connected across a 24-volt difference in potential. The current flowing through the lamp is 4 A. (a) What power does the lamp use? (b) How much electric energy does the lamp use in 10 min?

23:5　Ohm's Law

The German scientist Georg Simon Ohm (1787–1854) discovered that the ratio of the potential difference between the ends of a wire and the current flowing through the wire is a constant. This ratio is known as the **resistance** of a wire. It is constant for any given wire. This relationship, known as **Ohm's law**, states that *the current that flows through a given wire varies directly with the applied voltage.*

$$i = \frac{V}{R}$$

The electron current flow, i, is in amperes. The potential difference, V, is in volts. The resistance of the conductor R is given in ohms. An **ohm** (Ω) is the resistance which permits a current of 1 A to flow between a potential difference of 1 volt.

A higher voltage causes a greater current flow between the ends of a conductor. To obtain a higher voltage, a more intense charge must be placed on the plates. This higher voltage (greater potential difference) causes the electric field between the plates to become more intense. The more intense field moves more electrons per unit time between the plates.

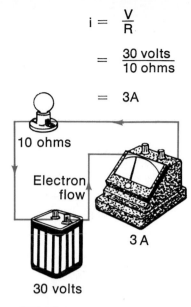

$$i = \frac{V}{R}$$
$$= \frac{30 \text{ volts}}{10 \text{ ohms}}$$
$$= 3\text{A}$$

10 ohms

Electron flow

3 A

30 volts

FIGURE 23-3. Ohm's law.

Example:　Ohm's Law

What current flows between a potential difference of 120 volts through a resistance of 30 ohms?

Solution:

$$i = \frac{V}{R}$$
$$= \frac{120 \text{ volts}}{30 \text{ ohms}}$$
$$= 4 \text{ A}$$

The current in an electric circuit varies directly with the applied voltage and inversely with the resistance.

PROBLEMS

17. A resistance of 30 ohms is placed across a 90-volt battery. What current flows in the circuit?

18. A voltage of 75 volts is placed across a 15-ohm resistor. What current flows through the resistor?

19. A current of 0.5 A flows through a lamp when it is connected to a 120-volt source. (a) What is the resistance of the lamp? (b) What is the wattage of the lamp?

20. A motor with an operating resistance of 30 ohms is connected to a voltage source. Four amperes of current flow in the circuit. What is the voltage of the source?

21. A transistor radio uses 0.2 A of current when it is operated by a 3-volt battery. What is the resistance of the radio circuit?

22. A resistance of 60 ohms allows 0.4 A of current to flow when it is connected across a battery. What is the voltage of the battery?

23:6 Diagramming Electric Circuits

Figure 23-4a shows a simple electric circuit. Figure 23-4b is a diagram of the same circuit. The jagged line in the diagram represents the resistance (or the electric device being operated). The alternate long and short lines represent a battery. The short lines indicate negative terminals. The long lines indicate positive terminals.

(a)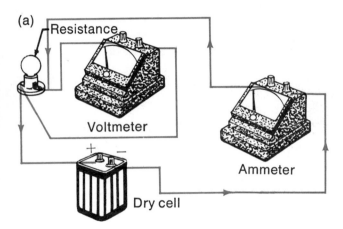

(b)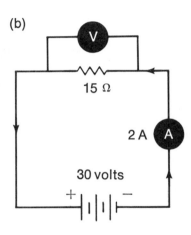

FIGURE 23-4. Simple electric circuit represented both pictorially (a) and schematically (b).

A voltmeter measures the drop in potential across the resistance. The voltmeter is connected to both sides of the resistance. Thus, the voltmeter is said to be in parallel with the resistance. An ammeter measures the current flowing in the circuit. It is connected directly into the circuit, and the entire current flows through the ammeter. Thus, the ammeter is said to be in series with the resistance.

In Figure 23-4 the resistance in the circuit is a light bulb. In a precise measurement the resistance of the connecting wires must also be included. But the resistance of such wires is usually low enough to overlook.

PROBLEMS

23. (a) Draw a diagram to show a circuit that includes a 90-volt battery, an ammeter, and a resistance of 60 ohms. (b) What does the ammeter read?

24. (a) Draw a circuit diagram to include a 60-volt battery, an ammeter, and a resistance of 12.5 ohms. (b) Indicate the ammeter reading.

25. (a) Draw a circuit diagram to include a 16-ohm resistor, a battery, and an ammeter that reads 1.75 A. (b) Indicate the voltage of the battery.

23:7   Controlling Current in a Circuit

There are two ways to control the current that flows in a circuit. Since $i = V/R$, i can be changed by varying either V, R, or both. Figure 23-5 shows a simple circuit. When V is 60 volts and R is 30 ohms, the current flow is 2 A. This may be more current than the resistance should have flowing through it for proper use. To reduce the current some of the dry cells can be removed and the

Current in a circuit can be controlled by adjusting either voltage or resistance.

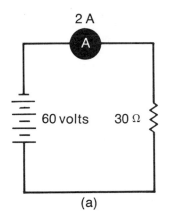

(a)

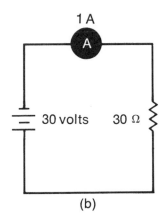

(b)

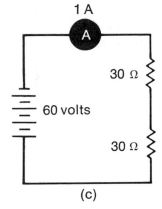

(c)

voltage lowered to 30 volts (Figure 23-5b). The current can also be reduced by increasing the resistance to 60 ohms by adding a resistor to the circuit (Figure 23-5c). Both of these methods will reduce the current to 1 A. Resistors used to control the current flow in electric circuits are control resistors. Control resistors are used to send the proper amount of current through circuits or parts of circuits. Radios and other electric circuits use such resistors.

Sometimes it is necessary to vary the current flow through a resistor. The electric motors used on ripple tanks are usually arranged so that the current through them can be varied. As a result, the motor can run fast or slow. This is done by adding a variable resistor to the circuit (Figure 23-6). A variable resistor consists of a coil of wire and a sliding contact point. By moving the contact point to various positions along the coil, the amount of wire added to the circuit is varied. With more wire placed in the circuit, the resistance of the circuit increases. Thus, less current flows, in accordance with Ohm's law. In this way, the speed of the motor can be adjusted. The same type of device controls

FIGURE 23-5. The current flow through a simple circuit (a) can be regulated by removing some of the dry cells (b), or by increasing the resistance of the circuit (c).

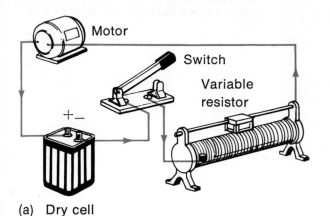

(a)   Dry cell

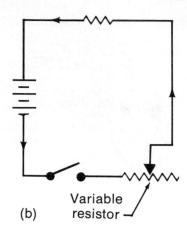

(b)   Variable resistor

FIGURE 23-6. A variable resistor can be used to regulate current in an electric circuit.

the speed of electric fans, electric mixers, and many other electric appliances.

The resistance of a resistor can change during use. Sometimes the temperature of a resistor increases during use. This temperature change causes its resistance to change. Light bulbs increase in resistance after they have been on for a while. If the resistance of a circuit changes while it operates, the current flow changes accordingly.

23:8 Heating Effect of Electric Currents

The power (energy/sec) used by an electric circuit is equal to the voltage multiplied by the current. From Ohm's law we know that $V = iR$. Substituting this expression into the equation for electric power

$$P = Vi$$
$$= iR \times i$$
$$= i^2R$$

The power used by a resistor varies directly with the square of current in the resistor.

The power also varies directly with the resistance.

The power used by a resistor is proportional to the square of the current that passes through it to its resistance.

The power supplied to a circuit can be used in different ways. A motor converts electric energy into mechanical energy. An electric light generates light. But not all of the electric energy used by a motor or an electric light ends up as work or light. All electric devices also generate heat. Some devices are designed for the purpose of supplying heat.

The total energy supplied to any device is the product of power and time.

The energy supplied to a resistor is the power used by the resistor multiplied by the time of its operation.

$$\text{Energy} = Pt$$
$$= \text{watts} \times \text{sec}$$
$$= \text{J/sec} \times \text{sec}$$
$$= \text{J}$$

John Morgan

FIGURE 23-7. Water in this cup is boiled by heat generated as an electric current flows through this metal heating coil.

The expression for power is i^2R. The total energy supplied to any device, Pt, is i^2Rt.

The heat developed by a heating coil, assuming 100 percent of the electric energy is converted to heat, equals the energy consumed during the time it is operated. Thus

$$H = i^2Rt$$

The heat energy developed in a resistor is given by the equation $H = i^2Rt$.

This equation expresses heat energy in joules. To convert heat in joules to heat in calories, use the mechanical equivalent of heat.

$$H = \frac{i^2Rt}{4.2 \text{ J/cal}}$$

Example: Heat Produced by an Electric Current

A heating coil has a resistance of 10 ohms. It is designed to operate on 120 volts. (a) What current flows through the coil? (b) What electric energy in joules is supplied to the heater in 10 sec? (c) How many calories of heat does the heater produce in 10 sec?

Solution:

(a) $i = \dfrac{V}{R}$

$= \dfrac{120 \text{ volts}}{10 \text{ ohms}}$

$= 12 \text{ A}$

(b) Energy $= i^2Rt$

$= (12 \text{ A})^2 (10 \text{ ohms}) (10 \text{ sec})$

$= 14\,400 \text{ J}$

(c) $H = \dfrac{i^2Rt}{4.2 \text{ J/cal}}$

$= \dfrac{14\,400 \text{ J}}{4.2 \text{ J/cal}}$

$= 3430 \text{ cal}$

PROBLEMS

26. (a) What current flows through a 15-ohm electric heater when it operates on a 120-volt outlet? (b) What energy in joules is used by the heater in 30 sec? (c) What heat in calories is liberated by the heater during this time?

27. (a) What current flows through a 30-ohm resistor connected to a 60-volt battery? (b) What energy in joules does the resistor use in 5 min? (c) All of the energy is converted to heat. How many calories are produced during the 5 min?

28. The resistance of an electric stove element at operating temperature is 11 ohms. (a) 220 volts are applied to it. What current flows through the element? (b) What energy in joules does the element use in 30 sec? (c) How much heat in calories does the stove develop in this time?

29. An electric heater is rated at 500 watts. (a) How many joules of energy does the heater use in half an hour? (b) How many calories of heat does the heater generate during this time?

30. A 100-watt light bulb is 20 percent efficient. (a) How many joules does the light bulb convert into heat each minute it is in operation? (b) How many calories of heat does the light bulb produce each minute?

23:9   Transmission of Current Over Long Distances

An energy source is not always located near areas where electricity is in the greatest demand. Electric power must often be transmitted over long distances. But, as the electricity is transmitted, heat is generated in the wires. This heat serves no useful purpose. Therefore, this wasted energy must be kept to a minimum. To do this, $H = i^2Rt$ indicates that it is important to keep the resistance of the wires low. Even more important, the current flowing in the lines needs to be kept low. Low current is more important than low resistance because heat loss depends on the square of the current.

Wire of large diameter and of good conductivity lowers the resistance of transmission lines. Such wires provide a wide path for large transmission of electrons and low resistance to current flow. However, the longer the wire, the greater the resistance. Thus, over long distances, transmission lines do have some heat loss.

High-voltage lines are needed to transmit electric energy over long distances with minimum energy loss.

The heat generated is proportional to the square of the current. Thus the current passing through the lines must be as small as possible. Since $P = Vi$, the current is reduced by making the voltage in the lines very high. Thus, long-distance transmission lines are called high-voltage lines. In this way, large amounts of power are transmitted over long distances with minimum energy loss.

FIGURE 23-8. High-voltage transmission lines carry electricity over large distances.

23:10   The Electronvolt

The charge carried by a single electron is 1.6×10^{-19} coul. The energy required to move 1 coul of charge through a potential difference of 1 volt is 1 J. Thus, the energy required to move a single electron through a potential difference of 1 volt is 1.6×10^{-19} J. This energy is defined to be one electronvolt (eV). Often it is used as a unit of energy to deal with extremely low energy values, such as those found in nuclear physics. A million times the energy of an electronvolt is another useful energy unit. It is a million electronvolts (1 MeV = 1.6×10^{-13} J).

One electronvolt (eV) is the energy required to move one electron through one volt.

SUMMARY

The purpose of an electric current is to transfer energy from place to place. To create an electric potential difference, work must be done to move a charge against an electric field. The work done on the charge is measured in joules per coulomb. A joule per coulomb is called a volt. Ten volts of potential difference means that every coulomb of charge residing on the charged plates required ten joules of work to be placed there. As the charge flows back from the negative plate to the positive plate, each coulomb of charge will deliver ten joules of energy to the circuit.

An ampere is a current flow of a coulomb per second. Electric power is found by multiplying voltage by current ($V \times i$). Volts multiplied by amperes would be joules per second, or watts. Thus, electric power is measured in watts.

Ohm's law states that the current flowing in an electric circuit varies directly with the applied voltage and varies inversely with the resistance of the circuit. The current in a circuit can be increased by increasing the voltage or by decreasing the resistance of the circuit.

QUESTIONS

1. Define a volt in terms of work done against an electric field.
2. Show how multiplying volts times amperes yields watts.

3. A 12-volt battery is connected to a 4-ohm resistor. (a) What current flows in the circuit? (b) State two ways to reduce the current to 1.5 amperes.

4. What quantities must be kept small to transmit electric energy over long distances economically?

5. What is the electronvolt? What does it represent?

PROBLEMS

1. The electric field intensity between two charged plates is 1500 N/coul. The plates are 0.08 m apart. What is the difference in potential between them in volts?

2. A voltmeter indicates that the difference in potential between two plates is 50 volts. The plates are 0.02 m apart. What field intensity exists between them?

3. What voltage is applied to a pair of parallel plates 0.04 m apart to develop a field intensity of 2500 N/coul?

4. How much work is done to transfer 1 coul of charge through a potential difference of 220 volts?

5. A generator transfers 20 coul of charge through a potential difference of 90 volts. (a) How much work does the generator perform? (b) The generator accomplishes this transfer in 60 sec. How much work does it do per sec? (c) What power does the generator deliver in watts?

6. A 60-volt battery transfers 22 coul of negative charge from its negative plate to its positive plate. How much work is done?

7. How much work is done to transfer 6 coulombs of charge through a potential difference of 1.5 volts?

8. A force of 50 N is needed to move a negative charge of 1 coul from a positive plate to a negative plate. (a) What is the intensity of the electric field between the two plates? (b) How much work is done to move the charge between the two plates if they are 5 cm (0.05 m) apart? (c) What is the potential energy in joules of the charge after it is moved between the plates? (d) What is the difference in potential between the plates in joules per coulomb? (e) What is the difference in potential between the plates in volts?

9. A 12-volt battery is connected to an electric motor. The current through the motor is 2 A. (a) How many joules of energy does the battery deliver to the motor each second? (b) What power does the motor use in watts? (c) How much energy does the motor use in 10 min?

10. (a) What power does a 120-volt generator deliver to an electric lamp that draws 0.5 A? (b) How many joules of energy does the lamp use in 5 min?

11. A resistance of 15 ohms is placed across a 45-volt battery. What current flows through the resistance?

12. A 20-ohm resistor is connected to a 30-volt battery. What current flows through the resistor?

13. What voltage is applied to a 20-ohm resistor if the current through it is 1.5 A?

14. What is the resistance of a lamp that is connected to a 120-volt source and draws 1.5 A of current?

15. What current flows through an electric device that is of 15 ohms resistance and designed to operate on 6 volts?

16. The resistance of an electric motor is 7 ohms. The motor operates properly on a voltage of 12 volts. What current does it require?

17. What voltage is placed across a motor of 15 ohms operating resistance to deliver 8 A of current?

18. A heating coil has a resistance of 4 ohms and operates on 120 volts. (a) What current flows through the coil while it is operating? (b) What energy in joules is supplied to the coil in 5 min? (c) How many calories of heat does the coil provide during the 5 min?

19. (a) What current passes through a 6-ohm resistor connected to a 15-volt battery? (b) How much heat is produced in 10 min?

20. (a) How many joules of energy does a 60-watt light bulb use in half an hour? (b) The light bulb is 25 percent efficient. How many calories of heat does it generate during the half hour?

PROJECTS

1. You can make a simple electric meter by wrapping several turns of copper wire around a small compass. Touch the ends of the wire to the top and bottom of a flashlight battery and watch the compass needle. Wrap one end of the wire lead from your meter around a nail. Dip the nail and the other end of the wire into a glass of salt water. Watch the compass needle.

2. Locate the electric meter in your house. Notice that it contains a circular metal disk that spins. The more electric power being used, the faster the disk spins. Shut off every electric device in the house (except clocks which use very little power). The circular disk should be turning very slowly. Turn on a 100-watt light bulb and count the time it takes the disk to turn ten times. Shut off the light bulb and turn on the largest TV set you have in the house. Can you estimate the wattage of the TV set?

3. Electricity experts think that our present-day batteries (dry cells) are not very good. The development of a low-cost battery that could deliver a strong current for a long time would be an important breakthrough in the electric industry. It would make possible the development of inexpensive nonpolluting electric cars. It would also have many other uses. You may want to join in the search for a better dry cell. To do so, you will need a fairly sensitive meter. These are not too difficult to find. Your science teacher may have an old one you can use or an electric worker in your neighborhood may be able to help you. Once you have the meter, arrange a small lab at home and test as many solutions and electrode materials as you can. CAUTION: *Observe all necessary precautions in handling these materials.*

READINGS

Brandt, N. B., and Ginzburg, N. I., "Superconductivity at High Pressure." *Scientific American,* April, 1971.

Dunsheath, Percy, *Giants of Electricity.* New York, Thomas Y. Crowell Co., 1967.

Millikan, R. A., *The Electron.* Chicago, Ill., The University of Chicago Press, 1963.

Seeger, Raymond J., *Benjamin Franklin* (Men and Physics Series). New York, Pergamon Press, Inc., 1974.

Shiers, George, "The First Electron Tube." *Scientific American,* March, 1969.

Suhr, Arthur G., "Ohm's Law." *The Science Teacher,* May, 1959.

The way in which resistors are connected into an electric circuit determines the total resistance in a circuit. It also determines how electric devices which are part of the circuit will function. Here you see a TV line amplifier-signal splitter. It amplifies the incoming TV signal and splits it so that it can be sent to two or more different places. Why do some strands of colored lights go out completely when only one bulb burns out, while other strands continue to function when only one bulb burns out?

SERIES AND PARALLEL CIRCUITS

You have flipped a switch to turn on an electric light. You may also have pushed a button to turn on a record player or an iron. In each case, you have completed an electric circuit. When a circuit is complete, an electric current flows through the circuit.

The way in which parts of a circuit are arranged affects the flow of current through the circuit. There are two basic types of circuits. One type is a series circuit. The other is a parallel circuit. A break in a series circuit stops the current flow in the whole circuit. A break in a parallel circuit stops the current flow in only a portion of the circuit. Let us take a closer look to see why these two types of circuits function as they do.

GOAL: You will gain knowledge and understanding of series and parallel circuits, and of the function of ammeters and voltmeters.

24:1 Series Circuits

When resistors are connected **in series,** current travels through each resistor one after the other. Figure 24-1 shows a series circuit. The electron current in the circuit passes through each appliance (resistance) in succession. The current through each resistance is exactly the same. The current flowing in a series circuit is the same everywhere along the wire.

The current, in turn, encounters resistance by each resistor. Thus, it is opposed by the sum of the resistances. The total resistance (R) of a series circuit is equal to the sum of the individual resistances in the circuit.

$$R = R_1 + R_2 + R_3 + \cdots$$

To find the current flowing in the circuit, first find the total resistance of the circuit. Then apply Ohm's law.

In a series circuit, the current is the same at all points along the wire.

The total resistance in a series circuit is the sum of the individual resistances.

355

Appliances

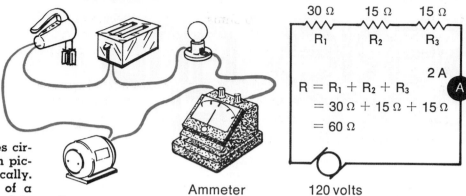

Generator   Ammeter   120 volts

$$R = R_1 + R_2 + R_3$$
$$= 30\,\Omega + 15\,\Omega + 15\,\Omega$$
$$= 60\,\Omega$$

FIGURE 24-1. A series circuit represented both pictorially and schematically. The total resistance of a series circuit is equal to the sum of the individual resistances.

Example: Current Flowing in a Series Circuit

Four 15-ohm resistors are connected in series across a 30-volt battery. What current flows in the circuit?

Solution:

Find the total resistance of the circuit.

$$R = R_1 + R_2 + R_3 + R_4$$
$$= 15\ \text{ohms} + 15\ \text{ohms} + 15\ \text{ohms} + 15\ \text{ohms}$$
$$= 60\ \text{ohms}$$

Then apply Ohm's law to the circuit.

$$i = \frac{V}{R}$$
$$= \frac{30\ \text{volts}}{60\ \text{ohms}}$$
$$= 0.5\ \text{A}$$

PROBLEMS

1. Three 20-ohm resistors are connected in series across a 120-volt generator. (a) What is the total resistance of the circuit? (b) What current flows in the circuit?

2. A 10-ohm resistor, a 15-ohm resistor, and a 5-ohm resistor are connected in series across a 90-volt battery. (a) What is the total resistance of the circuit? (b) What current flows in the circuit?

3. Ten Christmas tree bulbs have equal resistances. When connected to a 120-volt outlet, a current of 0.5 A flows through the bulbs. (a) What is the total resistance of the circuit? (b) What is the resistance of each bulb?

4. A 16-ohm resistor, a 14-ohm resistor, and a 30-ohm resistor are connected in series across a 45-volt battery. (a) What is the

total resistance of the circuit? (b) What current flows in the circuit?

5. A lamp having a resistance of 10 ohms is connected across a 15-volt battery. (a) What current flows through the lamp? (b) What resistance must be connected in series with the lamp to reduce the current to 0.5 A?

6. (a) What current flows through a 60-watt bulb when it is connected across a 120-volt outlet? (b) What is the resistance of two 60-watt bulbs connected in series? (c) What current flows through the two bulbs when connected in series and placed across a 120-volt outlet?

24:2   Voltage Drops in a Series Circuit

When resistors are connected in series, each resistor uses a part of the voltage applied to the circuit. According to Ohm's law, the voltage used is proportional to the resistance. To determine the voltage drop across each resistor, multiply the current in the circuit by the resistance. Thus, in Figure 24-2

> In a series circuit, the sum of the voltage drops equals the voltage drop across the entire circuit.

$$V_1 = iR_1 = 2 \text{ A} \times 10 \text{ ohms} = 20 \text{ volts}$$
$$V_2 = iR_2 = 2 \text{ A} \times 20 \text{ ohms} = 40 \text{ volts}$$
$$V_3 = iR_3 = 2 \text{ A} \times 30 \text{ ohms} = 60 \text{ volts}$$
$$\overline{\hspace{4cm}}$$
$$V = 120 \text{ volts}$$

The total resistance of the circuit in Figure 24-2 is 10 ohms + 20 ohms + 30 ohms, or 60 ohms. By Ohm's law, the current in the circuit is 120 volts/60 ohms = 2 A. To find the voltage drop

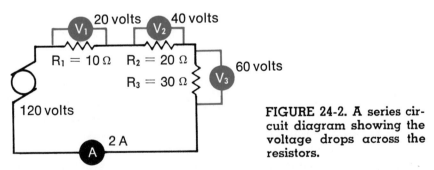

FIGURE 24-2. A series circuit diagram showing the voltage drops across the resistors.

across each resistor, apply Ohm's law to that resistor. Ohm's law may be applied to the entire circuit or to any part of the circuit. Since $V = iR$, the voltage drop across the first resistor is iR_1. Thus, V_1 is 2 A $\times$ 10 ohms = 20 volts. Use the same method to find V_2 and V_3. The voltage drops are 40 volts and 60 volts respectively. The sum of the voltage drops across the resistors is equal to the voltage drop across the entire circuit.

$$V = V_1 + V_2 + V_3$$

Example: Voltage Drops in a Series Circuit

A 5-ohm resistor and a 10-ohm resistor are connected in series and placed across a 45-volt potential difference. (a) What is the total resistance of the circuit? (b) What current flows through the circuit? (c) What is the voltage drop across each resistor? (d) What is the total voltage drop across the circuit?

Solution:

(a) $R = R_1 + R_2$
      $= 5 \text{ ohms} + 10 \text{ ohms}$
      $= 15 \text{ ohms}$

(b) $i = \dfrac{V}{R}$
      $= \dfrac{45 \text{ volts}}{15 \text{ ohms}}$
      $= 3 \text{ A}$

(c)   The voltage drop across R_1 is
      $V_1 = iR_1$
        $= 3 \text{ A} \times 5 \text{ ohms}$
        $= 15 \text{ volts}$

      The voltage drop across R_2 is
      $V_2 = iR_2$
        $= 3 \text{ A} \times 10 \text{ ohms}$
        $= 30 \text{ volts}$

(d) $V = V_1 + V_2$
      $= 15 \text{ volts} + 30 \text{ volts}$
      $= 45 \text{ volts}$

PROBLEMS

7. A 20-ohm resistor and a 30-ohm resistor are connected in series and placed across a 100-volt potential difference. (a) What is the total resistance of the circuit? (b) What current flows through the circuit? (c) What is the voltage drop across each resistor? (d) What is the total voltage drop across the circuit?

8. Three 30-ohm resistors are connected in series and placed across a difference in potential of 135 volts. Calculate (a) the total resistance of the circuit, (b) the current flowing in the circuit, (c) the voltage drop across each resistance, and (d) the total voltage drop across all three resistors.

9. Three resistors of 3 ohms, 5 ohms, and 4 ohms are connected in series across a 12-volt battery. (a) What is the combined resistance of the three resistors? (b) What current flows in the circuit? (c) What is the voltage drop across each resistor? (d) What is the total voltage drop across the circuit?

10. Four resistors of 6 ohms each are connected in series and placed across a voltage source. The current flowing in the circuit is 1.6 A. (a) What is the total resistance of the circuit?

(b) What is the voltage of the source? (c) What is the voltage drop across each of the resistors?

11. A 10-ohm resistor and a variable resistor are connected in series and placed across a 12-volt source. The variable resistor is adjusted until the current flowing in the circuit is 0.6 A. (a) At what resistance is the variable resistor set? (b) What are the voltage drops across the resistor and across the variable resistor?

12. A 40-ohm resistor and a variable resistor are connected in series across a 120-volt outlet. At what value is the variable resistor set if the current in the circuit is (a) 2 A? (b) 0.5 A?

24:3   Parallel Circuits

Figure 24-3 shows three resistors connected **in parallel** across a 120-volt potential difference. The wires running from the generator to points A and B have very little resistance and are not

In a parallel circuit, each resistor provides a new path for electrons to flow.

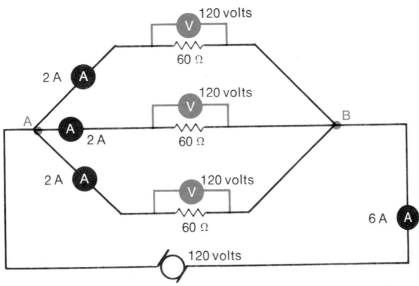

FIGURE 24-3. In a parallel circuit, the reciprocal of the total resistance is equal to the sum of the reciprocals of the individual resistances. Here you see three 60-ohm resistors connected in parallel. For each resistor, the voltage drop is 120 volts and the current is 2 A.

considered to be resistors. Each line from A to B is a complete circuit across the generator and behaves as if the other lines are not present. A 60-ohm resistor across a difference in potential of 120 volts draws 2 A of current. Each 60-ohm resistor in Figure 24-3 draws 2 A of current. The three 60-ohm resistors together draw three times as much current as would flow if only one of the resistors were connected across the generator. Thus, the circuit has a total resistance of only one-third that of any one resistor it contains. Placing resistors in parallel always decreases the total resistance of the circuit. The total resistance decreases because each new resistor provides a new path for the electrons to follow.

The total resistance of a parallel circuit decreases as each new resistor is added.

To find the total resistance of a parallel circuit, use the equation

$$\frac{1}{R} = \frac{1}{R_1} + \frac{1}{R_2} + \frac{1}{R_3} + \cdots$$

The total resistance of the circuit shown in Figure 24-3 is

$$\frac{1}{R} = \frac{1}{60 \text{ ohms}} + \frac{1}{60 \text{ ohms}} + \frac{1}{60 \text{ ohms}} = \frac{3}{60 \text{ ohms}}$$

Thus, $R = 20$ ohms

According to Ohm's law, the current in the circuit is

$$\frac{V}{R} = \frac{120 \text{ volts}}{20 \text{ ohms}} = 6 \text{ A}$$

Total current in a parallel circuit is the sum of the currents in its branches.

This current is the total current. It is found by adding together the 2-A currents in each of the three resistors. The total current in a parallel circuit is the sum of the currents in the separate branches.

$$i = i_1 + i_2 + i_3 + \cdots$$

The voltage drop across each branch is equal to the voltage of the generator.

In Figure 24-3, the voltage drop across each resistor is the difference in potential between A and B. It is the same across each resistor. This voltage drop is the voltage of the generator, or 120 volts.

Example: Total Resistance and Current in a Parallel Circuit

Three resistors of 60 ohms, 30 ohms, and 20 ohms are connected in parallel across a 90-volt difference in potential (Figure 24-4). Find (a) the total resistance of the circuit, (b) the current flowing in the entire circuit, and (c) the current flowing through each branch of the circuit.

Solution:

(a)
$$\frac{1}{R} = \frac{1}{R_1} + \frac{1}{R_2} + \frac{1}{R_3}$$
$$= \frac{1}{60 \text{ ohms}} + \frac{1}{30 \text{ ohms}} + \frac{1}{20 \text{ ohms}}$$
$$= \frac{6}{60 \text{ ohms}}$$

Thus, $R = 10$ ohms

FIGURE 24-4

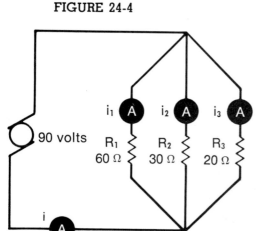

(b)
$$i = \frac{V}{R}$$
$$= \frac{90 \text{ volts}}{10 \text{ ohms}}$$
$$= 9 \text{ A}$$

(c) The voltage drop across each resistor is 90 volts.

$$\text{for } R_1, \ i_1 = \frac{V}{R_1} = \frac{90 \text{ volts}}{60 \text{ ohms}} = 1.5 \text{ A}$$

$$\text{for } R_2, \ i_2 = \frac{V}{R_2} = \frac{90 \text{ volts}}{30 \text{ ohms}} = 3 \text{ A}$$

$$\text{for } R_3, \ i_3 = \frac{V}{R_3} = \frac{90 \text{ volts}}{20 \text{ ohms}} = 4.5 \text{ A}$$

The sum of the current in the lines is 9 A as predicted by part (b). Dividing the voltage by the sum of the currents yields the total resistance of the circuit. The same solution is found as was found in part (a).

PROBLEMS

13. Three 15-ohm resistors are connected in parallel and placed across a difference in potential of 30 volts. (a) What is the total resistance of the parallel circuit? (b) What current flows through the entire circuit? (c) What current flows through each branch of the circuit?

14. Two 10-ohm resistors are connected in parallel and placed across the terminals of a 15-volt battery. (a) What is the total resistance of the parallel circuit? (b) What current flows in the circuit? (c) What current flows through each branch of the circuit?

15. A 120-ohm resistor, a 60-ohm resistor, and a 40-ohm resistor are connected in parallel and placed across a potential difference of 120 volts. (a) What is the total resistance of the parallel circuit? (b) What current flows through the entire circuit? (c) What current flows through each branch of the circuit?

16. A 6-ohm resistor, an 18-ohm resistor, and a 9-ohm resistor are connected in parallel and placed across a 36-volt potential difference. (a) What current flows through each resistor? (b) What total current flows in the circuit? (c) What is the total resistance of the circuit?

17. A 75-ohm heater and a 150-ohm lamp are connected in parallel across a potential difference of 150 volts. (a) What current flows through the 75-ohm heater? (b) What current flows through the 150-ohm lamp? (c) What current flows through the entire circuit? (d) What is the total resistance of the entire circuit? (e) Divide the voltage by the total resistance. Does the result agree with the solution to part (c)?

24:4   Characteristics of Parallel Circuits

Figure 24-3 shows three 60-ohm resistors connected in parallel across a 120-volt source. Two amperes of current flow through each resistor, and the total current in the circuit is 6 A. Figure 24-5 shows the same circuit but with a switch in one of the lines opened. Since the voltage across each line is still 120 volts, the current flowing through each of the remaining lines is still 2 A. The total resistance of the circuit increases from 20 ohms to 30 ohms.

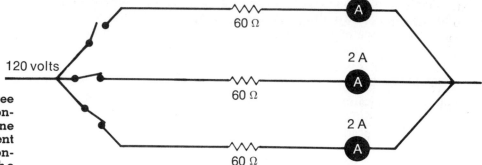

FIGURE 24-5. Here, three 60-ohm resistors are connected in parallel and one switch is open. The current through each of the connected resistors is the same as when all three resistors are connected.

In a parallel circuit, each resistor can be operated independently.

Parallel circuits are used for house wiring.

The important fact about a parallel circuit is that each resistor in the circuit can be operated independently. If one of the lines is opened so that no current flows through it, the current in the other parts of the circuit is not affected in any way. In contrast, when a switch is opened or a resistor burns out at any place in a series circuit, current does not flow anywhere in the circuit. Therefore, a series circuit is not practical for house wiring. A house wired in series would require every device to be on in order to use any one of them.

Figure 24-6 shows a general plan of house wiring. Generators at the power station provide a source of 120 volts potential difference. Two lines run from this outside source to the house. These two lines are close together and parallel to each other as they run through the walls of the house. At wall outlets, when appliances and lamps are plugged in, the circuit between these two wires is completed and current flows.

Connecting two wires of the diagram are three resistors. One resistor is a 10-ohm heater, another a 20-ohm refrigerator, and the third a 60-ohm lamp. Each device forms a complete circuit across

FIGURE 24-6. (a) House-wiring diagram indicating the parallel nature of the circuit. This arrangement permits the use of one or more appliances at the same time. (b) An example of parallel wiring.

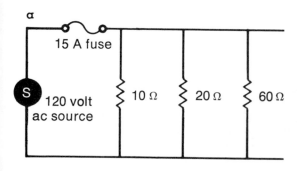

the 120-volt source. Each device operates independently of the others in the circuit. However, if all three devices operate at the same time, the total resistance is

$$\frac{1}{R} = \frac{1}{60 \text{ ohms}} + \frac{1}{20 \text{ ohms}} + \frac{1}{10 \text{ ohms}} = \frac{10}{60 \text{ ohms}}$$

Thus, $R = 6$ ohms

The current flowing through the lines is

$$i = \frac{V}{R} = \frac{120 \text{ volts}}{6 \text{ ohms}} = 20 \text{ A}$$

Fuses and circuit breakers are automatic switches in the line that act as safety devices. They prevent circuit overloads which

The current flowing into a house increases as additional appliances are turned on.

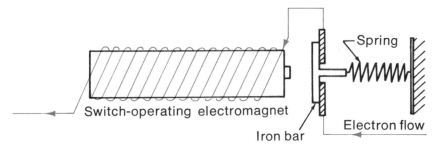

Switch-operating electromagnet

Iron bar

Spring

Electron flow

FIGURE 24-7. General plan of a circuit breaker. When current in the circuit becomes too great, the metal bar is pulled away from its contact points. Then current stops flowing in the circuit.

occur when too many appliances are turned on at the same time. The appliances are connected in parallel. Thus, each additional appliance causes more current to flow through these lines. This current increase may produce a heating effect (i^2R) large enough to cause a fire. A fuse is a short piece of metal which melts when the heating effect of the current reaches a set magnitude. A circuit breaker is an automatic switch that cuts off when the current reaches some set value. If an overload occurred in Figure 24-6, the fuse would melt. Then no current would flow anywhere in

Fuses and circuit breakers are safety devices which prevent too much current from flowing in a circuit.

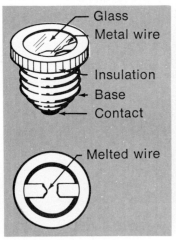

Glass
Metal wire

Insulation
Base
Contact

Melted wire

John Morgan

FIGURE 24-8. Several types of fuses can be used to prevent circuit overload and thus prevent fires.

the circuit. Usually, houses are wired so that separate circuits lead to different parts of the house. Such an arrangement prevents a circuit overload.

A short circuit occurs when a piece of low resistance wire is placed across the circuit. When a short circuit occurs, the current in the circuit becomes very large. This large current could start a fire if there were no fuse or circuit breaker in the circuit. For example, if a lamp cord becomes frayed, its wires could be accidentally brought together. A piece of copper wire in the lamp cord might have a resistance of 0.01 ohms. When placed across 120 volts, this resistance draws 120 volts/0.01 ohms, or 12 000 A. The fuse or circuit breaker immediately blows. Thus, the wire is prevented from becoming hot and starting a fire.

24:5 Series-Parallel Circuits

Often a circuit consists of both series and parallel connections. To determine how the current or the potential difference is distributed in the various parts of the circuit, Ohm's law is used. Ohm's law is applied to each part of the circuit as well as to the whole circuit.

Ohm's law can be used on each separate part of a series–parallel circuit.

Example: Series-Parallel Circuit

In Figure 24-9a, a 30-ohm resistor is connected in parallel with a 20-ohm resistor. The parallel connection is placed in series with an 8-ohm resistor across a 60-volt difference of potential. (a) What is the total resistance of the parallel portion of the circuit? (b) What is the resistance of the entire circuit? (c) What current flows in the circuit? (d) What is the voltage drop across the 8-ohm resistor? (e) What is the voltage drop across the parallel portion of the circuit? (f) What current flows through each line of the parallel portion of the circuit?

FIGURE 24-9

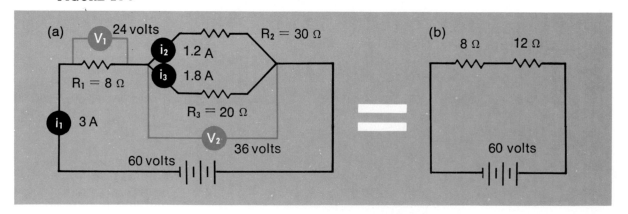

Solution:

(a) R_2 and R_3 are connected in parallel. Their combined resistance is

$$\frac{1}{R} = \frac{1}{R_2} + \frac{1}{R_3}$$

$$= \frac{1}{30 \text{ ohms}} + \frac{1}{20 \text{ ohms}}$$

$$= \frac{5}{60 \text{ ohms}}$$

Thus, $R = 12$ ohms

(b) The circuit is now a series circuit (Figure 24-9b) with an 8-ohm resistor and a 12-ohm resistor in series.

$$R = R_1 + R_{2,3}$$

$$= 8 \text{ ohms} + 12 \text{ ohms}$$

$$= 20 \text{ ohms}$$

(c) The current flowing in the circuit is

$$i = \frac{V}{R}$$

$$= \frac{60 \text{ volts}}{20 \text{ ohms}}$$

$$= 3 \text{ A}$$

(d) The voltage drop across the 8-ohm resistor is

$$V = iR_1$$

$$= 3 \text{ A} \times 8 \text{ ohms}$$

$$= 24 \text{ volts}$$

(e) The parallel portion of the circuit behaves as a 12-ohm resistor. Therefore, the voltage drop across it is

$$V = iR_{2,3}$$

$$= 3 \text{ A} \times 12 \text{ ohms}$$

$$= 36 \text{ volts}$$

(f) The 36-volt drop across the parallel portion of the circuit is the same across all parts of the circuit. Therefore, the current through the 30-ohm resistor is

$$i = \frac{V}{R_2}$$

$$= \frac{36 \text{ volts}}{30 \text{ ohms}}$$

$$= 1.2 \text{ A}$$

The current through the 20-ohm resistor is

$$i = \frac{V}{R_3}$$

$$= \frac{36 \text{ volts}}{20 \text{ ohms}}$$

$$= 1.8 \text{ A}$$

The total current through the parallel part of the circuit is 1.2 A plus 1.8 A, or 3 A. This total agrees with the value for current calculated in part (c).

PROBLEMS

18. Two 60-ohm resistors are connected in parallel. This parallel arrangement is connected in series with a 30-ohm resistor. The entire circuit is then placed across a 120-volt potential difference. (a) What is the resistance of the parallel portion of the circuit? (b) What is the resistance of the entire circuit? (c) What current flows in the circuit? (d) What is the voltage drop across the 30-ohm resistor? (e) What is the voltage drop across the parallel portion of the circuit? (f) What current flows in each branch of the parallel portion of the circuit?

19. Three 15-ohm resistors are connected in parallel. This arrangement is connected in series with a 10-ohm resistor. The entire circuit is then placed across a 45-volt difference in potential. (a) What is the resistance of the parallel portion of the circuit? (b) What is the resistance of the entire circuit? (c) What current flows in the circuit? (d) What is the voltage drop across the 10-ohm resistor? (e) What is the voltage drop across the parallel portion of the circuit? (f) What current flows in each branch of the parallel portion of the circuit?

20. Three 15-ohm resistors are connected in parallel. They are connected in series to a second set of three 15-ohm resistors, also connected in parallel. The entire circuit is then placed across the terminals of a 12-volt battery. (a) What is the total resistance of the circuit? (b) What current flows through the circuit? (c) What current flows through each resistor?

FIGURE 24-10. (a) Ammeters are placed in series with resistors during measurements of current flow. (b) Watthour meters measure the amount of electric energy used by a consumer. The more current being used at a given time, the faster the horizontal disk in the center of the meter turns.

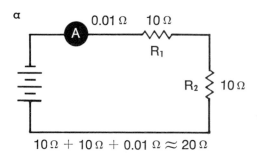

$10\,\Omega + 10\,\Omega + 0.01\,\Omega \approx 20\,\Omega$

24:6   Ammeters and Voltmeters

An **ammeter** is used to measure the current in a circuit. An ammeter is placed in a circuit in series with the resistors. Therefore, the resistance of an ammeter must be very low. Otherwise it would change the total resistance of the circuit in which it is placed. If the total resistance of the circuit were changed, the current flowing in the circuit would also be altered. Thus, the ammeter would defeat its own purpose.

A **voltmeter** is used to measure the voltage drop across a part of a circuit or an entire circuit. A voltmeter is placed in parallel with the resistor where voltage drop is to be measured. A voltmeter must have a very high resistance so that it does not affect the resistance of that part of the circuit where the voltage is being measured. A low-resistance voltmeter placed in parallel with a resistor would constitute a parallel circuit of lower resistance than that of the resistor. This lower resistance would cause an increase of current in the circuit. The voltage drop across the resistor would increase. A low-resistance voltmeter would defeat its own purpose. The resistance of a voltmeter is usually a minimum of 10 000 ohms. A 10 000-ohms resistance placed in parallel with a 10-ohm resistance keeps that part of the circuit resistance at 10 ohms.

Ammeters and voltmeters have many everyday uses. For example, the condition of a car battery is tested with a special ammeter. A voltmeter is used to check TV circuits and the circuits of other electronic devices.

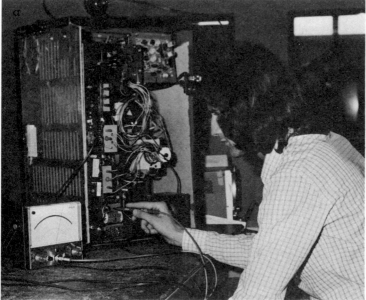

John Morgan

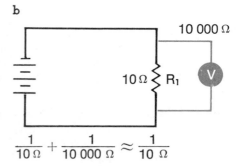

FIGURE 24-11. (a) This electronics student is using a voltmeter to check for proper voltage levels at various points in a receiver. **(b)** Voltmeters are connected in parallel with resistors during measurements of potential difference.

$$\frac{1}{10\ \Omega} + \frac{1}{10\ 000\ \Omega} \approx \frac{1}{10\ \Omega}$$

PROBLEM

21. Determine the reading of each ammeter and voltmeter in Figure 24-12.

FIGURE 24-12

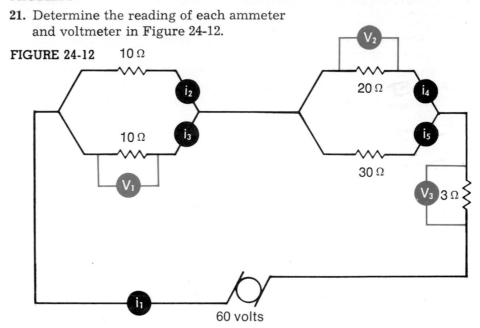

SUMMARY

When resistors are connected in series, the current is the same throughout the circuit. The total resistance of the circuit is equal to the sum of the individual resistances. When resistors are connected in parallel, the current will divide and flow through all branches of the circuit. Each branch will carry a portion of the current that is inversely proportional to its resistance. The voltage drop is the same across all branches of the parallel circuit. The reciprocal of the total resistance is equal to the sum of the reciprocals of the individual resistances. The sum of the currents in the branches must equal the total current in the circuit.

If any branch of a parallel circuit is opened so that no current flows through it, the current in the remaining branches does not change. When additional branches are added to a parallel circuit, the current through the entire circuit increases. This increased current may produce a heating effect large enough to cause a fire. Fuses and circuit breakers act as safety devices to prevent such a circuit overload.

Often a circuit consists of both series and parallel connections. To determine how the current or the potential difference is distributed in the various parts of the circuit, Ohm's law is used. Ohm's law may be applied to the whole circuit as well as to any part of the circuit.

An ammeter is used to measure current in a circuit. It is always placed in a circuit in series with the resistors. A voltmeter is used to measure the voltage drop across a circuit or a part of a circuit. It is always placed in parallel with a resistor.

QUESTIONS

1. Circuit *A* contains three 60-ohm resistors in series. Circuit *B* contains three 60-ohm resistors in parallel. How does the current flowing in the second 60-ohm resistor change if a switch cuts off the current to the first 60-ohm resistor in the (a) series circuit? (b) parallel circuit?

2. What is the difference in total resistance between three 60-ohm resistors connected in series and three 60-ohm resistors connected in parallel?

3. An engineer needs a 10-ohm control resistor and a 15-ohm control resistor. But, there are only 30-ohm resistors in stock. Must new resistors be bought? Explain.

4. The total current flowing through a parallel circuit is equal to the sum of the current flowing through its branches: $i = i_1 + i_2 + i_3$, and so on. Since the voltage across each branch of a parallel circuit is the same, this equation written in Ohm's law form is $\dfrac{V}{R} = \dfrac{V}{R_1} + \dfrac{V}{R_2} + \dfrac{V}{R_3}$. Remember that the voltages are all equal. Now rewrite this equation in a simplified form.

5. For each part of this question, write the form that applies: series circuit or parallel circuit.
   (a) The current is the same throughout.
   (b) The total resistance is equal to the sum of the individual resistances.
   (c) The total resistance is less than the resistance of the lowest value resistor in the circuit.
   (d) The voltage drop is the same across each resistor.
   (e) The voltage drop is proportional to the resistance.
   (f) Adding a resistor decreases the total resistance.
   (g) Adding a resistor increases the total resistance.
   (h) If one resistor is turned off or broken, no current flows in the entire circuit.
   (i) If one resistor is turned off, the current through all other resistors remains the same.
   (j) Suitable for house wiring.

6. Explain the function of a fuse in an electric circuit.

7. Why does an ammeter have a very low resistance?

8. Why does a voltmeter have a very high resistance?

9. What is a short circuit? Why is a short circuit dangerous?

PROBLEMS

1. Two resistors of 5 ohms and 7 ohms are connected in series across a 12-volt battery. (a) What is the total resistance of the circuit? (b) What current flows through the 5-ohm resistor? (c) What current flows through the 7-ohm resistor? (d) What is the voltage drop across each resistor?

2. Two 6-ohm resistors and a 3-ohm resistor are connected in series. A potential difference of 6 volts is applied to the circuit. (a) What is the total resistance of the circuit? (b) What current flows in the circuit? (c) What is the voltage drop across each resistor?

3. A light bulb has a resistance of 2 ohms. It is connected in series with a variable resistor. A difference in potential of 6 volts is applied to the circuit. An ammeter indicates that the current of the circuit is 0.5 A. At what resistance is the variable resistor set?

4. What resistance is connected in series with an 8-ohm resistor that is connected to a 60-volt generator if the current through the resistors is 4 A?

5. Ten Christmas tree lights are connected in series. When they are plugged into a 120-volt outlet, the current flowing through the lights is 0.75 A. What is the resistance of each light?

6. A 20-ohm lamp and a 5-ohm lamp are connected in series and placed across a difference in potential of 50 volts. (a) What is the total resistance of the circuit? (b) What current flows in the circuit? (c) What is the voltage drop across each resistor?

7. A 20-ohm lamp and a 5-ohm lamp are connected in parallel and placed across a difference in potential of 50 volts. (a) What is the total resistance of the circuit? (b) What current flows in the circuit? (c) What current flows through each resistor? (d) What is the voltage drop across each resistor?

8. A 16-ohm, a 20-ohm, and an 80-ohm resistor are connected in parallel. A difference in potential of 40 volts is applied to the combination. (a) Compute the total resistance of the parallel circuit. (b) What total current flows in the circuit? (c) What current flows through the 16-ohm resistor?

9. A household circuit contains six 240-ohm lamps (60-watt bulbs) and a 10-ohm heater. The voltage across the circuit is 120 volts. (a) What current flows in the circuit when four lamps are on? (b) What current flows when all six lamps are on? (c) What current flows in the circuit if all six lamps and the heater are operating?

10. Determine the reading of each ammeter and each voltmeter in Figure 24-13.

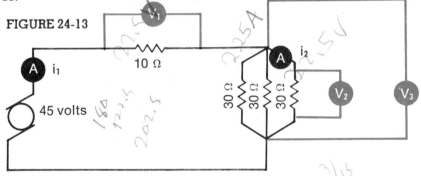

FIGURE 24-13

11. Find the reading of each ammeter and each voltmeter in Figure 24-14.

FIGURE 24-14

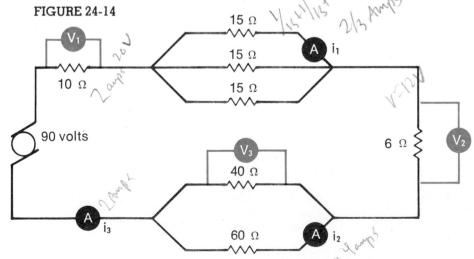

12. Determine the power in watts consumed by each resistance shown in Figure 24-13.

In a house, circuits are wired in parallel. Thus, when additional appliances or lights are used, the flow of current through the circuit increases. As the current increases, the heat produced in the wire increases. Certain circuits in your home are designed with heavy gauge wire to handle larger amounts of current. These circuits will have fuses or circuit breakers with higher amperage limits. Therefore, electric coffee pots, toasters, and other high-wattage appliances should not be used in bedrooms.

1. Calculate the resistance of some of the appliances in your home. Each will have its wattage printed somewhere on the outside. Remember that $P = Vi$ and note that $V = 120$ volts for a normal wall outlet.

2. Calculate the current in the circuit if these appliances are plugged in (a) one at a time, (b) two at a time, (c) three together, and so on. At what point is the circuit overloaded? (Calculate, don't demonstrate.)

Azbel', Kaganov and Lifshitz, "Conduction Electrons in Metals." *Scientific American*, January, 1973.

Dunsheath, Percy, *Electricity: How It Works*. New York, Thomas Y. Crowell Co., 1960.

Upton, Monroe, *Electronics for Everyone*. New York, New American Library, 1973.

Early Greeks knew about magnetism. They knew that iron is magnetized by a special kind of rock which we now call lodestone. They also knew that a piece of magnetized iron, when suspended by a string, always comes to rest in a north-south direction. They used this crude arrangement as a compass. We now know that magnetism can also be caused by an electric current. This principle has been used to build special magnets called electromagnets. Electromagnets can be turned on and off by turning the current on and off. What are some uses of magnets?

THE MAGNETIC FIELD

Magnetism plays an important role in any study of electricity. In fact, whenever an electric current appears, magnetism also appears. The two cannot be separated. The operation of many devices such as radios, TV sets, motors, and electric meters depends on the magnetic effects of electric currents.

GOAL: You will gain knowledge and understanding of permanent magnets, electromagnets, magnetic fields, and the forces exerted on charged particles.

25:1 General Properties of Magnets

Many of the principles of magnetism may already be familiar to you. You may have played with small magnets. Perhaps you have a magnetic bulletin board. Your cupboard doors may have magnetic closings. Let us begin our study of magnetic fields by reviewing some elementary principles of magnetism.

1. A magnet has polarity. The end of a suspended magnet that points north is the north-seeking pole (N pole) of the magnet. The end that points south is its south-seeking pole (S pole). These poles are distinct. However, they cannot be separated.

2. Magnetic poles which are alike repel one another. Unlike poles attract one another.

3. Iron, cobalt, and nickel are important magnetic substances. Permanent magnets are made from these metals. Permanent magnets keep their magnetism for a long time.

Carl England

FIGURE 25-1. A permanent magnet causes these paper clips to become temporary magnets.

4. Iron, cobalt, and nickel are magnetized by induction. When a magnetic substance is close to or touches a magnet, it becomes a magnet also. An iron nail becomes a temporary magnet when it comes in contact with a bar magnet. When removed from the magnet, the nail quickly loses its magnetic properties.

5. A compass is a small suspended needle-shaped magnet. The north-seeking pole of the compass needle points north. The magnetic north pole of the earth and the geographic north pole of the earth are not in the same place. A compass needle points toward the magnetic north pole.

25:2 Magnetic Fields Around Permanent Magnets

The presence of a magnetic field around a permanent magnet can be shown. Cover the magnet with a piece of paper. Sprinkle small iron filings onto the paper. The iron filings arrange themselves in lines running from pole to pole (Figure 25-2). These lines are called field lines or **magnetic flux lines.**

Magnetic flux lines are imaginary lines which indicate the direction and magnitude of the field about a magnet.

Magnetic flux lines are actually imaginary lines. The whole group of lines together is called **magnetic flux.** The magnetic flux shows the magnetic field around the magnet. The **magnetic flux density** is the number of lines per unit area. The strength of the magnetic field is proportional to the flux density.

Magnetic flux density is magnetic flux per unit area.

The direction of the magnetic field lines is the direction the N pole of a compass points in the magnetic field. Outside the magnet, the field lines run from the N pole of the magnet to its S pole. Field lines always form closed loops. Inside the magnet, the field lines run from the S pole to the N pole of the magnet. These rules are important when studying the behavior of charged particles in magnetic fields.

Magnetic fields outside a magnet run from north pole to south pole.

374

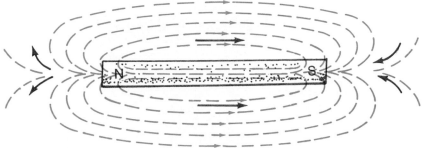

FIGURE 25-2. Magnetic flux lines extend from the N pole to the S pole outside the magnet and from the S pole to the N pole inside the magnet.

Magnetic field lines never overlap. In fact, they repel one another and follow well-defined paths. Field lines leave the N pole and enter the S pole. The lines are most concentrated at the poles. The field is strongest at the poles of the magnet.

25:3   Magnetic Fields Between Like and Unlike Poles

Place the poles of two bar magnets close together. Put a piece of paper over the magnets. Sprinkle iron filings on the paper. Tap the paper so the filings line up in patterns (Figure 25-3). Note the pattern of the filings when the two like poles are placed near

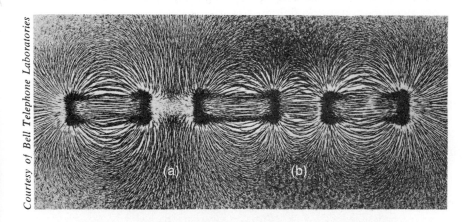

Courtesy of Bell Telephone Laboratories

FIGURE 25-3. (a) Repulsion of like poles. (b) Attraction of unlike poles.

one another. Then observe the pattern of the filings when two unlike poles are placed close together. From these patterns, we find that the magnetic field between unlike poles shows attraction. The field between like poles shows repulsion.

Unlike poles attract, like poles repel.

25:4   Electromagnetism

In 1820, the Danish physicist Hans Christian Oersted (1777–1851) made a very important discovery about magnetism. He was

A. D. Little Company

FIGURE 25-4. The lead sphere floats between two lead rings that carry electric currents when the temperature is near absolute zero. The repulsion between magnetic fields of the sphere and rings balances the sphere's weight so that it floats.

experimenting with electric current in wires. Oersted noticed that one of his wires was lying across the top of a small compass. He also saw that each time he sent a current through the wire, the compass needle moved. A compass needle is a small magnet. The magnetic field around a magnet will interact only with another magnetic field. Thus, the presence of an electric current in the wire somehow was causing a magnetic field to appear around the wire. Further studies by Oersted showed that any wire carrying an electric current has a magnetic field around it. Electric currents produce magnetic fields.

Magnetic fields are the result of electric currents.

25:5 Magnetic Fields Around a Current-Bearing Wire

The magnetic field around a current-bearing wire can easily be studied. Place a wire vertically through a piece of cardboard. Pass

FIGURE 25-5. Magnetic field produced by current in a straight-wire conductor.

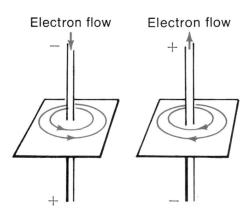

Courtesy of Kodansha

an electric current through the wire. Sprinkle iron filings on the cardboard around the wire. Tap the cardboard until the filings form a pattern around the wire. The pattern consists of concentric circles (circles with a common center) around the wire.

The circular lines indicate that the magnetic field lines form closed loops. The strength of the magnetic field around the wire varies directly with the magnitude of the current flowing in the wire.

The following left-hand rule can be used to find the direction of the magnetic field around a current-bearing straight wire. *Grasp the wire with the left hand. Keep the thumb of that hand pointed in the direction of electron flow. The fingers of the hand circle the wire pointing in the direction of the magnetic field.*

25:6 Magnetic Field Around a Coil

When an electric current flows through a single circular loop of wire, a magnetic field appears all around the loop. By applying the left-hand rule as in Figure 25-7b, it can be shown that the direction of the field inside the loop is always the same. In the case shown in the diagram, it is always to the right.

Suppose wire is looped several times to form a tight coil. When a current flows through the coil, the field around all loops will be in the same direction. The result is a smooth magnetic field inside the coil which acts in a single direction. The field outside the coil will also be uniform. However, it will act in the opposite direction.

When an electric current flows through a coil of wire, the coil acts like a permanent magnet. When this current-bearing coil is

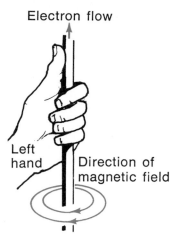

FIGURE 25-6. Left-hand rule for a current-bearing straight wire.

A left-hand rule is used to determine the direction of the magnetic field about a current carrying wire.

When current flows through a coil, a magnetic field is produced inside the coil. This field acts in one direction only.

FIGURE 25-7. Magnetic field about a circular loop of current-carrying wire.

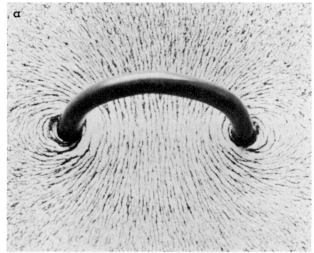

Courtesy of Kodansha

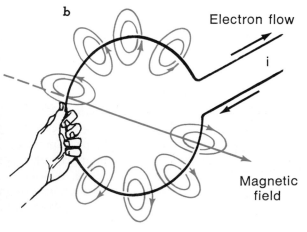

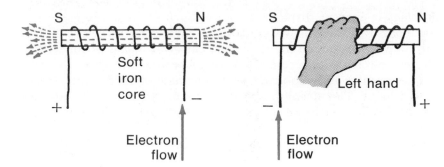

FIGURE 25-8. Left-hand rule for polarity of an electromagnet.

An electromagnet is a current-carrying coil of wire that acts like a magnet.

A second left-hand rule can be used to find the north and south poles of an electromagnet.

The strength of the field about an electromagnet can be increased by placing an iron core inside the coil.

The strength of the field about an electromagnet varies with the current.

The field about an electromagnet also varies with the number of loops in the coil.

brought close to a suspended bar magnet, one end of the coil repels the north pole of the magnet. The other end of the coil attracts the north pole of the magnet. Thus, the current-bearing coil has a north and south pole and is itself a magnet. This type of magnet is called an **electromagnet.**

The polarity of an electromagnet may be found by using a second left-hand rule. *Grasp the coil with the left hand. Curl the fingers around the loops in the direction of electron flow. Then, the thumb points toward the N pole of the electromagnet.*

The strength of an electromagnet can be increased by placing a soft iron core inside the coil. The iron is influenced by the field inside the coil. Thus, the iron core is magnetized by the magnetic field existing inside the coil.

The strength of the magnetic field around a current-bearing wire is proportional to the current flowing in the wire. Likewise, the strength of the field around an electromagnet is proportional to the current flowing through the wire. Also note that each loop of a coil produces the same field as any other loop. These individual fields are in the same direction and can be added. Thus, the more loops in an electromagnet, the stronger is the field. The strength of an electromagnet's magnetic field is proportional to the current, the number of loops, and the nature of the core.

25:7 Theory of Magnetism

The behavior of an electromagnet is similar to that of a permanent bar magnet. Can this be explained? In the early 19th century, a theory of magnetism was proposed by Andre Ampere (1775–1836). Ampere knew that the magnetic effects of an electromagnetic coil result when an electric current flows through its loops. Knowing this, he reasoned that the effects of a bar magnet must result from tiny "loops" of current within the bar. In essence, Ampere's reasoning was correct. The magnetic effect of a permanent magnet results from the spinning of electrons on their axes as they move in atoms. Therefore, we can see why the be-

The magnetism of a permanent magnet is due to the spinning motion of electrons in atoms.

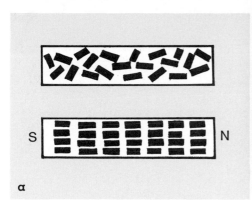

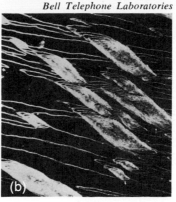

Bell Telephone Laboratories

FIGURE 25-9. (a) Model of the domain theory in which magnetic properties appear only when domains align. (b) Magnetic domains in iron-nickel-molybdenum alloy.

havior of an electromagnet is very similar to that of a permanent bar magnet.

The atoms in a magnet are not independent of surrounding atoms. Instead, the atoms act in groups or domains. Within each domain, the atoms are coupled and lined up in the same direction. The magnetic effects of the atoms of one domain act together to make a tiny magnet. Although domains are much larger than individual atoms, they are still very small. Thus, even a small sample of iron contains a huge number of domains. Usually the domains are not lined up. The result is that their magnetic fields cancel one another. Therefore, a piece of iron does not always show magnetic effects. But, if an iron bar is placed in a strong magnetic field, the domains tend to align with the external field. Iron, cobalt, nickel, and their alloys often keep this domain alignment after being removed from the external field. Thus, they become permanent magnets.

Atoms within a permanent magnet are arranged in domains.

All the atoms in a domain are lined up in the same direction.

Magnetic effects are observed when domains align with one another.

25:8 Interaction of Magnetic Fields

Ampere did other experiments with magnetic fields. He observed two parallel wires carrying current in the same direction. He found that the wires attract one another. He also observed two parallel wires carrying current in opposite directions. These wires repel one another. These forces of attraction and repulsion result from the magnetic fields around the wires.

The strength of a magnetic field is called **magnetic induction.** Magnetic field strength might seem to be a better term for this quantity. However, to avoid confusion with other terms used with magnetic fields, we will use the term magnetic induction. Magnetic induction is a vector quantity. The symbol for magnetic induction is B.

Magnetic field vectors ($\vec{\mathbf{B}}$) are shown pointing in several different directions in Figure 25-10a. In Figure 25-10b, magnetic field vectors are directed into the plane of the page. Those directed into the page are indicated by crosses. In Figure 25-10c, magnetic

Magnetic induction, the strength of a magnetic field, is a vector quantity.

Magnetic induction is another name for magnetic flux density.

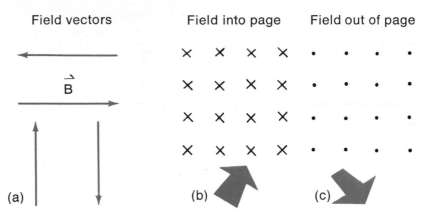

FIGURE 25-10. Directions of magnetic fields are indicated (a) by directional arrows when the field is in the same plane as the page, (b) by crosses when the field is into the page, and (c) by dots when the field is out of the page toward you.

field vectors are directed out of the page. Those directed out of the page are indicated by dots. Think of the vectors as a flight of arrows. The dots represent points approaching the reader head-on. The crosses represent tail feathers going away from the reader. This convention is used when three dimensions are considered.

Figure 25-11 shows that the direction of the magnetic field around each of the current-bearing wires follows the left-hand rule. In Figure 25-11a, we see that the fields between the wires

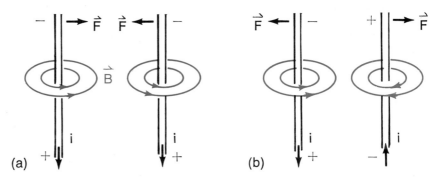

FIGURE 25-11. Two current-bearing conductors (a) are attracted when the currents are in the same direction, and (b) are repelled when the currents are in opposite directions.

are in opposition. Since magnetic fields add vectorially, the field between the wires is weak. The field outside the wires remains normal strength. Thus, the wires are forced together, or attract each other.

In Figure 25-11b, we see the opposite situation. Here, the fields between the wires act in the same direction. Thus, the field between the wires is strengthened. Outside the wires, the fields are at normal strength. Thus, the wires are forced apart by the stronger field between them.

The behavior of a small segment of wire placed at right angles to an external magnetic field is of interest. As a current is sent through the wire, a magnetic field appears around the wire. The two magnetic fields interact. In Figure 25-12a, the field due to the

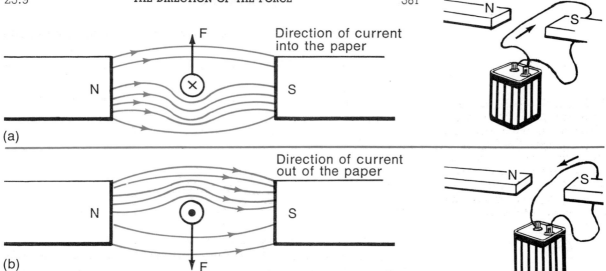

(a)

(b)

FIGURE 25-12. Force on a current-carrying wire in a magnetic field when (a) current is into the page, and (b) current is out of the page.

current in the wire is directed counterclockwise. Thus, above the wire, the field due to the current opposes the field due to the magnets. Below the wire, the two fields are in the same direction, and the resultant field is strengthened. The result is a net upward force. This force is perpendicular to both the external field and the direction of the current in the wire. In Figure 25-12b, the electrons flow in the opposite direction in the wire. Therefore, the field around the wire is directed clockwise. The wire is forced down.

25:9   The Direction of the Force

The force on a current-bearing wire in a magnetic field is determined by the interaction between the field around the wire and the external magnetic field. A faster way to find the direction of the force is to use a third left-hand rule. *Point the fingers of*

A third left-hand rule is used to determine the direction of force on a current-bearing wire placed in a magnetic field.

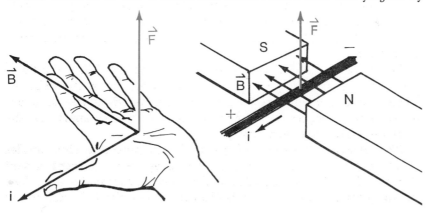

FIGURE 25-13. Left-hand rule for direction of force when current and magnetic fields are known.

the left hand in the direction of the magnetic field. Point the thumb in the direction of the electron flow of the wire. The palm of the hand then faces in the direction of the force acting on the wire.

25:10 Measuring the Force on the Wire

Michael Faraday (1791–1867) discovered that when a wire and a magnetic field are at right angles, a force acts on the wire due to the interaction of the fields. The force is proportional to three factors.

(1) the magnetic induction or strength (B) of the field

(2) the electron current (i) in the wire

(3) the length (l) of the wire that lies in the magnetic field

If B is in the proper units, the expression is

$$F = Bil$$

Solving for B,

$$B = \frac{F}{il}$$

The unit for magnetic induction is the newton/ampere-meter.

The strength, or induction, of a magnetic field is measured in newtons per ampere-meter (N/A-m). That is, the strength of a magnetic field is measured in terms of the force it exerts on a standard magnetic field. The standard magnetic field is the field around a wire which is one meter long and carries a current of one ampere. Thus, the magnetic induction, B, of a magnetic field indicates the force that the field can produce when it interacts with the standard field found around one meter of wire carrying one ampere of current.

All interactions are field interactions. In order to study the physical aspects of the universe, the physicist must be able to evaluate fields. Force is simply another term for magnitude of field interactions. Scientists can often find the magnitude of fields. But, they still do not completely understand fields.

Example: Magnetic Induction

A wire 1 m long carries a current of 5 A. The wire is at right angles to a uniform magnetic field. The force on the wire is 0.2 N. What is the magnetic induction (B) of the field?

Solution:

$$B = \frac{F}{il}$$
$$= \frac{0.2 \text{ N}}{(5 \text{ A}) (1 \text{ m})}$$
$$= 0.04 \text{ N/A-m}$$

Example: Force on a Current-Carrying Wire in a Magnetic Field

A wire 10 cm long is at right angles to a uniform magnetic field. The field has magnetic induction 0.06 N/A-m. The current through the wire is 4 A. What force acts on the wire?

Solution:

$$F = Bil$$
$$= 0.06 \frac{N}{A\text{-}m} \, (4 \text{ A}) \, (0.1 \text{ m})$$
$$= 0.024 \text{ N}$$

PROBLEMS

1. A wire 0.10 m long carrying a current of 2.0 A is at right angles to a magnetic field. The force on the wire is 0.04 N. What is the magnetic induction of the field?

2. A wire 0.5 m long carrying a current of 8 A is at right angles to a field of magnetic induction 0.40 N/A-m. What force acts on the wire?

3. A wire 75 cm long carrying a current of 6 A is at right angles to a uniform magnetic field. The force acting on the wire is 0.6 N. What is the magnetic induction of the field?

4. A magnetic field produces a force of 1.0 N on a wire. The wire is 25 cm long and carries a current of 5 A. What is the magnetic induction?

5. A copper wire 40 cm long carries a current of 6 A and weighs 0.35 N. Placed in a certain magnetic field, the wire remains suspended in the field. What is the magnetic induction of the field?

6. A wire 60 cm long is in a field of magnetic induction 0.4 N/A-m. The force acting on the wire is 1.8 N. What current is in the wire?

7. A wire 0.03 m long carrying a current of 5 A is at right angles to a magnetic field. The force acting on the wire is 9.0×10^{-3} N. What is the magnetic induction of the field?

25:11   The Force on a Single Charged Particle

The development of efficient air pumps made it possible to manufacture large vacuum tubes. A vacuum tube contains a pair of metal electrodes (Figure 25-14). A high voltage is applied across the electrodes. A stream of electrons leaves the negative electrode (cathode) and moves across the tube to the positive electrode (anode). By applying a magnetic field to the tube, the beam of electrons is deflected.

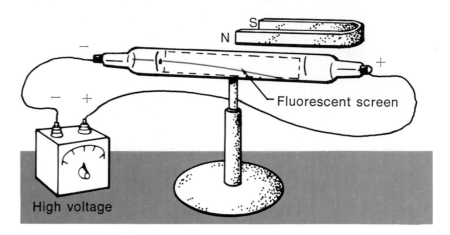

The force Bil acts on a short wire at right angles to a magnetic field. B is the induction of the field in newtons per ampere-meter.

$$F = Bil$$
$$= B \times \frac{\text{coul}}{\text{sec}} \times \text{m}$$
$$= B \times \frac{q}{\text{sec}} \times \text{m}$$

Rearranging this becomes

$$F = B \times q \times \frac{\text{m}}{\text{sec}}$$

Since m/sec is a velocity unit,

$$F = Bqv$$

The force acting on a single charged particle as it moves through a magnetic field is Bqv.

B is the induction of the magnetic field; q is the charge on the particle; and v is the speed of the particle. This equation gives the force exerted on a charged particle as it moves through a magnetic field.

Example: Force on a Charged Particle in a Magnetic Field

A beam of electrons travels at 3.0×10^6 m/sec through a uniform magnetic field. The magnetic induction is 4.0×10^{-2} N/A-m. (a) The beam is at right angles to the magnetic field. What force acts on each electron? (b) What force acts on a proton moving at the same speed and in the same direction as the electron in part (a)?

Solution:

(a) $F = Bqv$
   $= (4.0 \times 10^{-2} \text{ N/A-m}) (1.6 \times 10^{-19} \text{ coul})$
   $(3.0 \times 10^6 \text{ m/sec})$
   $= 1.9 \times 10^{-14} \text{ N}$

(b) The force is exactly the same on a proton as it is on an electron. The proton and the electron have exactly the same charge. But because the proton has the opposite sign, it is deflected in the opposite direction.

PROBLEMS

Use 1.6×10^{-19} coul as the elementary unit of charge.

8. A beam of electrons moves at right angles to a magnetic field of magnetic induction 6.0×10^{-2} N/A-m. The electrons have a speed of 2.5×10^{7} m/sec. What force acts on each electron?

9. An electron passes through a magnetic field at right angles to the field at a speed of 4.0×10^{6} m/sec. The strength of the magnetic field is 0.5 N/A-m. What force acts on the electron?

10. A stream of doubly-ionized particles (missing 2 electrons and thus carrying a net charge of 2 elementary charges) moves at a speed of 3.0×10^{4} m/sec perpendicularly to a magnetic field of 9.0×10^{-2} N/A-m. What force acts on each ion?

11. Triply ionized particles in a beam carry a net positive charge of three elementary charge units. The beam enters a field of magnetic induction 4.0×10^{-2} N/A-m at right angles to the field. The particles have a speed of 9.0×10^{6} m/sec. What force acts on each particle?

25:12   Electric Motors

The current passing through a wire loop in a magnetic field goes in one side of the loop and out the other side. Apply the third left-hand rule to each side of the loop. We find that one side of the loop is forced down while the other side of the loop is forced up. The loop will rotate. An electric motor operates on this principle.

A simple loop of wire in a magnetic field will not rotate more than 180°. In Figure 25-15, the force acting upward on the right side of the loop pushes the loop up. At the same time, the force acting downward on the left side of the loop pushes that side

An electric motor consists of a loop of wire in a magnetic field. When current flows in the loop, the loop rotates.

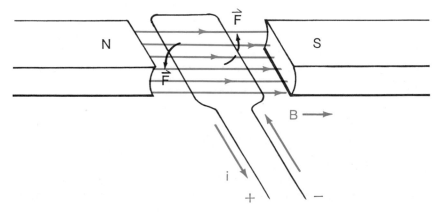

FIGURE 25-15. A wire loop is placed in a magnetic field. When current flows in the wire, the loop rotates.

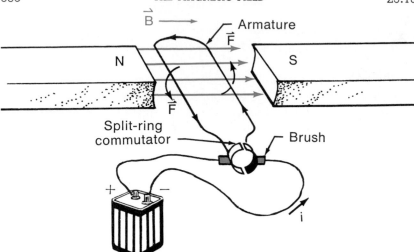

FIGURE 25-16. The principle of the electric motor. Split-ring commutators allow the wire loops in an electric motor to rotate 360°.

A split-ring commutator enables the loop in a motor to rotate 360°.

down. The loop turns until it reaches the vertical position. The loop would not continue to turn because the force acting on the right side of the loop is still directed up. It cannot move down through the field. Also, the left side of the loop would not move up through the field because the force acting on it is still directed down.

For the loop to rotate 360° in the field, the current running through the loop must reverse direction just as the loop reaches the vertical position. This causes the loop to rotate (Figure 25-16). To reverse current direction, a split-ring commutator is used. The split-ring commutator conducts current into the loop by rubbing against the brushes. The split ring is arranged so that each half of the commutator changes brushes just as the loop reaches the vertical position. Then the current in the loop is reversed and the direction of the force on each side of the loop is changed. The loop rotates. The process is repeated each half-turn. Thus the loop spins in the magnetic field.

In practice, electric motors have several rotating loops. Together they make up the armature of the motor. The total force acting on the armature is proportional to Bil. The force acting on the armature can be varied by changing the magnetic field. The force can also be varied by changing the current or by changing the number of loops in the armature.

25:13   Electric Meters

An electric meter measures current by measuring the distance a coil turns in a magnetic field due to the current.

The force acting on a wire loop placed in the field of a permanent magnet depends on the amount of current in the loop. Figure 25-17 shows how the force exerted on a loop of wire in a magnetic field can be used to measure current. A small coil of

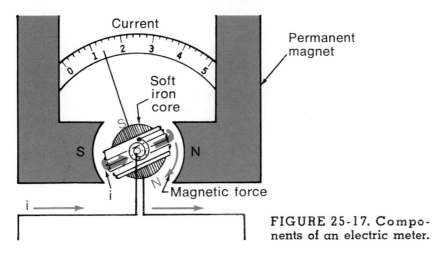

FIGURE 25-17. Components of an electric meter.

wire is placed in the strong magnetic field of a permanent magnet. The current to be measured is directed through the coil. The current produces a magnetic field about the coil. The magnetic induction of the field varies with the intensity of the current. Therefore, the force acting on the coil is proportional to the magnitude of the current. The coil turns against the restraining action of a small spring. The meter is calibrated by finding out how much the coil turns when known currents are sent through it. The meter is then used to measure other unknown currents.

SUMMARY

Magnetic poles which are alike repel each other. Unlike magnetic poles attract each other. The magnetic field around a magnet runs from north pole to south pole. Magnetic field lines always form closed loops. Thus, a magnetic field inside a magnet runs from the south pole to the north pole.

Whenever an electric current flows in a wire, a magnetic field appears around the wire. A coil through which an electric current flows also has a magnetic field. The field around the coil will be similar to the field about a permanent magnet.

When a current-bearing wire is placed in a magnetic field, the magnetic field around the wire interacts with the external magnetic field. This interaction produces a force. The intensity of a magnetic field is called magnetic induction. Magnetic induction is measured in newtons per ampere-meter.

An electric motor consists of a coil of wire placed in a magnetic field. When a current is introduced into the coil, the coil will begin to rotate in the external field. To keep the coil rotating, a split-ring commutator is included in the motor.

The force exerted on a loop of wire in a magnetic field can be used to measure electric current. This principle is used in the construction of an electric meter.

QUESTIONS

1. What is meant by poles of a magnet?
2. State the law of magnetic attraction and repulsion.
3. Name the three most important magnetic elements.

4. How does a temporary magnet differ from a permanent magnet?

5. Draw a small bar magnet to show the magnetic field lines as they appear about a magnet. Use arrows to show the direction of the field lines.

6. Draw the field between two like magnetic poles. Show the direction of the field.

7. Draw the field between two unlike magnetic poles. Show the direction of the field.

8. Draw the field around a straight current-bearing wire. Show its direction.

9. Explain the left-hand rule to determine the direction of a magnetic field around a straight current-bearing wire.

10. Explain the left-hand rule to determine the polarity of an electromagnet.

11. List three factors that control the strength of an electromagnet.

12. Describe a theory of magnetism.

13. Explain the left-hand rule to determine the direction of force on a current-bearing wire placed in a magnetic field.

14. What three factors control the force that acts on a wire carrying a current in a magnetic field?

PROBLEMS

1. A wire 0.5 m long carrying a current of 8 A is at right angles to a uniform magnetic field. The force on the wire is 0.4 N. What is the strength of the magnetic field?

2. A wire 20 cm long is at right angles to a uniform magnetic field of magnetic induction 0.3 N/A-m. The current through the wire is 6 A. What force acts on the wire?

3. A wire 1.5 m long carrying a current of 10 A is at right angles to a uniform magnetic field. The force acting on the wire is 0.6 N. What is the induction of the magnetic field?

4. The current through a wire 0.8 m long is 5 A. The wire is perpendicular to a magnetic field of induction 0.6 N/A-m. What force acts on the wire?

5. The force on a wire 0.8 m long which is perpendicular to a magnetic field of induction 6.0×10^{-2} N/A-m is 0.12 N. What current flows through the wire?

6. The force acting on a wire at right angles to a magnetic field is 3.6 N. The current flowing through the wire is 7.5 A. The magnetic field has an induction of 0.8 N/A-m. How long is the wire?

7. A stream of electrons travels through a magnetic field of induction 0.6 N/A-m at a speed of 4.0×10^{6} m/sec. The electrons travel at right angles to the field. What force acts on each of them?

8. Doubly-ionized helium atoms (alpha particles) are traveling at right angles to a magnetic field at a speed of 4.0×10^{4} m/sec. The induction of the field is 5.0×10^{-2} N/A-m. What force acts on each particle?

9. A beta particle (high-speed electron) is traveling at right angles to a magnetic field of induction 0.6 N/A-m. It has a speed of 2.5×10^{7} m/sec. What force acts on the particle?

10. The mass of an electron is about 9.0×10^{-31} kg. What acceleration does the beta particle in Problem 9 undergo in the direction of the force acting on it?

11. The induction of a magnetic field is 0.3 N/A-m. A wire in the field has 4.0×10^{20} free electrons moving through it at a speed of 2.0×10^{-2} m/sec. What total force acts on the wire?

1. An iron bar can be magnetized easily by holding it in a north-south direction and tapping its end lightly with a hammer. Find an iron bar in your school workshop and try to magnetize it. You can find out whether or not the bar is magnetized by testing it with a few paper clips.
2. Find a small toy electric motor and take it apart. Note its construction. Put the motor together. Using two, three, and then four batteries, find out how well the motor runs under different voltages.'
3. Make your own compass. Push a needle through a cork. With a magnet, stroke the needle in one direction only. Place the cork and needle on its side in a bowl of water. The needle will align itself in a north-south direction.
4. Tie a string around the center of a bar magnet. Suspend the magnet from the end of a table or chair. The magnet will align itself in a north-south direction. Verify the direction with a compass.

Becker, Joseph J., "Permanent Magnets." *Scientific American,* December, 1970.

Bitter, Francis, *Magnets: The Education of a Physicist.* New York, Doubleday and Co., Inc., 1959.

Cohen, David, "Magnetic Fields in the Human Body." *Physics Today,* August, 1975.

Dyal, Freeman J., and Parkin, Curtis W., "The Magnetism of the Moon." *Scientific American,* February, 1971.

Keffer, Frederic, "The Magnetic Properties of Materials." *Scientific American,* September, 1967.

An electric current produces a magnetic field. Conversely, a magnetic field, under certain conditions, can induce an electric current in a wire. This effect is called electromagnetic induction. The principle of electromagnetic induction is used in the operation of transformers. The transformer used in the operation of this model train decreases the voltage of alternating current coming in from the power line so that the train can be operated safely and effectively. In what other instances are transformers used to increase or decrease voltage?

ELECTRO- MAGNETIC INDUCTION

An electric current flowing through a wire produces a magnetic field. This discovery led some scientists to wonder if a magnetic field could produce an electric current. In 1831, Joseph Henry of the United States and Michael Faraday of England answered this question. They experimented and found that a magnetic field could indeed produce an electric current in a wire. An electric generator operates on this principle.

GOAL: You will gain knowledge and understanding of the use of magnetic fields in generating electric currents, the design of generators and transformers, and the nature of ac current.

26:1 Faraday's Discovery

Faraday experimented with a moving wire in a magnetic field. He found that when a wire is moved through a magnetic field, an electric current is induced in the wire. Figure 26-1 shows Faraday's experiments. A wire that is part of a closed (complete) circuit is held in a magnetic field. When the wire is moved through the field the meter indicates that an electric current flows in the wire. If the wire moves up through the field, the current flows in one direction in the wire. When the wire moves down through the field, the current flows in the opposite direction. If the wire is held still in the field or is moved parallel to the field, no current flows in the circuit. An electric current is generated in a wire only when the wire cuts through the magnetic field.

For a current to be produced, either the conductor can move through a field or the field can move past the conductor. The wire may be held still and the magnet moved up and down. Or, the wire may be moved in the magnetic field. In both cases, an electric current is generated in the wire. It is the relative motion between the wire and the magnetic field that produces the current. The process of generating a current in this way is **electromagnetic induction.**

When a wire is moved through a magnetic field, a current is generated in the wire.

Electromagnetic induction is the process of generating a current by the relative motion between a wire and a magnetic field.

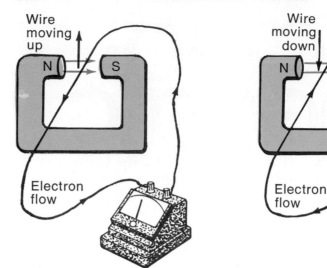

FIGURE 26-1. When a wire is moved in a magnetic field, an electric current flows in the wire, but only while the wire is moving. The direction of electron current flow depends on the direction the wire is moving through the field.

Suppose a wire moves through a magnetic field at an angle to the field. Only that component of the wire's velocity that is perpendicular to the direction of the field generates a current. The current is proportional to the size of the angle between the wire and the field.

26:2   Direction of a Current in a Wire

The force acting on the free electrons in a wire as the wire moves through a magnetic field is perpendicular to both the direction in which the wire is moving and the direction of the magnetic field. To find the direction of the electron current that flows in a conductor moving through a magnetic field, use the left-hand rule described in Chapter 25. Hold the left hand so the thumb points in the direction in which the wire is moving and the fingers point in the direction of the magnetic field. The palm of the hand will point in the direction of the force acting on the electrons.

A left-hand rule indicates the direction of the induced current.

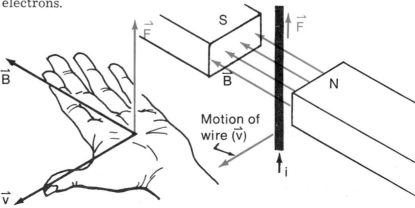

FIGURE 26-2. Left-hand rule for a conductor moving in a magnetic field.

26:3   Induced EMF

When we studied Ohm's law we learned that a voltage must be present if an electric current is to flow in a wire. This voltage is also called **electromotive force**, or EMF. Electromotive force is the energy given to the electrons in the wire. When a wire is moved through a magnetic field, electrons flow in the wire because a voltage appears across the wire. This voltage is referred to as the **induced electromotive force.** It is equal to the work done as the wire is moved through the field. The work that must be done to move a wire through a magnetic field depends on the magnetic induction (B), the length of the wire in the field (l), and the rate at which the wire is moved in the field (v). Thus,

$$EMF = Blv$$

EMF is measured in volts. It represents the work done to give energy to the current that flows in the wire. Note that no current would flow in a simple length of wire moved in a magnetic field. Electricity flows only in complete circuits. If a length of wire is formed into a closed loop and then a part of the loop is moved through a magnetic field, a current flows in the loop.

EMF is the energy given to electrons in a wire.

Induced EMF is the energy given to electrons when a wire moves through a magnetic field.

EMF is the product of magnetic induction, wire length, and speed of the wire.

Example: Induced EMF

A wire 0.2 m long moves perpendicularly through a magnetic field of magnetic induction 8.0×10^{-2} N/A-m at a speed of 7 m/sec. (a) What EMF is induced in the wire? (b) The wire is a part of a circuit which has a resistance of 0.5 ohms. What current flows in the circuit?

Solution: (a) $EMF = Blv$

$$= (8.0 \times 10^{-2} \text{ N/A-m}) \,(0.2 \text{ m})\,(7 \text{ m/sec})$$

$$= 0.11 \, \frac{\text{(N) (m) (m)}}{\left(\dfrac{\text{coul-m}}{\text{sec}}\right)(\text{sec})}$$

$$= 0.11 \, \frac{\text{N-m}}{\text{coul}}$$

$$= 0.11 \text{ J/coul}$$

$$= 0.11 \text{ volts}$$

      (b) $i = \dfrac{V}{R}$

$$= \frac{0.11 \text{ volts}}{0.5 \text{ ohms}}$$

$$= 0.22 \text{ A}$$

PROBLEMS

1. A wire 0.5 m long cuts straight up through a field of magnetic induction 0.4 N/A-m at a speed of 20 m/sec. (a) What EMF is

induced in the wire? (b) The wire is part of a circuit of total resistance 6 ohms. What current flows in the circuit?

2. A wire has a total length of 0.6 m perpendicular to a field of magnetic induction 0.5 N/A-m. The wire is moved through the field at a speed of 20 m/sec. (a) What EMF is induced in the wire? (b) The wire is part of a circuit of total resistance 15 ohms. What current flows in the circuit?

3. An instructor connects both ends of a copper wire of total resistance 0.5 ohms to the terminals of a galvanometer. The instructor then holds part of the wire in a field of magnetic induction 2.0×10^{-2} N/A-m. The length of the wire between the magnetic poles is 10 cm. If the instructor quickly moves the wire up through the field at 5 m/sec, what current will the galvanometer indicate?

4. A wire 30 m long moves at 2 m/sec perpendicularly through a field of magnetic induction 1 N/A-m. (a) What EMF is induced in the wire? (b) The total resistance of the circuit of which the wire is a part is 15 ohms. What current flows?

5. A wire 16 m long is perpendicular to a field of magnetic induction 0.5 N/A-m. The wire is moved through the field at 15 m/sec. (a) What EMF is induced in the wire? (b) The wire is part of a circuit of 20 ohms resistance. What current flows?

26:4   The Electric Generator

A generator consists of loops of wire placed in a magnetic field. As the loops are turned, current is induced in the wire.

All of the wire loops together form the armature of the generator.

The **electric generator** converts mechanical energy to electric energy. The electric generator was invented by Michael Faraday. In essence, an electric generator consists of a number of wire loops placed in a strong magnetic field. All of the loops together form what is known as an **armature** (AHR muh chuhr). The wire loops are mounted so that they rotate freely in the field. As the loops turn, they cut through magnetic field lines. Thus, a current is in-

FIGURE 26-3. (a) Generation of an electric current in a wire loop as the loop rotates. (b) Cross-sectional view showing the position of the loop when maximum current is generated and when no current is generated.

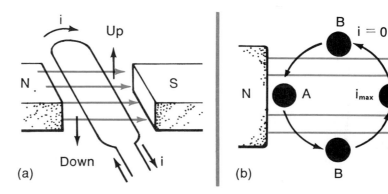

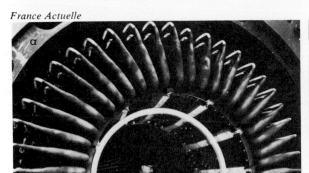

FIGURE 26-4. Giant coils of wire (a) are used to produce the magnetic field of a generator (b).

duced. The more loops in the armature, the longer the length of the wire in the field. Thus, the greater is the induced EMF. Figure 26-3 shows one loop of a generator.

Using Figure 26-3 and the left-hand rule, notice that the current induced in the loop moves in opposite directions in the two sides of the loop. Therefore, a current flows around the entire loop. Only while the loop is in a horizontal position do the two segments cut through the field at a right angle. In this position, the current is a maximum. This maximum occurs because the loop cuts through the maximum number of magnetic field lines per unit time in this position. As the loop moves from the horizontal to the vertical position, it cuts through the magnetic field lines at an ever increasing angle. Thus, it cuts through fewer magnetic field lines per unit time and the current decreases. When the loop is in the vertical position, the segments move parallel to the field and the current is zero. As the loop continues to turn, the segment that was moving up begins to move down. The segment that was moving down begins to move up. Thus, the direction of the current in the loop changes. This change in direction takes place each time the loop turns through 180°. The current changes smoothly from zero to some maximum value and back to zero during each half-turn of the loop. Then it reverses direction. The graph of current versus time yields the sine curve of Figure 26-5.

In the previous section we found that the EMF, or voltage, developed in a wire moving through a magnetic field is equal to the

The current induced in a wire loop changes direction each time the loop rotates 180°.

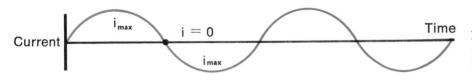

Current i_{max} $i = 0$ i_{max} Time

FIGURE 26-5. Variation of current with time as the loop rotates.

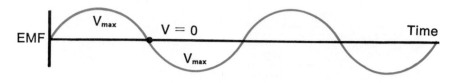

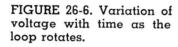

FIGURE 26-6. Variation of voltage with time as the loop rotates.

product Blv. A generator consists of a coil of wire rotating in a strong magnetic field. Thus, the EMF, or voltage, developed by the generator depends upon the magnetic induction (B), the length of wire rotating in the field (l), and the rate at which the coil (armature) turns in the field (v).

As the armature turns in the magnetic field, its loops cut through the field at different angles. Thus, the voltage changes in the same way that the current changes. The voltage is at maximum value when the loops are moving at right angles to the field. The voltage is zero when the loops are moving parallel to the field (Figure 26-6).

Maximum current and voltage are produced when the loops move at right angles to the field.

Zero current and voltage are produced when the loops move parallel to the field.

26:5 Alternating Current Generator

The armature of a generator is rotated in the magnetic field by the energy source at a set number of turns per second (rev/sec). Commercially, this frequency is usually 60 hertz. The current changes direction after each half-turn. Therefore, the current changes direction, or alternates, 120 times a second.

In Figure 26-7, an alternating current in an armature is transmitted to the rest of the circuit. The brush-slip-ring arrangement permits the armature to turn freely while still allowing the current to pass into the external circuit. As the armature turns, the alternating current varies between some maximum value and zero. But, the light in the circuit does not appear to dim or brighten because the changes are too fast for the eye to detect.

The effective value of an alternating current is found by comparing it to a direct current. If an alternating current is applied to a heater, the heat the current produces in one minute can be measured. The direct current needed to produce the same amount of heat in the same time is then calculated. The ac current is then compared to the dc current. Such measurements always show that the effective value of an alternating current is equal to its maximum value multiplied by 0.707. Likewise, the effective value of the alternating EMF is 0.707 × the maximum value. (The sine of 45° is 0.707.)

The effective current is 0.707 maximum current.

The effective voltage is 0.707 maximum voltage.

$$i_{\text{eff}} = 0.707\ i_{\text{max}}$$
$$V_{\text{eff}} = 0.707\ V_{\text{max}}$$

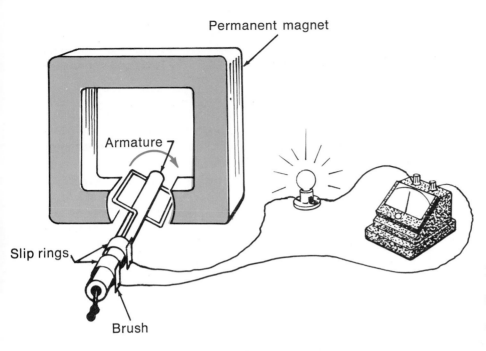

Permanent magnet

Armature

Slip rings

Brush

FIGURE 26-7. Alternating current generators transmit current to an external circuit by way of a brush-slip ring arrangement.

Example: Effective Voltage and Effective Current

An ac generator develops a maximum voltage of 100 volts and delivers a maximum current of 20 A to a circuit. (a) What is the effective voltage of the generator? (b) What effective current is delivered to the circuit? (c) What is the resistance of the circuit?

Solution: (a) $V_{eff} = 0.707\, V_{max}$
$$= 0.707\,(100 \text{ volts})$$
$$= 70.7 \text{ volts}$$

         (b) $i_{eff} = 0.707\, i_{max}$
$$= 0.707\,(20 \text{ A})$$
$$= 14.1 \text{ A}$$

         (c) $R = \dfrac{V_{eff}}{i_{eff}}$
$$= \frac{70.7 \text{ volts}}{14.1 \text{ A}}$$
$$= 5.0 \text{ ohms}$$

PROBLEMS

6. A generator in a power plant develops a maximum voltage of 170 volts. (a) What is the effective voltage? (b) A 60-watt light bulb is placed across the generator. A maximum current of 0.7 A flows through the bulb. What effective current flows through the bulb?

7. The effective voltage of an ac household outlet is 117 volts. (a) What is the maximum voltage across a lamp connected to the outlet? (b) The effective current through the lamp is 5.5 A. What maximum current flows in the lamp during a complete cycle?

8. An ac generator delivers a maximum voltage of 250 volts. (a) What effective voltage is available to a circuit? (b) An 88-ohm resistor is placed across the generator. What effective current flows through it? (c) What is the maximum current through the resistor?

9. (a) What is the effective EMF across a circuit connected to a generator that delivers a maximum voltage of 310 volts? (b) What effective current does this generator deliver if the resistance of the circuit is 55 ohms?

10. An ac generator delivers a peak voltage of 425 volts. (a) What is the effective voltage in a circuit placed across the generator? (b) The resistance of the circuit is 500 ohms. What effective current flows in it?

26:6 Generators and Motors

A generator converts mechanical energy to electric energy; a motor converts electric energy to mechanical energy.

Generators and motors are identical in construction, but they serve opposite purposes. The purpose of a generator is to convert mechanical energy to electric energy. The purpose of a motor is to convert electric energy to mechanical energy. When an electric current is made to flow through an armature in a magnetic field, the armature turns. This device is a motor. But when an armature is turned in a magnetic field, an electric current is produced. This device is an electric generator. An electric motor can be used as an electric generator. In France, all trains are electric. The same motor that drives a train up a hill is used as a generator when the train rolls downhill. The engineer throws a switch and the motors serve as generators. Thus, the kinetic energy of the train is used to produce electric energy. This electric energy is sent back into the power lines to be used by other trains.

Recently, much interest in electric cars and trucks has developed because of fuel shortages. Such vehicles use batteries for power. Their operating range is limited by the batteries in use. To conserve as much energy as possible, the braking system of electric vehicles are made so that when the driver steps on a brake pedal, contacts are switched to change the motor to a generator. As the electric car slows down, it gives its kinetic energy to the generator. The generator produces electric energy to help recharge the batteries. Thus, electric cars can travel a greater distance before their batteries need to be completely recharged.

FIGURE 26-8. An electric car (a) with a close-up of its motor and electronic circuitry (b).

26:7 Lenz's Law

As soon as the armature of a generator starts to turn, current flows in its wires. As a result, a generator must also act like a motor. The motor effect of a generator tries to turn the armature in the opposite way from which it is turning. If the armature of a hand generator is turned clockwise, the current that flows tries to turn the armature counterclockwise. Therefore, the armature is more difficult to turn.

Lenz's law states that *an induced current always acts in such a direction that its magnetic properties oppose the change by which the current is induced.*

Lenz's law also applies to motors. As soon as the armature of a motor begins to turn in a magnetic field, it will generate an electric current. The generator effect of a motor attempts to produce current in direct opposition to the current that makes the armature turn. This generator effect of a motor is quite noticeable. It is called the **"back-EMF"** of the motor. When the armature of the motor is turning, back-EMF opposes the current put into the motor. If a motor is to operate properly, it must have a resistance that accounts for back-EMF. For this reason, a motor's resistance is low. Thus, when a motor is first turned on, it draws a large current. This large current can cause a voltage drop across the entire circuit. Suppose a second device, such as a light bulb, is in the same circuit when the motor is turned on. The voltage across the light decreases for a moment and the light dims. As the motor begins to turn, back-EMF appears. The back-EMF opposes the current flowing into the motor. Thus, in effect, it reduces the current flowing in the entire circuit. The excess voltage drop in the lines is eliminated and the circuit returns to normal.

The current in a generator produces a motor effect. The motor effect opposes the turning of the generator.

A motor produces a back-EMF as it rotates. The generated current opposes the current operating the motor.

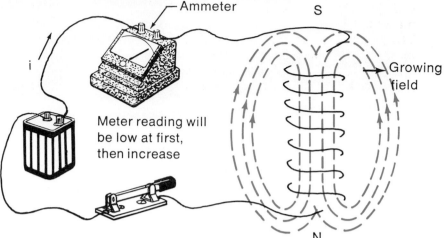

FIGURE 26-9. Self-inductance of a coil causes opposition to the flow of current in a circuit. In this dc circuit the opposition to current flow disappears as soon as the current becomes steady.

26:8 Self-Induction

As current in a coil changes, an induced EMF appears in that same coil. This effect is called self-induction.

Whenever a coil of wire is part of an electric circuit, it produces an effect called **self-induction**. Consider the coil in Figure 26-9. When the switch is closed, a current begins to flow in the circuit. The current causes a magnetic field to appear about the coil. The field does not reach its full magnitude at once. It grows as the current increases toward its maximum value. As it grows, the field moves out and cuts through adjacent loops of the coil. As the field cuts through these loops, an EMF is induced in the coil. By Lenz's law, this induced EMF tends to oppose the current flowing in the loops. The current is prevented from reaching its maximum value for a short time.

In a dc circuit, such as Figure 26-9, the self-inductance of the coil disappears rapidly. It disappears because as soon as the current reaches its maximum value, the field becomes stable and does not move. However, if the source of dc current is replaced with an ac source, the field about the coil constantly changes as the current in the circuit changes. Thus, the field is constantly moving in and out from the coil and cutting through the loops of the coil. This produces an induced current. By Lenz's law, the induced current will always oppose the current in the coil. For this reason, any coil placed in an alternating current circuit presents a strong opposition to the flow of current in that circuit. This opposition (which is not a true resistance) to current flow in an alternating current circuit is called **inductive reactance.**

Inductive reactance impedes the flow of current in an ac circuit.

26:9 Transformers

A **transformer** has two coils wound around the same core. One coil is called the primary coil. The other is called the secondary coil. The introduction of an alternating current into the primary coil causes the magnetic field about the coil to fluctuate. The current in the coil constantly changes between zero and its maximum. Thus, the magnetic field is always changing. It changes direction every half cycle. This varying field cuts through the loops of the secondary coil. Thus, it induces an EMF in the second coil.

This induced EMF can be found by using the relationship EMF = Blv. The rate of change of magnetic flux is the same about both coils. Thus, B is the same around both coils. The velocity v is also the same for both coils because the flux passes over both coils in the same time. If the secondary coil has more turns on it than the primary coil, it has a greater length, l, than the primary coil. The lengths are in direct proportion to the number of turns on each coil. Thus, the EMF is greater in the secondary coil. If the secondary coil has fewer turns than the primary coil, its EMF is less. The ratio of the EMF in the secondary coil to the EMF in the primary coil is equal to the ratio of the number of turns on the secondary to the number of turns on the primary.

$$\frac{\text{Primary voltage}}{\text{Secondary voltage}} = \frac{\text{Number of turns on primary}}{\text{Number of turns on secondary}}$$
$$\frac{V_p}{V_s} = \frac{N_p}{N_s}$$

A transformer may be a step-up or a step-down transformer. A step-up transformer is used to increase voltage. A step-down transformer is used to decrease voltage. In an "ideal" transformer,

In a transformer, two coils of different lengths are wound around the same core.

A transformer can be used to increase voltage or to decrease voltage.

FIGURE 26-10. (a) A large step-up transformer increases the voltage of the current as it leaves the power station. **(b)** A pole transformer greatly reduces the voltage of the current before it is sent to individual users.

Columbus and Southern Ohio Electric Co.

Primary   Secondary

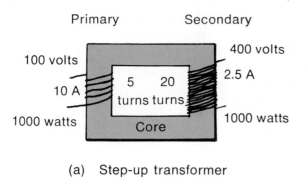

(a)   Step-up transformer

Primary   Secondary

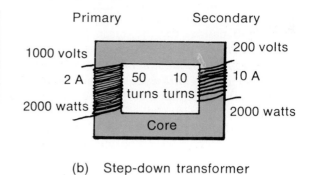

(b)   Step-down transformer

FIGURE 26-11. The ratio of input voltage to output voltage depends upon the ratio of the number of turns of the primary to the number of turns of the secondary.

the power input is equal to the power output. Since electric power is voltage times current $(P = Vi)$, a transformer that increases voltage must decrease current. A transformer that decreases voltage will increase current. In all cases the power introduced into the primary of a transformer is equal to the power induced in the secondary of the transformer.

$$V_p i_p = V_s i_s$$

Example: Step-up Transformer

A step-up transformer has 200 turns on its primary coil and 3000 turns on its secondary coil. (a) The primary coil is supplied with an alternating current at 90 volts. What is the voltage in the secondary circuit? (b) The current in the primary circuit is 30 A. What current flows in the secondary circuit? (c) What is the power in the primary? In the secondary?

Solution:

(a) $\dfrac{V_p}{V_s} = \dfrac{N_p}{N_s}$

$\quad V_s = \dfrac{V_p N_s}{N_p}$

$\qquad = \dfrac{90 \text{ volts} \times 3000}{200}$

$\qquad = 1350 \text{ volts}$

(b) $V_p i_p = V_s i_s$

$\quad i_s = \dfrac{V_p i_p}{V_s}$

$\qquad = \dfrac{90 \text{ volts} \times 30 \text{ A}}{1350 \text{ volts}}$

$\qquad = 2 \text{ A}$

(c) $V_p i_p = 90 \text{ volts} \times 30 \text{ A}$

$\qquad = 2700 \text{ watts}$

$\quad V_s i_s = 1350 \text{ volts} \times 2 \text{ A}$

$\qquad = 2700 \text{ watts}$

PROBLEMS

11. An ideal step-up transformer's primary has 50 turns. Its secondary has 1500 turns. The primary is connected to an ac generator having an EMF of 120 volts. (a) Calculate the EMF of the secondary. (b) Find the current in the secondary circuit if the current in the primary is 90 A. (c) What power develops in the primary? In the secondary?

12. The secondary of a step-down transformer has 50 turns. The primary has 1500 turns. (a) The EMF of the primary is 3600 volts. What is the EMF of the secondary? (b) The current in the primary is 3 A. What current flows in the secondary?

13. A step-up transformer has 300 turns on its primary and 90 000 turns on its secondary. The EMF of the generator to which the primary is attached is 60 volts. (a) What is the EMF in the secondary? (b) The current flowing in the primary coil is 150 A. What current flows in the secondary?

14. A step-down transformer has 7500 turns on its primary and 125 turns on its secondary. The voltage across the primary is 7200 volts. (a) What voltage is across the secondary? (b) The current in the primary is 0.6 A. What current flows in the secondary?

15. A step-up transformer is connected to a generator that delivers 120 volts and 100 A. The ratio of the turns on the secondary to the turns on the primary is 1000 to 1. (a) What voltage is in the secondary? (b) What current flows in the secondary? (c) What is the power input? (d) What is the power output?

16. The primary of a transformer has 150 turns. It is connected to a 120-volt source. Calculate the number of turns on the secondary to supply (a) 600 volts, (b) 300 volts, and (c) 6 volts.

SUMMARY

Faraday discovered that when a wire is moved through a magnetic field, an electric current is induced in the wire. The direction taken by the current in the wire depends upon the direction in which the wire cuts through the field. The amount of current produced depends on the angle between the wire and the field. The maximum current is produced when the wire is perpendicular to the magnetic field. The current is zero when the wire is parallel to the magnetic field.

Electromotive force (EMF) is the energy imparted to each unit of charge by the energy source. The EMF induced in a wire moving through a magnetic field is measured in volts and is the product of three factors. These factors are the magnetic induction, B, the length of the wire in the field, l, and the speed of the moving wire, v. $EMF = Blv$.

An electric generator consists of a number of wire loops placed in a magnetic field. Some energy source must turn the coil. Since each side of the loops moves alternately up and then down through the field, the current alternates direction in the loops. The generator develops alternating current.

Generators and motors are identical in construction, but they serve opposite purposes. A generator converts mechanical energy to electric energy. A motor converts electric energy to mechanical energy.

Lenz's law states that an induced current always acts in such a direction that its magnetic properties oppose the change by which the current is induced. In a motor, the "back-EMF" opposes the current put into the motor.

When a coil is placed in an electric circuit, it produces an effect called self-induction. When the current flowing through the circuit changes, a magnetic field is produced around the coil. This generates an induced current which opposes the current flowing in the loops. This effect is not important in dc circuits but is highly significant in ac circuits.

A transformer has two coils wound around the same core. The introduction of an ac current into the primary coil produces an EMF in the secondary core. The voltages and currents in alternating current circuits may be stepped up or down by the use of transformers.

QUESTIONS

1. Explain how a wire and a strong magnet generate an electric current.
2. What is the difference between the current generated in a wire when the wire is moved up through a magnetic field and when the wire is moved down through the same field?
3. What causes an electron to move in a wire when the wire is moved through a magnetic field?
4. What is EMF?
5. Substitute units to show that $Blv = $ volts.
6. Sketch and describe an ac generator.
7. What is the armature of an electric generator?
8. What is the difference between a generator and a motor?
9. How is the effective value of an ac current determined?
10. What factors determine the EMF of a generator?
11. State Lenz's law.
12. What causes the back-EMF of an electric motor?
13. Why is the self-inductance of a coil an important factor when the coil is in an ac circuit and a minor factor when the coil is in a dc circuit?
14. Upon what does the ratio of the EMF in the primary of a transformer to the EMF in the secondary of the transformer depend?

PROBLEMS

1. A wire segment 30 cm long moves straight up through a field of magnetic induction 4.0×10^{-2} N/A-m at a speed of 15 m/sec. What EMF is induced in the wire?
2. A wire 0.75 m long cuts straight up through a field of magnetic induction 0.3 N/A-m at a speed of 16 m/sec. (a) What EMF is induced in the wire? (b) The wire is part of a circuit of total resistance 4.5 ohms. What current flows in the circuit?
3. A wire 20 m long moves at 4 m/sec perpendicularly through a field of magnetic induction 0.5 N/A-m. What EMF is induced in the wire?
4. An ac generator develops a maximum voltage of 150 volts. It delivers a maximum current of 30 A to an external circuit. (a) What is the effective voltage of the generator? (b) What effective current does it deliver to the external circuit?
5. An electric stove is connected to a 220-volt ac source. (a) What is the

maximum voltage across one of the stove's elements when it is operating? (b) The resistance of the operating element is 11 ohms. What effective current flows through it?

6. An ac generator develops a maximum EMF of 565 volts. What effective EMF does the generator deliver to an external circuit?

7. A step-up transformer has 80 turns on its primary coil. It has 1200 turns on its secondary coil. The primary coil is supplied with an alternating current at 120 volts. (a) What voltage is in the secondary coil? (b) The current in the primary coil is 50 A. What current flows in the secondary circuit? (c) What is the transformer power input and output?

8. An ideal transformer has 300 turns on its primary coil. It has 9000 turns on its secondary coil. The primary is connected to a 90-volt generator. Calculate (a) the EMF of the secondary; (b) the current in the secondary if the current in the primary is 60 A; and (c) the power developed in the primary and the secondary.

9. The primary of a transformer has 300 turns. It is connected to a 150-volt source. Calculate the number of turns on the secondary to supply (a) 900 volts, (b) 270 volts, (c) 12.5 volts, and (d) 6 volts.

10. In a hydroelectric plant, electric energy is generated at 1200 volts. It is transmitted at 240 000 volts. (a) What is the ratio of the turns on the primary to the turns on the secondary of a transformer connected to one of the generators? (b) One of the plant generators delivers 40 A to the primary of its transformer. What current flows in the secondary?

PROJECTS

1. Make a homemade electromagnet using one of the following procedures. (a) Get some insulated copper wire, a large nail, and an empty thread spool. Wrap several turns of wire around the spool. Always wind the wire in the same direction. Leave the ends of the wire free. Scrape the insulation from the ends of the wire and connect the ends to a battery. Then pass the nail through the middle of the spool to test it for magnetic properties. (b) Wrap several coils of insulated copper wire around a large nail. Connect the ends to a battery and test for magnetic properties.

2. Construct a homemade telegraph set by following the accompanying diagram closely. You will need about a meter of insulated copper wire, two small pieces of scrap wood (10 cm × 15 cm), two short lengths of spring steel (from a packing case), two nails, two small screws, a wooden block about 5 cm on each edge, and a few batteries. Wind the wire around the nail at least 20 times to form a strong electromagnet. Then construct the circuit of Figure 26-12. When you close the key, the electromagnet should draw the clicker down to produce a clicking sound. If needed, make adjustments in the distance between the top of the nail and the clicker.

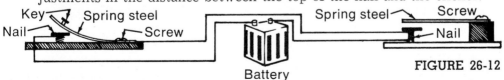

FIGURE 26-12

READINGS

Beiser, Germaine and Arthur, *The Story of Cosmic Rays.* New York, E. P. Dutton and Co., Inc., 1962.

Carrigan, Richard A., "Quest for the Magnetic Monopole." *The Physics Teacher,* October, 1975.

Shiers, George, "The Induction Coil." *Scientific American,* May, 1971.

The electromagnetic spectrum includes radiation with wavelengths as short as 10^{-14} meters and as long as 10^7 meters. Toward the short-wavelength end of the spectrum we find X rays. At the opposite end we find radio waves. Very long radio waves originating in outer space are detected with large radio antennas. These waves tell us about processes occurring in distant stars and galaxies. Shorter radio waves can be used to transmit messages long distances without wires. What kinds of equipment can be used to send and receive messages in this way?

ELECTRO-MAGNETIC FIELD APPLICATIONS

We have seen that when a conductor is placed in a changing magnetic field, an induced EMF appears. This EMF indicates that an electric field is present. The electric field pushes electrons through the conductor. A changing magnetic field always generates an electric field.

GOAL: You will gain knowledge and understanding of the generation and transmission of electromagnetic waves and of the behavior of charged particles in electric and magnetic fields.

27:1   The Generation of Electromagnetic Waves

In 1864, James Clerk Maxwell showed that conductors are not needed to generate magnetic or electric fields. Maxwell predicted that a magnetic field moving in space generates an electric field moving in space which generates a magnetic field moving in space, and so on. The fields pass through space at the speed of light in the form of a wave. Maxwell predicted that the magnetic and electric parts of a wave are always at right angles to each other. Also, they are both at right angles to the direction of propagation of the wave. Experiments confirm this prediction.

A changing magnetic field generates a changing electric field.

A changing electric field generates a changing magnetic field.

To generate an electromagnetic wave, a changing magnetic field or a changing electric field is needed. To produce a changing magnetic field, the current in the wire must be constantly changing. A changing electric current means a changing rate of flow. This changing rate of flow means that charged particles are being accelerated. Accelerated charged particles produce electromagnetic waves which travel off into space.

To produce an electromagnetic wave, a changing field is needed.

Accelerated charges generate electromagnetic waves.

407

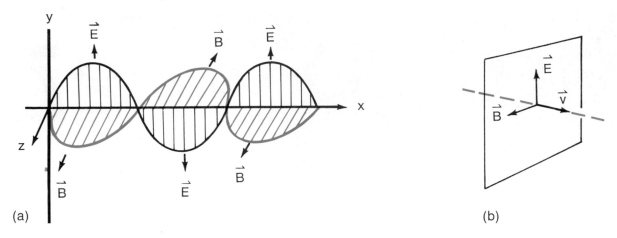

(a)   (b)

FIGURE 27-1. A model of an electromagnetic wave. Note that the electric and magnetic fields are perpendicular to one another and that they are both perpendicular to the direction in which the wave is traveling.

Light waves are electromagnetic waves generated by the acceleration of electrons within an atom.

Radio waves are generated by accelerating electrons in an antenna.

This relationship between the accelerating charged particles and electromagnetic waves explains several issues. Electromagnetic waves travel at the speed of light as Maxwell predicted. This implies that light waves are electromagnetic waves. Since electrons are charged particles, the energy transitions of electrons within the atom are thought to be the origin of the characteristic spectra of an atom. This supports the idea that electromagnetic waves are due to the acceleration of charged particles. Electrons accelerate as they move between two different energy levels within an atom. The accelerating electrons produce electromagnetic waves in the visible and nonvisible regions of the spectrum.

Maxwell's theory had an important implication. If electrons can vibrate in a wire at a constant frequency, an electromagnetic wave of the same frequency should leave the region of the wire. Thus, Maxwell predicted the propagation of radio waves. Maxwell did not live to see his prediction confirmed. In 1887 Heinrich Hertz generated and detected the first radio waves.

27:2   The Discovery of X Rays

In 1895 in Germany, Wilhelm Roentgen sent electrons through an evacuated discharge tube. Roentgen used very high voltage across the tube. This voltage accelerated the electrons to very high speeds. The electrons struck the electrode located at the opposite end of the tube. Roentgen noted a glow on a phosphorescent screen a short distance away. He concluded that some kind of highly penetrating rays were coming from the discharge tube. Because of the excitations on the screen, Roentgen recognized that the rays could pass through materials.

X rays are high-frequency electromagnetic waves generated when electrons strike an anode.

Because Roentgen did not know what these strange rays were, he called them **X rays**. X rays are now known to be electromag-

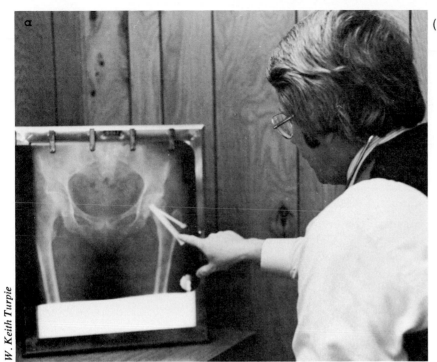

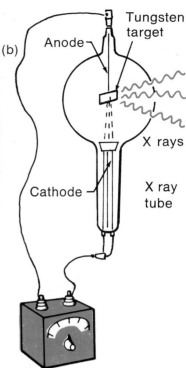

High voltage; 10^5 volts

W. Keith Turpie

netic waves of very high frequency. They are produced by the extremely high rate of deceleration of the electrons as they strike the anode of the tube. The high frequency of X rays indicates the high energy of the electromagnetic wave. The energy of an electromagnetic wave is equal to Planck's constant times the frequency of the wave, $E = hf$. Much of the kinetic energy of the high-speed electrons is converted to the energy of the X rays that result when the particles are decelerated at the anode.

FIGURE 27-2. (a) Negative produced by X rays. (b) Apparatus for producing X rays.

The energy of an X ray is equal to the energy loss of an electron as it strikes the anode.

Example: Accelerating an Electron in a Discharge Tube

Assume an electron starts from rest at one end of a cathode ray tube where the voltage is 10^5 volts. Find the speed of the electron when it reaches the other end of the tube. The mass of an electron is 9×10^{-31} kg.

Solution:

By the definition of a volt, we know that 100 000 J of work are done to transfer 1 coul of charge across a 10^5 volt potential difference. There are 6.25×10^{18} electrons in 1 coul of charge. Thus, the work done on a single electron to move it through the potential difference is

$$\frac{100\ 000 \text{ J/coul}}{6.25 \times 10^{18} \text{ electrons/coul}} = 1.6 \times 10^{-14} \text{ J/electron}$$

The electron converts this energy to kinetic energy as it travels to the anode.

Therefore, at the anode, $KE = \dfrac{mv^2}{2} = 1.6 \times 10^{-14}$ J

and
$$v = \sqrt{\frac{2\,(1.6 \times 10^{-14})\,J}{m}}$$
$$= \sqrt{\frac{3.2 \times 10^{-14}\,J}{9 \times 10^{-31}\,kg}}$$
$$= \sqrt{3.6 \times 10^{16}\,m^2/sec^2}$$
$$= 1.9 \times 10^8\ m/sec$$

Example: Radiation Produced by Electrons in a Discharge Tube

Assume the energy found in the preceding example is roughly correct. (a) Calculate the frequency of the radiation emitted if all the energy of the electron is converted to electromagnetic radiation when the electron strikes the anode. (b) X rays have frequencies between 10^{16} and 10^{21} Hz. Is the radiation of part (a) of this problem in the X-ray region?

Solution:

Use Planck's constant $(6.6 \times 10^{-34}$ J-sec) in the relation $E = hf$.

(a)
$$f = \frac{E}{h}$$
$$= \frac{1.6 \times 10^{-14}\,J}{6.6 \times 10^{-34}\,J\text{-sec}}$$
$$= 2.4 \times 10^{19}\ Hz$$

(b) Since the frequency is between 10^{16} and 10^{21} Hz, the rays are X rays.

PROBLEMS

1. (a) Find the energy given to an electron transferred through a potential difference of 80 000 volts. (b) What energy does the electron give up as it strikes the anode?

2. The electrons in Problem 1 are accelerated across a discharge tube by 80 000 volts. Assume the electrons start from rest. What speed do they attain before reaching the anode?

3. All the energy given up by each electron in Problem 1 is converted to electromagnetic radiation. What is the frequency of the electromagnetic wave that is produced?

4. An electron falls through a potential difference of 10 000 volts. (a) What energy is given up by the electron? (b) The electron passes through a discharge tube while giving up the energy. What speed does it attain?

5. A proton has a mass of 1.7×10^{-27} kg. What maximum speed does it attain in falling through a potential difference of 100 000 volts?

27:3   Transmission of Electromagnetic Waves

Maxwell showed that accelerated charged particles generate electromagnetic waves. He also predicted that it should be possible to send messages through long distances without the use of wires (wireless). To send such messages, electromagnetic waves of the proper frequency must be generated and detected.

All electromagnetic waves travel through space at the speed of light, 3×10^8 m/sec. They differ from one another only in wavelength and frequency. The frequency of the wave is the same as the frequency of the vibrating charge that produces it.

The standard wavelength of an AM radio wave is about 300 meters. To produce waves of this wavelength, electrons must be made to oscillate at about 10^6 vibrations per sec in the broadcast antennas of a radio station. FM radio and TV use wavelengths of only about 3 meters. Stations broadcasting at these wavelengths must oscillate electrons in their antennas at about 10^8 vibrations per sec. This frequency is a hundred times greater than those used by AM stations.

AM radio waves have frequencies of about 10^6 hertz.

FM radio and TV waves have frequencies of about 10^8 hertz.

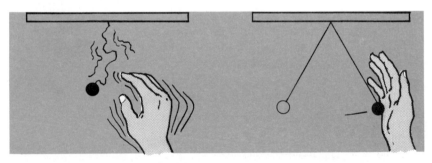

FIGURE 27-3. Energy can be transferred to a pendulum easily only when the frequency of energy input is equal to the natural frequency of the pendulum.

An understanding of radio and TV broadcasting depends on an understanding of **resonance.** Your first encounter with resonance probably came at a very early age when you first learned to "pump" a swing. At that time you found that a pendulum (you, ropes, seat) would accept energy only when it is offered at the right frequency. This is the frequency at which the pendulum naturally vibrates. To verify this, construct a simple pendulum as shown in Figure 27-3. Strike the bob rapidly. You will find that although you are offering the system a good deal of energy, most of it is rejected. Now try to push the pendulum in time with the natural frequency at which it vibrates. The pendulum will gain energy rapidly.

Radio and TV transmission and reception depend on resonance.

A system readily accepts energy that is offered at the natural frequency of the system.

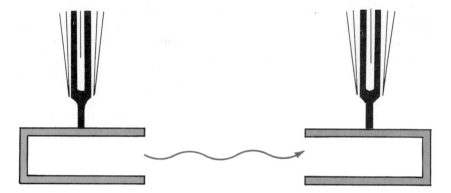

FIGURE 27-4. A sound wave can cause a tuning fork to vibrate if the frequency of the incoming wave is the same as the frequency at which the fork naturally vibrates.

The presence of waves of a given frequency can be detected by applying the principle of resonance. Consider the two tuning forks in Figure 27-4. Both forks vibrate at the same frequency. If one tuning fork is struck by a rubber hammer, it will vibrate and emit a sound wave that has the same frequency as its rate of vibration. The sound wave will travel through the air and cause the second tuning fork to vibrate. The rate of energy input from the sound wave resonates with the natural frequency of the second tuning fork. Each tuning fork will vibrate in response to a sound wave from the other.

Two objects do not need to be identical in size to vibrate at the same frequency. A picture on a wall can vibrate in response to the sound of a passing truck. The vibrations of a car's engine can explain some noises that occur in other parts of the car. In the same way, the AM radio in your home is not the same size as the radio station that is broadcasting the electromagnetic waves. But, the radio must be able to oscillate charge in its antenna in response to that wave. In effect, your radio is a smaller version of the broadcasting station.

A home radio is a smaller version of a transmitting station.

Consider the pump-water tank arrangement in Figure 27-5a. Suppose the pump attempts to pump water from one tank to the

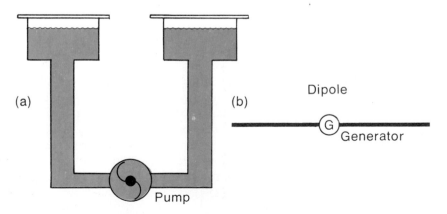

FIGURE 27-5. Diagram of (a) pump-water tank arrangement and (b) dipole antenna.

other. It could only do so for a brief interval. One of the tanks would soon be full and no further water could flow in the pipes. But suppose that instead of trying to pump water in just one direction, the pump caused the water to oscillate back and forth. In that event the pump could operate. The pump could operate best at the one frequency that changes the direction of flow precisely when each tank became full.

Now consider the generator-wire arrangement (antenna) shown in Figure 27-5b. Such an arrangement is called a **dipole.** A direct-current generator could not cause charge to flow in the dipole for the same reason that the water pump could not pump water in one direction in its system. In the case of a direct-current generator, electrons would build up in one of the wires. This buildup would stop all further current in the system. But an alternating-current generator could cause charge to oscillate in the dipole. It could do this by sending the current back and forth quickly enough to prevent a strong charge from building up at either end of the dipole. The dipole will have a natural frequency of oscillation that depends on its length. Just as a pendulum will accept energy at a particular frequency, a dipole will best accept electric energy at one particular input rate. This rate is the natural frequency of the dipole.

Suppose that a radio or TV station is causing electrons to oscillate in its antenna at the natural frequency of the antenna. If the electrons are oscillating, they are constantly being accelerated. According to Maxwell's prediction, electromagnetic waves will develop about the antenna. As electrons are accelerated in one direction in the dipole, radio waves in the form of closed loops build up around the dipole. When the current is accelerated in the opposite direction, new radio waves develop. But they will form loops of opposite direction.

In Figure 27-6, the electric field lines are shown for one complete cycle of the oscillator. Note that the electric field lines

An ac generator causes electrons in a dipole antenna to oscillate.

A dipole operates most efficiently at one particular frequency.

When electrons oscillate in a dipole, electromagnetic waves are generated.

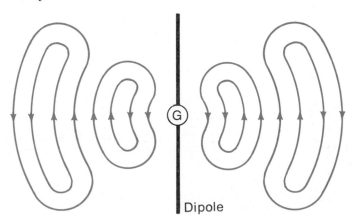

Dipole

FIGURE 27-6. Electric field lines produced by oscillating charges in a broadcast antenna.

FIGURE 27-7. This moving TV news truck is equipped with transmitting and receiving antennas.

from different half-cycles (loops of opposite direction) that are next to each other have the same direction. Electric field lines with the same direction repel each other. Because of this repelling force, each oncoming wave pushes the wave before it into space at the speed of light. Only electric field lines are shown in the diagram. But, magnetic field lines would also be present. The magnetic field lines would be perpendicular to the electric field lines. They would project into and out of the page.

Suppose there is another wire antenna some distance from the transmitting antenna. The electric charges in that wire will oscillate in response to the electric and magnetic fields that pass over it. Moving magnetic fields cause electrons to flow in a wire.

The antenna of a radio or TV receiver is always exposed to electromagnetic waves that originate from many different radio and TV stations. But the length of an antenna can be adjusted so that its natural frequency of electric oscillation matches only one station. Then, the antenna will respond only to that station. In effect, every time you turn a tuning dial on your radio or TV set, you are adjusting the set to respond to one certain station. The radio or TV will exclude all other stations.

A radio or TV receiver is adjusted to resonate in response to only one station.

In practice the frequency of commercial broadcasts range from 500 thousand Hz to 1500 thousand Hz. No generator can be built to rotate that rapidly. Therefore, to generate high frequencies, most stations use a small crystal. Small crystals vibrate naturally in this frequency range. The exact frequency of a given crystal depends on its size and shape. Usually these crystals are quartz. Each station must use the proper size crystal. The station uses the crystal to control the frequency at which electrons are sent along its transmitting antenna. Higher frequencies require smaller

Crystals are used to generate high-frequency waves.

The natural frequency of a crystal depends on its size and shape.

John Morgan

FIGURE 27-8. Assorted crystals used in transmitters and receivers.

crystals. The generation of radar waves requires the smallest crystals that can be made.

The crystals needed to generate infrared (heat) waves would be about the size of a molecule. This suggests that heat waves are developed by vibrating molecules and atoms. To generate frequencies in the range of visible light, particles that are even smaller than molecules are needed. We find that these particles must be about the size of electrons. This finding agrees with present theory about the origin of light waves. That is, light is a result of the vibration of electrons within atoms.

27:4 Millikan's Oil-Drop Experiment

Figure 27-9 shows the method used by Robert A. Millikan to measure the charge carried by a single electron. Fine oil drops are sprayed into the air from an atomizer. These drops often have small charges. The charges are a result of the transfer of electrons from the atomizer to the oil drops. These drops then fall through

From Millikan's oil-drop experiment, the charge of an electron was determined.

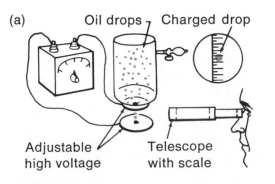

(a) Oil drops — Charged drop

Adjustable high voltage

Telescope with scale

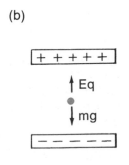

(b)

$$+ + + + +$$

$\uparrow Eq$

$\downarrow mg$

$$- - - - -$$

FIGURE 27-9. (a) Diagram of the apparatus used by Millikan to determine the charge on an electron. (b) Diagram of an oil drop suspended between two oppositely charged plates.

the air. A few enter the hole in the top plate of the apparatus. The two plates are given opposite charges. Thus, an electric field is created between the plates. The electric field between the plates and the electric field around a charged particle interact. An oil drop with a negative charge is attracted toward the positive plate. If the top plate is the positive plate, the oil drop is acted on by two forces. The force due to its weight causes it to fall. The other force due to the electric field causes it to rise. The charge on the plates can be adjusted to suspend a charged drop between the plates. Then, the downward force of the weight and the upward force of the electric field are equal.

$$Eq = mg$$

The intensity of the electric field, E, is found from the voltage across the plates. A second measurement is made to determine the weight of the droplet, mg. The weight of a tiny oil drop is too small to measure by ordinary methods. To make this measurement, a suspended drop is observed and its rate of fall is timed when the electric field is shut off. Because of friction, an oil drop quickly reaches a uniform or "terminal" speed. The speed is related to the mass of the drop by a formula devised by the British physicist George G. Stokes. This formula is used to calculate the weight of the drop, mg. Since both E and mg are known, q can be calculated.

Millikan had no way to know whether a drop of oil carried one or several extra charges. The smallest value obtained for q was 1.6×10^{-19} coul. All other values were exact multiples of this value. The value 1.6×10^{-19} coul is now accepted as the charge carried by the electron and the proton.

Example: Finding the Charge on an Oil Drop

An oil drop weighs 1.92×10^{-14} N. It is suspended in an electric field of intensity 4×10^4 N/coul. (a) What is the charge on the oil drop? (b) If the drop behaves as a negative particle in the field, how many excess electrons does the drop have?

Solution:

(a)
$$mg = Eq$$
$$q = \frac{mg}{E}$$
$$= \frac{1.92 \times 10^{-14} \text{ N}}{4 \times 10^4 \text{ N/coul}}$$
$$= 4.8 \times 10^{-19} \text{ coul}$$

(b)
$$\text{no. of electrons} = \frac{\text{Total charge on drop}}{\text{Charge per electron}}$$
$$= \frac{4.8 \times 10^{-19} \text{ coul}}{1.6 \times 10^{-19} \text{ coul/electron}}$$
$$= 3 \text{ electrons}$$

PROBLEMS

6. An oil drop weighs 1.92×10^{-15} N. It is suspended in an electric field of intensity 6.0×10^3 N/coul. (a) What is the charge on the oil drop? (b) The particle is negative. How many excess electrons does it carry?

7. A positively-charged oil drop weighs 6.4×10^{-13} N. It becomes suspended between two charged plates when the intensity of the electric field is 4.0×10^6 N/coul. (a) What is the charge on the drop? (b) How many electrons is the drop missing?

8. A negatively-charged oil drop weighs 8.5×10^{-15} N. The drop is suspended between two charged plates that produce an electric field of 5.3×10^{-3} N/coul. (a) What is the charge on the drop? (b) How many excess electrons does it carry?

9. During a Millikan experiment, a student records the weight of five different oil drops. A record is also made of the field intensity necessary to hold each drop stationary. (a) Plot the readings on a graph of W vs E. Plot W vertically. (b) Determine the slope of the line. What does the slope represent?

W (N)	E (N/coul)
1.7×10^{-14}	1.06×10^5
5.6×10^{-14}	3.5×10^5
9.3×10^{-14}	5.8×10^5
2.9×10^{-14}	1.8×10^5

27:5   Determining the Mass of the Electron

The British scientist Sir J. J. Thomson (1856–1940) constructed a discharge tube similar to the one in Figure 27-10. Electrons that leave the cathode of this tube are accelerated toward the anode.

From Thomson's experiment, the value of m/e was determined.

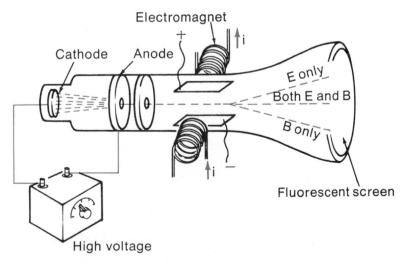

FIGURE 27-10. A cathode ray tube similar to the one shown here was used by J. J. Thomson to determine the charge-to-mass ratio of the electron.

Thomson observed the deflection of electrons in both electric and magnetic fields.

There is a small hole in the anode. Some of the high-speed electrons pass through this hole. A second metal plate beyond the anode guarantees that a straight beam of electrons passes through the remainder of the tube. Only electrons that align with the holes in both plates can pass on. Farther down the tube a pair of charged plates is arranged to deflect the negative electrons upward toward the positive plate. The force of the electric field acting on each electron is Ee. Here, E represents the electric field intensity, and e the charge on the electron. A magnetic field is also introduced. It acts at right angles to the charged plates. The force of the magnetic field on the electrons, Bev, deflects the electrons downward.

The electric field, the magnetic field, and the electron beam are all perpendicular to one another.

When both the electric and magnetic fields are present, the fields can be adjusted until the beam of electrons follows a straight or undeflected path. Then the force on the electrons due to the electric field is equal to the force due to the magnetic field.

$$Bev = Ee$$

Solving this equation for v, we obtain the expression

$$v = \frac{Ee}{Be}$$
$$= \frac{E}{B}$$

To find the velocity of the electrons, the fields are adjusted until electrons follow an undeflected path.

If the potential difference is removed from the plates, the only force acting on the electrons is due to the magnetic field. This force acts at a 90° angle with the direction of motion of the electrons. Thus, it is a centripetal force and causes the electrons to follow a circular path. When the electric field is absent,

When electrons move through a magnetic field, they follow a circular path of radius r.

$$Bev = \frac{mv^2}{r}$$

Solving for Br/v, we obtain the expression

$$\frac{Br}{v} = \frac{m}{e}$$

The value of m/e can be calculated when B, r, and v are known.

Thomson measured the distance between the undeflected spot and the position of the spot when the electrons were subjected only to the magnetic field. Thomson measured the radius, r, or the circular path given to the electrons by the magnetic field. He also measured the magnetic induction. He found the value of v from E/B. Thus, Thomson could calculate Br/v. This also gave him the value of m/e. Thomson consistently obtained the value 5.68×10^{-12} kg/coul. Millikan's value of e, 1.6×10^{-19} coul, allows the mass of the electron m to be calculated. Since

Millikan's value for e allowed the determination of m.

$$\frac{m}{e} = 5.68 \times 10^{-12} \text{ kg/coul}$$

then,
$$m = (5.68 \times 10^{-12} \text{ kg/coul}) (e)$$
$$= (5.68 \times 10^{-12} \text{ kg/coul}) (1.6 \times 10^{-19} \text{ coul})$$
$$= 9.1 \times 10^{-31} \text{ kg}$$

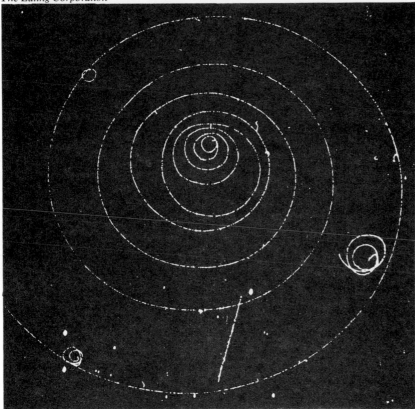

FIGURE 27-11. Spiral track made by an electron as it passes through a magnetic field in a bubble chamber. The radius of curvature is proportional to the velocity of the electron.

Thus, the mass of the electron equals 9.1×10^{-31} kg.

These equations also apply to a beam of protons sent across a discharge tube in the same way as the electrons. To obtain protons, a small amount of hydrogen gas is placed in the path of high-speed electrons that are traveling through a discharge tube. The electrons ionize many of the hydrogen atoms. A hydrogen atom consists of a single proton and a single electron. Thus, an ionized hydrogen atom is a proton. The protons are drawn into a tube similar to the one used to measure the mass of the electron. The mass of a proton is 1.7×10^{-27} kg.

The mass of a proton can be measured by the same method.

Example: Straight-Line Motion of an Electron in a Discharge Tube

A beam of electrons travels an undeflected path in a discharge tube. E is 7.0×10^3 N/coul. B is 3.5×10^{-2} N/A-m. What is the speed of the electrons as they travel through the tube?

Solution:

$$v = \frac{E}{B}$$
$$= \frac{7.0 \times 10^3 \text{ N/coul}}{3.5 \times 10^{-2} \text{ N/A-m}}$$
$$= 2.0 \times 10^5 \text{ m/sec}$$

Example: Path of an Electron in a Magnetic Field

An electron of mass 9.1×10^{-31} kg moves with a speed of 2.0×10^5 m/sec across a magnetic field. The magnetic induction is 8.0×10^{-4} N/A-m. What is the radius of the circular path followed by the electrons while in the field?

Solution:

$$\text{Since, } Bev = \frac{mv^2}{r}$$

$$r = \frac{mv}{Be}$$

$$= \frac{(9.0 \times 10^{-31}\,\text{kg})\,(2.0 \times 10^5\,\text{m/sec})}{(8.0 \times 10^{-4}\,\text{N/A-m})\,(1.6 \times 10^{-19}\,\text{coul})}$$

$$= 1.4 \times 10^{-3}\ \text{m}$$

PROBLEMS

Assume the direction of all moving charged particles is perpendicular to any fields.

10. Protons passing through a field of magnetic induction 0.6 N/A-m are deflected. An electric field of intensity 4.5×10^3 N/coul is introduced. The protons are brought back to their undeflected path. What is the speed of the moving protons?

11. A proton moves at a speed of 7.5×10^3 m/sec as it passes through a field of magnetic induction 0.6 N/A-m. Find the radius of the circular path. The mass of a proton is 1.7×10^{-27} kg. The charge carried by the proton is equal to that of the electron but is positive.

12. Electrons move through a field of magnetic induction 6.0×10^{-2} N/A-m. An electric field of 3.0×10^3 N/coul prevents the electrons from being deflected. What is the speed of the electrons?

13. Calculate the radius of the circular path the electrons in Problem 12 follow in the absence of the electric field. The mass of an electron is 9.0×10^{-31} kg.

14. A proton enters a magnetic field which has a magnetic induction of 6.0×10^{-2} N/A-m with a speed of 5.4×10^4 m/sec. What is the radius of the circular path it follows?

15. A proton moves across a field of magnetic induction 0.36 N/A-m. It follows a circular path of radius 0.2 m. What is the speed of the proton?

16. Electrons move across a field of magnetic induction 4.0×10^{-3} N/A-m. They follow a circular path of radius 2.0×10^{-2} m. (a) What is their speed? (b) An electric field is applied perpendicularly to the magnetic field. The electrons then follow a straight-line path. Find the magnitude of the electric field.

27:6 The Mass Spectrograph

A mass spectrograph is an offspring of the Thomson tube. It is used to measure masses of atoms. A diagram of a mass spectrograph appears in Figure 27-13b. In this device, a cathode and an anode are located at one end of the tube. If a high potential difference is placed across these electrodes, electrons will be accelerated from the cathode to the anode. When an element in the gas state is placed between the cathode and the anode, its atoms are constantly bombarded by electrons. In this way, many of the atoms of the gas are ionized. These positive ions are then accelerated toward the cathode. Many of the ions pass through the small opening in the cathode and move down the tube at high velocity.

The mass spectrograph is used to measure the masses of atoms.

There is no way of knowing how many electrons have been removed from any one atom as a result of collisions between electrons and atoms. The atoms that emerge from the opening in the cathode may have a single, double, or triple positive charge. To be sure that all ions in the beam moving down the tube have the same charge, the beam is made to pass between two charged plates. The ions are deflected by the electric field between the plates. The charge on the plates is adjusted so that only ions having the same charge can pass through the slit beyond the plates. Ions having too large a charge are deflected so much that they miss the slit and strike the metal instead.

In a mass spectrograph, the beam of ions is first deflected in an electric field so that only ions of the same charge continue through the discharge tube.

The beam of uniformly charged particles that passes through the slit is subjected to a strong magnetic field. This field is produced by two electromagnets. In the previous section, we found that charged particles moving through a magnetic field move in a

When the beam of uniformly charged ions passes through a strong magnetic field, it moves in a circular path.

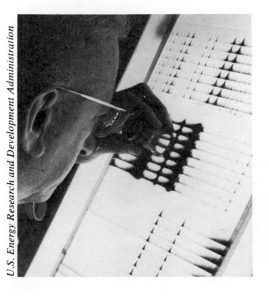

U.S. Energy Research and Development Administration

FIGURE 27-12. Scientist examining plates from a mass spectrograph to check the relative amounts of radioactive materials in a sample.

b

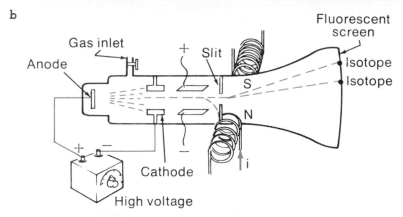

Gas inlet

Anode

Fluorescent
screen

Slit

Isotope

Isotope

S

N

Cathode

High voltage

i

FIGURE 27-13. (a) A complete mass spectrometer showing the source region, the magnet, and the collector end of the flight path where the components of the ion beam are collected and measured mass by mass. (b) A diagram of a variation of the mass spectrometer, called a spectroscope, in which isotopes register on a fluorescent screen. (c) The ion source region of the mass spectrometer.

circular path. The radius of the circular path can be found by using the equation $Bev = mv^2/r$.

$$r = \frac{mv}{Be}$$

Hence, the mass of any particle passing through the tube is proportional to its radius of curvature in the magnetic field. Also, because the charged atoms often have more than a single charge, e is expressed as q which is a multiple of e. Therefore,

$$m = \frac{Bqr}{v}$$

The radius of curvature of a charged particle in the spectrograph is found by turning the magnetic field off and on. When the field is absent, the ions travel straight down the tube and strike the center of the fluorescent screen. When the field is on, the particles are deflected in proportion to their masses. They will strike the screen above the central position. In a well calibrated spectrograph, the mass of the particle can be read directly from the screen itself.

Ions are deflected in proportion to their masses.

The first spectrograph was designed by F. W. Aston in England in 1913. When it was put into use, Aston was surprised by the appearance of more than one spot above the center of the screen. This occurred each time he attempted to measure the mass of an atom. It could only mean that some elements have atoms with the same chemical properties but with differing masses. Aston had verified the existence of isotopes.

Example: The Mass of a Neon Atom

These measurements were made in a mass spectrograph for a beam of doubly-ionized neon atoms.

$$B = 5.0 \times 10^{-2}\,\text{N/A-m}$$
$$q = 2e = 2 \times 1.6 \times 10^{-19}\,\text{coul}$$
$$r = 0.053\,\text{m}$$
$$v = 2.5 \times 10^4\,\text{m/sec}$$

Calculate the mass of a neon atom.

Solution:

$$m = \frac{Bqr}{v}$$
$$= \frac{(5.0 \times 10^{-2}\,\text{N/A-m})\,(3.2 \times 10^{-19}\,\text{coul})\,(0.053\,\text{m})}{2.5 \times 10^4\,\text{m/sec}}$$
$$= 3.4 \times 10^{-26}\,\text{kg}$$

PROBLEMS

17. A mass spectrograph gives data for a beam of doubly-ionized argon atoms. The values are $B = 5.0 \times 10^{-2}\,\text{N/A-m}$, $q = 2e = 2\,(1.6 \times 10^{-19}\,\text{coul})$, $r = 0.106\,\text{m}$, and $v = 2.5 \times 10^4\,\text{m/sec}$. Find the mass of an argon atom.

18. A mass spectrograph gives data for a beam of singly-ionized oxygen atoms. The values are $B = 7.2 \times 10^{-2}$ N/A-m, $q = 1.6 \times 10^{-19}$ coul, $r = 0.85$ m, and $v = 3.6 \times 10^5$ m/sec. Calculate the mass of an oxygen atom.

19. A mass spectrograph yields data for a beam of doubly-ionized sodium atoms. These values are $B = 8.0 \times 10^{-3}$ N/A-m, $q = 2e = 2(1.6 \times 10^{-19}$ coul$)$, $r = 0.77$ m, and $v = 5.0 \times 10^4$ m/sec. Calculate the mass of a sodium atom.

20. Measurements are made with a mass spectrograph for a beam of doubly-ionized neon atoms. The data obtained are $B = 5.0 \times 10^{-2}$ N/A-m, $q = 2e = 2(1.6 \times 10^{-19}$ coul$)$, $r = 0.058$ m, and $v = 2.5 \times 10^4$ m/sec. (a) Calculate the mass of a neon atom. (b) Compare this solution with the one given in the example. What accounts for the difference in mass?

SUMMARY

In 1864, James Clerk Maxwell predicted that a changing magnetic field would generate a changing electric field which would generate a changing magnetic field, and so on. In this manner, electromagnetic waves are propagated through space. If electrons are made to vibrate in a wire, a changing magnetic field will appear around the wire. An electromagnetic wave will travel through space at the speed of light. In 1887, Hertz generated an electromagnetic (radio) wave in this manner.

When high-speed electrons strike the anode of an evacuated tube, the electrons produce electromagnetic waves of very high energy. These waves are called X rays. The energies of the rays are equal to the change in energy of the electrons. The transmission and detection of electromagnetic waves is possible because of electric resonance.

Robert Millikan measured the electric charge carried by a single electron. He did this by balancing the weight of charged oil drops with an electric force. J. J. Thomson determined the mass of the electron by measuring the deflection of electrons in magnetic and electric fields.

The mass spectrograph is a device used to measure the masses of atoms and molecules. A mass spectrograph ionizes particles and sends them through a magnetic field. The deflection of the particles in the field is proportional to their masses.

QUESTIONS

1. Describe the directions of the electric and magnetic field components of an electromagnetic wave in respect to the direction of the wave.
2. What must always occur if an electromagnetic wave is to be generated?
3. Why does an X-ray tube require extremely high voltage?
4. Every time a classroom projector is rewound, it begins to vibrate. This happens for only a short part of the rewinding of the film. How would you explain this vibration?
5. What happens when you turn the tuning dial of a radio?
6. What causes an electron to accelerate as it passes from the cathode to the anode of a discharge tube?
7. Substitute units to show that E/B yields m/sec.
8. What is the function of a mass spectrograph? What principles are involved in its operation?

1. The potential difference between the cathode and anode of a discharge tube is 2.5×10^4 volts. What maximum speed does an electron reach as it travels across the tube? Assume the electron starts from rest.

2. Find the speed an electron reaches in falling through a potential difference of 3.2×10^4 volts. Assume the electron starts from rest.

3. What speed does a proton develop as it falls through a potential difference of 3.4×10^4 volts? The proton starts from rest.

4. The difference in potential between the cathode and anode of a spark plug is 10 000 volts. (a) What energy does an electron give up as it passes between the electrodes? (b) One fourth of the energy given up by the electron is converted to electromagnetic radiation. What is the frequency of the waves emitted?

5. (a) What energy is given to an electron to transfer it across a difference in potential of 4.0×10^5 volts? (b) The energy is converted to electromagnetic radiation. What is the frequency of the wave emitted?

6. A beam of electrons returns to its undeflected position when a field of magnetic induction 6.5×10^{-2} N/A-m is placed at right angles to the deflecting electric field of 1.3×10^3 N/coul. What is the speed of an electron passing through the crossed fields?

7. A stream of protons maintains its path without deflection as it passes through a field of magnetic induction 1.8×10^{-2} N/A-m perpendicular to an electric field of 3.6×10^4 N/coul. (a) What is the speed of the protons? (b) The protons enter a field of magnetic induction 4.0×10^{-2} N/A-m and follow a circular path of 0.53 m. What is the proton's mass?

8. A stream of singly-ionized lithium atoms does not deflect as it passes through a field of magnetic induction 1.5×10^{-3} N/A-m perpendicular to an electric field of 6.0×10^2 N/coul. (a) What is the speed of the lithium atoms as they pass through the crossed fields? (b) The lithium atoms move into a field of magnetic induction 0.18 N/A-m. They follow a circular path of radius 0.165 m. What is the mass of a lithium atom?

9. An oil drops weighs 9.6×10^{-15} N. It is suspended in an electric field of 2×10^4 N/coul. (a) What is the charge on the oil drop? (b) How many excess electrons does it carry?

10. A positively-charged oil drop weighs 9.6×10^{-13} N. It becomes suspended in an electric field of intensity 6.0×10^6 N/coul. (a) What is the charge on the oil drop? (b) How many electrons does it lack?

1. Turn on an oscilloscope. Adjust it so that a spot appears in the center of its screen. Bring a strong magnet close to the sides and top of the oscilloscope. Reverse the magnet and repeat this procedure. Explain your observations in terms of a left-hand rule.

2. Obtain information on citizen-band and ham-radio transmitters and receivers. Explain their operation.

Kellerman, K. I., "Intercontinental Radio Astronomy." *Scientific American,* February, 1972.

McKown, Robin, *The Fabulous Isotopes*. New York, Holiday House, Inc., 1962.

Solomon, Joan, *The Structure of Matter*. New York, Halsted Press, 1974.

In the early 1900's, scientists became aware that light has properties of particles as well as properties of waves. In studying the particle nature of light, it became apparent that bundles of light energy, or photons, could be used to release electrons from certain materials and thus could be used to generate electricity. Photocells in this communications satellite use this principle to convert light from the sun into electric energy. This electric energy is then used to operate instruments, guidance systems, and other devices. What are some other uses for photocells?

THE QUANTUM THEORY

In our study of light, we found that light follows the behavior patterns of waves. We will now study light as it behaves as a particle. In these cases, we assume that light consists of discrete bundles of energy. These bundles of energy are called **quanta**. Quanta are also called **photons**. In our study of light, we must develop a dual model that fits both the wave nature and the particle nature of electromagnetic radiation.

GOAL: You will gain knowledge and understanding of the particle nature of light and of the wave nature of particles.

Light is emitted and observed in discrete packets of energy called quanta or photons.

28:1 The Photoelectric Effect

The **photoelectric effect** is the emission of electrons from a metal plate exposed to light of certain frequencies. This effect is studied by the use of a photocell circuit (Figure 28-1). Two metal electrodes are sealed in an evacuated tube made of quartz. One of the electrodes is coated with zinc. A difference in potential is placed across the electrodes. A variable resistor is also included in the circuit. With this resistor, the difference in potential can be varied.

When light is absent, current does not flow in the circuit. When light of the proper frequency falls on the zinc electrode, a current flows in the circuit. Light causes electrons to leave the negative zinc plate. These electrons travel to the positive plate. Thus, the circuit is completed. The electrons ejected from the metal plate by the light are called **photoelectrons**. Photoelectrons are the same as any other electrons.

The emission of electrons from a metal plate exposed to light of certain frequencies is called the photoelectric effect.

Photoelectrons are electrons which are emitted by a metal plate when it is struck by light of certain frequencies.

William Maddox

α

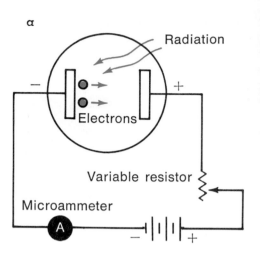

FIGURE 28-1. (α) Diagram of a photocell circuit. (b) This photographic light meter contains a photocell.

Threshold frequency is the minimum frequency (f_0) of light needed to eject electrons from a plate.

Light with a frequency higher than f_0 imparts KE to the electrons.

Stopping potential is the opposing potential necessary to stop electrons from traveling across the gap between the electrodes.

The KE imparted to electrons by light can be found by calculating the work done to stop these electrons.

Incident light of a certain minimum frequency is needed to eject electrons from the zinc plate. This minimum frequency varies with the nature of the plate. It is called the **threshold frequency** (f_0) of that metal. Light of a frequency below f_0 does not eject electrons from the metal, no matter how great the intensity of the light. On the other hand, light of the threshold frequency or higher causes electrons to leave the metal immediately, even if the light is very faint. According to the wave theory of light, this should not be the case. More intense light means more energy along the wave fronts. Thus, more electrons will leave the plate. If we think of light as photons, threshold frequency is readily explained. Photons with frequencies below f_0 do not have enough energy to give even an easily removed surface electron enough energy to escape the metal.

When light of frequency higher than f_0 strikes a zinc plate in an evacuated tube, electrons travel across the tube with increased kinetic energy. Electrons ejected from the surface of the zinc have the highest energy. Electrons ejected from below the surface have a lower energy. The kinetic energy of electrons having maximum energy can be measured. To do this, a difference in potential is placed across the tube. That is, the zinc plate is made slightly positive and the second metal plate is made slightly negative. The voltage tends to prevent the electrons from leaving the zinc plate. The opposing potential difference is increased until no electrons have enough energy to travel across the tube. This potential difference is the **stopping potential.** Work is done to stop the electrons having maximum kinetic energy. The work done is equal to the maximum kinetic energy of these electrons and is given by the equation

$$KE_{max} = V_0 e$$

Here, V_0 is the stopping potential in volts (joules per coulomb), and e is the charge on the electron (1.6×10^{-19} coulomb). The work done on the electrons having maximum kinetic energy is done at the expense of photons falling on the metal. The sum of work done to stop the electrons and the work done to free the electrons from the metal surface represents the energy of the photons falling on the metal.

Example: Maximum Kinetic Energy of a Photoelectron

The stopping potential to prevent electrons from flowing across a photoelectric cell is 4.0 volts. What maximum kinetic energy is given to the electrons by the incident light?

Solution:

$$KE_{max} = V_0 e$$
$$= 4 \text{ J/coul} \times 1.6 \times 10^{-19} \text{ coul}$$
$$= 6.4 \times 10^{-19} \text{ J}$$

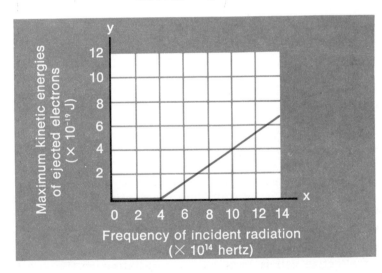

FIGURE 28-2. Graph of kinetic energy of ejected electrons versus frequency of incident radiation.

Figure 28-2 is a plot of the maximum kinetic energies of the electrons ejected from a metal versus the frequencies of the incident radiations. The resulting graph is a straight line. All metals give similar graphs with the same slopes. The graphs differ only in the point of origin. The point of origin varies with the threshold frequency of the metal. The slope of the line is Planck's constant (h).

$$h = \frac{\Delta y}{\Delta x} = \frac{\text{Maximum kinetic energies of ejected electrons}}{\text{Frequency of incident radiations}}$$
$$= 6.6 \times 10^{-34} \text{ J-sec}$$

The energy needed to free a surface electron from the metal is called the **work function** of the metal. The work function is the

The work function of a metal is the energy needed to free a surface electron from the metal.

The work function or energy needed to free the surface electrons from a metal is the product of Planck's constant (h) and threshold frequency (f_0).

product of the threshold frequency and Planck's constant. It is expressed as hf_0. The energy of the incident photon can be written as hf, where f is the frequency of the incident photon. The maximum kinetic energy of the emitted electron can then be calculated from the photoelectric equation which is

$$KE_{max} = hf - hf_0$$

Example: Photoelectric Equation

The threshold frequency of sodium is 5.6×10^{14} Hz. (a) What is the work function of sodium? (b) Sodium is exposed to radiation of frequency 8.6×10^{14} Hz. What is the maximum kinetic energy of the ejected electrons?

Solution:

(a) Work function $= hf_0$
$$= 6.6 \times 10^{-34} \text{ J-sec} \times 5.6 \times 10^{14} \text{ Hz}$$
$$= 3.7 \times 10^{-19} \text{ J}$$

(b) $KE_{max} = hf - hf_0$
$$= (6.6 \times 10^{-34} \text{ J-sec} \times 8.6 \times 10^{14} \text{ Hz}) -$$
$$3.7 \times 10^{-19} \text{ J}$$
$$= 2.0 \times 10^{-19} \text{ J}$$

PROBLEMS

1. The stopping potential to prevent electron flow through a photocell is 3.2 volts. Calculate the maximum kinetic energy of the photoelectrons within the cell.

2. The stopping potential to stop electron flow through a photoelectric cell is 5.7 volts. Calculate the maximum kinetic energy of the photoelectrons within the cell.

3. The threshold frequency of zinc is 9.7×10^{14} Hz. (a) What is the photoelectric work function of zinc? (b) Zinc used in a photoelectric cell is irradiated by radiation of frequency 4.5×10^{15} Hz. What is the maximum kinetic energy of the photoelectrons within the cell?

4. The threshold frequency of calcium is 6.5×10^{14} Hz. (a) What is the photoelectric work function of calcium? (b) An electronvolt (eV) is needed to transfer one electron through a potential difference of one volt. An electronvolt is 1.6×10^{-19} J. What is the work function of calcium in electronvolts?

5. The work function of chromium is 4.6 eV. What is the threshold frequency of chromium?

6. The work function of potassium is 2.2 eV. (a) What is the work function of potassium in joules? (b) What is the threshold frequency of potassium?

28:2 The Quantum Theory of Light

The photoelectric equation can be rearranged to give the following equation:

$$hf = KE_{max} + hf_0$$

This form of the equation shows that the total energy of photons may be calculated. The photocell is exposed to photons of known frequency. The stopping potential is found and the maximum kinetic energy of the ejected electrons is calculated. This energy is then added to the work function to give the total energy of the incident photons. Note that the total energy of photons always turns out to be the product of Planck's constant and the frequency of the photon. All photons have definite frequencies and Planck's constant never changes. Thus, photons must also have definite energy contents. In this way, it was determined that light energy consists of quanta. In other words, light energy is made up of discrete bundles of energy.

The total energy of an incident photon can be found by adding the work function and the maximum kinetic energy of the ejected electron.

In classical physics, a mass is assumed to have a continuous range of potential energies which depends on how far a mass is from the earth's surface. However, even though they have many of the properties of particles, photons have a range of potential energies which is not continuous. Instead, the potential energies are multiples of Planck's constant.

Photons have a range of potential energies that are multiples of Planck's constant.

For example, consider a ball placed on a step (Figure 28-3). The potential energy of the ball in this case can be thought of as quantized. In other words, the ball can have any potential energy which corresponds to a whole number multiple of steps. The ball cannot have a potential energy value between these multiples.

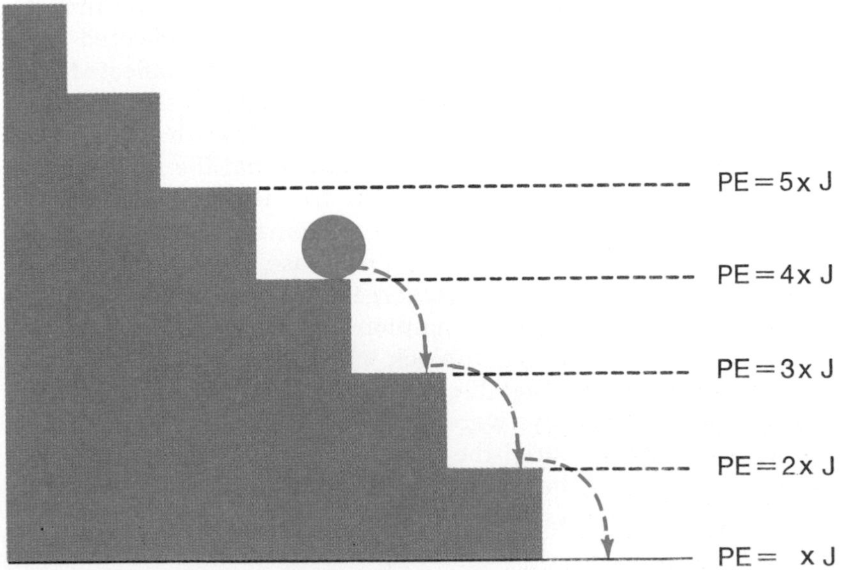

PE = 5x J

PE = 4x J

PE = 3x J

PE = 2x J

PE = x J

FIGURE 28-3. The potential energies of photons are quantized and can be compared to the potential energies of a ball as it rests on each of these steps.

The photoelectric effect shows that energy is quantized. It also indicates that Planck's constant contains clues about the structure of the atom. Light is emitted and absorbed in discrete amounts as electrons move between energy levels within an atom. Thus, these atomic energy levels must be related by a factor equal to hf. The way in which the physicist Niels Bohr was able to relate atomic structure and Planck's constant will be discussed in the next chapter.

To explain the dual nature of light, the quantum theory of light assumes that light and all other electromagnetic radiation consists of streams of photons. Each photon is characterized in space by a **probability wave.** The wave determines the position of the photon at any given time. Accordingly, it is more probable for a photon to be located where the amplitude of the probability wave is high. The probability wave also accounts for interference and diffraction phenomena.

Photons escaped notice for many years because of their very small size. Each electromagnetic wave contains a very large number of these tiny particles. Photons acting together make the particle nature of the wave hard to observe. Photons are noticeable only when they interact with other very small particles such as electrons. The quantum theory is not easy to visualize. But the fundamental behavior of light and other electromagnetic waves requires this description.

> According to the quantum theory, light is made up of a stream of photons.

> The highest probability of locating a certain photon in space at a given time is given by its probability wave.

28:3   The Compton Effect

In 1922, Arthur Compton experimented with X rays aimed at a carbon block. He observed two phenomena. First, he saw that the X rays that emerged from the block often were deflected from their original paths. Also, he found that when the deflected rays were sent through a grating and their wavelengths were measured, the wavelengths of the emergent rays were longer than the wavelengths of the incident X rays. It was shown that the frequency of the emergent X rays was less than the frequency of the incident X rays. The energy content of an electromagnetic wave varies directly with its frequency. Thus, a decrease in frequency meant that the energy content of the emergent waves was less than the energy of the incident rays. Compton also noticed that electrons were ejected from the carbon block when it was bombarded with X rays. He concluded that X rays were colliding with electrons. In the process, the X rays were giving up energy to the electrons.

Compton then measured the kinetic energy of the ejected electrons. The energy of the incident X-ray photons is hf_1. The energy of the emergent X rays is hf_2. Compton calculated the difference between hf_1 and hf_2. He found that the energy gained by an

FIGURE 28-4. Sir Arthur Compton demonstrated the particle nature of X rays in 1922.

Brown Brothers

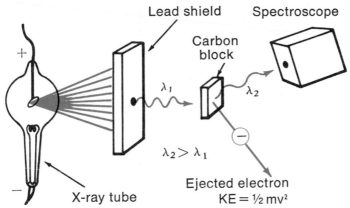

Lead shield   Spectroscope

Carbon block

λ_1

λ_2

$\lambda_2 > \lambda_1$

X-ray tube

Ejected electron
KE $= \frac{1}{2} mv^2$

FIGURE 28-5. Diagram of apparatus used by Compton to study the nature of photons.

By observing photon and electron interactions, Compton found that photons have properties of particles.

ejected electron, $mv^2/2$, is equal to the difference in the energy content of the incident and emergent rays. Also, the laws of conservation of energy and conservation of momentum were upheld. Compton was led to a startling conclusion. Electromagnetic radiation has particle properties and mass!

28:4   The Heisenberg Uncertainty Principle

The German scientist Werner Heisenberg (1901–1976) stated a very important point in the use of photons to study electrons. He said that any attempt to study the nature and motion of electrons by bombarding them with photons would change the motion and position of the electron, and thus would lead to uncertainty. This statement is now known as the Heisenberg **uncertainty principle**. The uncertainty principle applies only to measurements on the subatomic scale. It applies to any attempt to observe electrons closely enough to find out whether they are particles or waves, or both.

The photon is the finest measuring tool a physicist has. To study the nature and motions of an electron, photons are bounced off the electron. For accurate measurements, a photon of very short wavelength must be used. In other words, the photon has a high frequency and also high energy. But as the Compton effect shows, quanta of high energy, for example, in the X-ray range, change the motions of electrons. Photons with short wavelengths change the position of the electron too much to be useful in position measurements. If a photon of long wavelength and low energy is used, the interaction between the photon and the electron is smaller. However, inaccurate values result from the long wavelength of the photon. At present, the scientist cannot control a more finite measuring tool than the photon. Thus, a closer look at electron motion is not possible at this time.

The Heisenberg uncertainty principle refers to the inability to measure accurately both the position and momentum of an electron at a given time.

28:5 Matter Waves

Compton's studies showed that the momentum (mv) of a photon is given by the equation

$$mv = \frac{h}{\lambda}$$

Here, h is Planck's constant, and λ is the wavelength of the photon. Thus, λ would be expressed by the equation

$$\lambda = \frac{h}{mv}$$

De Broglie reasoned that if light behaves as particles, particles should behave as waves.

The French scientist Louis-Victor de Broglie (1892–   ) reasoned that if light has particle properties, then matter must have wave properties. He postulated that particles of matter obey a wave equation just as photons do. He assumed that the wavelength of the wave associated with a particle is equal to Planck's constant divided by the momentum of the particle.

$$\lambda = \frac{h}{mv}$$

This is the same equation that describes the wavelength associated with a photon. Thus, de Broglie said that matter and electromagnetic radiation are more closely related than had been believed.

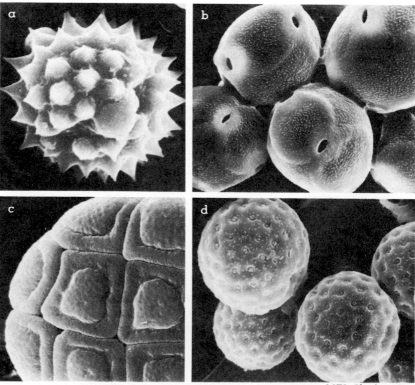

FIGURE 28-6. An electron microscope makes use of the wave properties of electrons to photograph these pollen grains of (a) goldenrod, (b) alder, (c) acacia, and (d) lamb's quarters at a magnification of 6000X.

MEI-Charlton, Inc.

He also said that matter and light display the same wave and particle properties.

The wave properties of matter had never been observed. Thus, de Broglie's concept of matter waves met with much doubt. But in 1927, G. L. Thomson, son of J. J. Thomson, succeeded in diffracting electrons by use of a beam of electrons and a small crystal. The spacing of the atoms in the crystal lattice acted as a diffraction grating for the electrons. Since diffraction is a wave phenomenon, Thomson had shown the wave nature of matter.

De Broglie's equation for the wavelength of matter waves explains why the wave nature of large particles is not observed. Consider the de Broglie wavelength of a baseball with a mass of 0.25 kg when it leaves a bat with a speed of 20 m/sec.

$$\lambda = \frac{h}{mv}$$
$$= \frac{6.6 \times 10^{-34} \text{ J-sec}}{0.25 \text{ kg} \times 20 \text{ m/sec}}$$
$$= 1.3 \times 10^{-34} \text{ m}$$

This wavelength is far too small to be observed. On the other hand, calculate the de Broglie wavelength of one of Thomson's electrons moving with a typical speed of 10^6 m/sec.

$$\lambda = \frac{h}{mv}$$
$$= \frac{6.6 \times 10^{-34} \text{ J-sec}}{9.1 \times 10^{-31} \text{ kg} \times 10^6 \text{ m/sec}}$$
$$= 7.3 \times 10^{-10} \text{ m}$$

This wavelength approximates the distance between the atoms in a crystal. It makes the wavelength suitable for diffraction and interference effects if a crystal is used as a grating. Thus, the wavelengths of very small particles of matter are readily observable.

G. L. Thomson's success in diffracting electrons gave strong support to de Broglie's theory.

PROBLEMS

7. What is the de Broglie wavelength of a proton moving with a speed of 10^6 m/sec? The mass of a proton is 1.67×10^{-27} kg.

8. Calculate the de Broglie wavelength of a Ping-Pong ball of mass 0.015 kg moving at a speed of 3 m/sec.

9. What is the de Broglie wavelength of a 75-kg student running at a speed of 10 m/sec?

10. Calculate the de Broglie wavelength of a neutron traveling at a speed of 10^3 m/sec. The mass of a neutron is 1.67×10^{-27} kg.

11. Determine the de Broglie wavelength of a ship of mass 2×10^6 kg moving at a speed of 8 m/sec.

12. The earth has a mass of 6.0×10^{24} kg. Its average speed is 2.7×10^4 m/sec. Determine the de Broglie wavelength of the earth.

SUMMARY

When light of a minimum frequency, called the threshold frequency, falls on certain metals, electrons are ejected from the metals. This event can be explained only if light is assumed to consist of particles.

The threshold frequency is the lowest frequency a photon can have and still contain enough energy to eject the easily dislodged surface electrons. Photons of higher frequency not only eject electrons but also accelerate them. This acceleration gives the electrons kinetic energy. By giving the metal plate a positive charge and the opposing electrode a negative charge, a potential difference that works against the ejected electron can be created. The potential difference that is just able to stop the most energetic electron from crossing between the plates is a measure of the energy of the electron.

When the kinetic energies of photoelectrons are plotted against the frequencies of the incident light, a straight line with the same slope always results. The threshold frequency varies from metal to metal. However, the slope of the line never changes. The slope of the line is Planck's constant, h.

The quantum theory assumes that light and all other electromagnetic radiations consist of streams of particles called quanta or photons. The energy of any photon, in joules, is equal to its frequency multiplied by Planck's constant.

The Compton effect clearly indicates that X rays can collide with electrons in the same way as particles. The Heisenberg uncertainty principle points out that the interactions between photons and electrons makes it impossible to measure the momentum and position of fundamental particles.

Louis de Broglie theorized that particles should display wave characteristics just as waves display particle characteristics. This hypothesis was verified experimentally in 1927.

QUESTIONS

1. The removal of an electron from nickel requires more energy than the removal of an electron from potassium. Which metal has the higher work function? Which metal has the higher threshold frequency?
2. How does the photoelectric effect show the particle nature of light?
3. What is the constant of proportionality between the energy possessed by a photon and the frequency of the photon?
4. Which has higher energy, photons of long wavelength or photons of short wavelength?
5. Express h/mv in fundamental units. Prove that the expression yields length.
6. Why is it difficult to detect the particle nature of light?
7. Suppose that the smallest thermometer that could possibly be made is as large as a baseball bat. A biologist wants to measure the temperature of a glass of water. Compare the task of this biologist with the task of a physicist who is attempting to track the movements of an electron.
8. Which particle is more likely to have a detectable de Broglie wavelength associated with it, a high-speed electron or a speeding bullet? Use the de Broglie equation to explain your choice.

PROBLEMS

1. The stopping potential to prevent electron flow through a photocell is 5.2 volts. What is the maximum kinetic energy of the photoelectrons within the cell?
2. To prevent electron flow in a photocell, a stopping potential of 3.8 volts is used. What is the maximum kinetic energy of the photoelectrons within the cell?

3. The threshold frequency of tin is 1.1×10^{15} Hz. (a) What is the work function of tin? (b) Radiation of frequency 1.8×10^{15} Hz falls on tin. What is the maximum kinetic energy of the ejected electrons?

4. The work function of iron is 7.5×10^{-19} J. (a) What is the threshold frequency of iron? (b) Iron is exposed to radiation of frequency 6.2×10^{15} Hz. What is the kinetic energy of the ejected electrons?

5. The threshold frequency of magnesium is 9.0×10^{14} Hz. (a) What is the work function of magnesium? (b) Radiation of frequency 2.0×10^{15} Hz falls on magnesium. What is the kinetic energy of the ejected electrons?

6. Find the de Broglie wavelength of a deuteron of mass 3.3×10^{-27} kg that moves with a speed of 2.5×10^4 m/sec.

7. A spacecraft blasts off and reaches a speed of 1.2×10^3 m/sec. The mass of the spacecraft is 2.0×10^3 kg. What is the de Broglie wavelength of the spacecraft?

8. A proton of mass 1.67×10^{-27} kg moves in a particle accelerator at a speed of 2×10^8 m/sec. What is the de Broglie wavelength of the proton?

PROJECTS

1. You can demonstrate the ejection of electrons from a metal plate by using an electroscope and a mercury-vapor lamp. Charge the electroscope by using a rubber rod which has been rubbed with fur. The electroscope will have a negative charge. Expose the knob of the electroscope to ultraviolet rays from the mercury-vapor lamp. If electrons are being ejected, the leaves should fall rapidly.

2. Use reference materials to make a list of practical uses of photoelectric cells. How many examples of the use of photoelectric cells can you find in your own community?

READINGS

Cline, Barbara, *The Questioners*. New York, Thomas Y. Crowell Co., 1965.

De Broglie, Louis, *The Revolution in Physics: A Non-Mathematical Survey of Quanta*. New York, Farrer, Straus, and Giroux, Inc., 1953.

Gamow, George, *Mr. Tompkins in Paperback*. New York, Cambridge University Press, 1965.

Gamow, George, *Thirty Years That Shook Physics*. New York, Doubleday and Co., Inc., 1966.

Jammer, Max, *The Conceptual Development of Quantum Mechanics*, text ed. New York, McGraw Hill Book Co., 1966.

Litke and Wilson, "Electron-Positron Collisions." *Scientific American*, October, 1973.

Weart, Spencer T., "Scientists With a Secret." *Physics Today*, February, 1976.

Weisskopf, Victor F., "How Light Interacts with Matter." *Scientific American*, September, 1968.

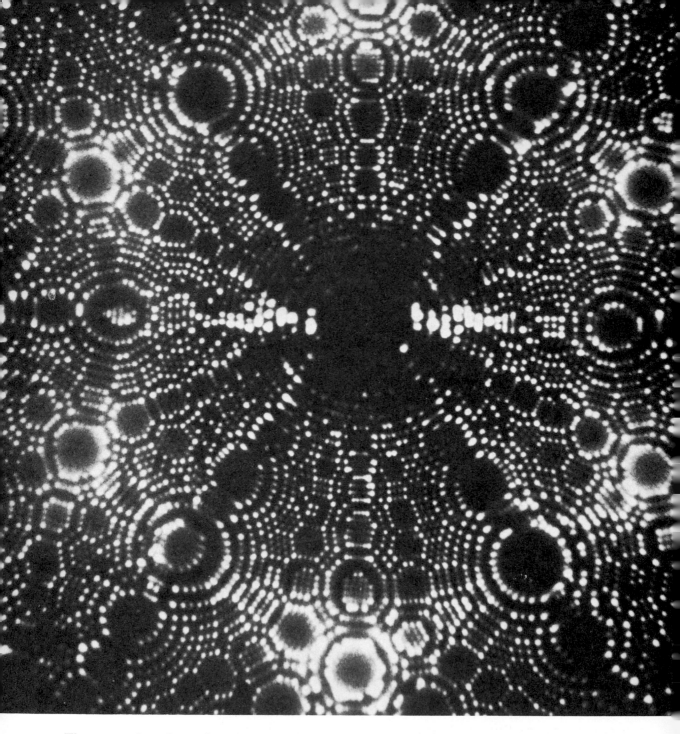

The atom has long been a puzzle. Even now, scientists are not able to see an individual atom. However, using a field ion emission microscope scientists can study some crystal patterns like that of tungsten shown in this photograph. Theorizing that all substances are made up of the same kinds of fundamental particles, how can you explain the great differences in their properties such as chemical activity, solubility, crystal structure, color, and conductivity?

THE ATOM

Once the electron and the proton were identified, they were thought to be the major particles that make up atoms. Both J. J. Thomson (1856–1940) and Sir Ernest Rutherford (1871–1937) tried to find out how these particles are arranged to form atoms. Their work met with much success.

GOAL: You will gain knowledge and understanding of the basic structure of the atom and of interactions among atoms.

29:1 Radioactivity

The experiments Rutherford performed to probe the atom were based on work of a French physicist, Henri Becquerel (1852–1908). In 1896, Becquerel was working with compounds of the element uranium. To his surprise, he found that even when these uranium compounds were kept some distance from unexposed photographic plates, the plates became fogged or partially exposed. This fogging suggested that some kind of ray had passed through the plate coverings. Becquerel also found that unexposed plates, even when shielded by several thin sheets of lead, were exposed when placed near the uranium. Only thick layers of lead seemed able to absorb this radiation. At first, he thought he had found some sort of invisible rays similar to X rays. Soon it was revealed that the radiation did not consist of X rays. Several materials other than uranium or its compounds also emitted these rays. Materials which emit this kind of radiation are called **radioactive materials.**

Becquerel discovered that radiation was being emitted from uranium compounds.

439

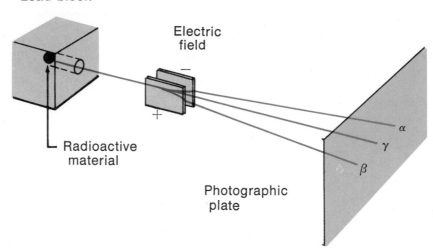

Lead block

Electric field

Radioactive material

Photographic plate

α

γ

β

FIGURE 29-1. Rutherford's apparatus for studying radioactive substances. Note the directions in which the emitted radiations are deflected on passing through an electric field.

Figure 29-1 illustrates the method Rutherford used to study radioactive materials. A small amount of radioactive substance was placed at the bottom of a hole drilled in a lead block. The radiation which escaped from the box was limited to a small beam that left the radioactive substance in a direct line with the hole. The rest was absorbed by the lead. He then caused this emergent radiation to pass through a strong electric field and to fall on a photographic plate. When the plate was developed, three distinct spots were found on the plate. The spots indicated three distinct types of radiation. These were named alpha (α), beta (β), and gamma (γ) rays. Alpha, beta, and gamma are the first three letters of the Greek alphabet. A study was made of the behavior of these rays in electric and magnetic fields. It was found that **alpha particles** are doubly-ionized helium nuclei.* It was also found that **beta particles** are high-speed electrons, and **gamma rays** are photons of very high frequency.

Rutherford found that naturally radioactive materials emit three types of radiation.

Alpha particles are doubly-ionized helium nuclei.

Beta particles are high-speed electrons.

Gamma rays are high-frequency photons.

29:2 Discovery of the Nucleus

Rutherford studied atomic structure by bombarding metal foils with alpha particles.

To explore the structure of atoms, Rutherford's research team of Geiger and Marsden directed alpha rays at very thin sheets of metal which had a thickness of several hundred atoms. They placed a small fluorescent screen in front of a movable telescope. Then, they observed alpha particles passing through the metal being studied. Each time an alpha particle passed through the foil

---

*The helium atom contains two electrons, each with a negative charge, and two protons, each with a positive charge. It also contains two uncharged particles. An alpha particle is a helium atom with a deficit of two electrons. The alpha particle thus has a 2+ charge, or is "doubly-ionized."

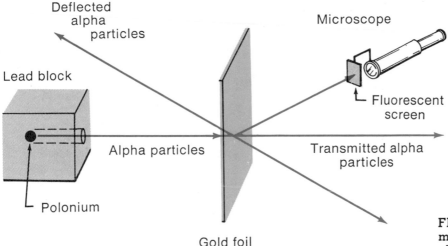

FIGURE 29-2. **Bombardment of gold foil with alpha particles.**

Radiation causes some materials to scintillate, or emit brief flashes of light.

and struck the fluorescent screen in front of the telescope, a small flash of light, or a **scintillation** (sint uhl AY shuhn), was observed on the screen. The scintillation was the result of the excitation of the fluorescent material on the screen by the alpha particle.

Rutherford's team also found that most of the particles passed straight through the foil. Since the foil was at least several hundreds of atoms thick, it appeared that atoms are mostly empty space. A few alpha particles were deflected as they passed through the foil. A few alpha particles even rebounded from the foil.

After observing the angles through which the particles were deflected, Rutherford's team concluded that most of the mass of the atom is located in a very small core or nucleus. Those alpha particles which rebounded from the foil apparently had interacted with nuclei in the foil.

Rutherford's team also measured the velocity of the alpha particles as they approached the foil. Since they knew the charge and

The nature of the deflection of alpha particles by atoms in the metal foil indicates that most of the mass of an atom is located in a central nucleus.

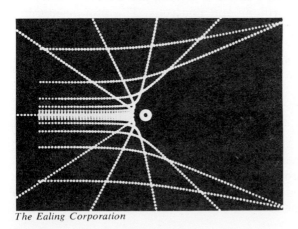

The Ealing Corporation

FIGURE 29-3. **Simulation of bombardment of a nucleus with alpha particles.**

the mass of the alpha particles, they could apply Coulomb's law and Newton's laws of motion. In a brilliant series of experiments and analysis of results, they determined the total charge carried by the nuclei of several different atoms. Since each proton carries one elementary charge, they then determined the number of protons in the nucleus of each atom under study.

29:3   The Neutron

As Rutherford's team determined the number of protons in the nucleus, another fact soon became clear. The mass of the nucleus of a given atom could not be explained in terms of the protons alone. Rutherford postulated the existence of a neutral particle within the nucleus. Such a particle could have no net charge. Rutherford called this particle a neutron. In 1932, James Chadwick demonstrated the existence of the neutron. The neutron was found to have a mass approximately equal to the mass of the proton, approximately one atomic mass unit (a.m.u.) The mass of the protons in an atom plus the mass of the neutrons in the atom account for the mass of the nucleus. Therefore, the approximate number of mass units of a nucleus in atomic mass units is the same as the number of protons plus the number of neutrons within that nucleus. Since the electrons outside the nucleus are of negligible mass, the mass of the nucleus is taken to be the mass of the atom.

Example: Number of Neutrons in a Nucleus

An atom of iron has an atomic mass of 56 a.m.u. The atomic number of iron is 26. How many neutrons are in the nucleus of an atom of this isotope?

Solution:

Since the mass of the atom is 56 a.m.u., the nucleus must contain a total of 56 protons and neutrons. The atomic number tells us that there are 26 protons in the nucleus. The number of neutrons is the difference between 56 and 26. Thus, this iron nucleus contains 30 neutrons.

29:4   Planetary Model of the Atom

Rutherford knew that ordinarily most materials bear no net charge. He reasoned that each atom, unless it had been ionized, contains as many electrons as protons. Because electrons often are easily removed from the atom, he further postulated that the electrons were located outside the nucleus. Figure 29-4 shows the planetary model of the atom as put forth after Rutherford's work.

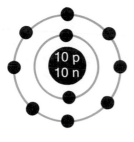

Neon

Atomic number (Z) = 10
Atomic mass (A) = 20

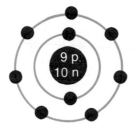

Fluorine

Atomic number (Z) = 9
Atomic mass (A) = 19

FIGURE 29-4. Planetary models of a neon atom and a fluorine atom. How does this model differ from more recent models?

29:5 Isotopes

For some time, scientists all over the world were puzzled by the fact that the masses of the atoms of most of the elements, measured in atomic mass units, were not exactly whole numbers. If, as was thought, the nucleus is made up of protons and neutrons each with a mass of approximately 1 a.m.u., then the total mass of any atom should be near a whole number. However, most measurements showed that the masses of atoms are not whole numbers. For example, careful measurements of the mass of the boron atom consistently yield 10.8 a.m.u.

The problem presented by decimal values for the mass of the atoms was solved with the use of the mass spectrometer (Chapter 27). The mass spectrometer showed that an element has atoms of different masses. For example, neon has atoms of two different masses. Using a pure sample of neon, it was found that not one, but two spots appeared on the screen of the spectrometer. Careful measurements showed that the two spots represented neon atoms of different mass. One neon atom has a mass of about 20 a.m.u. The second neon atom has a mass of about 21 a.m.u. All neon atoms have ten protons in their nuclei. In other words, one "kind" of neon has ten neutrons in its nucleus while the other has eleven neutrons in its nucleus. Thus, neon is a mixture of neon atoms which have different numbers of neutrons in their nuclei. When the mass of neon was determined prior to the invention of the mass spectrometer, the result had always given the average mass of 20.183 a.m.u. for the two kinds of neon. Hence, while the mass of any individual atom of neon is close to a whole number, the mass of any given sample of neon is not.

Further study revealed that the situation described for neon was the usual case and not the exception. Chromium, for example, was found to have four kinds of atoms differing only in the number of neutrons contained in their nuclei. These different

Isotopes are atoms which contain the same number of protons but different numbers of neutrons.

FIGURE 29-5. Isotopes of neon.

(a)

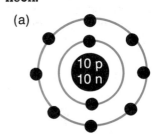

Neon
(Z = 10, A = 20)

(b)

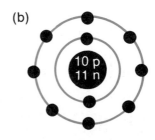

Neon
(Z = 10, A = 21)

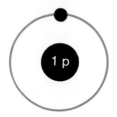

Protium

Atomic number = 1
Mass number = 1

Deuterium

Atomic number = 1
Mass number = 2

Tritium

Atomic number = 1
Mass number = 3

FIGURE 29-6. Hydrogen's three known isotopes.

The atomic number of an element is represented by the letter Z.

The atomic mass of an element is represented by the letter A.

The general form for the symbol of an isotope is $_Z^A$E, where E represents the symbol for the element.

forms of the element chromium are called the **isotopes** of chromium. Most elements have several isotopes. Hydrogen is known to have three isotopes.

A special method is used to express the isotopes of the elements. A small subscript for the atomic number (Z) is written to the lower left of the symbol of that element. A small superscript is written to the upper left of the symbol for the mass number (A). This takes the form $_Z^A$E. To illustrate, for oxygen of atomic number 8 and mass number 16, the form is $_8^{16}$O. For neon of mass number 20 and atomic number 10, the form is $_{10}^{20}$Ne.

PROBLEMS

1. An isotope of oxygen has a mass number of 15. If the atomic number of oxygen is 8, how many neutrons are in the nuclei of this isotope?

2. Three isotopes of uranium have mass numbers of 234, 235, and 238 respectively. How many neutrons are in the nuclei of each of these isotopes if the atomic number of uranium is 92?

3. How many neutrons are in an atom of the mercury isotope $_{80}^{200}$Hg?

4. Write the symbolic expression for the three isotopes of hydrogen in Figure 29-6.

5. Under certain circumstances, the nucleus of the isotope $_{92}^{238}$U absorbs another neutron. (a) Write the symbolic expression for this new isotope of uranium. (b) How many neutrons are in the nuclei of each of these isotopes?

6. After $_{92}^{238}$U absorbs the neutron described in Problem 5, an electron is ejected from the nucleus. What new nucleus is formed?

29:6   The Bohr Model of the Atom

The planetary model of the atom showed electrons circling the nucleus of the atom. This model was severely criticized. It has been found that whenever a charged particle is accelerated, energy is emitted in the form of electromagnetic radiation. If an electron follows a circular path, it undergoes continuous acceleration and it should continuously emit radiation. As the electron lost energy, it would spiral down into the nucleus of the atom. In short, on the basis of the planetary model, atoms should not exist.

Another objection to the planetary model was that it failed to account for the quantum nature of electromagnetic radiations. The photoelectric effect clearly showed that each photon of light carries a definite quantity of energy. Also, the spectrum of each element, as seen in a spectroscope, is always the same. In other words, the electromagnetic radiation emitted by any given

Rutherford's model did not account for (1) the lack of emission of radiation as electrons orbit the nucleus, and (2) the unique spectrum of each element.

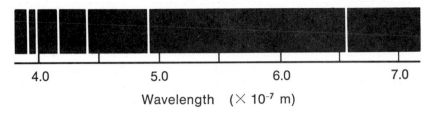

Wavelength $(\times\ 10^{-7}\ m)$

FIGURE 29-7. Line spectrum of hydrogen. The lines correspond to definite electron transitions within the atom.

element is always the same. Maxwell had shown that electromagnetic radiation is the result of the accelerations of charged particles. Assuming that atoms emit this kind of radiation as their electrons are accelerated, the electrons within an atom must undergo some very definite transitions. Rutherford did not provide for this in his atomic model. If the electrons could orbit anywhere about the nucleus, then all wavelengths of radiation should be seen for that element within a set range. Thus, the elements should emit a continuous spectrum. This does not happen. Thus, a new model of the atom was needed.

The Danish physicist Niels Bohr (1885–1962) extended Rutherford's model of the atom. He presented two bold theories. First, Bohr said that electrons can move around the nucleus of an atom without radiating energy. Second, he introduced the idea of the energy states of the atom, suggesting that the positive nucleus and the orbiting negative electrons give the atom energy. The energy state of an atom can be changed when it absorbs or emits radiation. Although orbits no longer are considered to exist, electrons can be imagined as circling around the nucleus of an atom in certain allowed orbits. Figure 29-8 illustrates the general idea of the Bohr atom. The energy levels represent higher energy as the electron's distance from the nucleus increases. This increase in energy occurs because the force between an electron and the nucleus is one of attraction. Work must be done on the electron to move it farther away from the nucleus. The system gains energy when the electron moves from an inner to an outer orbit. Thus, the

Bohr suggested that negative electrons could orbit the positive nucleus without the emission of radiation.

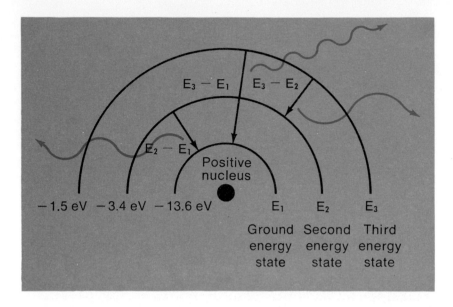

energy content of an electron at E_2 is greater than the energy content of an electron at E_1. A base level ($PE = 0$) is chosen at an infinite distance from the nucleus. Since an electron loses energy as it approaches the nucleus, the energy states must be expressed in negative values.

According to Bohr, the atom emits no radiation as long as the electrons occupy their allowed orbital paths. However, if the atom absorbs energy, an electron can move to a higher energy level. In this way, the potential energy of the atom is increased. Usually, the atom returns immediately to its normal energy state as the electron returns to its normal level. During the down-transition, a photon of energy is released. By the law of conservation of energy, the energy content of the photon (hf) is equal to the energy difference represented by the electron transition, that is

$$hf = E_{\text{initial}} - E_{\text{final}}$$

Thus, Bohr directly relates the energy changes within the atom to Einstein's photoelectric equation for the energy of a photon. The photon's energy is the energy released by an atom as its energy content decreases during the transition of an electron from a higher to a lower energy level.

29:7 Bohr's Equations

Section 29:6 treats Bohr's picture of the atom qualitatively. That is, a description is given of how the atom could be arranged so that the discrete spectrum of the atoms and the energy of photons can be explained. If this had been all that Bohr had contributed, his concept of the atom might have been ignored. But

446

Bohr did much more than this. Using Coulomb's law, he defined the force of attraction between the electron and the positive nucleus. Then, he applied Newton's conditions for angular momentum and centripetal force. Adding one or two brilliant hypotheses, he derived several equations. He determined an equation for the radius of the hydrogen orbits, an equation for the energy content of the allowed orbits, and an equation that predicted the frequencies and wavelengths of the hydrogen spectrum in precise agreement with experimental evidence. This type of mathematical evidence lends great strength to theory. Bohr's model of the atom was generally accepted.

The derivations of the Bohr equations are straightforward and easily understood by anyone familiar with simple algebra and Newtonian mechanics. The derivations are omitted here. However, the equations and their applications are presented. Note that these equations apply only to the hydrogen atom.

The radius of hydrogen orbits is given by the equation

$$r = \frac{n^2h^2}{4\pi^2Kme^2}$$

where n represents whole number values for the orbits beginning with 1 for the innermost orbital level. K is the constant 9.0×10^9 N-m²/coul² used in Coulomb's law, h is Planck's constant, m is the mass of the electron, and e is the charge in coulombs.

Bohr showed mathematically that electron transitions could account for atomic spectra.

The radius of a hydrogen orbital can be calculated with the Bohr equation.

Example: Radius of a Hydrogen Orbit

Calculate the radius of the innermost orbital level of the hydrogen atom.

Solution:

$n = 1$
$K = 9.0 \times 10^9$ N-m²/coul² $m = 9.1 \times 10^{-31}$ kg
$e = 1.6 \times 10^{-19}$ coul
$h = 6.6 \times 10^{-34}$ J-sec $r = \dfrac{n^2h^2}{4\pi^2Kme^2}$

$$r = \frac{(1)^2 (6.6 \times 10^{-34} \text{ J-sec})^2}{(4)(9.86)\left(\dfrac{9.0 \times 10^9 \text{ N-m}^2}{\text{coul}^2}\right)(9.1 \times 10^{-31} \text{ kg})(1.6 \times 10^{-19} \text{ coul})^2}$$

$$= 5.3 \times 10^{-11} \text{ m}$$

The orbital energy of electrons in the hydrogen atom is given by the equation

$$E = \frac{-2\pi^2K^2me^4}{n^2h^2}$$

where K, m, e, and h are the same constants used in the equation for the radii of the hydrogen orbits. The constants are combined to give a simplified version of the equation. Hence,

$$E = \frac{-2.17 \times 10^{-18}}{n^2} \text{ J}$$

The orbital energy of electrons in the hydrogen atom can be calculated with the Bohr equation.

Since an electronvolt (eV) is equal to 1.60×10^{-19} J, the above equation may also be written

$$E = \frac{-13.6 \text{ eV}}{n^2}$$

Example: Orbital Energy of Electrons in the Hydrogen Atom

(a) Determine the energy associated with the innermost orbit of the hydrogen atom ($n = 1$). (b) Determine the energy associated with the second orbit of the hydrogen atom. (c) What energy does an incoming photon possess to raise an electron from the first to the second allowed orbit of the hydrogen atom?

Solution:

$$\begin{aligned}
\text{(a)} \quad E &= \frac{-13.6 \text{ eV}}{n^2} \\
&= \frac{-13.6 \text{ eV}}{1^2} \\
&= -13.6 \text{ eV}
\end{aligned}$$

$$\begin{aligned}
\text{(b)} \quad E &= \frac{-13.6 \text{ eV}}{n^2} \\
&= \frac{-13.6 \text{ eV}}{2^2} \\
&= -3.4 \text{ eV}
\end{aligned}$$

$$\begin{aligned}
\text{(c)} \quad hf &= E_f - E_i \\
&= -3.4 \text{ eV} - (-13.6 \text{ eV}) \\
&= 10.2 \text{ eV}
\end{aligned}$$

The frequency and wavelength of emitted photons can easily be calculated. Since $hf = E_f - E_i$

$$f = \frac{E_f - E_i}{h}$$

Also, since $c = f\lambda$

$$\lambda = \frac{c}{f}$$

Example: Frequency and Wavelength of Emitted Photons

An electron drops from the second energy level to the first energy level within an excited hydrogen atom. (a) Determine the energy of the photon emitted. (b) Calculate the frequency of the photon emitted. (c) Calculate the wavelength of the photon emitted.

Solution:

Beginning with the information from the solution to the preceding example, the energy of the photon equals $E_2 - E_1 = 10.2$ eV.

$$\begin{aligned}
\text{(a)} \quad hf &= E_2 - E_1 \\
&= (-3.4 \text{ eV}) - (-13.6 \text{ eV}) \\
&= 10.2 \text{ eV}
\end{aligned}$$

(b) Since $hf = 10.2$ eV

$$f = \frac{10.2 \text{ eV}}{h}$$

$$= \frac{10.2 \text{ eV} (1.6 \times 10^{-19} \text{ J/eV})}{6.6 \times 10^{-34} \text{ J-sec}}$$

$$= 2.5 \times 10^{15} \text{ Hz}$$

(c) $$\lambda = \frac{c}{f}$$

$$= \frac{3.0 \times 10^8 \text{ m/sec}}{2.5 \times 10^{15} \text{ Hz}}$$

$$= 1.2 \times 10^{-7} \text{m}$$

PROBLEMS

7. The example on page 447 shows how to calculate the radius of the innermost orbit of the hydrogen atom. Note that all factors in the formula are constants with the exception of n^2. Use the solution to the example to find the radius of the second, third, and fourth allowable energy levels in the hydrogen atom.

8. Calculate the energy associated with the second, third, and fourth energy levels in the hydrogen atom.

9. Calculate the energy difference between E_3 and E_2 in the hydrogen atoms. Do the same between E_4 and E_3.

10. Determine the frequency and wavelength of the photon emitted when an electron drops from E_3 to E_2 in an excited hydrogen atom.

11. Determine the frequency and wavelength of the photon emitted when an electron drops from E_4 to E_3 in an excited hydrogen atom.

12. What is the difference between the energy associated with the energy level E_4 and E_1 of the hydrogen atom?

13. Determine the frequency and wavelength of the photon emitted when an electron drops from E_4 to E_1 in an excited hydrogen atom.

29:8   Success of Bohr's Model of the Atom

The Bohr model of the atom was a major contribution to quantum mechanics. Bohr had placed Rutherford's orbiting electrons in definite rings around the nucleus. He had shown that an orbital electron radiates energy only when it moves from a higher energy level to a lower energy level, and *not* when it is accelerating around the nucleus. Bohr had also shown that the energy of a photon emitted by the hydrogen atom is equal to the *difference* in two of its energy levels and obeys the relationship $E = hf$.

The Bohr model of the atom was a major contribution to quantum mechanics.

Using visible spectra of the elements, Bohr was able to diagram the energy levels of many of those elements. He was also able to predict several X-ray frequencies by assuming that electrons could make transitions to the innermost levels. These X-ray frequencies were later confirmed experimentally. Bohr was also able to calculate the ionization energy of a hydrogen atom. The ionization energy of an atom is the energy needed to eject an electron completely from that atom. His calculated values for ionization energy were soon confirmed experimentally.

There is one aspect of the Bohr model of the atom that should not be overlooked. The Bohr model provided an explanation of many of the general chemical properties of the elements. The idea that the atoms of each element have unique electron arrangements about their nuclei is the foundation for much of our knowledge of chemical bonding.

Bohr's model of the atom explained many of the chemical properties of elements.

29:9 Present Model of the Atom

Two features of the Bohr model of the atom confused many investigators including Bohr himself. First, it did not explain how electrons, which are negatively charged particles, could accelerate around nuclei and yet not radiate energy. According to classical physics, the electrons should give up energy and spiral into their nuclei. From the classical viewpoint, the universe should have ended long ago in a brilliant flash of violet light, the so-called "violet death" of the universe. This had obviously not happened. Thus, scientists were left with no other choice than to assume that electrons can orbit the nucleus of an atom and not radiate light. Secondly, the notion that electrons may occupy only certain levels was a further contradiction of accepted physical law. It would seem that electrons should be able to orbit the nucleus at any distance, the distance depending only on the speed of the electron.

De Broglie suggested that particles have wave characteristics.

Louis de Broglie (1892–   ) introduced the possibility that particles have wave characteristics just as light waves have particle characteristics. If the electron is considered to be a wave rather than a particle, the energy levels proposed by Bohr can be readily understood. In this view, a Bohr orbit will exist only when the circumference of the orbit is a whole number multiple of the wavelengths of the orbiting electrons. Thus, the wave can reinforce itself constructively and never lose energy. In other words, electrons do not spiral into nuclei. They must occupy only certain levels.

FIGURE 29-9. Orbiting electrons occupy levels which have a circumference equal to a multiple of their de Broglie wavelengths. The innermost orbit has a circumference of one wavelength.

de Broglie orbit

Bohr orbit

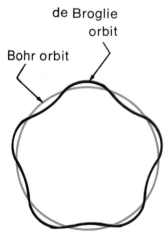

De Broglie was able to show mathematically that the Bohr orbits do indeed turn out to be exactly equal to whole number multiples of their de Broglie wavelengths. Thus, he had provided strong evidence to support both Bohr's model of the atom and his own theory of matter waves.

The present model of the atom is a further modification of de Broglie's version of the Bohr atom. The German physicist Erwin Schrödinger (1887–1961) expanded de Broglie's matter wave concept to develop a completely mathematical model of the atom. Schrödinger replaced matter waves with "probability" waves which can only give the probable position of an electron at any given instant, not an exact position. The highest probability turns out to be that an electron will be found at a distance from the nucleus which agrees with one of Bohr's radii.

De Broglie showed that Bohr orbitals exist at levels that are whole number multiples of the wavelength of the electron.

The present model of the atom is a mathematical model. It gives the probability of the location of an electron at any given time.

SUMMARY

In 1896 Becquerel discovered that uranium compounds emit highly penetrating radiations. Rutherford later determined the nature of these radiations by causing them to pass through electric and magnetic fields and noting their deflections. He found that there are three types of radiations from radioactive substances. Alpha rays are doubly-ionized helium nuclei; beta rays are high-speed electrons; and gamma rays are high-energy photons.

Rutherford's team directed alpha particles at thin gold sheets. They found that most of the particles passed straight through the sheets. This observation showed that atoms consist mostly of empty space. A few alpha particles were deflected. The angles of deflection implied that the mass of an atom is concentrated in a nucleus.

Rutherford recognized that the nucleus is too large to consist of protons alone. He postulated the existence of a second type of particle which had no charge in the nucleus. James Chadwick discovered neutrons in 1932.

The Rutherford model of the atom pictures a nucleus containing protons and neutrons. Electrons orbit around this nucleus at some distance. Niels Bohr revised the Rutherford model of the atom to account for the observed electromagnetic radiations that atoms are capable of emitting. The Bohr model of the atom differs from the Rutherford model in that the orbital electrons are confined to specific energy levels. Electrons are restricted to transitions between these levels. Thus, electromagnetic radiations are quantized.

The de Broglie model of the atom treats electrons as waves. With this model it was possible to explain why electrons move only in definite levels. It also explained why electrons do not lose energy and fall into the nucleus.

The present model of the atom is a mathematical model. Rather than matter waves, it describes electrons in terms of probability waves. These waves give the probable position of the electron at a given time, not the exact position.

QUESTIONS

1. Describe Rutherford's method of analyzing radioactive materials.
2. Name and describe the three types of radiation emitted by naturally radioactive materials.
3. Describe the neutron. How does its mass compare with the mass of a proton?
4. Upon what does the mass of a nucleus depend?
5. What are isotopes?

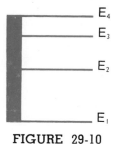

E₄

E₃

E₂

E₁

FIGURE 29-10

6. A certain atom has four distinct energy levels as shown in Figure 29-10. If an electron can make transitions between any two levels, how many spectral lines can the atom emit? Which transition emits the photon of highest energy?

7. What two basic assumptions did Bohr make in order to modify Rutherford's model of the atom?

8. How does the Bohr model of the atom account for the emission of radiation by atoms?

9. What two features of the Bohr atom were in direct conflict with classical physics?

10. How did de Broglie explain Bohr orbits?

PROBLEMS

1. An atom of an isotope of magnesium has an atomic mass of 24 a.m.u. The atomic number of magnesium is 12. How many neutrons are in the nucleus of this atom?

2. An atom of an isotope of nitrogen has an atomic mass of 15 a.m.u. The atomic number of nitrogen is 7. How many neutrons are in the nucleus of this isotope?

3. List the number of neutrons in an atom of each of these isotopes:
   (a) $^{112}_{48}Cd$ (d) $^{80}_{35}Br$ (f) $^{40}_{18}Ar$
   (b) $^{209}_{83}Bi$ (e) $^{1}_{1}H$ (g) $^{132}_{54}Xe$
   (c) $^{208}_{83}Bi$

4. Calculate the radius of the allowed energy levels E_5 and E_6 of the hydrogen atom.

5. What energy is associated with the hydrogen atom energy levels E_2, E_3, E_4, E_5, and E_6?

6. Calculate these values for the hydrogen atom:
   (a) $E_6 - E_5$ (d) $E_5 - E_2$
   (b) $E_6 - E_3$ (e) $E_5 - E_3$
   (c) $E_4 - E_2$

7. Use Problem 6 solutions to determine the frequencies of the photons emitted when the hydrogen atom passes through the energy differences.

8. Use Problem 7 solutions to determine the wavelengths of the photons having the frequencies listed.

9. A photon of energy 16 eV enters a hydrogen atom whose electron is in the ground state. The photon ejects an electron from the atom. What is the kinetic energy of the electron in electronvolts?

Use Figure 29-11 to solve Problems 10 through 13. The left side of the diagram gives the energy level for mercury in electronvolts. The right side gives the energy required to raise the atom from the ground state to each energy level.

10. An electron is accelerated by a potential difference of 7.7 volts. (a) What energy does the electron possess in electronvolts? (b) The electron strikes a mercury atom in its ground state. To which energy level is the mercury atom raised?

11. A mercury atom is in the excited state when its energy level is 6.67 eV above the ground state. A photon of energy 2.15 eV strikes the mercury atom and is absorbed by it. To which energy level is the mercury atom raised?

12. A mercury atom drops from 8.81 eV above its ground state to 6.67 eV above its ground state. What is the energy of the photon emitted by the mercury atom?

13. In Problem 12, calculate the photon's (a) frequency, and (b) wavelength.

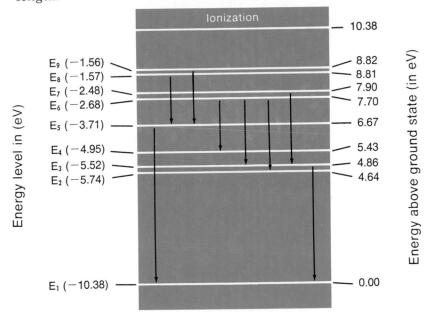

FIGURE 29-11. Ionization energy table for a mercury atom.

1. The Bohr equation for the energy levels of the hydrogen atom can be used as a basis for determining Planck's constant. To do this, measure the wavelengths of the four principal lines of the hydrogen spectrum as outlined in any standard physics laboratory manual. Solve for Planck's constant by using the following form of the Bohr equation:

$$h = \frac{13.6\lambda}{c}\left(\frac{1}{2^2} - \frac{1}{n^2}\right)$$

where h is Planck's constant, λ is the wavelength of the observed line in meters, and c is 3×10^8 m/sec. For the red line, $n = 2$; for the blue-green line, $n = 3$; for the blue-violet line, $n = 4$; and for the violet line (very faint), $n = 5$. The value you obtain for Planck's constant should be very close to the accepted value of 6.63×10^{-34} joule-second.

Andrade, E. N., *Rutherford and the Nature of the Atom.* New York, Doubleday and Co., Inc., 1964.

Baranger, Michel, and Sorenson, Raymond A., "The Size and Shape of Atomic Nuclei." *Scientific American,* August, 1969.

Drietlein, Joseph, "The New Particles—What Good Are They?" *The Physics Teacher,* November, 1975.

Fermi, Laura, *Atoms in the Family: My Life with Enrico Fermi.* Chicago, The University of Chicago Press, 1954.

Watson, E. C., "Robert Millikan—A Physicist Who Has Changed the Course of History." *The Physics Teacher,* January, 1964.

The nucleus of an atom is the target of much research today. Early in the 20th century, scientists found that the atom contains energy. They soon found that the atom is a source of tremendous amounts of energy. For example, one kilogram of uranium atoms can release as much energy as 73 million kilograms of TNT. Currently, scientists are studying ways of using nuclear energy to produce electric energy. By what processes do atomic nuclei release such great amounts of energy?

THE NUCLEUS

The radioactive properties of uranium were discovered by Becquerel. The search for other radioactive elements by Pierre and Marie Curie resulted in the discovery of polonium and radium. Further investigations led to the discovery of the radioactive properties of thorium and actinium. Rutherford discovered radon, an inert gas which is radioactive.

30:1 Atomic Number and Mass Number

The nuclei of naturally radioactive elements are unstable. An unstable nucleus undergoes a series of changes until it becomes stable. For example, $^{238}_{92}U$, an unstable isotope of uranium, undergoes fourteen separate transformations before becoming $^{206}_{82}Pb$, a stable lead isotope.

The identity of the element to which a nucleus belongs depends only upon the number of protons in the nucleus. The number of protons in the nucleus is the atomic number (Z) of the nucleus.

In Chapter 29, the number of neutrons in the nucleus of an atom was determined by subtracting the number of protons from the atomic mass (A) of the nucleus. This method works only when the atomic mass of the isotope of any given element is stated in terms of a whole number. The standard for the atomic mass unit is defined as 1/12 of the mass of an atom of $^{12}_{6}C$. Precise atomic mass measurements do not yield whole numbers. However, the numbers come close to being whole numbers. These whole numbers are the **mass numbers** of isotopes. For example, the mass of a helium isotope in atomic mass units is 4.00260 a.m.u. Its mass number is 4. Recall that the number of neutrons in a nucleus is found by subtracting its atomic number from its mass number. In future sections, we will call the superscript accompanying the symbol of an element the mass number.

30:2 Radioactive Transmutation

An unstable nucleus emits radiation in the form of alpha, beta, and gamma rays. An alpha particle is a helium nucleus. A helium nucleus consists of two protons and two neutrons. If the nucleus of a uranium atom, $^{238}_{92}U$, emits an alpha particle, it loses two protons and two neutrons. Thus it loses four units of mass from its nucleus. Since the number of protons in the nucleus determines the identity of the element, the atom is no longer uranium.

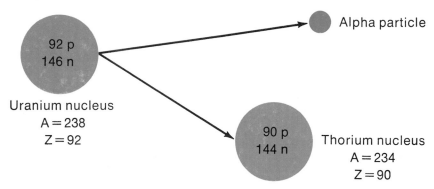

92 p
146 n

Alpha particle

Uranium nucleus
A = 238
Z = 92

90 p
144 n

Thorium nucleus
A = 234
Z = 90

FIGURE 30-1. Emission of an alpha particle by $^{238}_{92}U$.

Transmutation is the change of one element into another through a change in proton number.

A beta particle is an electron which is emitted by an atomic nucleus when a neutron breaks up to form a proton and an electron.

After the loss of two protons, the nucleus has an atomic number $Z = 90$. From Appendix B, we find that $Z = 90$ is thorium. Its mass number is $238 - 4$, or 234. Thus, a thorium isotope, $^{234}_{90}Th$, is formed. The uranium isotope has undergone transmutation. **Transmutation** is the change of one element into another element by a change in the number of protons.

A radioactive atom undergoes beta decay by emitting an electron from the nucleus. This happens when a neutron in the nucleus disintegrates and forms a proton and an electron. The electron is ejected as a beta particle. The proton remains in the nucleus. The nucleus is changed correspondingly by an increase of one positive charge. Thus the atomic number of the element is raised by one. The mass of an electron is insignificant. Therefore, the atomic mass of a nucleus is not changed by the emission of a beta particle. However, the increase in the atomic number by one brings about a change in the identity of the nucleus. For example, after a uranium atom becomes thorium, the newly formed thorium atom emits a beta particle. In this transmutation, the number of

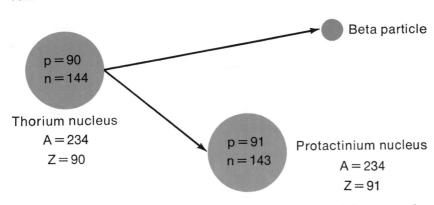

$$p = 90$$
$$n = 144$$

Beta particle

Thorium nucleus
$$A = 234$$
$$Z = 90$$

$$p = 91$$
$$n = 143$$

Protactinium nucleus
$$A = 234$$
$$Z = 91$$

FIGURE 30-2. Emission of a beta particle by $^{234}_{90}$ Th.

protons in the thorium nucleus is increased by one. However, the thorium nucleus undergoes no change in mass. Thus, $^{234}_{90}$ Th becomes a protactinium isotope, $^{234}_{91}$Pa.

When a gamma ray is emitted by a nucleus, no transmutation takes place. A gamma ray is a quantum of energy that does not have a net charge. By the emission of a gamma ray, excess energy is released from a nucleus as it is rearranged during decay.

The emission of a gamma ray does not result in a change in the identity of the nucleus.

30:3   Nuclear Equations

Nuclear reactions are expressed in equation form. The use of nuclear equations makes the calculation of atomic number and mass numbers in a transformation quite simple. For example, the word equation for the nuclear reaction for the transmutation of uranium to thorium due to the emission of an alpha particle is

The symbol for an alpha particle is $^4_2$He.

Uranium 238 $\longrightarrow$ Thorium 234 + Alpha Particle

The nuclear equation for this reaction is

$$^{238}_{92}U \longrightarrow {}^{234}_{90}Th + {}^4_2He$$

No nuclear particles are destroyed during the transmutation process. Thus, the sum of the superscripts on the right side of the equation must equal the sum of the superscripts on the left side of the equation. The sum of the superscripts on the right is 238 and is equal to the sum of the superscripts on the left. Electric charge is also conserved. Hence, the sum of the subscripts on the right is equal to the sum of the subscripts on the left.

In a nuclear equation, the sum of the superscripts on the right side must be equal to the sum of the superscripts on the left side.

In a nuclear equation, the sum of the subscripts on the right side must be equal to the sum of the subscripts on the left side.

Example: Nuclear Equation—Alpha Decay

Write the equation for the transmutation of a radioactive radium isotope, $^{226}_{88}$Ra, into a radon isotope, $^{222}_{86}$ Rn, by the emission of an alpha particle.

Solution:

$$^{226}_{88}Ra \longrightarrow {}^{222}_{86}Rn + {}^4_2He$$

A beta particle is represented by the symbol $_{-1}^{0}e$. This indicates that the electron has one negative charge and an atomic mass number of zero. The equation for the transmutation of a thorium atom by the emission of a beta particle is

$$_{90}^{234}\text{Th} \longrightarrow {}_{91}^{234}\text{Pa} + {}_{-1}^{0}e$$

The sum of the superscripts on the right side of the equation equals the sum of the superscripts on the left side of the equation. Also, the sum of the subscripts on the right side of the equation equals the sum of the subscripts on the left side of the equation.

Example: Nuclear Equation—Beta Decay

Write the equation for the transmutation of a radioactive lead isotope, $_{82}^{209}\text{Pb}$, into a bismuth isotope, $_{83}^{209}\text{Bi}$, by the emission of a beta particle.

Solution:

$$_{82}^{209}\text{Pb} \longrightarrow {}_{83}^{209}\text{Bi} + {}_{-1}^{0}e$$

PROBLEMS

1. Write the nuclear equation for the transmutation of a radioactive uranium isotope, $_{92}^{234}\text{U}$, into a thorium isotope, $_{90}^{230}\text{Th}$, by the emission of an alpha particle.

2. Write the nuclear equation for the transmutation of a radioactive thorium isotope, $_{90}^{230}\text{Th}$, into a radioactive radium isotope, $_{88}^{226}\text{Ra}$, by the emission of an alpha particle.

3. Write the nuclear equation for the transmutation of a radioactive radium isotope, $_{88}^{226}\text{Ra}$, into a radon isotope, $_{86}^{222}\text{Rn}$, by the emission of an alpha particle.

4. A radioactive lead isotope, $_{82}^{214}\text{Pb}$, can change to a radioactive bismuth isotope, $_{83}^{214}\text{Bi}$, by the emission of a beta particle. Write the nuclear equation.

5. A radioactive bismuth isotope, $_{83}^{214}\text{Bi}$, emits a beta particle. Use Appendix B to determine the element formed. Write the nuclear equation.

6. A radioactive polonium isotope, $_{84}^{210}\text{Po}$, emits an alpha particle. Use Appendix B to determine the element formed. Write the nuclear equation.

30:4   Nuclear Bombardment

The nuclei of atoms can be studied by bombarding them with smaller particles such as alpha particles or neutrons. When such particles strike the nucleus of an atom, the nucleus disintegrates.

Much is learned by studying the rays and particles emitted as the nucleus breaks down.

When a sample of an element emits radiation only after nuclear bombardment, the sample is said to be artificially radioactive. Nuclear bombardment often results in the artificial transmutation of elements. New elements with atomic numbers higher than that of uranium can be created. These elements are called **transuranium elements**.

Transuranium elements are those elements with atomic numbers above 92.

30:5   The Cyclotron

In 1930, the cyclotron (SY kluh trahn) was developed by E. O. Lawrence. The cyclotron is a device which accelerates protons and deuterons to very high speeds. A **deuteron** is a nucleus of the hydrogen isotope $^2_1$H. These speeds give them sufficient energy to enter the nuclei of atoms. A cyclotron consists of two hollow half-cylinders. They are called "dees" because of their D-shapes. The dees are enclosed in an evacuated chamber and placed between the poles of a powerful electromagnet. The dees are also connected to a source of high frequency (10^7 Hz) alternating voltage of at least 50 000 volts. With this alternating voltage the charge on each dee is changed during each half-cycle.

Figure 30-4 shows how the cyclotron works. A proton is introduced at A. Protons are obtained by removing the only electron from hydrogen atoms. When the proton enters at A, it moves

The cyclotron accelerates charged particles to extremely high velocities.

A deuteron is a deuterium nucleus. It consists of one proton and one neutron.

U.S. Energy Research and Development Administration

FIGURE 30-3. A cyclotron accelerates charged particles to high speeds and energies.

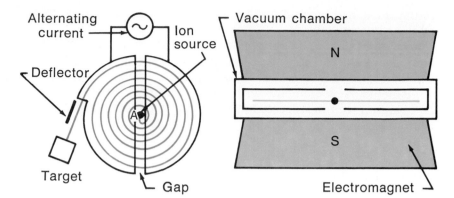

FIGURE 30-4. The internal structure of the cyclotron.

slowly. The strong magnetic field causes it to follow a circular path. Soon it reaches the gap between the two dees. The applied voltage across the dees is synchronized so that the dee which the proton is leaving is charged positively. The opposite dee is charged negatively. Hence, the proton is accelerated across the 50 000-volt difference of potential. The increased velocity causes the proton to follow a circular path of larger radius since the electromagnetic field is kept constant. Each time the proton crosses the gap between the dees, its velocity increases. Therefore, the radius of its circular path also increases. The proton is accelerated to a very high velocity. Then it is directed at a target. The particles bombard the nuclei of elements that make up the target. The transformations that result are then studied.

30:6 Linear Accelerators

Linear accelerators use potential differences to accelerate charged particles.

A linear accelerator consists of a long series of hollow evacuated tubes. The tubes are connected to a source of high-frequency alternating voltage. As the protons leave each tube, the alternating

U.S. Energy Research and Development Administration

FIGURE 30-5. Electrons are accelerated in this linear accelerator.

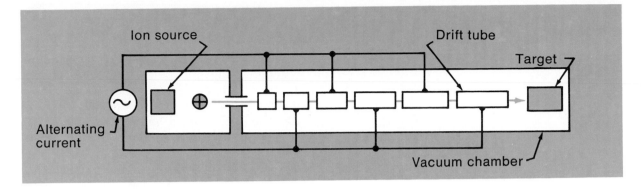

voltage is arranged so that the tube from which the proton exits has a positive charge. The next tube is given a negative charge. Thus, the proton is accelerated as it leaves one tube and enters another. The total energy given to the proton depends on both the length of the accelerator and the difference in potential placed across the tubes.

FIGURE 30-6. The internal structure of a linear accelerator.

30:7 Particle Detectors

Photographic plates become "fogged" or exposed when alpha particles, beta particles, or gamma rays strike them. Thus, photographic plates can be used to detect these rays. Many other devices can also be used to detect charged particles and gamma rays. Most of these devices use the principle that a high-speed particle removes electrons from atoms. The high-speed particles ionize the matter which they bombard. For example, some substances fluoresce when exposed to certain types of radiation. Thus, fluorescent substances can be used in detecting radiation.

The Geiger-Müller tube employs an avalanche effect (Figure 30-7). The tube contains a gas at low pressure (0.1 atm). At one end of the tube is a very thin "window" through which charged particles or gamma rays are allowed to pass. Inside the tube is a

Photographic plates can be used to detect radioactive substances.

Some fluorescent substances can be used to detect radiation.

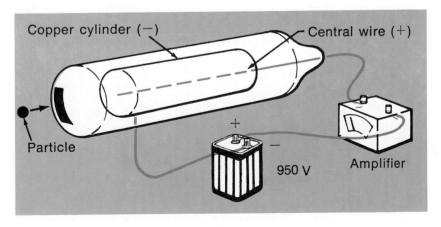

Copper cylinder (−)

Central wire (+)

Particle

+

950 V

−

Amplifier

FIGURE 30-7. A Geiger counter.

metal cylinder with a negative charge. A rigid wire with a positive charge runs down the center of this cylinder. The voltage across the wire and cylinder is kept just below the point where a spontaneous discharge occurs. When a charged particle or gamma ray enters the tube, it ionizes a gas particle located between the metal cylinder and the wire. The ionized gas particle which has a positive charge is accelerated toward the metal cylinder by the potential difference. The electron is accelerated toward the positive wire. As these particles move, they strike other particles. In this way, more ions are formed. These ions, in turn, move toward the negatively-charged cylinder and ionize even more atoms in their path. Thus, an avalanche of charged particles is created and the tube discharges. This discharge can be amplified sufficiently to cause an audible signal such as a click or to operate a counter. To operate the tube continuously, a temporary drop in voltage is placed across the tube to "quench" the discharge. This quenching is done electronically as an automatic reaction to the discharge. Thus, the tube is ready for the beginning of a new avalanche when another particle or gamma ray enters it.

Another device used to detect particles is the Wilson cloud chamber. This chamber creates an area that is supersaturated with water vapor. When ions travel through the chamber, the water vapor tends to condense on the ions. In this way, visible trails of water particles, or fog, are formed.

FIGURE 30-8. Radiation is being checked by this technician at a nuclear center in Puerto Rico.

U.S. Energy Research and Development Administration

The bubble chamber operates on a similar principle but is much more sensitive than the cloud chamber. Particles, such as neutrinos, that cannot be detected in a cloud chamber can be detected in a bubble chamber.

FIGURE 30-9. Neutrons passing through this model affect a photographic plate. In this way, the mechanism of this model can be inspected.

Reprinted with permission of General Electric.

30:8   Artificial Transmutation

The first deliberate artificial transmutation of an element was achieved by Lord Rutherford. Rutherford bombarded pure nitrogen gas with alpha particles. Oxygen gas appeared in the once pure sample of nitrogen.

By bombarding an element with alpha particles, a new element can be formed.

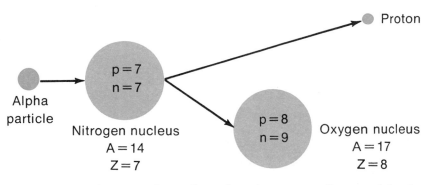

FIGURE 30-10. Artificial transmutation involving the bombardment of nitrogen gas with alpha particles.

Here an alpha particle strikes the nitrogen nucleus and is absorbed. During the process it ejects a proton from the nitrogen atom. The symbol for a proton is ^1_1H. This symbol shows that a hydrogen nucleus has an atomic number of one and a mass number of one. By absorbing the alpha particle, the nitrogen nucleus gains one proton to become oxygen. The net addition of one proton and two neutrons increases the mass number to seventeen. This reaction is written

$$\text{Nitrogen} + \text{Alpha Particle} \longrightarrow \text{Oxygen} + \text{Proton}$$
$$^{14}_{7}N \quad + \quad ^{4}_{2}He \quad \longrightarrow \quad ^{17}_{8}O \quad + \quad ^{1}_{1}H$$

In 1932, James Chadwick confirmed the existence of neutrons. He bombarded beryllium nuclei with alpha particles. Carbon atoms and neutrons were formed according to the equation

$$\ _4^9\mathrm{Be} + \ _2^4\mathrm{He} \longrightarrow \ _6^{12}\mathrm{C} + \ _0^1 n$$

Beryllium 9 + Alpha particle →
Carbon 12 + Neutron

The symbol for a neutron is $_0^1 n$. This symbol shows that a neutron has an atomic number of zero and a mass number of one. The beryllium nucleus gains two protons. Thus, the atomic number increases from 4 to 6 and a carbon nucleus is formed. The ejected neutrons are excellent particles for bombarding the nuclei of other elements because they have no net charge. Thus, neutrons are not repelled as they approach the positively-charged nucleus of an atom.

30:9   Artificial Radioactivity

Stable nuclei may become unstable after bombardment with neutrons, alpha particles, beta particles, and accelerated protons. The resulting unstable nuclei emit radiation until they become stable. Artificially radioactive substances, like naturally radioactive substances, can emit alpha and beta particles. Artificially radioactive substances also can emit a particle called a **positron** (PAHZ uh trahn). A positron is a positive electron. It has the same mass as an electron. Unlike an electron, a positron has a positive charge. Its symbol is $_{+1}^0 e$. A positron results from the conversion of a proton into a neutron. A **neutrino** (noo TREE noh) is also formed in the process. A neutrino has no charge and has very little mass. Just as a neutron can produce a proton by emitting a negative electron and an antineutrino, a proton can produce a neutron by emitting a positive electron and a neutrino.

Not only alpha and beta particles but also positrons and neutrinos can be emitted from artificially radioactive substances.

A positron has one positive charge. Like an electron, it has negligible mass.

A neutrino has negligible mass and no charge.

Proton → Positron + Neutrino
      + Neutron
Neutron → Electron + Proton
      + Antineutrino

When a proton produces a neutron by the emission of a positive electron, the atomic number (Z) of the nucleus containing the proton decreases by one. Hence, transmutation takes place. For example, artificially radioactive phosphorus decays by the emission of a positron and forms stable silicon. The equation is

Phosphorus 30 → Silicon 30
      + Positron

$$\ _{15}^{30}\mathrm{P} \longrightarrow \ _{14}^{30}\mathrm{Si} + \ _{+1}^0 e$$

PROBLEMS

7. Use Appendix B to complete the following nuclear equations:
   (a) $\ _6^{14}\mathrm{C} \longrightarrow \ ? + \ _{-1}^0 e$ (b) $\ _{24}^{55}\mathrm{Cr} \longrightarrow \ ? + \ _{-1}^0 e$
8. Write the nuclear equation for the transmutation of a uranium isotope, $\ _{92}^{238}\mathrm{U}$, into a thorium isotope, $\ _{90}^{234}\mathrm{Th}$, by the emission of an alpha particle.
9. Write the nuclear equation for the transmutation of a radioactive radium isotope, $\ _{88}^{226}\mathrm{Ra}$, by alpha decay.

10. A radioactive polonium isotope, $^{214}_{84}$Po, decays by alpha emission and becomes lead. Write the nuclear equation.

11. Write the nuclear equations for the beta decay of these isotopes:
    (a) $^{210}_{82}$Pb   (b) $^{210}_{83}$Bi   (c) $^{234}_{90}$Th   (d) $^{239}_{93}$Np

12. When bombarded by protons, a lithium isotope, $^{7}_{3}$Li, absorbs a proton and then ejects two alpha particles. Write the nuclear equation for this reaction.

13. Complete the nuclear equations for these transmutations:
    (a) $^{30}_{15}$P $\longrightarrow$? + $^{0}_{+1}e$ (b) $^{205}_{82}$Pb $\longrightarrow$? + $^{0}_{+1}e$

14. The radioactive nuclei indicated in each equation disintegrate by emitting a positron. Complete each nuclear equation.
    (a) $^{21}_{11}$Na $\longrightarrow$? + $^{0}_{1}e$ (b) $^{49}_{24}$Cr $\longrightarrow$? + $^{0}_{1}e$

15. Each of the nuclei given below can absorb an alpha particle. Complete the equations. Assume that no secondary particles are emitted by the nucleus that absorbs the alpha particle.
    (a) $^{14}_{7}$N + $^{4}_{2}$He $\longrightarrow$?   (b) $^{27}_{13}$Al + $^{4}_{2}$He $\longrightarrow$?

16. In each of these reactions, a neutron is absorbed by a nucleus. The nucleus then emits a proton. Complete the equations.
    (a) $^{65}_{29}$Cu + $^{1}_{0}n$ $\longrightarrow$? + $^{1}_{1}$H   (b) $^{14}_{7}$N + $^{1}_{0}n$ $\longrightarrow$? + $^{1}_{1}$H

30:10   Half-Life

The time required for half of the atoms in any given quantity of a radioactive element to disintegrate is the **half-life** of that element. The half-life of a pure radioactive isotope is unique to that

The half-life of an element is the time required for half of the quantity of the radioactive element to decay.

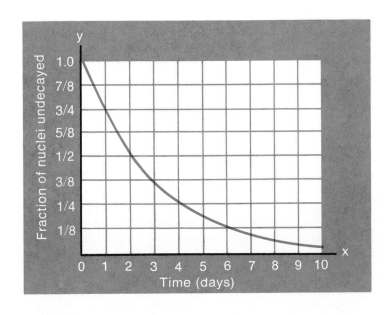

FIGURE 30-11. Half-life graph for $^{238}_{93}$Np. The half-life of this isotope is 2 days. What does the shape of the graph indicate?

particular isotope. For example, the half-life of radium isotope, $^{226}_{88}$Ra, is 1600 years. In other words, in 1600 years, half of a given quantity of the sample of $^{226}_{88}$Ra will disintegrate and form other substances. In another 1600 years, half of the remaining sample will have disintegrated. Only one-fourth of the original amount will remain at that time.

Table 30–1
HALF-LIFE OF SELECTED ISOTOPES

Element	Isotope	Half-Life	Radiation Produced
hydrogen (tritium)	$^{3}_{1}$H	12.3 years	beta
carbon	$^{14}_{6}$C	5730 years	beta
iodine	$^{131}_{53}$I	8.07 days	beta and gamma
lead	$^{212}_{82}$Pb	10.6 hours	beta and gamma
polonium	$^{194}_{84}$Po	0.6 seconds	alpha
polonium	$^{210}_{84}$Po	138 days	alpha
uranium	$^{227}_{92}$U	1.3 minutes	alpha
uranium	$^{235}_{92}$U	7.1×10^8 years	alpha and gamma
uranium	$^{238}_{92}$U	4.51×10^9 years	alpha and gamma
plutonium	$^{236}_{94}$Pu	2.85 years	alpha and gamma
plutonium	$^{242}_{94}$Pu	3.79×10^5 years	alpha

30:11   Binding Force Within the Nucleus

The electrons that surround the positively-charged nucleus of an atom are held in place by a force of electric attraction. The nucleus consists of positively-charged protons and neutral neutrons. The protons are very close together. Normally, the strong electric repulsive force between the protons would cause them to fly apart. This does not happen because an even stronger force exists within the nucleus to hold it together. This force is called the **nuclear binding force.** The nuclear binding force exists only when the particles that make up the nucleus are very close together. The particles that make up the nucleus are called **nucleons**. To develop the binding force, mass is converted into energy. The lost mass equals the binding energy. For example, the helium nucleus, $^{4}_{2}$He, consists of 2 protons and 2 neutrons. The mass of a proton is 1.007825 a.m.u. The mass of a neutron is 1.008665 a.m.u. Thus, the mass of a helium nucleus should be equal to the sum of the masses of 2 protons and 2 neutrons, or 4.032980 a.m.u. Careful measurement shows the mass of a helium nucleus to be only 4.00260 a.m.u. Thus, when a helium atom is formed, 0.03038 a.m.u. is missing. Hence, the mass of the helium nucleus is less than the mass of its constituent parts. This difference is called the **mass defect** of the nucleus.

The mass represented by the mass defect of a nucleus is changed into energy in the form of radiation. It is in keeping with the equation $E = mc^2$. Before a nucleus can be separated into its parts, the same amount of energy must be restored to it. For example, before a helium nucleus can be split into 2 protons and 2 neutrons, energy in the amount of $(0.03038$ a.m.u.$)c^2$ must be added to it.

The mass defect of the nucleus is the amount of the atomic mass that has been converted into nuclear binding energy ($E = mc^2$).

30:12   Calculating Binding Energy

The mass defect of a nucleus provides its binding energy. It follows that the binding energy of any nucleus can be calculated if its mass and the number of protons and neutrons in it are known. First, find the mass defect. Then, use $E = mc^2$ to determine the energy equivalent of the mass defect.

Mass defects are determined in atomic mass units. If the energy equivalent of 1 a.m.u. is found, this quantity can be multiplied by any mass defect. Thus, we have a way to convert mass defects to binding energies. An atomic mass unit is equivalent to 1.66×10^{-27} kg. The energy equivalent of 1 a.m.u. is

$$E = mc^2$$
$$= (1.66 \times 10^{-27} \text{ kg}) (3.0 \times 10^8 \text{ m/sec})^2$$
$$= 14.9 \times 10^{-11} \text{ J}$$

Recall that an electronvolt is 1.6×10^{-19} J. This value for the energy equivalent of 1 a.m.u. can be calculated.

$$\text{Energy equivalent for 1 a.m.u.} = \frac{14.9 \times 10^{-11} \text{ J}}{1.6 \times 10^{-19} \text{ J/eV}}$$
$$= 9.31 \times 10^8 \text{ eV}$$

It is customary to express mass-energy equivalents as millions of electronvolts (MeV).

$$1 \text{ a.m.u.} = 931 \text{ MeV}$$

Example: Mass Defect and Nuclear Binding Energy

The mass of a proton is 1.007825 a.m.u. The mass of a neutron is 1.008665 a.m.u. The mass of the nucleus of a helium isotope, $_2^4$He, is 4.00260 a.m.u. (a) What is the nuclear mass defect of this helium nucleus? (b) What is the binding energy of this helium nucleus?

Solution:

    (a) As indicated by the superscript and subscript in the symbol for helium, its nucleus contains 2 protons and 2 neutrons. Its mass defect can be found as follows:

Mass of 2 protons $= 2 \times 1.007825$ a.m.u. $= 2.015650$ a.m.u.
Mass of 2 neutrons $= 2 \times 1.008665$ a.m.u. $= 2.017330$ a.m.u.
Total $= 4.032980$ a.m.u.
Mass of helium nucleus $= 4.00260$ a.m.u.
Mass defect $= 0.03038$ a.m.u.

    (b) Since 1 a.m.u. is equivalent to 931 MeV, the binding energy of the helium nucleus can be calculated.

Binding energy of $^4_2$He nucleus $= 0.03038$ a.m.u. $\times 931$ MeV/a.m.u.
$= 28.3$ MeV

PROBLEMS

Use these values in the following problems: mass of a proton = 1.007825 a.m.u., mass of a neutron = 1.008665 a.m.u., and 1 a.m.u. = 931 MeV.

17. A carbon isotope, $^{12}_6$C, has a nuclear mass of 12.0000 a.m.u. (a) Calculate its mass defect. (b) Calculate its binding energy in MeV.

18. The isotope of hydrogen that contains 1 proton and 1 neutron is called deuterium. The mass of its nucleus is 2.0140 a.m.u. (a) What is its mass defect? (b) What is the binding energy of deuterium in MeV?

19. A nitrogen isotope, $^{15}_7$N, has 7 protons and 8 neutrons. Its nucleus has a mass of 15.00011 a.m.u. (a) Calculate the mass defect of this nucleus. (b) Calculate the binding energy of the nucleus.

30:13 Nuclear Particles

When the nucleus is bombarded, many types of particles may be emitted.

    Neutrons and protons are the major nuclear particles. In addition, many other particles can be produced from the nucleus. Many of these particles have been discovered as a result of bombardment and detection techniques. Some of the particles appear to be constituent parts of protons and neutrons. Other particles seem to be formed at the moment the bombarding particle strikes the nucleus. Nuclear particles are classified according to mass as follows:

Nuclear particles are classified by their mass.

    Leptons—from the lightest to 210 times the electron mass
    Mesons—from 210 times the electron mass to the mass of the proton
    Hyperons—from the mass of the proton (a hyperon) up

The discovery and identification of the neutron as the second major nuclear particle led the Japanese physicist Hideki Yukawa (1907–   ) to theorize about the force needed to hold the nucleus together. Yukawa thought this force resulted from particles of "middle mass," or **mesons**. The mesons could pass back and forth between the neutrons and the protons. Yukawa predicted the mass of the meson to be about 300 times the mass of the electron. Eventually, two definite types of mesons were discovered. These were pi (π) mesons (pions) and K mesons (kaons).

Pi mesons have a mass of about 273 times the mass of the electron. They fit into Yukawa's theory. Actually, there are three pi mesons. One has a single positive charge (π^+), one has a single negative charge (π^-), and the other is a neutral meson (π^0). When a proton emits a π^+ meson, it becomes a neutron. When a neutron absorbs a π^+ meson, it becomes a proton. Similarly, when a neutron emits a π^- meson, the neutron becomes a proton. If a proton absorbs the π^- meson, the proton becomes a neutron. The passing of mesons back and forth between neutrons and protons holds the nucleus together.

The discovery of mesons explained nuclear binding forces. However, the origin of the beta particles was still in question. The beta particle is an electron which is emitted from the nucleus. For some time, physicists thought the nucleus contained individual electrons. The nuclear electrons seemed to explain how the nucleus is held together. However, it was soon found that free electrons do not exist in the nucleus. First, mesons alone satisfactorily explained the nuclear binding force. Second, matter waves associated with electrons did not fit the diameter of the nucleus. Studies finally showed that beta particles are formed in the transformation of a nuclear neutron into a nuclear proton. During the transformation, beta particles receive energy and leave the nucleus at high speed.

One fact still puzzled physicists. All the beta particles did not leave their respective nuclei with the same amount of energy. This observation did not agree with the law of conservation of energy. The contradiction led to the prediction of yet another particle to share energy with the beta particle during the transformation of a neutron into a proton. The new particle would have almost zero mass and no charge. The predicted particle was the **neutrino,** or little neutron. The small mass and absence of charge made the neutrino a very difficult particle to detect. Finally, experiments showed that neutrinos do exist.

The bombardment of nuclei with protons and electrons led to the identification of many other particles. Seemingly, every particle has an **antiparticle.** The proton has the antiproton; the neutron has the antineutron; the electron has the positron, and so on.

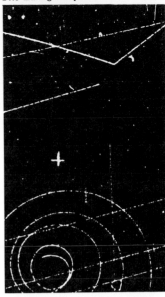

The Ealing Corporation

FIGURE 30-12. A photograph of tracks of hyperons in a bubble chamber.

Mesons pass back and forth between neutrons and protons. This exchange holds the nucleus together.

There appears to be an antiparticle for every particle.

From "Women in Science" by Dinah Moche, distributed by the American Association of Physics Teachers

Annihilation occurs when a particle meets an antiparticle.

A particle and an antiparticle undergo **annihilation** (uh ny uh LAY shuhn) when they meet. In this process, the particles destroy each other. The annihilation is accompanied by the emission of gamma radiation. The radiation carries away the momentum and energy of the particles.

30:14 Nuclear Fission

Fission is the splitting of a nucleus into two or more fragments of almost equal size. Fission is accompanied by the release of large amounts of energy.

During fission (FIZH uhn), a nucleus is split into two or more nearly equal fragments. When fission occurs, the mass of the fragments is less than the mass of the original nucleus. The mass difference is converted into energy in the form of radiation. The observed value for this energy agrees with the value calculated with the equation $E = mc^2$. The best known example of nuclear fission is the fission of the uranium isotope $^{235}_{92}\text{U}$. The $^{235}_{92}\text{U}$ nucleus splits when struck by a neutron of proper speed. The split sometimes forms the elements barium and krypton. The reaction is

$$^{235}_{92}\text{U} + ^{1}_{0}n \longrightarrow ^{92}_{36}\text{Kr} + ^{141}_{56}\text{Ba} + 3\,^{1}_{0}n + 200 \text{ MeV}$$

The splitting of a $^{235}_{92}\text{U}$ nucleus is accompanied by the liberation of free neutrons. These neutrons can cause other $^{235}_{92}\text{U}$ nuclei to split. If the sample of $^{235}_{92}\text{U}$ is large enough, the neutrons freed in the splitting of these atoms have a high probability of striking the nuclei of other $^{235}_{92}\text{U}$ atoms. Then a chain reaction occurs. If the sample is too small, the free neutrons have a high probability of escaping the sample without hitting other nuclei. Then a chain reaction is highly improbable.

Fermi, Bohr, Teller and other scientists who helped to produce the first chain reaction had one major problem. Uranium samples consist mainly of the isotope $^{238}_{92}U$. Only a tiny quantity of $^{235}_{92}U$ is found in any sample of uranium. However, only $^{235}_{92}U$ could sustain the chain reaction. Thus, the isotopes had to be separated. Separation of these isotopes was a problem because their mass difference is extremely small and their chemical properties are identical.

30:15 The Nuclear Reactor

A chain reaction cannot take place in an ordinary sample of uranium even when the sample is large. Ordinary uranium contains many more atoms of $^{238}_{92}U$ than $^{235}_{92}U$. Neutrons released by fissioning atoms of $^{238}_{92}U$ are **fast neutrons**. Fast neutrons are easily absorbed by $^{238}_{92}U$ nuclei. When a $^{238}_{92}U$ absorbs a neutron, it does not undergo fission. It only increases its atomic mass number by 1 a.m.u. and becomes a new uranium isotope, $^{239}_{92}U$. The tendency of $^{238}_{92}U$ to absorb neutrons keeps most of the neutrons in the sample from reaching the fissionable $^{235}_{92}U$ atoms. Thus, a chain reaction cannot take place in the sample.

Enrico Fermi suggested that a chain reaction might be possible in an ordinary sample of uranium if the sample is broken into small pieces and placed among rods of graphite. Graphite is a

International News Photo

FIGURE 30-14. Enrico Fermi, famous Italian-born physicist and Nobel prize winner, directed the first controlled fission chain reaction at the University of Chicago, December 2, 1942.

FIGURE 30-15. Diagram of a nuclear pile reactor indicating graphite block moderators, the cadmium control rods, and the $^{235}_{92}U$ fuel cylinders.

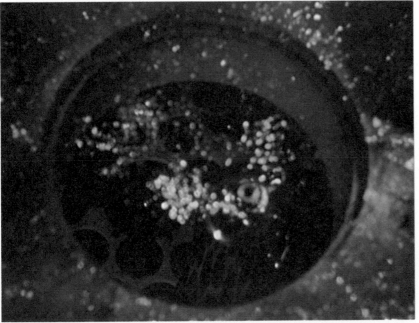

Courtesy of Kodansha

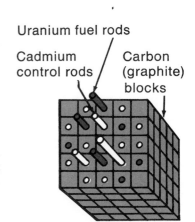

Uranium fuel rods

Cadmium control rods

Carbon (graphite) blocks

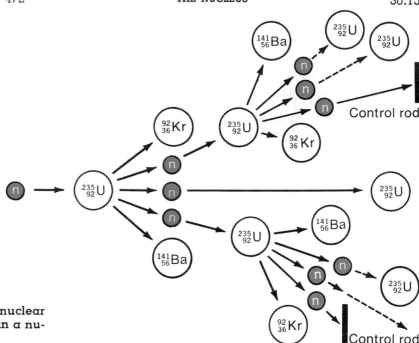

FIGURE 30-16. A model of a nuclear fission chain reaction of $^{235}_{92}U$ in a nuclear reactor.

Fast neutrons are neutrons released by fissioning atoms.

A slow neutron is a more effective bombarding particle than a fast neutron.

A nuclear moderator slows down particles in a nuclear reactor without stopping them.

In a nuclear reactor, materials are bombarded with slow neutrons. The rate of release of energy by fission is controlled in a nuclear reactor.

Control rods regulate energy release in a nuclear reactor by absorbing neutrons.

special form of carbon. Carbon atoms are small enough to recoil when struck by a neutron. The carbon atom absorbs some of a neutron's momentum. In this way, the neutron loses speed or becomes a **slow neutron.** Thus, the graphite creates many slow neutrons in the system. A substance which slows down but does not stop particles in a reactor is called a **nuclear moderator.**

Slow neutrons are much more likely to be absorbed by $^{235}_{92}U$ than by $^{238}_{92}U$. Accordingly, the abundance of slow neutrons in the system greatly increases the possibility that a neutron released by a $^{235}_{92}U$ atom will cause some other $^{235}_{92}U$ atom to undergo fission. If there is enough uranium in the pile, a chain reaction can occur.

A **nuclear reactor** consists of many metric tons of graphite blocks that surround rods of uranium. Between the uranium rods are cadmium rods. Cadmium absorbs neutrons quite easily. The cadmium rods are lifted in and out of the reactor to control the rate of energy release. For this reason, these rods are called **control rods.** When these control rods are placed completely in the pile, they absorb so many neutrons that the reaction stops completely. As they are lifted out of the pile, the rate of energy release increases.

The energy released by the fission of uranium inside the reactor can be converted to electric energy (Figure 30-17). The reactor is surrounded with water. The water is heated by the energy from the nuclear reaction and forms steam. The steam is used to operate steam turbines which generate electricity.

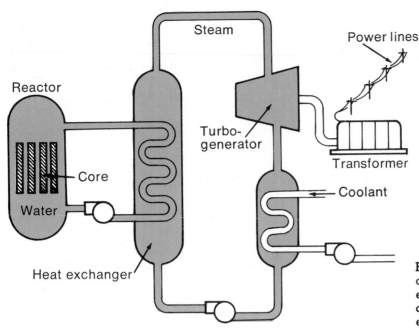

FIGURE 30-17. Diagram of a nuclear power plant in which heat energy released in nuclear reactions is converted to electric energy.

When the $^{235}_{92}\text{U}$ atoms in a nuclear reactor split, they release other elements with less mass as well as energy. These other elements must eventually be removed from the reactor. Another important product of a reactor is the new element plutonium. Plutonium fissions in much the same way as $^{235}_{92}\text{U}$.

The production of plutonium in reactors is the result of the absorption of neutrons by $^{238}_{92}\text{U}$. An atom of $^{238}_{92}\text{U}$ does not fission when a neutron enters its nucleus. Instead, it becomes the uranium isotope $^{239}_{92}\text{U}$.

$$^{238}_{92}\text{U} + ^{1}_{0}n \longrightarrow ^{239}_{92}\text{U}$$

The isotope $^{239}_{92}\text{U}$ is unstable. It has a half-life of 23.5 minutes. When $^{239}_{92}\text{U}$ decays, it emits a beta particle. When a beta particle is emitted by the breakup of a neutron, a proton is also formed. Thus, the atomic number of the atom increases by one. Neptunium is formed in this reaction.

$$^{239}_{92}\text{U} \longrightarrow ^{239}_{93}\text{Np} + ^{0}_{-1}e$$

Neptunium is also unstable. It has a half-life of only 2.35 days. Neptunium also decays by the emission of a beta particle. Plutonium is formed.

$$^{239}_{93}\text{Np} \longrightarrow ^{239}_{94}\text{Pu} + ^{0}_{-1}e$$

Plutonium is relatively stable and has a half-life of 24 400 years. Plutonium can be produced in quantity in the nuclear reactor. It can then be removed from the reactor and used to fuel other reactors.

When U-235 undergoes fission, elements with less mass are produced. Vast quantities of energy are also released.

Uranium 238 + Neutron → Uranium 239

Uranium 239 → Neptunium 239 + Beta particle

Neptunium 239 → Plutonium 239 + Beta particle

FIGURE 30-18. Plutonium is produced from $^{238}_{92}$U by a stepwise process in a nuclear reactor. The plutonium can then be recovered and used to fuel other reactors.

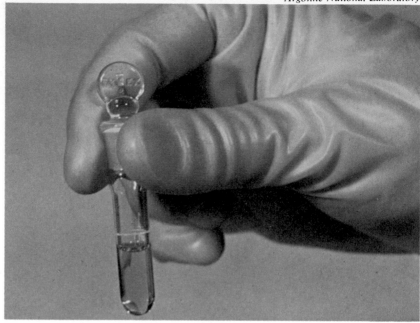

Nuclear reactors are an important source of electric energy.

Nuclear reactors are becoming important sources of electric energy. Operation of nuclear reactors results in much less environmental pollution than the operation of fossil-fueled power plants. By 1980, it is expected that more than 100 reactors will be generating about 40 percent of the electricity requirements of the United States.

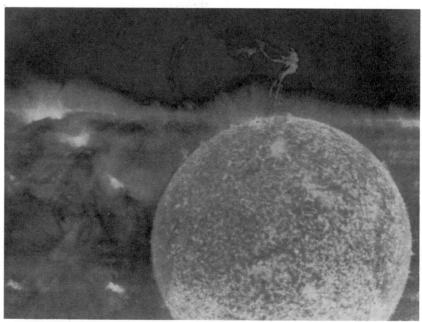

FIGURE 30-19. Nuclear fusion occurs on the sun and is the source of the sun's radiation. In this process, four hydrogen nuclei fuse to form a helium nucleus.

30:16 Breeder Reactors

A **breeder reactor** can actually produce more fissionable fuel than it uses. If plutonium and $^{238}_{92}U$ are both present in the reactor, the plutonium will undergo fission in the manner of $^{235}_{92}U$. During the process, many of the free neutrons from the fission of plutonium are absorbed by the $^{238}_{92}U$. In this reaction, $^{239}_{92}U$ is formed. As described earlier, this isotope soon becomes plutonium by beta emission. For every two plutonium atoms that undergo fission, three new ones are formed. Soon, more fissionable fuel can be recovered from this reactor than was originally present.

A breeder reactor produces more atoms of fissionable material than it originally contained.

30:17 Nuclear Fusion

During **fusion** (FYOO zhuhn), the nuclei of elements with very small masses combine to form nuclei with larger masses. In this process, huge amounts of energy are released. A typical example of fusion is the process which occurs on the sun. Four hydrogen nuclei fuse in several steps to form one helium nucleus. The mass of four separate hydrogen nuclei is larger than the mass of one helium nucleus. The mass lost during the reaction is converted to energy in accordance with the relationship $E = mc^2$.

Fusion is the union of small nuclei to form larger nuclei.

The mass difference is the result of the work that must be done to separate the particles. To separate the particles of a helium nucleus, a great deal of work must be done on the particles. A cyclotron or other high-energy device is needed. This work, or energy input, does not appear in the form of kinetic energy. It appears as an increase in the mass of the particles, in keeping with $E = mc^2$. Should the particles recombine, they must release the same amount of energy needed to separate them. This recombination would result in a corresponding decrease in mass. This mass decrease in the case of helium produces about 27 000 000 eV of energy. In comparison, the explosion of a dynamite molecule releases about 20 eV of energy.

During fusion, mass is converted to energy.

Fusion reactions release even larger quantities of energy than fission reactions.

Nuclear fusion takes place only when temperatures are extremely high, about 2×10^7 °K. Fusion reactions are called **thermonuclear reactions**. Temperatures in the interior of the sun are suitable for the fusion of hydrogen. This reaction is responsible for the sun's radiant energy.

Fusion reactions are also called thermonuclear reactions because they take place at extremely high temperatures, such as those of the sun's interior.

30:18 Controlled Fusion

Scientists are investigating methods for producing controlled fusion reactions. Controlled fusion would give the world an almost limitless source of energy. In order to control fusion, some very difficult problems must be solved.

Lawrence Radiation Laboratory

FIGURE 30-20. A magnetic field can be used to contain plasma at temperatures higher than the melting point of all material containers.

The pinch effect refers to the compression of plasma rotating in the changing magnetic field.

The Tokamak reactor is a research device for studying the control of fusion reactions.

To start fusion, the temperature of hydrogen isotopes must be raised to millions of degrees Celsius. Initially, hydrogen gas is passed through an electric arc. In this arc, the temperature of the gas is raised and atoms are stripped of their electrons. The gas then consists of high-temperature, charged particles and is called a plasma. The temperature of the plasma can be greatly increased by compressing it.

The major problem in raising a substance to fusion temperature is finding a container for the plasma. The temperature of the plasma must be raised to millions of degrees. However, all known materials melt at less than 5000° C. Magnetic fields can be used to contain a plasma. A magnetic field is not a material and therefore is not affected in the same way as a material container. A plasma can be kept rotating in a magnetic bottle. When the plasma is rotating, quick changes in field strength compress the plasma by "pinching" it. This is known as the **pinch effect**. Fusion has been achieved in such magnetic bottles. So far, instabilities in the plasma flow have prevented the achievement of a sustained reaction. Controlling the plasma flow is currently being researched.

One of the most promising fusion reactors under development is the Tokamak reactor. Essentially, the Tokamak provides a doughnut-shaped field in which the plasma rotates. The purpose of the Tokamak is to maximize plasma-flow research.

A second and totally new approach to controlled fusion is the multiple-laser, pellet-implosion program. In this process, liquid pellets of the hydrogen isotopes deuterium ($^2_1$H) and tritium ($^3_1$H) are subjected to intense radiation from multiple laser

FIGURE 30-21. This Tokamak reactor is a controlled fusion device which uses giant magnets to confine plasma.

U.S. Energy Research and Development Administration

FIGURE 30-22. This long-path, glass disc laser made of neodymium glass is being used to conduct laser-fusion research.

beams. The radiation causes the pellet to **implode,** or burst inward, with great violence. In this process, the temperature of the hydrogen isotopes can be raised to fusion levels.

Implosion is being studied as a means of raising the temperature of hydrogen isotopes to fusion temperatures.

SUMMARY

Nuclear transmutation is the change in the identity of a radioactive element. The identity of the element depends upon the number of protons in its nuclei. The number of protons in the nucleus is called the atomic number of the atom. The number of protons plus the number of neutrons in a nucleus is called the mass number of the atom.

An alpha particle is a helium nucleus. It consists of 2 protons and 2 neutrons. When a nucleus emits an alpha particle, the atomic number of the nucleus decreases by two and the atom changes identity. Also, the mass number of the atom decreases by four.

A nucleus emits a beta particle (an electron) from its nucleus as the result of the decay of a neutron into a proton and an electron. The atomic number of the atom then increases by one. The mass of an electron is not enough to cause a change in mass number.

The emission of a gamma ray causes no change in the atomic number of an atom. Gamma rays are given off by the nucleus of an atom as a result of rearrangement of particles in the nucleus during decay.

The cyclotron and linear accelerators are used to bombard nuclei with high energy particles. Only charged particles can be accelerated in these devices. Neutrons have no charge and thus cannot be accelerated in these devices.

Artificially radioactive substances often emit positive electrons called positrons. In the emission of a positron by a proton in the formation of a neutron, a neutrino is also emitted. When an atom emits a positron, the atomic number of the atom decreases by one.

The half-life of a radioactive substance is the time required for half of the atoms of any given quantity of a radioactive substance to disintegrate. The half-lives of elements vary widely. Among isotopes of the same elements, the half-lives may show wide variations.

Nuclear binding force is the force that holds the nucleus together. The nuclear binding force opposes the strong electric force of repulsion between the protons.

477

During nuclear fission, an atom absorbs a neutron and then splits into fragments. During fission, a huge amount of energy and free neutrons are released. Fission can be controlled in a nuclear reactor. In this way, fission can be used to generate large quantities of electric energy. A chain reaction is the fission of a large number of unstable particles. In a breeder reactor, more fissionable material is produced than was originally present.

Nuclear fusion is a process in which the nuclei of elements of very small mass combine to form nuclei of larger mass. During this process, a huge amount of energy is released. Fusion takes place only when temperatures are extremely high. Fusion reactions are called thermonuclear reactions. Fusion is the process which goes on in the sun. Fusion is the source of radiant energy given off by the sun.

QUESTIONS

1. What is meant by the term transmutation as used in nuclear physics?
2. What determines to which element an atom belongs?
3. What happens to the atomic number and atomic mass of an atom that ejects an alpha particle?
4. What happens to the atomic number and atomic mass of an atom that ejects a beta particle?
5. Distinguish between natural and artificial radioactivity.
6. Describe the change that takes place within a nucleus when it emits a positron.
7. What changes take place in a nucleus when it emits a gamma ray?
8. Describe the construction and operation of the cyclotron.
9. Write the symbol of the following particles:
   (a) proton
   (b) electron
   (c) positron
   (d) neutron
   (e) alpha particle
10. Explain what is meant by the half-life of a radioactive element.
11. What is the mass defect of a nucleus? What does it account for?
12. Why is it difficult to separate $^{235}_{92}U$ from $^{238}_{92}U$?
13. Explain how it is possible for a modern power reactor to produce more fissionable fuel than it uses. What are such reactors called?
14. Of what advantage would it be to control the fusion process? What two different processes are presently being studied in hopes of controlling fusion?

PROBLEMS

1. An unstable chromium isotope, $^{56}_{24}Cr$, emits a beta particle. Write a complete equation and show the element formed.
2. An aluminum isotope, $^{25}_{13}Al$, when bombarded by alpha particles absorbs an alpha particle and then emits a neutron. Write a nuclear equation for this transmutation.
3. When a boron isotope, $^{10}_{5}B$, is bombarded with neutrons, it absorbs a neutron and then emits an alpha particle. (a) What element is also formed? (b) Write the nuclear equation for this reaction.
4. The first fusion reaction produced artificially involved the use of deuterons, or heavy hydrogen nuclei. The symbol for a deuteron is $^{2}_{1}H$. During this reaction, two deuterons combine to form a helium isotope, $^{3}_{2}He$. What other particle is produced?

5. On the sun, the nuclei of four ordinary hydrogen atoms combine to form a helium isotope, $_{2}^{4}\text{He}$. What type of particle is missing from the following equation for this reaction?

$$4\,(_{1}^{1}\text{H}) \longrightarrow \,_{2}^{4}\text{He} + 2\,(?)$$

6. A mercury isotope, $_{80}^{200}\text{Hg}$, is bombarded with deuterons ($_{1}^{2}\text{H}$). The mercury nucleus absorbs the deuteron and then emits an alpha particle. (a) What element is formed by this reaction? (b) Write the nuclear equation for the reaction.

7. A nitrogen isotope, $_{7}^{14}\text{N}$, has 7 protons and 7 neutrons in its nucleus. Its nuclear mass is approximately 14.00307 a.m.u. (a) Calculate the mass defect of the nucleus. (b) What is the binding energy of this nucleus?

8. Assume that each nucleon shares equally in the binding energy of the nucleus. Calculate the energy needed to eject a neutron from the nucleus of a nitrogen isotope, $_{7}^{14}\text{N}$.

9. A carbon isotope, $_{6}^{13}\text{C}$, has a nuclear mass of approximately 13.00335 a.m.u. (a) What is the mass defect of this isotope? (b) What is the binding energy of its nucleus?

10. An oxygen isotope, $_{8}^{16}\text{O}$, has a nuclear mass of about 15.99491 a.m.u. (a) What is the mass defect of this isotope? (b) What is the binding energy of its nucleus?

PROJECTS

1. Obtain a packet of Polaroid camera film (Pola Pan type 57). Place a key or metal washer on an unopened film envelope. Then place a watch or clock with a luminous dial face down on top of it. Leave the combination in a place where it will not be disturbed for several days. You can develop the film by rolling it with any suitable roller. Wait a minute or so after rolling and then open the film packet. What do you observe on the film?

2. Take a watch with a luminous dial into a dark room. After allowing your eyes to adjust to the dark, look at the dial of the watch with a strong magnifying glass. You should be able to see tiny individual flashes as the alpha particles ejected from radium nuclei strike the molecules of zinc sulfide.

READINGS

Blow, Michael, and Watson, William W., *The History of the Atomic Bomb* (American Heritage Junior Library). New York, Harper and Row Publishers, Inc., 1968.

Coppi, Bruno, and Rem, Jan, "The Tokamak Approach in Fusion Research." *Scientific American*, July, 1972.

Emmett, John L., Nuckolls, John, and Wood, Lowell, "Fusion Power by Laser Implosion." *Scientific American*, June, 1974.

Feld, Bernard T., "Nuclear Proliferation." *Physics Today*, July, 1975.

Hughes, Donald J., *The Neutron Story*. New York, Doubleday and Co., Inc., 1959.

Korff, Serge A., "Cosmic Rays and Eclipses." *The Physics Teacher*, September, 1975.

Poole, L., *Carbon 14 and Other Science Methods that Date the Past*. New York, McGraw-Hill Book Co., 1961.

Romer, Alfred, *The Restless Atom*. New York, Doubleday and Co., Inc., 1960.

Seaborg, Glenn T., and Bloom, Justin L., "Fast Breeder Reactors." *Scientific American*, November, 1970.

APPENDICES

ANSWERS
TO ODD-NUMBERED PROBLEMS

INDEX

APPENDIX A

A:1 Table A-1

Trigonometric Functions

Angle	sin	cos	tan	Angle	sin	cos	tan
0°	.0000	1.0000	.0000	45°	.7071	.7071	1.0000
1°	.0175	.9998	.0175	46°	.7193	.6947	1.0355
2°	.0349	.9994	.0349	47°	.7314	.6820	1.0724
3°	.0523	.9986	.0524	48°	.7431	.6691	1.1106
4°	.0698	.9976	.0699	49°	.7547	.6561	1.1504
5°	.0872	.9962	.0875	50°	.7660	.6428	1.1918
6°	.1045	.9945	.1051	51°	.7771	.6293	1.2349
7°	.1219	.9925	.1228	52°	.7880	.6157	1.2799
8°	.1392	.9903	.1405	53°	.7986	.6018	1.3270
9°	.1564	.9877	.1584	54°	.8090	.5878	1.3764
10°	.1736	.9848	.1763	55°	.8192	.5736	1.4281
11°	.1908	.9816	.1944	56°	.8290	.5592	1.4826
12°	.2079	.9781	.2126	57°	.8387	.5446	1.5399
13°	.2250	.9744	.2309	58°	.8480	.5299	1.6003
14°	.2419	.9703	.2493	59°	.8572	.5150	1.6643
15°	.2588	.9659	.2679	60°	.8660	.5000	1.7321
16°	.2756	.9613	.2867	61°	.8746	.4848	1.8040
17°	.2924	.9563	.3057	62°	.8829	.4695	1.8807
18°	.3090	.9511	.3249	63°	.8910	.4540	1.9626
19°	.3256	.9455	.3443	64°	.8988	.4384	2.0503
20°	.3420	.9397	.3640	65°	.9063	.4226	2.1445
21°	.3584	.9336	.3839	66°	.9135	.4067	2.2460
22°	.3746	.9272	.4040	67°	.9205	.3907	2.3559
23°	.3907	.9205	.4245	68°	.9272	.3746	2.4751
24°	.4067	.9135	.4452	69°	.9336	.3584	2.6051
25°	.4226	.9063	.4663	70°	.9397	.3420	2.7475
26°	.4384	.8988	.4877	71°	.9455	.3256	2.9042
27°	.4540	.8910	.5095	72°	.9511	.3090	3.0777
28°	.4695	.8829	.5317	73°	.9563	.2924	3.2709
29°	.4848	.8746	.5543	74°	.9613	.2756	3.4874
30°	.5000	.8660	.5774	75°	.9659	.2588	3.7321
31°	.5150	.8572	.6009	76°	.9703	.2419	4.0108
32°	.5299	.8480	.6249	77°	.9744	.2250	4.3315
33°	.5446	.8387	.6494	78°	.9781	.2079	4.7046
34°	.5592	.8290	.6745	79°	.9816	.1908	5.1446
35°	.5736	.8192	.7002	80°	.9848	.1736	5.6713
36°	.5878	.8090	.7265	81°	.9877	.1564	6.3138
37°	.6018	.7986	.7536	82°	.9903	.1392	7.1154
38°	.6157	.7880	.7813	83°	.9925	.1219	8.1443
39°	.6293	.7771	.8098	84°	.9945	.1045	9.5144
40°	.6428	.7660	.8391	85°	.9962	.0872	11.4301
41°	.6561	.7547	.8693	86°	.9976	.0698	14.3007
42°	.6691	.7431	.9004	87°	.9986	.0523	19.0811
43°	.6820	.7314	.9325	88°	.9994	.0349	28.6363
44°	.6947	.7193	.9657	89°	.9998	.0175	57.2900
45°	.7071	.7071	1.0000	90°	1.0000	.0000	∞

APPENDIX B

B:1   Table B-1

International Atomic Masses

Element	Symbol	Atomic number	Atomic mass	Element	Symbol	Atomic number	Atomic mass
Actinium	Ac	89	227*	Mercury	Hg	80	200.59
Aluminum	Al	13	26.98154	Molybdenum	Mo	42	95.94
Americium	Am	95	243*	Neodymium	Nd	60	144.24
Antimony	Sb	51	121.75	Neon	Ne	10	20.179
Argon	Ar	18	39.948	Neptunium	Np	93	237.0482*
Arsenic	As	33	74.9216	Nickel	Ni	28	58.70
Astatine	At	85	210*	Niobium	Nb	41	92.9064
Barium	Ba	56	137.34	Nitrogen	N	7	14.0067
Berkelium	Bk	97	247*	Nobelium	No	102	255*
Beryllium	Be	4	9.01218	Osmium	Os	76	190.2
Bismuth	Bi	83	208.9804	Oxygen	O	8	15.9994
Boron	B	5	10.81	Palladium	Pd	46	106.4
Bromine	Br	35	79.904	Phosphorus	P	15	30.97376
Cadmium	Cd	48	112.40	Platinum	Pt	78	195.09
Calcium	Ca	20	40.08	Plutonium	Pu	94	244*
Californium	Cf	98	251*	Polonium	Po	84	209*
Carbon	C	6	12.011	Potassium	K	19	39.098
Cerium	Ce	58	140.12	Praseodymium	Pr	59	140.9077
Cesium	Cs	55	132.9054	Promethium	Pm	61	145*
Chlorine	Cl	17	35.453	Protactinium	Pa	91	231.0359*
Chromium	Cr	24	51.996	Radium	Ra	88	226.0254
Cobalt	Co	27	58.9332	Radon	Rn	86	222*
Copper	Cu	29	63.546	Rhenium	Re	75	186.207
Curium	Cm	96	247*	Rhodium	Rh	45	102.9055
Dysprosium	Dy	66	162.50	Rubidium	Rb	37	85.4678
Einsteinium	Es	99	254*	Ruthenium	Ru	44	101.07
Erbium	Er	68	167.26	Samarium	Sm	62	150.4
Europium	Eu	63	151.96	Scandium	Sc	21	44.9559
Fermium	Fm	100	257*	Selenium	Se	34	78.96
Fluorine	F	9	18.99840	Silicon	Si	14	28.086
Francium	Fr	87	223*	Silver	Ag	47	107.868
Gadolinium	Gd	64	157.25	Sodium	Na	11	22.98977
Gallium	Ga	31	69.72	Strontium	Sr	38	87.62
Germanium	Ge	32	72.59	Sulfur	S	16	32.06
Gold	Au	79	196.9665	Tantalum	Ta	73	180.9479
Hafnium	Hf	72	178.49	Technetium	Tc	43	98.9062*
Helium	He	2	4.00260	Tellurium	Te	52	127.60
Holmium	Ho	67	164.9304	Terbium	Tb	65	158.9254
Hydrogen	H	1	1.0079	Thallium	Tl	81	204.37
Indium	In	49	114.82	Thorium	Th	90	232.0381
Iodine	I	53	126.9045	Thulium	Tm	69	168.9342
Iridium	Ir	77	192.22	Tin	Sn	50	118.69
Iron	Fe	26	55.847	Titanium	Ti	22	47.90
Krypton	Kr	36	83.80	Tungsten	W	74	183.85
Lanthanum	La	57	138.9055	Uranium	U	92	238.029
Lawrencium	Lr	103	256*	Vanadium	V	23	50.9414
Lead	Pb	82	207.2	Xenon	Xe	54	131.30
Lithium	Li	3	6.941	Ytterbium	Yb	70	173.04
Lutetium	Lu	71	174.97	Yttrium	Y	39	88.9059
Magnesium	Mg	12	24.305	Zinc	Zn	30	65.38
Manganese	Mn	25	54.9380	Zirconium	Zr	40	91.22
Mendelevium	Md	101	258*	Element 104†		104	257*
				Element 105†		105	260*

* The mass number of the isotope with the longest known half-life.

† Names for elements 104 and 105 have not yet been approved by the IUPAC. The USSR has proposed Kurchatovium (Ku) for element 104 and Bohrium (Bh) for element 105. The United States has proposed Rutherfordium (Rf) for element 104 and Hahnium (Ha) for element 105.

APPENDIX C

Physical Constants and Conversion Factors

C:1 Physical Constants

Avogadro's number: $N_o = 6.02 \times 10^{23}$

Speed of light in vacuum: $c = 2.99793 \times 10^8$ m/sec

Gravitational constant: $G = 6.670 \times 10^{-11}$ m^3/kg-sec^2

Universal gas constant: $R = 8.31$ J/mole-K$°$

Planck's constant: $h = 6.626 \times 10^{-34}$ J-sec $= 4.136 \times 10^{-15}$ eV-sec

Constant in Coulomb's law: $K = 8.988 \times 10^9$ N-m^2/coul^2

Acceleration due to gravity at sea level, lat. $45°$: $g = 9.806$ m/sec^2

Absolute zero of temperature: $0°K = -273°C$

Charge of electron: $e = -1.602 \times 10^{-19}$ coul

Mass of electron: $m_e = 9.109 \times 10^{-31}$ kg

Mass of proton: $m_p = 1.672 \times 10^{-27}$ kg

Mean wavelength of sodium light: 5.893×10^{-7} m

Standard atmospheric pressure: 1 atm $= 1.013 \times 10^5$ N/m^2

C:2 Conversion Factors

1 atomic mass unit $= 1.66 \times 10^{-27}$ kg

1 electronvolt $= 1.602 \times 10^{-19}$ J

1 joule $= 1$ N-m

1 joule $= 1$ volt-coulomb

1 calorie $= 4.184$ J

1 coulomb $= 6.242 \times 10^{18}$ elementary charge units

APPENDIX D

Useful Equations

Quadratic equation: A quadratic equation may be reduced to the form

$$ax^2 + bx + c = 0$$

then

$$x = \frac{-b \pm \sqrt{b^2 - 4ac}}{2a}$$

Remember that the sign immediately preceding the coefficient is carried with the coefficient in solving for the two values of x.

Circumference of a circle: $C = 2\pi r$ or $C = \pi d$

Area of a circle: $A = \pi r^2$

Volume of a cylinder: $V = \pi r^2 h$

Surface area of a sphere: $A = 4\pi r^2$

Volume of a sphere: $V = \dfrac{4\pi r^3}{3}$

APPENDIX E

Physics-Related Careers

Careers in physics-related fields are many and varied. Requirements for some jobs in these fields may consist only of on-the-job training. Others may consist of seven or eight years of formal college training plus experience through on-the-job programs.

Below is a list of just a few of the jobs open in physics-related fields. This list includes brief job descriptions and minimum training requirements. These may vary somewhat from place to place or job to job. You will want to check with local companies, schools, and professional groups for details.

Training and Education Key

Job	= On-the-job training	BS	= Bachelor of Science degree
VoTech	= Vocational or technical school	MS	= Master of Science degree
JC	= Junior college (2 yr)	PhD	= Doctor of Philosophy degree (science)

PHYSICIST

Physicists attempt to discover the basic interactions between matter and energy. Some physicists perform research to learn facts. Others (theoretical physicists) analyze data and invent theoretical models. Many theoretical and research physicists are also involved in teaching.

Career	Training	Job Description
Acoustical scientist	BS, MS	does research in the control of sound; develops acoustical systems
Astrophysicist	BS, MS, PhD	studies the structure and motion of the universe and all its bodies
Biophysicist	BS, MS, PhD	applies physics to biology, medical fields, and related areas
Elementary-particle physicist	BS, MS, PhD	studies properties of the electron, the proton, and the many other particles produced in high-energy collisions
Low-temperature physicist	BS, MS	studies the behavior of materials at extremely low temperatures
Nuclear physicist	BS, MS, PhD	studies the structure of atomic nuclei and their interactions with each other
Optical scientist	BS, MS	develops optical systems; does laser research

Career	Training	Job Description
Plasma physicist	BS, MS, PhD	studies matter in the plasma state; does research directed toward the control of fusion
Radiological physicist	BS	detects radiation and plans health and safety programs at nuclear power plants
Teacher (High school)	BS	instructs students about general areas of physics
Teacher (College)	BS, MS, PhD	instructs students about general and specific areas of physics

ENGINEER

It is often difficult to distinguish between the duties of a physicist and an engineer. It is not unusual to find an engineer engaged in pure research or a physicist designing a specialized piece of equipment. Generally, engineers apply scientific principles to practical problems. They design equipment, develop new materials, and find methods for making raw materials and power sources into useful products. Engineers are also frequently involved in sales.

Career	Training	Job Description
Aerospace engineer	BS	designs and develops flight systems, aircraft, and spacecraft
Biomedical engineer	BS	develops instruments and systems to improve medical procedures; studies the engineering aspects of the biological systems of humans and animals
Ceramic engineer	BS	develops methods for processing clay and other nonmetallic minerals into a variety of products, such as glass and heat-resistant materials
Chemical engineer	BS	plans, designs, and constructs chemical plants; develops processes
Civil engineer	BS	designs bridges, buildings, dams, and many other types of structures
Electrical engineer	BS	designs electric equipment and systems for the generation and distribution of power
Electronics engineer	BS	designs TV, radio, stereo systems; often works in the computer field
Mechanical engineer	BS	designs and develops machines that produce power, such as engines and nuclear reactors
Metallurgical engineer	BS	develops methods to process metals and convert them into useful products

TECHNICIAN

Technicians work directly with physicists and engineers. They are specially trained in certain aspects of science, math, and technology. They help in developing and testing laboratory and industrial equipment and processes, and are frequently involved in sales. Many opportunities exist for technicians in a variety of fields of specialization.

Career	Training	Job Description
Aeronautical technician	VoTech, JC	works with engineers and scientists to develop aircraft; works in field service
Chemical technician	JC	helps to develop, sell, distribute chemical products and equipment; conducts routine tests
Civil engineering technician	JC, Job	assists civil engineers in planning, designing and constructing bridges, dams, and other structures
Computer technician	VoTech, JC	operates and services sophisticated computers
Electronics technician	VoTech, Job	develops, constructs, and services a wide range of electronic equipment
Mechanical technician	VoTech, Job	helps to develop and construct automotive tools and machines
Nuclear technician	Job, JC	operates monitoring systems; supports and assists nuclear engineers

Additional Information

Following is a list of addresses for a few sources of additional information. Further information about physics-related careers and a more complete listing of additional sources can be found in the *Occupational Outlook Handbook* and *Keys to Careers in Science and Technology*. Check also with your school guidance counselors for any information they may be able to supply.

American Institute of Physics
335 East 45th Street
New York, New York 10017

Encyclopedia of Careers and Vocational Guidance
Doubleday and Co., Inc.
501 Franklin Avenue
Garden City, New York 11530

Keys to Careers in Science and Technology
National Science Teachers Association
1742 Connecticut Avenue, N.W.
Washington, D. C. 20009

Occupations
Armed Forces Vocational Testing Group
Universal City, Texas 78148

Occupational Outlook Handbook
U.S. Department of Labor
Bureau of Labor Statistics
Washington, D. C. 20212

U.S. Civil Service Commission
Washington, D. C. 20415

ANSWERS TO ODD-NUMBERED PROBLEMS

Chapter 1: Fundamental Mathematics

1. (a) $8 = 2 \times 4$, (b) $4 = 8/2$
3. (a) $t^2 = 2\,s/a$, (b) $a = 2\,s/t^2$,
   (c) $2 = at^2/s$
5. (a) $h = P/D$, (b) $D = P/h$
7. (a) 5.8×10^3, (b) 4.5×10^5,
   (c) 6×10^4, (d) 8.6×10^{10}
9. (a) 3×10^8, (b) 1.86×10^5,
   (c) 9.3×10^7
11. (a) 5×10^{21}, (b) 1.66×10^{-19}
13. (a) 8×10^{-7}, (b) 7×10^{-3},
   (c) 3.96×10^{-19}, (d) 9.8×10^{-12}
15. (a) 2×10^{-8}, (b) 1.9×10^{-12},
   (c) 3.0×10^{-9}
17. (a) 5.4×10^{-7}, (b) 6.2×10^{-3},
   (c) 3.2×10^{-14}
19. (a) 8×10^{12}, (b) 6×10^{10},
   (c) 3×10^{-11}, (d) 6.25×10^9
21. (a) 2×10^4, (b) 2×10^{12},
   (c) 3×10^8, (d) 3×10^1

23. (a) Student graph, (b) opp = 2.05 cm,
   adj = 5.64 cm
25. opp = 13 cm, adj = 7.5 cm
27. (a) 16 cm, (b) 20 cm
29. (a) Student graph, (b) 15.6 cm
31. 33°
33. (a) incorrect, (b) correct, (c) incorrect

Chapter end problems

1. (a) $x = W/f$, (b) $x = f/g$, (c) $x = my$,
   (d) $x = \sqrt{2s/a}$
3. (a) 2.5×10^{-2}, (b) 2.5×10^{-4},
   (c) 6×10^{-4}, (d) 1.9×10^{-13}
5. (a) 5.2×10^{-8}, (b) 2.0×10^7,
   (c) 5.4×10^{-8}, (d) 1.4×10^{12}
7. (a) 2×10^7, (b) 2.2×10^{18},
   (c) 6.5×10^{-5}, (d) 9.7×10^4
9. 4.4 cm, 9.0 cm
11. side $a = 9.8$ cm, side $b = 8.0$ cm

Chapter 2: Measurement

1. (a) 4, (b) 3, (c) 2, (d) 4,
   (e) 2, (f) 3
3. 26.3 cm
5. 71.7 kg
7. 2.5 g
9. 48.2 kg
11. (a) 2.7 cm, (b) 0.3 cm, (c) 4.7 m

Chapter end problems

1. (a) 3, (b) 4, (c) 1, (d) 5
3. 34.7 m
5. 46.00 cm²
7. (a) 1.7 cm², (b) 21 m²,
   (c) 188 cm², (d) 12.0 cm³
9. 240 cm³
11. (a) 682 g, (b) 6.3 cm³
13. (a) a straight line, (b) The acceleration
   of the mass varies directly with the applied force.

Chapter 3: Motion in a Straight Line

1. (a) 58 km/hr, (b) 16 m/sec
3. (a) 40 000 km/hr, (b) 11 100 m/sec
5. 1.5×10^8 km
7. 2 m/sec²
9. 2.5 m/sec²
11. 9.8 m/sec²
13. 4×10^6 m/sec²
15. 95 m/sec
17. 3.9×10^3 m/sec
19. 160 m
21. 1650 m
23. 1350 m
25. 1800 m
27. (a) 7.6 m/sec², (b) 95 m
29. 55 m/sec
31. 25 m/sec

33. 225 m
35. 59.2 m/sec
37. 44 m
39. (a) 37.4 m/sec, (b) 68 m
41. (a) 15 sec, (b) 1100 m

Chapter end problems

1. 6 m/sec²
3. 2×10^5 m/sec²
5. 24 m/sec
7. 924 m
9. 225 m
11. 2×10^5 m/sec²
13. 71 m/sec
15. (a) 276 m, (b) 7.5 sec
17. 48 m/sec

Chapter 4:   Graphical Analysis of Motion

1. (a)

t (sec)	s (m)
0	0
1	50
2	100
3	150
4	200
...	...
20	1000

(b) Straight line with slope,
(c) Should give 50 m/sec,
(d) Horizontal straight line,
(e) 150 m

3. (a) 10 m/sec, (b) 0 m/sec, (c) 10 m/sec, (d) 20 m/sec

5.

t (sec)	v (m/sec)
0	0
10	10
20	10
30	10
40	10
50	0
60	0
70	0
80	−10
90	−10
100	−20

7. (a) Straight line with slope,

(b) $\dfrac{\Delta y}{\Delta x} = 40$ m/sec,

(c) Horizontal straight line. The area under the line is vt and thus represents total distance traveled during a given time interval. (d) 40 m. The distance traveled during one second.

Chapter end problems

1. (a) Student diagram, (b) 8 m, (c) 32 m, (d) 110 m, (e) 4 m/sec² (acceleration), (f) 0 (constant speed, i.e. no acceleration)

3. (a) 6 m/sec², (b) 0 m/sec², (c) −2 m/sec², (d) −4 m/sec²

5. A-B = acceleration, B-C = constant speed, C-D = deceleration, D-E = rest, E-F = acceleration in opposite direction, F-G = constant speed, G-H = deceleration

7. (a)

t (sec)	s (m)
1	4.9
2	19.6
3	44.1
4	78.4
5	122.5

(b) parabola, (c) should turn out to be about 19.6 m/sec and 39 m/sec

9. (a) Constant speed, (b) speed

11. (a) Uniform acceleration, (b) the acceleration, (c) distance

13. (a) A parabola, (b) speed, (c) larger, indicates higher speed

Chapter 5:   Vectors

1. 112 m/sec, 27° west of north

3. (a) 18.4 m/sec, 29° south of east
(b) 8.5 sec, (c) 76.5 m

5. 79 km, 43° east of north

7. (a) 120 N, (b) 115 N, (c) 104 N, (d) 85 N, (e) 0 N

9. 16.4 m/sec², 66°

11. 112 N, 27° east of north

13. (a) 8.8 m/sec, 65° with respect to direction of water flow, (b) 5 sec, (c) 19 m

15. (a) 20 N, (b) 19 N, (c) 14 N, (d) 10 N, (e) 0 N

17. (a) 100 N, 37° east of north, (b) 100 N, 37° west of south

19. 100 N, 8° south of east

21. 40 N

23. (a) 250 km/hr, (b) 433 km/hr

25. (a) 35 N, (b) 54 N, (c) 61 N

27. 200 N

Chapter end problems

1. 35 N east

3. (a) 9 m/sec, (b) 30 sec, (c) 120 m

5. 273 N

7. 193 km north, 230 km east

9. (a) $F_h = 45$ N, $F_v = 78$ N, (b) $F_h = 78$ N, $F_v = 45$ N

11. (a) 3.1 m/sec, (b) 6.7 m/sec

13. 87 N, 87 N

Chapter 6:   Dynamics

1. 2.5 m/sec^2
3. 7.5 kg
5. (a) 4 m/sec^2, (b) 2 m/sec^2,
   (c) 1 m/sec^2, (d) 0.5 m/sec^2,
   (e) 0.2 m/sec^2
7. 5.6 × 10^5 N
9. 47 N
11. 196 N
13. 9800 N
15. 9.8 m/sec^2
17. (a) 0.5 kg, (b) 128 m/sec^2
19. (a) 1.5 kg, (b) 3 m/sec^2 downward

21. (a) 49 N, (b) 9.8 m/sec^2,
    (c) 98 m/sec upward, (d) 49 N
    (its weight), (e) 10 sec

Chapter end problems
1. 5 m/sec^2
3. (a) 137 N, (b) 4.2 N, (c) 6.9 N
5. 20 N
7. (a) 1000 kg, (b) 13 800 N
9. 3.75 m/sec^2
11. 4.9 m/sec^2
13. The meteoroid just touches the spaceship.

Chapter 7:   Momentum and Its Conservation

1. (a) 800 kg, (b) 2 × 10^4 N-sec,
   (c) 20 sec
3. 1200 N
5. (a) 5500 N-sec, (b) 92 N
7. (a) 2 × 10^4 N-sec, (b) 300 N
9. 16 cm/sec in the same direction
11. 6.7 m/sec, in the original direction of the car.
13. 42 cm/sec, in its original direction.
15. 7.5 m/sec
17. 2.9 m/sec, in a direction opposite to that of the first camper.

19. 9 cm/sec to the right
21. (a) Student graph, $mv_A = 11.5$ kg-m/sec
                        $mv_B = 13.8$ kg-m/sec
    (b) $v_A = 1.9$ m/sec, $v_B = 2.3$ m/sec

Chapter end problems
1. 100 N-sec
3. (a) 3 × 10^4 N-sec, (b) 1000 N
5. (a) 32 000 kg-m/sec, (b) 40 sec
7. 62 m/sec

Chapter 8:   Motion in Two Dimensions

1. 64 m
3. 378 m
5. 47 m
7. 20 m
9. (a) $v_v = 170$ m/sec, $v_h = 98$ m/sec,
   (b) 34.6 sec, (c) 3391 m
11. (a) 20 sec, (b) It hits the archer.
    (c) 700 m
13. 20 m/sec^2
15. (a) 1.18 × 10^4 N, (b) 19.8 m/sec^2
17. 2.7 × 10^{-3} m/sec^2
19. 1.7 km/sec

21. 1.4 sec
23. 9.9 m/sec^2

Chapter end problems
1. 32 m
3. (a) 10 sec, (b) 2000 m
5. 6.6 m/sec
7. 250 m
9. (a) $v_v = 39.2$ m/sec, (b) $v_h = 68$ m/sec
11. 250 N
13. 0.56 m

Chapter 9:   Universal Gravitation

1. 8.0 × 10^{-8} N
3. 8.3 N
5. 1.9 × 10^{20} N
7. 1.02 × 10^{-47} N

Chapter end problems
1. 0.667 N
3. 1.4 × 10^{-5} N
5. 22 years

Chapter 10:   Work and Power

1. 3.2×10^4 J
3. 1920 J
5. 7536 J
7. (a) 24 000 J, (b) 1.44×10^5 J
9. 2940 J
11. 1420 J
13. (a) 2175 N, (b) 4.35×10^5 J
15. (a) 2000 watts, (b) 2 kw
17. (a) 196 N, (b) 58 800 J,
    (c) 238 800 J, (d) 133 watts,
    (e) 0.133 kw
19. 3.25 kw

Chapter end problems
1. 900 J
3. (a) 9800 N-m, (b) 9800 J
5. (a) 9000 J, (b) 450 watts
7. 450 watts
9. 490 watts

Chapter 11:   Energy and Its Conservation

1. 19 600 J
3. (a) 3150 J, (b) 3150 J
5. (a) 3×10^4 J, (b) 500 watts,
    (c) 50 minutes
7. (a) 55 100 J, (b) 223 000 J,
    (c) $\approx 4:1$
9. 6.0×10^{-13} J
11. (a) 490 J, (b) 245 J, (c) 245 J,
    (d) 9.9 m/sec
13. 940 J
15. (a) 6272 J, (b) 6272 J, (c) 35.4 m/sec
17. 20 m
19. (a) 12.5 m/sec, (b) 784 J
21. (a) yes, (b) 2000 J, 1000 J, no,
    (c) yes, yes

23. (a) 4.0×10^6 kg-m/sec, (b) 4.0×10^6 kg-m/sec, (c) KE before = 1.6×10^7 J, KE after = 8.0×10^6 J, (d) While momentum was consumed during the collision, KE was not. Energy was converted to heat and sound.

Chapter end problems
1. (a) 4900 J, (b) 4900 J, (c) 4900 J
3. 675 000 J
5. (a) 200 m, (b) 1650 N, (c) 3.3×10^5 J
7. (a) 19 600 J, (b) 19 600 J,
    (c) 44 m/sec
9. 9×10^{16} J
11. 3.3×10^{-16} kg
13. (a) E, (b) B, (c) E

Chapter 12:   Measurement of Heat

1. 313° K
3. 546° K
5. −73° K
7. (a) 373° K, (b) 173° K, (c) 573° K,
    (d) 293° K, (e) 250° K
9. 331 cal
11. 21 kcal
13. 32.5 kcal
15. 137.5 kcal
17. 63° C
19. 23° C
21. 12.6° C
23. 27 000 cal

25. 1.2×10^5 cal
27. 37 200 cal
29. 1.6×10^6 cal

Chapter end problems
1. (a) 323° K, (b) 423° K, (c) 73° K,
    (d) 573° K
3. 3925 kcal
5. 1111° C
7. 60° C
9. 0.041 cal/g-C°
11. 59 cal/g
13. 0.24 cal/g-C°

Chapter 13:   Heat as Energy

1. 4.7×10^2 cal
3. 0.23 C°
5. (a) 7140 cal, (b) 30 000 J, (c) 612 liters
7. 1285.7 kcal

Chapter end problems
1. 190 cal
3. 1.2 C°
5. 71.4 kcal
7. 1070 cal
9. (a) 633 cal, (b) 1.44 C°

Chapter 14:   Kinetic Theory

Chapter end problems
1. 0.7 cm
3. 0.8008 m

5. 4.5×10^{22} J
7. 8.2×10^{14} years

Chapter 15:   The Gas Laws

1. 30 m^3
3. 5.0 liters
5. 0.67 liter
7. 0.33 atm
9. 58 m^3
11. 666°K
13. 2 atm
15. 200 liters

Chapter end problems
1. (a) 0.5 atm, (b) 5 atm
3. (a) 200 m^3, (b) −205° C
5. 333° C
7. 2.33 m^3
9. 500 cm^3
11. 228 m^3

Chapter 16:   Waves and Energy Transfer

1. 325 m/sec
3. 28.8 cm/sec
5. (a) 1.5×10^9 Hz, (b) 6.7×10^{-10} sec
7. (a) 0.66 m, (b) 2×10^{-3} sec
9. It is attached to the wall.
11. (a) The pulse will be partially transmitted and partially reflected. It will be inverted. (b) The pulse will be almost totally reflected. It will be inverted.

13. (a) Boundary A is more rigid.
    (b) Boundary B is less rigid.
    (c) Boundary C is less rigid.
    (d) Boundary D is more rigid.

Chapter end problems
1. 6.6 m
3. (a) 1500 m/sec, (b) 1×10^{-3} sec, (c) 1×10^{-3} sec
5. 3.0×10^8 m/sec
7. 5.0×10^9 Hz
9. (a) 1×10^{24} Hz, (b) 3.0×10^{-16} m

Chapter 17:   The Nature of Light

1. 1.6×10^{-3} sec
3. (a) 3×10^5 km/sec, (b) 3×10^8 m/sec
5. By starting the mirror from rest and increasing its rate of revolution to the first rate that gives the brightest reflected spot.
7. The illumination at 90 cm is 1/9 that at 30 cm.
9. 450 candelas
11. 125 candelas

Chapter end problems
1. 3×10^8 m/sec
3. 3.9×10^5 km
5. 7.1 lumens/m^2
7. 320 candelas
9. 1000 lumens/m^2
11. (a) 16 lumens/m^2, 4 lumens/m^2, 1.78 lumens/m^2, 1.0 lumens/m^2, 0.64 lumens/m^2, (b) table, (c) graph, (d) Hyperbola.
    Light intensity varies inversely with the square of the distance.
13. 6.6×10^{-14} J
15. 7.5×10^{-8} m

Chapter 18:   Reflection and Refraction

1. Graph
3. 22°
5. (a) 17°, (b) diamond
7. (a) should measure 19°, (b) 19°, (c) 30°, (d) away from normal
9. 1.5

Chapter end problems
1. (a) 53°, (b) 106°
3. Graph
5. 26°
7. 45°
9. 2.26 $\times 10^8$ m/sec
11. 14°

Chapter 19:   Mirrors and Lenses

1. Graph
3. (a) graph, (b) 15 cm, (c) 4.5 cm
5. (a) 3.7 cm from mirror, (b) 4 cm, (c) 1 cm
7. 60 cm
9. -15 cm
11. -8.6 cm
13. -37.5 cm
15. Graph
17. (a) graph, (b) $d_i = 15$ cm, $s_i = 4.5$ cm
19. 4 cm
21. 40 cm

23. (a) -6 cm, (b) 3 cm
25. (a) 25 cm, (b) -60 cm, (c) virtual, (d) inverted

Chapter end problems
1. (a) graph, (b) 13.3 cm
3. (a) graph, (b) $d_i = 30$ cm, $s_i = 1.8$ cm
5. -15.2 cm
7. -5.96 cm
9. (a) graph, (b) 13.3 cm, (c) 1.0 cm
11. (a) $d_i = 420$ cm, (b) $s_i = 20\ s_0$

Chapter 20:   Diffraction of Light

1. 4.2×10^{-5} cm
3. 5.4×10^{-5} cm
5. 3.6×10^{-5} cm
7. 0.21 cm
9. 0.012 cm

Chapter end problems
1. 4.5×10^{-5} cm
3. 2×10^{-3} cm
5. 6.6×10^{-5} cm
7. 5×10^{-15} cm
9. 5.9×10^{-5} cm
11. 8.0×10^{-2} cm

Chapter 21:   The Origin of Light

Chapter end problems
1. 4.8×10^{14} Hz

3. 8.3×10^{14} Hz
5. 3×10^7 Hz

Chapter 22:   Static Electricity

1. 1.3 N
3. -4.4×10^3 N
5. 3×10^{-6} coul
7. 4×10^3 m/sec^2 per body
9. 12.5 N
11. 1 N/coul

Chapter end problems
1. -10 N
3. -90 N
5. -9.2×10^{-8} N
7. (a) 9.8×10^{-3} N, (b) 5.7×10^{-3} N, (c) 2.4×10^{-8} coul
9. (a) 4 N/coul, (b) Toward
11. 5×10^{-5} coul

Chapter 23:   Electric Currents

1. 400 volts
3. 2.5×10^4 N/coul
5. 125 volts
7. 7.5 J
9. (a) 5500 J, (b) 1100 J/sec, (c) 1100 watts, (d) 1.1 kilowatts
11. 180 watts
13. 144 watts
15. 3.6×10^4 J
17. 3 A
19. (a) 240 ohms, (b) 60 watts
21. 15 ohms
23. (a) Diagram, (b) 1.5 A
25. (a) Diagram, (b) 28 volts

27. (a) 2 A, (b) 3.6×10^4 J (c) 8570 cal
29. (a) 9×10^5 J, (b) 2.1×10^5 cal

Chapter end problems
1. 120 volts
3. 100 volts
5. (a) 1800 J, (b) 30 J/sec, (c) 30 watts
7. 9 J
9. (a) 24 J/sec, (b) 24 watts, (c) 14 400 J
11. 3 A
13. 30 volts
15. 0.4 A
17. 120 volts
19. (a) 2.5 A, (b) 5360 cal

Chapter 24:   Series and Parallel Circuits

1. (a) 60 ohms, (b) 2 A
3. (a) 240 ohms, (b) 24 ohms
5. (a) 1.5 A, (b) 20 ohms
7. (a) 50 ohms, (b) 2 A, (c) $V_1 = 40$ volts, $V_2 = 60$ volts, (d) 100 volts
9. (a) 12 ohms, (b) 1 A, (c) $V_1 = 3$ volts, $V_2 = 5$ volts, $V_3 = 4$ volts, (d) 12 volts
11. (a) 10 ohms, (b) $V_1 = 6$ volts, $V_2 = 6$ volts
13. (a) 5 ohms, (b) 6 A, (c) 2 A
15. (a) 20 ohms, (b) 6 A, (c) $i_1 = 1$ A, $i_2 = 2$ A, $i_3 = 3$ A
17. (a) 2 A, (b) 1 A, (c) 3 A, (d) 50 ohms (e) yes
19. (a) 5 ohms, (b) 15 ohms, (c) 3 A, (d) 30 volts, (e) 15 volts, (f) 1 A

21. $V_1 = 15$ volts, $V_2 = 36$ volts, $V_3 = 9$ volts, $i_1 = 3$ A, $i_2 = 1.5$ A, $i_3 = 1.5$ A, $i_4 = 1.8$ A, $i_5 = 1.2$ A

Chapter end problems
1. (a) 12 ohms, (b) 1 A, (c) 1 A, (d) $V_1 = 5$ volts, $V_2 = 7$ volts
3. 10 ohms
5. 16 ohms
7. (a) 4 ohms, (b) 12.5 A, (c) $i_1 = 2.5$ A, $i_2 = 10$ A, (d) 50 volts
9. (a) 2 A, (b) 3 A, (c) 15 A
11. $i = 0.67$ A, $i_2 = 0.8$ A, $i_3 = 2.0$ A $V_1 = 20$ volts, $V_2 = 12$ volts, $V_3 = 48$ volts

Chapter 25:   The Magnetic Field

1. 0.2 N/A-m
3. 0.13 N/A-m
5. 0.15 N/A-m
7. 6×10^{-2} N/A-m
9. 3.2×10^{-13} N
11. 1.7×10^{-13} N

Chapter end problems
1. 0.1 N/A-m
3. 0.04 N/A-m
5. 2.5 A
7. 3.8×10^{-13} N
9. 2.4×10^{-12} N
11. 0.38 N

Chapter 26:   Electromagnetic Induction

1. (a) 4 volts, (b) 0.67 A
3. 0.02 A
5. (a) 120 volts, (b) 6 A
7. (a) 165 volts, (b) 7.8 A
9. (a) 220 volts, (b) 4.0 A
11. (a) 3600 volts, (b) 3 A, (c) 10 800 watts, 10 800 watts
13. (a) 1.8×10^4 volts, (b) 0.5 A
15. (a) 1.2×10^5 volts, (b) 0.1 A, (c) 1.2×10^4 volts, (d) 1.2×10^4 watts

Chapter end problems
1. 0.18 volts
3. 40 volts
5. (a) 310 volts, (b) 20 A
7. (a) 1800 volts, (b) 3.3 A, (c) 6000 watts, 6000 watts
9. (a) 1800, (b) 540, (c) 25, (d) 12

Chapter 27:   Electromagnetic Field Applications

1. (a) 1.3×10^{-14} J/electron, (b) 1.3×10^{-14} J
3. 2.0×10^{19} Hz
5. 4.4×10^6 m/sec
7. (a) 1.6×10^{-19} coul, (b) one
9. (a) Graph, (b) 1.6×10^{-19} coul, electronic charge
11. 1.3×10^{-4} m
13. 4.7×10^{-6} m
15. 6.8×10^6 m/sec

17. 6.8×10^{-26} kg
19. (a) 3.94×10^{-26} kg

Chapter end problems
1. 9.4×10^7 m/sec
3. 2.5×10^6 m/sec
5. (a) 6.4×10^{-14} J, (b) 1×10^{20} Hz
7. (a) 2×10^6 m/sec, (b) 1.7×10^{-27} kg
9. (a) 4.8×10^{-19} coul, (b) 3 electrons

Chapter 28:   The Quantum Theory

1. 5.1×10^{-19} J
3. (a) 6.4×10^{-19} J, (b) 2.3×10^{-18} J
5. 1.1×10^{15} Hz
7. 4×10^{-13} m
9. 8.8×10^{-37} m
11. 4×10^{-41} m

Chapter end problems

1. 8.3×10^{-19} J
3. (a) 7.3×10^{-19} J, (b) 4.6×10^{-19} J
5. (a) 6×10^{-19} J, (b) 7×10^{-19} J
7. 2.8×10^{-40} m

Chapter 29:   The Atom

1. 7 neutrons
3. 120 neutrons
5. (a) $^{238}_{92}$U, (b) $^{238}_{92}$U contains 146 neutrons, $^{239}_{92}$U contains 147 neutrons
7. $r_2 = 2.1 \times 10^{-10}$ m, $r_3 = 4.8 \times 10^{-10}$ m $r_1 = 8.5 \times 10^{-10}$ m
9. 1.9 eV, 0.65 eV
11. $f = 1.6 \times 10^{14}$ Hz, $\lambda = 1.9 \times 10^{-6}$ m
13. $f = 3.1 \times 10^{15}$ Hz, $\lambda = 1 \times 10^{-7}$ m

Chapter end problems

1. 12 neutrons
3. (a) 64 neutrons, (b) 126 neutrons, (c) 125 neutrons, (d) 45 neutrons, (e) 0 neutrons, (f) 22 neutrons, (g) 78 neutrons
5. $E_2 = -3.4$ eV, $E_3 = 1.5$ eV, $E_4 = -0.85$ eV, $E_5 = -0.54$ eV, $E_6 = -0.38$ eV
7. (a) 4.0×10^{13} Hz, (b) 2.7×10^{14} Hz, (c) 6.0×10^{14} Hz, (d) 7.0×10^{14} Hz, (e) 2.4×10^{14} Hz
9. 2.4 eV
11. E_9
13. (a) 5.2×10^{14} Hz, (b) 5.8×10^{-7} m

Chapter 30:   The Nucleus

1. $^{234}_{92}$U $= {}^{230}_{90}$Th $+ {}^{4}_{2}$He

3. $^{226}_{88}$Ra $= {}^{222}_{86}$Rn $+ {}^{4}_{2}$He

5. $^{214}_{83}$Bi $= {}^{214}_{84}$Po $+ {}^{0}_{-1}e$

7. (a) $^{14}_{7}$N, (b) $^{55}_{25}$Mn

9. $^{226}_{88}$Ra $= {}^{222}_{86}$Rn $+ {}^{4}_{2}$He

11. (a) $^{210}_{82}$Pb $= {}^{210}_{83}$Bi $+ {}^{0}_{-1}e$

   (b) $^{210}_{83}$Bi $= {}^{210}_{84}$Po $+ {}^{0}_{-1}e$

   (c) $^{234}_{90}$Th $= {}^{234}_{91}$Pa $+ {}^{0}_{-1}e$

   (d) $^{239}_{93}$Np $= {}^{239}_{94}$Pu $+ {}^{0}_{-1}e$

13. (a) $^{30}_{14}$Si, (b) $^{205}_{81}$Tl

15. (a) $^{18}_{9}$F, (b) $^{31}_{15}$P

17. (a) 0.098940 a.m.u., (b) 92.1 MeV
19. (a) 0.123985 a.m.u., (b) 115.4 MeV

Chapter end problems

1. $^{56}_{24}$Cr $= {}^{56}_{25}$Mn $+ {}^{0}_{-1}e$

3. (a) Lithium

   (b) $^{10}_{5}$B $+ {}^{1}_{0}n = {}^{7}_{3}$Li $+ {}^{4}_{2}$He

5. a positron
7. (a) 0.112360 a.m.u.
   (b) 104.6 MeV
9. 0.104255 a.m.u., (b) 97.1 MeV

INDEX

Absorption spectrum, 313, 314

Acceleration, 31, 80, 82, 86, 94, 121, 122; centripetal, 115-120, 133; component, 122; and electromotive wave, 407, 408, 445; graphical analysis of, 51-54; of gravity, 41, 42, 123, 135; and light, 307-317; of particles, 459-462; from rest, 38-42, 51-54

Acceleration-time graph, 53, 54; illus., 54

Accuracy, 21

Achromatic lens, 290

Action-reaction law, 96, 97

Adhesion, 199

Air, ionization of, 327; refraction in, 264, 267, 269, 270

Alcohol, 168, 200

Alpha particle, 440, 441, 456, 461, 463, 464

Alternating current, 395-397, 400-402

Ammeter, 367; illus., 467

Ampere, 344

Ampere, Andre, 378, 379

Amplitude, 121, 123, 226, 227, 228, 232

Analyzer, 256

Aneroid barometer, 212

Angle, critical, 268

Angle of incidence, 261, 262, 265, 267

Angle of reflection, 261

Angle of refraction, 263, 265, 267

Annihilation, 470

Anode, 383, 409, 417, 418, 421

Antenna, 411, 412, 413, 414

Antineutrino, 464

Antinodal line, 296

Antiparticle, 469, 470

Area, 11; under curve, 50, 52, 53, 54

Aristotle, 15

Armature, 386, 394, 396, 398, 399

Aston, F. W., 423

Atmosphere, 211

Atom, electric forces in, 330; and electricity conduction, 206; excited, 308, 309, 415, 432; half-life of, 465; ionization of, 204, 419, 450; and light production, 307-317; magnetic, 379; mass of, 421, 423; nuclear forces in, 80, 466-468, 469

Atomic mass unit, 455

Atomic model, 321, 442, 444-451

Atomic nucleus, 455-477; binding force of, 80, 466-468, 469; fission of, 470-474; fusion of, 474-477; mass defect of, 467; transmutation of, 456, 457

Atomic number, 455, 456

Average speed, 32

Back-EMF, 399

Barometer, 212

Barrier, 295

Base level, 150

Battery, 148, 329, 346, 398

Becquerel, Henri, 439, 455

Beryllium, 464

Beta decay, 456

Beta emission, 474

Beta particle, 440, 456, 458, 461, 469, 473

Bimetallic strip, 196, 197; illus., 197

Binding energy, 467, 468

Binding force, 80, 466-468, 469

Black hole, 205

Bohr, Niels, 257, 432, 445

Bohr model, 444-451

Boiling point, 177, 201

Boundary, 262, 267; of waves, 228, 229, 234, 235, 236

Boyle's law, 26, 212, 213, 217

Brahe, Tycho, 128

Breeder reactor, 474

Broadcasting station, 411-417

Broglie, Louis-Victor de, 434, 450, 451

Brown, Robert, 194

Brownian motion, 194

Brush, 386

Bubble chamber, 462; illus., 462

Caloric, 165

Caloric theory, 165, 184

Calorie, 171

Calorimeter, illus., 174

Candela, 248

Candle, 248

Capillary action, 199

Carbon, 464, 472

Cathode, 383, 417, 421

Cathode ray tube, illus., 417

Cavendish, Henry, 133, 134

Cell, 329

Celsius scale, 169

Center of curvature, 277

Centripetal acceleration, 115-120, 133

Centripetal force, 115, 116, 118, 119, 120, 129

Cesium clock, illus., 18

Cesium-133, 18

Chadwick, James, 442, 464

Chain reaction, 149, 470, 471

Change of state, 176-179, 200

Charged particle, and light, 307-317

Charging body, 322

Charles, Jacques, 215

Charles' law, 215, 216, 217

Chemical bond, 149

Chemical bonding, 450

Chromatic aberration, 290

Chromium, 443, 444

Circuit, electric, 346-350, 355-365

Circuit breaker, 363, 364

Circuit diagram, 346

Circular motion, 114-120

Cobalt, 379

Coherent light, 314-317

Cohesive force, 176, 177, 193, 198, 199, 200, 202

Coil, 400, 401

Collision, 212, 213; elastic, 157-159; inelastic, 157, 159; and light production, 309, 310

Color, 251, 255, 271

Commutator, 386

Component, 141, 142

Component acceleration, 122

Component force, 71-75; non-perpendicular, 74, 75; perpendicular 71-74

Component velocity, 109-114

Compression, 225

Compton, Arthur, 432

Compton effect, 432, 433

Concave lens, 286, 289, 290, 291

Concave mirror, 277-282; focal length of, 278; spherical aberration in, 278

Concurrent force, 63, 69, 70

Condensation, 200

Conductivity, electric, 169; heat, 171

Conductor, 206, 207, 407; electric, 205-207; as electrical ground, 326

Conservation, of energy, 153-157, 170, 183, 189, 308, 446; of heat, 170, 174, 175; of mass-energy, 157; of matter, 156, 157; of momentum, 97-101, 158, 159, 205

Constructive interference, 231, 253, 254, 295-303, 450; illus., 253

Continuous spectrum, 313, 314

Control rod, 472

Convection current, 196

Converging lens, 286-289

Convex lens, 286-289, 291

Convex mirror, 282-285

Copernicus, 15

Cosine, 8

Cosine law, 9, 11

Coulomb, 329

Coulomb, Charles, 330
Coulomb's law, 330-332, 447
Crest, 295, 296
Critical angle, 268
Crystal, 202, 414, 415, 435; *illus.,* 415
Crystal radio, *illus.,* 415
Curie, Marie, 455
Curie, Pierre, 455
Curve of best fit, 24-26
Cyclotron, 459, 460; *illus.,* 459

Day, mean solar, 18
Dees, 459
Density, 16; magnetic flux, 374; optical, 263-265, 270
Dependent variable, 24, 25, 26
Destructive interference, 232, 236, 253, 254, 295-303; *illus.,* 253
Deuterium, 476
Deuteron, 459
Diffraction, 236, 237, 252-254, 295-303, 317; double slit, 295-299; single slit, 300-302
Diffusion, 261, 262
Digit, doubtful, 23, 24; nonzero, 22; significant, 22-24; uncertain, 23, 24
Dimensional quantity, 11
Dipole, 413
Direct current, 396, 400
Direct variation, 25, 26
Discharging tube, 408
Displacement, 62, 121
Distance, 62; from graphical area, 50, 52, 53; and uniform acceleration, 37, 38, 39
Distance-time graph, 48, 49, 52, 53; *illus.,* 48; 49; 51; 53
Diverging lens, 285
Diverging mirror, 282-285, 291
Domain, 379
Doppler effect, 237, 238
Double-slit interference, 295-299
Dry cell, 347
Dynamics, 79

Earth, 245, 246, 339; as electrical ground, 326; gravitational field of, 136; mass of, 4, 5
Eclipse, 245, 246
Efficiency, of light source, 248, 309; of point discharge, 327
Einstein, Dr. Albert, 89, 157, 257
Elastic collision, 157-159
Electric charge, 321-325; concentration of, 327; measurement of, 329; point, 322, 333, 334
Electric circuit, 346-350; parallel, 359-364; series, 355-359; series-parallel, 364, 365; short, 364
Electric conductivity, 169

Electric current, 328, 329, 339-350, 363, 364, 391-402, 407; alternating, 395-397, 400-402; direct, 396, 400; effective value of, 396; and magnetism, 376-383; measurement of, 386, 387
Electric energy, 342, 343; conduction of, 205-207; transmission of, 350
Electric field, deflection of particles by, 421, 440; on electromagnetic wave, 414; and increased voltage, 343, 345, 416; and induction, 391, 407, 418; plotting of, 332-334; work on, 340, 341, 342; *illus.,* 333
Electric field intensity, 334, 335, 339-341, 345, 416
Electric force, 80, 328, 330, 331, 332, 333, 334, 445, 447
Electric generator, 394-399
Electric meter, 386, 387
Electric motor, 343, 344, 385, 386, 398
Electric potential energy, 148, 149, 327, 328, 339-342, 343, 445, 446
Electric power, 344, 348-350, 402
Electric resistance, 205, 206, 207, 345, 346, 347, 348, 350, 357, 359, 361
Electricity, from kinetic energy, 342, 343; static, 321-325
Electromagnet, 375-383
Electromagnetic induction, 391
Electromagnetic wave, 222, 243, 244, 247, 271, 307-317, 407-417, 432; coherent, 314-317; generation of, 407-410; speed of, 411; transmission of, 411-415
Electromotive force, 393, 401; effective value of, 396
Electron, 343, 442, 450, 462, 464; as beta ray, 440, 456, 458, 461; charge on, 329, 415-417; diffraction of, 435; free, 326; kinetic energy of, 428-432; and light production, 307-317, 408, 415, 431-433; and magnetism, 378, 379, 393; mass of, 4, 5, 417-421; photo, 256, 257, 427, 428; in plasma, 204; potential energy of, 149; as a wave, 450, 451
Electron current, 206, 322, 355, 392
Electron gas, 326
Electron pump, 328, 329
Electron pumping, 316
Electron transition, 310-312
Electronvolt, 351
Electroscope, 323, 324, 326
Element, 312, 313, 444, 450; half-life of, 465, 466; radioactive, 456-459,

464, 473; transmutation of, 456, 457; transuranium, 459; *table,* half-life, 466
Emission spectrum, 312, 313
Energy, 147-159, 433, 449; absorption of, 310-312; of allowed orbits, 447; and amplitude, 226, 227; binding, 467, 468; bundles of, 427, 431; in collisions, 157-159; conservation of, 153-157, 170, 183, 189, 308, 446; electric, 205-207, 342, 343, 350; equivalency of, 183-189; external, 165; flow of, 171; from fission, 472; from fusion, 475; as gamma rays, 457; heat, 154, 158, 165-178, 194-198, 269, 270, 348, 349, 363, 364; internal, 165-167, 169; ionization, 450; kinetic, 148, 152-155, 157-159, 165-167, 169, 200, 342, 343, 428, 429, 430, 432; light, 244-257, 261-272, 275-291, 295-303, 307-317, 408, 415, 427-430; molecular, 165-167, 169; in a pendulum, 411; photons of, 257; potential, 148-150, 154, 156, 165-167, 176, 186, 327, 328, 339-342, 343, 445, 446; radiant, 205, 244; transfer of, 222, 227, 228; X ray, 408-410
Energy level, 308, 309, 311, 432, 445, 446, 449, 450
Entropy, 171
Equation, linear, 25; nuclear, 457, 458
Equation solving, 3, 4; mathematical units and, 11
Equilibrant force, 70
Equilibrium, 69, 75, 82
Errors in measurement, 20, 21
Evaporation, 200, 201
Expansion, of water, 202
Extrapolation, 215
Eye, 290, 291
Eyepiece, 291

Factor-label method, 33
Faraday, Michael, 382, 391, 394
Farsightedness, 291
Fast neutron, 471
Fermi, Enrico, 471
Fiber optics, 268
Field intensity, electric, 334, 335, 339-341, 345, 416; gravitational, 339
First-order line, 298
Fluid, 194, 195
Fluorescence, 309, 310
Fluorescent lamp, 248, 309, 310
Fluoroscope, 310
Focal length, 278, 280, 286, 291
Focal point, 277, 278, 286, 289, 291

Force, 79-89, 94; adhesive, 199; binding, 80, 466-468, 469; centripetal, 115, 116, 119, 129; cohesive, 176, 177, 179, 193, 198, 199, 200, 202; component, 71-75; concurrent, 63, 69, 70; on current-bearing wire, 380-384, 386, 387; effective, 194, 195, 199, 202; electric, 80, 328, 330, 332, 333, 334; electromotive, 393, 396; equilibrant, 70; external, 100-102; of friction, 81, 120, 328; graphical analysis of, 25; gravitational, 80, 120, 328; of gravity, 128-131, 132, 135, 205; internal, 100-102; magnetic, 80; net, 141, 194, 198; nuclear, 80; unit of, 83; van der Waals, 193; weak interaction, 80; and work, 139-142

Force vector, 63, 68, 69; component, 71-75; equilibrant, 70

Fraunhofer, 314

Fraunhofer line, 314

Free electron, 326

Freezing point, 202, 203

Frequency, 121, 224, 225, 237; change in medium, 227, 228, 231; doppler effect on, 257; natural, 413, 414; and photoelectric effect, 418; of photon, 431, 432, 433; threshold, 428, 430

Friction, 81, 82, 86, 87

Fuse, 363, 364

Galilei, Galileo, 15, 16, 80, 81

Gamma ray, 440, 457, 461, 470

Gas, 204, 314; conservation of momentum in, 98, 99; radioactive, 455

Gas law, 26, 211-217

Geiger, 440

Geiger-Müller tube, 461

General Conference of Weights and Measures, 18

Generator, 328, 343, 399

Gram, 18

Graph, 24-26; slope of, 48

Graphical analysis, of force, 25; of gas volume, 26; of motion, 47-54; of vectors, 60-75; *illus.,* 48; 49; 50; 51; 52; 53; 54

Graphite, 471

Gravitational constant, 131, 134, 135

Gravitational field, 135, 136, 205, 339

Gravitational field intensity, 339

Gravitational force, 80, 84, 85, 120, 128-131, 132, 135, 328

Gravitational law, 128-133

Gravitational mass, 88, 89

Gravitational potential energy, 148, 150, 151

Gravity, acceleration of, 41, 42, 123, 135

Grimaldi, Francesco, 253

Grounding, 325, 326

Half-life, 465, 466

Heat energy, 154, 157, 165-178; conservation of, 170, 174, 175; from electric current, 348, 349, 363, 364; and expansion, 194-198; flow of, 171; and kinetic energy, 165-167; and light production, 309; measurement of, 168-170; mechanical equivalent of, 183-189; and refraction, 269, 270; from sunlight, 278; transfer of, 196; *table,* specific heat, 172

Heat of fusion, 176; *table,* 176

Heat of vaporization, 177, 178; *table,* 178

Heat unit, 171-173

Heat wave, 415

Heisenberg, Werner, 433

Heisenberg uncertainty principle, 433-435

Helium, 466, 467, 474

Helmholtz, Hermann von, 189

Henry, Joseph, 391

Hertz, 121, 224

Hertz, Heinrich, 307, 408

High voltage line, 350

Holograph, *illus.,* 317

Hooke, Sir Robert, 25

Hooke's law, 25

Huygens, Christian, 252

Hydrogen, 459, 474, 476, 477; radius of, 447

Hydrogen atom, 449

Hydrogen gas, 419

Hyperbola, 25

Ice, expansion of, 202; specific heat of, 176

If-then process, 207, 208

Illuminance, 249, 250

Illuminated body, 243

Illumination, 248-250

Image, 279, 280-285, 286, 287-291

Implosion, 477

Impulse, 95, 98

Incandescent lamp, 248

Independence, of vector quantity, 63, 109-114

Independent variable, 24, 25, 26

Index of refraction, 266

Induced current, 400

Induced electromotive force, 393, 401

Inductive reactance, 400

Inelastic collision, 157, 159

Inertia, 81, 88

Inertial mass, 88

Inquisition, 16

Instantaneous speed, 32

Intensity, 416

Interference, 231-233, 435; constructive, 231, 253, 254, 295-303, 450; destructive, 232, 236, 253, 254, 295-303; *illus.,* 253

International System of Units, 18

Inverse square law, 132, 133

Inverse variation, 26

Inversion, 254

Ion, 204

Ionization, 419, 421, 462

Ionization energy, 450

Iron, 379

Isotope, 444, 459; discovery of, 423; fission of, 470, 471; fusion of, 476, 477; half-life of, 465, 466; radioactive, 455, 456, 465, 466, 473, 474; *table,* half-life, 466

Joule, 140, 150

Joule, James Prescott, 186

Jupiter, 245, 246

K meson, 469

Kelvin, Lord, 169, 216

Kelvin temperature scale, 169, 216

Kepler, Johannes, 128

Kepler's law, 127-131

Kilocalorie, 171

Kilogram, standard, 18

Kilowatt, 143

Kinematics, 15, 81

Kinetic energy, 148, 152-155, 157-159, 169; and change of state, 200; converted to electricity, 342, 343; of electrons, 428-432; and heat, 165-167, 169

Kinetic theory, 165-167, 169, 193-208, 213

Krypton-86, 18

Laser, 314-317; and fusion, 476, 477; *illus.,* 317; fusion, 477

Latent heat of fusion, 176; *table,* 176

Latent heat of vaporization, 178

Law, action-reaction, 96, 97; Boyle's 26, 212, 213, 217; Charles', 215, 216, 217; conservation of energy, 153-157, 170, 183, 308, 446; conservation of matter, 156, 157; conservation of momentum, 97-101, 158, 159; of cosines, 9, 10;

Coulomb's, 330-332, 447; first thermodynamics, 170, 174; gas, 211-217; Hooke's, 25; inverse square, 132, 133; Kepler's, 127-131; kinematic, 15; Lenz's, 399, 400; Newton's first, 80, 81, 115; Newton's second, 82, 86, 94, 120, 152; Newton's third, 96, 97; Ohm's, 345, 348, 349, 356-365; of reflection, 234, 235, 261; second thermodynamics, 171; of sines, 10, 11; Snell's, 264, 265

Lawrence, E. O., 459

Lead, 440

Left-hand rule, 377, 378, 380, 381, 392, 395; *illus.*, 392

Length, 11, 16; standard unit of, 17, 18

Lens, 285-291; achromatic, 290; concave, 286, 289, 290, 291; converging, 286-289, 291; convex, 286-289, 291; diverging, 286, 289, 290, 291; eyepiece, 291; in laser, 317; objective, 291, 302; resolving power of, 302, 303; *illus.*, contact, 291

Lens equation, 290

Lenz's law, 399, 400

Light energy, 261-272, 307-317; absorption of, 313, 314; coherent, 314-317; and color, 312, 313; color of, 251, 255, 271, 272, 290, 296; diffraction of, 252-254, 295-303, 317; diffusion of, 261, 262; and gravity, 205; incoherent, 314; intensity of, 248-250; monochromatic, 300; particle nature of, 252-257; and photoelectric effect, 427-430; photons of, 257; polarized, 256, 257; reflection of, 254, 255, 261, 262, 268, 269, 275-285; refraction of, 262-271, 285-291; speed of, 228, 245, 246, 262-272, 411; transmission of, 244, 245; wave nature of, 252-257; *illus.*, color, 251; lumen, 248; *table*, index of refraction, 264

Light source, 248, 309, 310; efficiency of, 248, 309

Linear accelerator, 460, 461; *illus.*, 460

Linear variation, 25, 26

Liquid, 199, 200, 201, 202; refraction in, 270

Longitudinal wave, 222, 225, 256

Lumen, 248, 249

Luminous body, 243

Luminous flux, 248, 249

Luminous intensity, 248, 250

Magnet, permanent, 374, 375; properties of, 373, 374

Magnetic bottle, 476

Magnetic field, 373-387, 391, 392, 396, 398, 399; containing plasma, 476; in electromagnetic wave, 407, 413, 414, 418; induced, 379, 387, 393, 396, 400, 401, 418; in mass spectrograph, 421, 423; in particle accelerators, 460

Magnetic flux, 374, 401

Magnetic flux density, 374

Magnetic flux line, 374

Magnetic force, 80

Magnetic induction, 379, 387, 393, 396, 400, 401, 418

Magnetic potential energy, 149

Magnetism, and electric current, 377-383; theory of, 440

Marsden, 440

Maser, 317

Mass, 16, 121, 123, 130, 134, 135, 136, 431, 455, 456, 457, 466, 475; acceleration of, 86, 87; of atom, 441, 442, 443; conservation of, 157; of Earth, 4, 5; of electron, 4, 5, 417-420; gravitational, 88, 89; and heat content, 172, 173, 174, 175; inertial, 88, 89; measurement of, 88, 89; and momentum, 93-104; of proton, 419, 423; standard, 18

Mass defect, 467

Mass-energy, conservation of, 157

Mass number, 455, 456

Mass spectrograph, 421-423; *illus.*, 422

Mass spectrometer, 443

Matter, 149; conservation of, 156, 157; expansion of, 194-198; micro-structure of, 321; states of, 198-205

Matter wave, 434, 435, 451, 469

Maxwell, James Clerk, 407, 411, 445

Maxwell's theory, 307, 408, 413

Mean solar day, 18

Measurement, accuracy of, 21; errors in, 20; significant digits in, 22-24; standard units of, 17-19

Mechanical equivalent of heat, 183-189, 349

Mechanical wave, 222

Mechanics, 16

Melting point, 176

Mercury, 168, 211, 212

Meson, 469

Metal, 326, 427, 428, 429

Meter, standard, 17, 18

Metric system, 16-19; prefixes used in, 18, 19; standard unit of, 17, 18; *table*, prefixes, 19

Michelson, Albert, 246

Microscope, 291

Microwave, 317

Millikan, Robert A., 415, 416

Mirror, 275-285; concave, 277-282; converging, 277-282; convex, 282-285; diverging, 282-285; in laser, 316; parabolic, 278; plane, 275, 276, 277, 279

MKS system, 16, 17, 18

Molecular motion, 165-167, 169

Molecule, 98, 173, 176, 198, 199, 200

Momentum, 93-104, 434; conservation of, 97-101, 158, 159, 205

Monochromatic light, 300

Moon, 245, 246, 339; centripetal acceleration on, 132, 133

Motion, curved, 31, 114-120; falling bodies, 15, 41, 42, 80, 81, 110, 111; first law of, 80, 81, 115; graphical analysis of, 47-54; and kinetic energy, 152-155; law of, 152; linear, 31-42; molecular, 165-167, 169; projectile, 109-114; second law of, 82, 86, 87, 91, 120; simple harmonic, 121-123; third law of, 96, 97; two-dimensional, 109-123

Motor, 343, 344, 398, 399; electric, 385, 386

Nearsightedness, 291

Neon, 443

Neptunium, 473

Net force, 194, 198

Neutral body, 322, 324, 325

Neutrino, 464, 469

Neutron, 205, 321, 456, 468, 469; discovery of, 442, 464; fast, 471; slow, 472

Neutron star, 205

Newton, 63, 83

Newton, Sir Isaac, 79, 252, 271

Newton's first law, 80, 81, 115

Newton's gravitational law, 128-133

Newton's second law, 82, 86, 87, 94, 120, 152

Newton's third law, 96, 97

Nickel, 379

Nitrogen, 463

Nodal line, 236, 296

Node, 232, 233

Nova, 205

Nuclear binding force, 80, 456, 457, 466-468, 469

Nuclear bombardment, 458, 459

Nuclear equation, 457, 458

Nuclear fission, 470, 471

Nuclear force, 80

Nuclear fusion, 205, 474-477; *illus.*, 477

Nuclear moderator, 472

Nuclear particle, 468-470

Nuclear reaction, 149
Nuclear reactor, 471-477
Nucleon, 466
Nucleus, 80, 321, 440-442, 445, 446, 447, 455-477; binding force of, 80, 456, 457, 466-468, 469; fission of, 470-474 fusion of, 474-477; mass defect of, 467; transmutation of, 456, 457

Objective lens, 291
Odor detection, 194
Oersted, Hans Christian, 275, 376
Ohm, Georg Simon, 345
Ohm's law, 345, 347, 348, 349, 356-365
Oil-drop experiment, 415-417
Opaque material, 245
Optical density, 263-265, 270
Optical device, 290, 291
Orbit, 245, 246
Origin, 25, 26
Oscillator, 411-417
Oxygen, 463

Parabola, 25, 53
Parabolic mirror, 278
Parallax, 20; illus., 20
Parallel circuit, 359-364
Pendulum, 121, 122, 123, 411; illus., 121; 411
Period, 118, 121, 122, 123
Permanent magnet, 374, 375
Phosphorescence, 309, 310
Photocell, 427
Photoelectric effect, 256, 257, 427-432, 445
Photoelectron, 256, 257, 427, 428
Photon, 257, 427, 428, 430, 431, 433, 440, 445, 446; collision of, 309; in laser, 315-317; momentum of, 434
Physics, 3
Pi meson, 469
Picture tube, 310
Pinch effect, 476
Planck, Max, 257
Planck's constant, 429, 430, 431, 432, 434
Plane mirror, 275, 276, 277, 279
Planet, 129, 130, 131
Planetary model, 442, 445
Plasma, 203-205, 476
Platinum, 169
Plutonium, 473, 474
Point charge, 332, 334
Point source, 248, 249
Polarization, 255, 256
Polarizer, 256
Pole, 374, 375, 378
Polonium, 455
Positron, 464

Potential difference, 328, 339-342, 428
Potential drop, 357, 360, 367
Potential energy, 154, 156, 165-167, 176, 446; electric, 148, 149, 327, 328, 339-342, 343, 445, 446; gravitational, 148, 150, 151; magnetic, 149
Power, 143, 144; electric, 344, 348, 349, 350, 402; of light source, 248; magnification, 280, 291; resolving, 302, 303
Precision, 21, 22
Pressure, and freezing point, 202, 203; and gas volume, 26; standard, 211, 212; and temperature, 217; and vaporization rate, 200, 201; and volume, 212, 213
Primary coil, 400, 401
Principal axis, 277, 278, 280, 283, 286, 288, 289
Principal focus, 279
Prism, 271
Probability wave, 432, 451
Projectile motion, 109-114
Protactinium, 457
Proton, 321, 322, 442, 443, 456, 457, 459, 468, 469; acceleration of, 460; atomic number of, 455; charge on, 329; mass of, 419, 423; production of, 419, 464, 473
Puddle effect, 269, 270
Pulsar, 205
Pulse, 223, 224, 228, 229, 232, 234
Pumping, 316
Pythagorean theorem, 66

Quanta, 427
Quantity, dimensional, 11; scalar, 59; variable, 24-26; vector, 59-75, 103, 104, 109-114; illus., 60; 61; 66; 67; 68; 69; 70; 71; 72; 74
Quantum theory, 257, 427-435

Radar wave, 415
Radiant energy, 205, 244, 308, 309
Radiation, 439, 440
Radio wave, 205, 307, 408, 411, 413; illus., 413
Radioactive element, 455, 456-459, 464, 473
Radioactive material, 439, 440
Radioactivity, 464
Radium, 455, 466
Radon, 455
Rainbow, 271, 272; illus., 271
Rarefaction, 225
Ray, beta, 440, 456, 458, 461; gamma, 440, 457, 461, 470; light, 247, 261-264, 266, 270, 275, 276, 279-283, 286, 288

Ray diagram, 235, 279, 287
Ray optics, 247
Real image, 279, 282, 286, 287
Red shift, 238
Reflection, 228, 229; from curved mirror, 277-285; internal, 268, 269; law of, 234, 235, 261; from plane mirror, 275, 276; and polarization, 256; from thin film, 254, 255
Reflector, 309
Refracting telescope, 291
Refraction, 235, 262-271, 285-291; index of, 266, 271; table, 264
Resistance, 205, 206, 207, 345, 347, 350, 355, 357, 359, 361
Resistor, 347, 348, 355, 357, 359, 361, 362, 427
Resolving power, 302, 303
Resonance, 411, 412
Resultant, 60, 66, 68, 70, 71, 103, 104
Retina, 290, 291
Ripple tank, 233, 234
Roemer, Olaf, 245, 246
Roentgen, Wilhelm, 408
Rumford, Count, 184
Rutherford, Sir Ernest, 439, 440, 441, 442, 445, 455, 463

Satellite orbit, 119, 120
Scalar quantity, 59, 139, 148
Schrödinger, Erwin, 451
Scientific method, 16
Scientific notation, 4-7, 22
Scintillation, 441
Second, standard, 18
Secondary coil, 400, 401
Second-order line, 298
Self-induction, 400
Series circuit, 355-359
Series-parallel circuit, 364, 365
Short circuit, 364
Significant digit, 22-24
Simple harmonic motion, 121-123
Sine, 8
Sine law, 10, 11
Single-slit diffraction, 300-302
Slope, 48, 49, 52, 53
Slow neutron, 472
Snell, Willibrord, 265
Snell's law, 264, 265
Solar wind, 205
Solid, 195
Solid state, 202, 203
Sound wave, 412; speed of, 228, 237, 238
Specific heat, 172, 173, 176; table, 172
Spectrograph, 421-423; illus., 422
Spectrometer, 313

Spectrum, 244, 251, 271, 272, 297, 408, 445; absorption, 313, 314; continuous, 313, 314; emission, 312, 313; sun's, 314; *illus.,* 271

Speed, 11, 32, 34, 48, 62, 200; and attraction force, 194, 195; average, 32, 37; and energy, 152; final, 36, 40; graphical analysis of, 47-54; of light, 228, 245, 246, 262-272, 411; of solar wind, 205; of sound, 228; of wave, 224, 227, 228, 231, 235

Speed-time graph, 50-52; *illus.,* 50; 52

Spherical aberration, 278

Spherical concave mirror, 277

Split-ring commutator, 386

Standard unit, 17-19

Standing wave, 233

Star, 205, 208, 238, 314

Static electricity, 321-325; grounding of, 325, 326; theory of, 322-324

Stokes, George G., 416

Stopping potential, 428, 429, 431

Straight line, 25

Sun, 130, 131, 204, 205, 314, 474; *illus.,* 204

Sunlight, 314

Superconductivity, 207

Surface tension, 198, 199, 200

Tangent, 8, 53, 66

Telescope, 291

Temperature, 166, 167, 174, 175, 200, 201, 476; and conductivity, 206, 207; and pressure, 217; and resistance, 348; and specific heat, 172, 173; and volume, 215, 216

Temperature scale, 169, 170, 216

Theory, caloric, 165, 184; if-then, 207, 208; kinetic, 165-167, 169, 193-208, 213; magnetic, 378, 379; Maxwell's, 307, 408, 413; quantum, 257, 427-435; static electricity, 322-324; Yukawa's, 469

Thermocouple, *illus.,* 170

Thermodynamics, first law of, 170, 174; second law of, 171

Thermometer, 168

Thermometry, 168, 169

Thermonuclear reaction, 475

Thermostat, 197; *illus.,* 198

Thomson, G. L., 435

Thomson, J. J., 417, 418, 439

Thoria, 248

Thorium, 455, 456, 457

Threshold frequency, 428, 430

Time, 16; standard unit of, 476

Tokamak reactor, 476; *illus.,* 476

Torsion balance, 330

Total internal reflection, 267, 268

Transformer, 400-403

Translucent material, 245

Transmission line, 350

Transmitted wave, 231

Transmutation, 456, 457; artificial, 463, 464

Transparent material, 244

Transuranium element, 459

Transverse wave, 222, 225, 256

Triangle, trigonometry of, 8-11, 66, 298, 299, 301

Trigonometry, 8-11, 66

Tritium, 476

Trough, 295, 296

Tube, picture, 310

Tuning fork, 412

Uncertainty principle, 433-435

Unit, consistent, 11; derived, 16; fundamental, 16; SI, 18; standard, 17-19

Unit conversion, 33

Universal constant, 131

Universal gravitational law, 128-133

Universe, conservation of momentum in, 101

Uranium, 439, 455, 456, 470, 471, 472

Vacuum tube, 383

Van der Waal's force, 193

Vaporization, 200, 201

Variable, 24-26

Variable resistor, 347

Vector addition, 60-70

Vector quantity, 59-75, 103, 104; independence of, 63, 109-114; resolved, 71-75, 109-114; *illus.,* 60; 61; 66; 67; 68; 69; 70; 71; 72; 74

Velocity, 31, 62, 115; average, 32, 37; component, 109-114; and energy, 152; final, 36, 40; graphical analysis of, 47-54; and momentum, 93-104; orbital, 120

Vibration, 121

Virtual image, 279, 281, 282, 285, 288, 289, 291

Volatile liquid, 199

Volt, 328, 340, 393; electron, 357

Voltage, 396

Voltage drop, 357, 367, 399

Voltaic cell, 328

Voltmeter, 346, 367; *illus.,* 367

Volume, 16

Water, boiling point of, 177, 201; Brownian movement in, 194; charging of, 325; expansion of, 202; freezing point of, 203; heat content of, 167, 171, 172, 174, 175; heat of fusion of, 176; heat of vaporization of, 178; melting point of, 176; refraction in, 270; as temperature standard, 169

Watt, 143, 344

Wave, 221-238; coherent, 314-317; at boundaries, 228, 229; detection of, 412; electromagnetic, 222, 243, 244, 247, 307-317, 407-417, 432; infrared, 415; longitudinal, 222, 225, 256; matter, 434, 435, 451, 469; mechanical, 222; polarized, 255, 256; probability, 432; radar, 415; radio, 307, 408, 411, 413; reflection of, 254, 255, 261, 262, 268, 269, 275-285; speed of, 411; sound, 225, 412; standing, 233; transmitted, 231; transverse, 222, 225, 256

Wave amplitude, 226, 227, 228, 232

Wave behavior, 296

Wave characteristics, 224

Wave diffraction, 236, 237

Wave frequency, 257

Wave interference, 231-233, 236

Wave inversion, 229

Wave refraction, 235

Wave speed, 224, 227, 228, 231, 235

Wavelength, 224, 228, 231, 237, 238, 254, 255, 271, 411, 432, 433; absorption of, 313, 314; and color, 251, 255, 271, 272, 290, 296, 312, 313; measurement of, 296-300; standard metric, 18

Weak interaction force, 80

Weight, 84, 85, 120, 134

Weights and Measures, General Conference of, 18

Wilson cloud chamber, 462

Work, 139-142, 339; and change of state, 176; in an electric field, 340, 341, 342, 343, 344, 393, 445, 475; and energy, 147, 148, 183, 184, 186, 187, 340; and heat, 166, 176; stopping electrons, 428, 429; units of, 150, 151; *illus.,* 141

Work function, 429, 431

X ray, 310, 316, 408-410, 432, 433, 450

Young, Thomas, 253, 254, 295

Yukawa, Hideki, 469

Zero, significant, 22